25. Mary Somerville
26. George Poulett Scrope
27. River valley reexcavated through a basaltic lava current, France
28. Valley, filled by a current of basaltic lava, being reexcavated by the stream flowing in it
29. Hills capped with basalt platforms, France
30. Tunnel of a Roman lead mine under basalt in the bank of the Sioule River, near Pont Gibaud
31. Lyell's and Murchison's geological section of the freshwater strata and overlying volcanic rock in the valley of the Couz d'Issoire River, Auvergne
32. *Ancylus elegans,* drawn by James Sowerby from specimens collected by Lyell
33. Lyell's and Murchison's geological section of freshwater strata at Aix-en-Provence
34. Ischia from the west

Between pages 336 and 337

35. The Temple of Serapis
36. The Val del Bove
37. Lyell's sketch of the view from the summit of Etna into the Val del Bove
38. Lyell's drawing of Etna from Lentini
39. Lyell's drawing of Gozzo degli Martiri
40. Lyell's drawing of the Val di Noto escarpment from the south side of the harbor of Syracuse
41. Lyell's drawing of the strata at Cape Passaro
42. Lyell's drawing of a view of Licata
43. The volcanoes of Olot
44. Mary Elizabeth Horner in 1831
45. Charles Lyell in 1836
46. John Murray II
47. Lyell's diagram of the geology of Valorsine
48. Sea level mark at Gräsö near Oregrund, Sweden
49. Sea level mark in the harbor of Löfgrund, Sweden
50. Sea level mark at Koon Island near Marstrand, Sweden
51. Emma Darwin in 1839 and Charles Darwin in 1837
52. Frontispiece to the *Elements,* 1838

Maps

1. The south of England with the places important in Lyell's boyhood — 13
2. Lyell's tour to Staffa in 1817 — 51
3. Lyell's tour in Switzerland with his family, 1818 — 61
4. Thomas Webster's tour of the Isle of Wight, 1811 — 98
5. Lyell's tour with Constant Prevost in the southwest of England, 1824, and the route of the Western Circuit of the Assizes — 127
6. Lyell's London, with places where he lived and worked — 150
7. Lyell's and Murchison's tour through France in 1828 and Lyell's tour to the Pyrenees in 1830 — 192
8. Some of the places visited by Lyell and Murchison in Auvergne and possible routes, 1828 — 195
9. Lyell's tour through Italy and Sicily, 1828–29 — 222
10. Lyell's excursions in the vicinity of Naples, November 1828 — 227
11. Lyell's route through Sicily, 1828 — 234
12. Lyell's tour in Spain and possible routes, July 1830 — 298
13. Charles and Mary Lyell's wedding tour through Germany and Switzerland — 365
14. Lyell's tour in Denmark and Sweden, 1834 — 393
15. Lyell's tour in Switzerland, August–September 1835 — 416
16. Lyell's tours in Suffolk and Norfolk to study the Crag — 479
17. Lyell's tour in Normandy and Touraine, July 1840 — 491

Preface

In 1959, while at the University of California at Berkeley, I first read Charles Lyell's *Principles of Geology* and immediately became interested in the man who had written such a thoughtful and delightful scientific book and one which had exerted such a profound and, I believe, revolutionary influence on the history of science. As a result I read for pleasure *The Life, Letters and Journals of Sir Charles Lyell*, edited by Katherine M. Lyell. The latter work revealed Lyell's interests in history, politics, and literature as well as in science and suggested the many points at which he had touched life during the early Victorian period. At the same time there was much that the *Life, Letters and Journals* did not tell. They omitted almost all discussion of Lyell's scientific work and of his travels in America. There were significant gaps between letters, with little to indicate what Lyell was doing in the meantime and little to explain the background of the letters that were included. Altogether, the *Life, Letters and Journals* aroused as many questions as they answered and I determined to discover whether more information might be obtained about Lyell.

To begin with I wrote to England to Mr. Victor Eyles, whose lectures on the history of geology I had attended earlier at University College London, to ask whether he knew the location of Sir Charles Lyell's personal papers or of any surviving members of his family. In reply Mr. Eyles told me that there was a large body of Lyell correspondence at the Department of Geology, University of Edinburgh, and that Lyell's family was still represented by Lord Lyell of Kinnordy, Kirriemuir, Angus, Scotland.

When I wrote to the Department of Geology, University of Edinburgh, they replied that the Lyell papers had been moved to the Edinburgh University Library. Mr. Charles P. Finlayson, Keeper of Manuscripts at the Edinburgh University Library, then informed me that the Lyell correspondence formed a very large uncatalogued collection of more than two thousand letters. In order to use such a large collection I should have to have it microfilmed, but the cost was beyond my means.

During 1959–60 I was teaching as a visiting assistant professor at Cornell University, but had already agreed to go to Yale University to work under Dr. John F. Fulton in the Department of the

History of Science and Medicine. When I told Dr. Fulton of the problem with which I was faced of having more than two thousand letters at the University of Edinburgh microfilmed, he told me immediately to go ahead and have the work done and he wrote to Mr. Finlayson to say that his Department would pay the cost. In retrospect I do not think that when Dr. Fulton gave this assurance he had any very clear idea of where the money was to come from, but I have now no means of knowing because Dr. Fulton died before I arrived at Yale. His encouragement was, however, vital at the time. The cataloguing and microfilming of the collection at Edinburgh took more than two years and ultimately most of the cost of the microfilming was paid by a grant from the National Science Foundation.

In reply to my inquiry to Lord Lyell of Kinnordy whether he had any papers of Sir Charles Lyell, his mother the Lady Lyell wrote to say that they had many letters, journals, and notebooks at Kinnordy House and that I was welcome to come to consult them. I visited Kinnordy House first in 1961 and both then and on a succession of later visits received much kindly hospitality from the Lady Lyell and Lord Lyell. I was also given assistance and hospitality by two successive factors of the Kinnordy estate and their wives, Mr. and Mrs. Neil Findlay and Mr. and Mrs. Ronald Thorborn, as well as by neighbors and friends of the Lyells. Lord Lyell very generously allowed me to have the letters, journals, and notebooks at Kinnordy microfilmed as I needed them. During a visit to Kinnordy House in 1966 I discovered additional valuable letters of Mary Lyell.

The research on which this biography is based has been supported by two grants from the National Science Foundation to Yale University: NSF G-16458 in 1961 and NSF GS-1277 in 1966. In July 1967 NSF Grant GS-1819 was awarded to the University of Minnesota for continued support of my Lyell research. In the summer of 1961 the first NSF grant enabled me to hire two Yale students as assistants. John Brandt made a most useful catalogue of the microfilms of the Lyell correspondence from the University of Edinburgh while Allan Weinstein, as part-time work, located Lyell letters in libraries and archives at Boston, Massachusetts.

The first draft of this volume was written during 1964–65 when I received a Junior Faculty Fellowship from Yale University. It was typed by Mrs. Elizabeth Musgrave and was read by my colleagues at Yale, Frederic L. Holmes, Lloyd G. Stevenson, and

Elizabeth H. Thomson and I benefited greatly from their criticisms and suggestions.

Mrs. Helen Mammen, my secretary at the University of Minnesota, has typed the final manuscript and Mrs. Patricia Burwell, Senior Cartographer in the Department of Geography, University of Minnesota, has drawn the maps from rough drafts prepared by my wife and myself.

From the foregoing it is clear that I am deeply indebted to institutions, to the National Science Foundation, Yale University, and the University of Minnesota for the financial support which has enabled me to research and write this book and to the individuals, libraries, and archives listed under Manuscript Sources in the Bibliography which have provided me with Lyell letters and other manuscripts. In particular I should mention the help of Dr. Walter F. Cannon of the Smithsonian Institution who drew my attention to the Lyell letters among the Whewell papers at Trinity College, Cambridge, and Dr. Martin Rudwick of Cambridge University, who discovered a box of Murchison papers at the Geological Society of London and wrote to tell me that there were Lyell letters among them. In addition I have incurred many personal obligations, particularly to the staffs of the Geology Library and the Medical Library at Yale and to the staff of the Biomedical Library at the University of Minnesota. To all of these institutions and persons I am very grateful and can only hope that the book will in some measure justify the help they have given.

Finally, I am indebted to the anonymous reader for the Yale Press who made many valuable suggestions and criticisms and to Mrs. Jane Pruett who edited the manuscript for the Press in a thoroughly competent fashion.

L. G. W.

Minneapolis
1971

CHARLES LYELL

The years to 1841: The revolution in geology

CHARLES LYELL

The years to 1841: The revolution in geology

By Leonard G. Wilson

New Haven and London, Yale University Press

1972

Published with assistance from
the Louis Stern Memorial Fund.

Library of Congress catalog card number: 72–75212.
International standard book number: 0-300-01486-4.

Designed by John O. C. McCrillis
and set in Baskerville type.
Printed in the United States of America by
Connecticut Printers, Inc., Hartford, Connecticut.

Published in Great Britain, Europe, and Africa by
Yale University Press, Ltd., London.
Distributed in Canada by McGill-Queen's University
Press, Montreal; in Latin America by Kaiman & Polon,
Inc., New York City; in Australasia and Southeast
Asia by John Wiley & Sons Australasia Pty. Ltd.,
Sydney; in India by UBS Publishers' Distributors
Pvt., Ltd., Delhi; in Japan by John Weatherhill, Inc.,
Tokyo.

To the memory of
George Edward Wilson
1874–1962
my father

Contents

Illustrations		viii
Maps		x
Preface		xi
1	The Setting	1
2	Boyhood of the Third Charles Lyell	11
3	Oxford and First Travels, 1816–1819	33
4	The State of Geology in 1819	65
5	Law Student and Amateur Geologist, 1819–1824	85
6	The Emerging Barrister, Scientist, and Writer, 1825–1827	135
7	Travels through France, 1828	183
8	Italy and Sicily, the Birth of a Scientific Revolution	218
9	The *Principles of Geology,* 1829–1830	262
10	The Second Volume of the *Principles,* 1830–1832	294
11	Marriage and Professorship, 1832–1833	340
12	The Mature Geologist, 1833–1836	382
13	Darwin and Lyell, 1836–1841	433
14	The Crag Question and the Classification of Tertiary Formations, 1836–1840	461
15	The Glacier Theory, 1840	496
16	The *Elements of Geology* and the Sixth Edition of the *Principles of Geology,* 1838–1841	503
Bibliography		519
Index		539

Illustrations

Between pages 48 and 49

1. The first Charles Lyell and his family ca. 1780
2. Kinnordy House before reconstruction in 1880
3. Silhouette of Mr. Lyell of Kinnordy
4. Silhouette of Charles Lyell: The Oxford undergraduate
5. The Reverend William Buckland lecturing at Oxford in 1823
6. Thomas Pennant's illustration of Fingal's Cave, Staffa
7. The Lyell brothers in 1819
8. Dr. James Hutton
9. The Reverend John Playfair
10. W. D. Conybeare's reconstruction of *Ichthyosaurus* and *Plesiosaurus*
11. Gideon Mantell in 1837
12. Vertical chalk strata at Handfast Point, Dorsetshire
13. Thomas Webster's theoretical sections of the Isle of Wight and adjacent part of Dorsetshire to the west
14. Thomas Webster's geological map of the Paris, London, and Isle of Wight basins
15. Two views of Sandown Bay
16. Lyell's section of Sandown Bay
17. View of Compton Bay, Isle of Wight

Between pages 176 and 177

18. Geological section of Compton Bay
19. W. H. Fitton's geological map of the Isle of Wight, 1824
20. Drawing of the skeleton of *Plesiosaurus* discovered at Lyme Regis in 1823
21. Geological section of part of Forfarshire from north to south through Bakie Loch
22. Lyell's geological map of Forfarshire
23. Roderick Murchison
24. Lyell's specimens of fossil *Chara* from the rock marl and living *Chara hispida*

CHAPTER 1

The Setting

IN THE FIRST HALF of the eighteenth century Scotland was backward and impoverished. In the countryside the lairds and their tenants were poor—not, in the Lowlands at least, because the land was barren, but because they had not the money to provide the drainage necessary even on upland slopes and there was little market for what they did produce. From this hard land it was natural that young men should migrate in search of better means to make a living. They were usually successful because they customarily possessed both vigor of character and superior education. They served in the British navy, very often as ship's surgeons, as bookkeepers in London counting houses, and on distant stations of the East India Company. As officers and men in the army and navy, as surgeons, accountants, and engineers, they made their way in the world. They offered in skill, training, and reliability what they may have lacked in influential connections. Perhaps assertive, and certainly clannish, they were an indispensable element in the far-flung activities, both commercial and military, of the British Empire.

The first Charles Lyell was such a man. He was born 17 September 1734, son of the farmer John Lyell and his wife Margaret Mudie, at Carcary in the parish of Farnell, county of Forfarshire, or Angus, in Scotland where the Lyells had farmed for several generations. In 1751 James Lyell took over the farm of Carcary, presumably because of the death of brother John. On 6 December of that year Charles Lyell was apprenticed to John Ritchie, a merchant at Montrose,[1] to learn "merchandizing and book-keeping" for a term of three years, his uncle James Lyell and his older brother, also James Lyell, serving as "Cautioners" and paying the indenture fee of fifteen pounds sterling.[2] On 16 January 1756, about a year after the completion of his apprenticeship, Lyell joined the navy and was entered as an able-bodied seaman on His Majesty's sloop *Firebrand* under the command of Captain Taylor

1. "Indenture Betwixt John Ritchie and Charles Lyall (1751)," 6 Dec. 1751, Kinnordy mss.
2. A. J. Warden, *Angus or Forfarshire* . . . (1880–85) vol. 4, pp. 113–14.

Penny. He is mentioned as acting as a captain's clerk so his training in accountancy was standing him in good stead. On 2 July he
was promoted to gunner's mate and on 13 May the next year to
midshipman.[3] However, a week later, on 20 May 1757, the *Firebrand* was paid off, and Lyell's service in the navy is obscure for
the next few years until on 13 June 1763 he was transferred from
H.M.S. *Mermaid* to H.M.S. *Romney* under command of Captain
James Ferguson. On 15 May 1766, while the *Romney* lay at Halifax, Nova Scotia, the purser of the ship died, and Lyell was appointed to the vacant post.[4]

The purser of a British naval ship in the eighteenth century was
essentially the businessman of the ship. He was not paid a full salary, but was expected to supplement his income by acting as a
purveyor to the ship at a profit. He had to supply caution money
as security for the bills which he might run up against the navy
and was to some extent an independent contractor. He had numerous perquisites, some legitimate, others illegitimate. Like
other businessmen he might interpret his role in a large or a small
way and thereupon might depend his success or failure.[5] Charles
Lyell seems to have exploited his business opportunities with
imagination. In 1770 in partnership with other men he became a
supplier to the British navy at the various ports along the Atlantic
coast of North America—Halifax, Boston, New York, Philadelphia,
Charleston—as well as at other points in the West Indies and at
London and Portsmouth in England.

Perhaps on the strength of his appointment as purser Lyell decided to marry. On 26 February 1767 he was excused duty from
the *Romney* and shortly afterward married Mary Beale of West
Looe, Cornwall. During the years 1767–70 he appears not to have
been on shipboard, and on 7 March 1769, while the Lyells were
living at Southampton Buildings, Holborn, Mary Lyell gave birth
to a son who on 31 March was baptized Charles after his father.[6]
After a few years they moved to a house in Queens Square, Bloomsbury (Fig. 1). The young Charles was presently entered at St.
Paul's School.

In May 1770 Charles Lyell was transferred from the *Romney* to

3. Admiralty 36. 5603.
4. Admiralty 6. 20, p. 120.
5. M. Lewis, *A Social History of the Navy 1793–1815* (1960) pp. 246–50.
6. Baptism register of St. Andrews, Holborn, London, 31 March 1769.

the *Salisbury*.[7] This was the year he entered into the partnership agreement to supply His Majesty's ships on the coast of North America. Three years later (12 October 1773) Lyell exchanged posts with Edward l'Epine, purser of the *Neptune*, and served as purser of that ship until 17 February 1778[8] when he was transferred to the *Warspight*. On 21 April he exchanged posts with the purser of the *Albion*, but remained only until June when, at the request of Admiral John Byron, he was appointed purser of Byron's flagship, the *Princess Royal*. Lyell was also to act as secretary to Admiral Byron and paymaster to the ships under his command. Earlier in the year Byron had been given command of a fleet of ships and ordered to proceed to America where Britain was at war with her former colonies.

Byron's expedition to America was unlucky. On the entry of France into the American war, a French fleet under the Comte d'Estaing sailed from Toulon on 12 April 1778. Byron sailed from Plymouth in pursuit of him on 9 June. After several encounters with D'Estaing's ships, on 6 July 1779 Byron engaged the French fleet off Grenada in the West Indies. The resulting battle was inconclusive and probably resulted in more damage to the British ships than to the French, but the French fleet withdrew and the British fleet sailed to St. Kitts to refit.[9] In August 1779 Admiral Byron returned to England and with him went his secretary, Charles Lyell, weary of the sea.

As a result of the prize money which he received from this voyage and which he continued to receive as the war progressed, Lyell felt himself in a position to fulfill what had probably been a long-held ambition—to buy an estate in his home county in Scotland. He went north in November 1780 for the purpose of looking at various properties. After considering the estates of Rossie and Kinnordy, both of which were for sale, he made an offer of £38,000 to the trustees of Sir John Ogilvy for the estates of Kinnordy and Invercarity at Kirriemuir, and on 25 November 1782 the sale was closed.[10] The castle of Invercarity was a ruin, but Kinnordy possessed a fine manor house. Thus Charles Lyell of Queen's Square,

7. Admiralty 6. 20, p. 276.

8. Admiralty 36. 7706. See also Muster book of the *Salisbury*, 11 Sept. 1773–25 Dec. 1774.

9. R. Beatson, Naval and Military Memoirs . . . (1804) vol. 4, pp. 340–41, 362–63, 369–71, 379, 457–75.

10. C. Lyell to D. Mudie, 1 Sept. 1781. Kinnordy mss.

Bloomsbury, became Charles Lyell of Kinnordy. Kinnordy and Invercarity at this time included about 5,000 acres of arable land plus moorlands and mills on different streams.[11] These lands lay on rising ground on the northern slope of the valley of Strathmore, a broad depression which runs east–west through the county of Forfarshire between the Grampians to the north and the line of the Sidlaw hills, which separate Strathmore from the estuary of the Tay, to the south. The loch of Kinnordy had been drained in 1740 to give access to its beds of marl—a useful conditioner of the soils of Angus.[12]

At some time in the next several years Charles Lyell moved from London to Kinnordy and immediately began to improve his estate (Fig. 2). The Reverend Thomas Ogilvy, describing the parish of Kirriemuir in the year 1792, wrote that "woodland is abundant in the parish especially on the estate of Kinnordy, the proprietor of which is giving his seat every embellishment which wood can bestow, as well as ornamenting the country, by planting every piece of waste ground on his estate." This was a time of great agricultural improvement throughout Scotland and these changes were especially noticeable at Kirriemuir. According to Ogilvy, the proprietors and tenants were draining the wet land, bringing all arable land into cultivation, and planting to trees what was not arable. An important element in the improvement of arable land was the application of marl from the marl beds opened by the drainage of Kinnordy loch in 1740, and the new owner of Kinnordy encouraged his tenants to use it for he "sells it considerably cheaper than any other marl in the county, though in quality, it is, by many, reckoned inferior to none." He also contributed "a handsome spire which is seen through the whole of Strathmore" to the new church of Kirriemuir which was built in 1787.[13]

The parish of Kirriemuir had therefore taken full part in the great revolution which had begun in Scottish agriculture about 1750. This revolution consisted in the abandonment of "run-rig" farming, a relic of the medieval open-field system in which the fields had been divided into long narrow strips, a certain number

11. Scottish Records Office, Edinburgh, Abridgements Kinnordy, 242.

12. *New Statistical Account of Scotland.* 15 vols., Edinburgh: William Blackwood and Sons (1845), vol. 11, p. 165.

13. J. Sinclair, *The Statistical Account of Scotland* . . . (1791–99) vol. 12, pp. 190, 191, 196.

of strips being assigned to each tenant. Instead the fields were enclosed by fences or hedges and divided into farms of suitable size. Each farm was let on a lease of nineteen years so that it became in the interest of the tenant to improve it. Plowing, draining, crop rotation, and the cultivation of turnips, potatoes, and improved grains all became part of the new system of farming. Fields of wheat and barley replaced expanses of heather. Land which could not be cultivated was planted to trees, and Scotland gradually lost the bare and treeless aspect lamented by Samuel Johnson in 1773. The leaders in this movement were not the tenants, for they lacked the necessary capital and knew only the old ways, but the landowners or lairds.[14] As a new laird in 1782, therefore, Charles Lyell brought to his task both capital and new ideas acquired during his years at London and abroad.

In 1783 Lyell added to his estates of Kinnordy and Invercarity, the adjoining property of Shielhill, and in 1784 he bought two farms, Muirhouses and Waulkmiln. By these additional purchases he became one of the great landowners in the vale of Strathmore.

On 21 February 1786 his son Charles, now almost seventeen, matriculated at Saint Andrews University where, however, he can have spent little more than a year and a half, because at the beginning of the Michaelmas term in the autumn of 1787 he matriculated at Peterhouse College, Cambridge.

The emerging character of this second Charles Lyell, who was to be known through most of his life as Charles Lyell, Esq. of Kinnordy, is of considerable interest not only because he was an original and engaging person but also because he was to be the dominant influence upon his eldest son—the future Sir Charles Lyell, geologist.

We know little about the second Charles Lyell's first year at Cambridge, but if we may speculate from the later nature of his inquisitive mind and strong but scattered and rambling interests, he probably read avidly, made friends easily, took long walks and rides, hunted, attended the races, enjoyed long and convivial dinners—did everything in fact except study. In short, he followed the usual student life of the period which was not very much different from that pursued by Charles Darwin some forty years later.[15] But whereas Darwin was intended for the church while he was at Cam-

14. H. G. Graham, *The Social Life of Scotland* ... (1937) pp. 201–27.
15. C. Darwin, *Autobiography* (1858) pp. 58–60.

bridge, Lyell was intended for the law. On 5 April 1788 he was entered at Lincoln's Inn although he would not go there until after he took his degree at Cambridge in 1791.

During the summer vacation of 1788 the younger Lyell visited France in company with the family of a fellow student. They went to Paris and then as far south as Tours. He was thus having the experience, more precious than he or anyone could then appreciate, of seeing France before the Revolution. On his later visits to France he was to contrast his impressions with this, his first and perhaps sharpest experience of that country.

In the autumn he returned to Cambridge and at the beginning of the winter term began to keep a diary.[16] The entry for 29 January is characteristic:

> Hired a horse, and at eight o'clock rode over with my gun to Newton—breakfasted with them.—and afterwards Pemberton and myself took our horses, a boy, and three pointers and proceeded to shoot—. . . . The day was exceedingly fine; & we saw an innumerable quantity of birds but wild.

On 2 March he recorded, "Attended Milner's Lectures on Chemistry—first time," but on 14 April "Rode a wretched horse over to Newmarket—a famous race between Meteor, Sir Peter Teazel and Gunpowder" and on Saturday 10 May "Went in the evening to see a sparring match between Big Ben—Lee—Ward and Ryan." But he and his friends also went to Lord Howard's house of Audley End to see the paintings there. After two weeks in London during June Lyell went north to Sedberg on the borders of the lake district, where he was to be tutored by a Mr. Dawson in order to learn the mathematics which he had not learned at Cambridge. With a fellow student he found accommodation with Mr. John Wallace "Where we are to have two bedrooms—a large sitting room and our board for 11/6 a week each." Dawson tutored a group of seventeen Cambridge students. He was not so demanding, however, but that they had time for expeditions to the lakes and to caves and waterfalls in the surrounding country. The youthful Lyell had a keen sense of the beauty and interest of the area. He remained at Sedberg until early in September, then went north to visit his parents at Kinnordy. In October he returned to London and proceeded

---

16. C. Lyell (1769–1849), "Journal at Cambridge, London, Sedberg, the Lakes, the Caves, St. Andrews, Kinnordy, London, Cambridge from 19 Jan. 1789 to 27 April 1790." Kinnordy mss.

to Cambridge early in November, but after only a few weeks he went again to Sedberg and did not go back to Cambridge until 6 February 1790. He also spent the summer of 1790 quite pleasantly at Sedberg, making long excursions in the lake district to Windermere, Coniston, Ambleside, and other places.[17]

On 21 October 1790 Lyell finally took leave of Mr. Dawson at Sedberg and paid him £4.10 for his tutoring although he doubted whether he had gained any benefit whatever from it, admitting, at the same time, that this was the result of his own idleness. He must have done some studying during the following year at Cambridge because he was 17th Wrangler when he was graduated B.A. in 1791. Apparently he then took up the study of law at Lincoln's Inn where he had already been admitted on 5 April 1788.[18]

Between April and October of 1792 he took an extended tour of France, Switzerland, and Holland. France was then still in the midst of the revolution, and he was advised to wear a cockade for safety's sake—an indignity he bitterly resented. At Paris he saw the royal prisoners. The king, he thought, looked "very dense," but the queen sadly noble. On visiting the National Assembly he was shocked by the violence and confusion of its members.

In Switzerland Lyell became romantically enthusiastic about mountain scenery. He had been prepared to admire it by his reading of Rousseau and of Saussure's *Voyages dans les Alpes*—a work which he thought every traveler to Switzerland should read before he went.[19] He also met members of the De Candolle family, who were to become famous as botanists. This visit to Switzerland had the effect on Lyell of extending his interest in scenery, already developed by his rambles in the lake district and over the Yorkshire moors, to a broader interest in natural history, particularly botany. It is probable that Lyell traveled also in the summer of 1793, but we have no record of his activities for that year.

After a vacation at Kinnordy during the summer of 1794, Lyell continued to study law at Lincoln's Inn in his easygoing and haphazard fashion. On 23 September 1794 he opened a notebook of "Memorandums" which gives a vivid picture of his life in London through 1794–95. He was now calling regularly at the house of

17. C. Lyell, "Journal at Cambridge, Sedberg, the Lakes, Maker, 5 May–30 Nov., 1790." Kinnordy mss.

18. J. A. Venn, *Alumni Cantabrigiensis, (1752–1900)* vol. 4, p. 243.

19. H. B. de Saussure. *Voyages dans les Alpes* . . . (1779–96). At this time Lyell only had access to the first three volumes which were published in 1779, 1786, and 1791 respectively.

Mr. Thomas Smith in St. Martin's Lane, attracted by the company of Miss Frances Smith. He also went sometimes with another college friend, Sheppard,[20] to the latter's home at Wickham, where Miss Smith also went to spend some weeks during the autumn with Miss Sheppard. When a box of game arrived from Kinnordy, Lyell sent "5 partridges and a Woodcock" to St. Martin's Lane. Lyell also attended the trials of Hardy and of Horne Tooke at the Old Bailey and regretted their acquittal, for he believed that "this acquittal will have the most dangerous consequences in giving encouragement to the popular Societies." He went frequently to the theater and occasionally to see sales of pictures and other sights. He had his portrait drawn by Miss Singleton and ruefully admitted, "She has certainly caught a likeness—there is a good natured vacant look in it."[21]

At the end of 1794 Lyell applied for the Bye fellowship at Peterhouse, Cambridge, which had just become vacant through the marriage of the incumbent, Burton, because, "The distinction of Fellow of Peter House may be an advantage to me hereafter if I go the Norfolk Circuit."[22] His application was successful and on 31 March 1795 he went to Cambridge where on 4 April he was inducted into the fellowship.

During the summer of 1795 Lyell toured Ireland passing through Wales on the way. He left London 2 July in company with his college friend Warrington.[23] He visited friends in the north of Ireland, among them the Heylands of Hillhead, County Antrim, the family of one of his college friends. On this tour he also met the Reverend William Richardson, rector of Moy and Clonfele, County Antrim, who had interested himself in the origin of the basalts and whinstones which are so conspicuous a feature of the geology of northern Ireland. Richardson was to argue in a long series of papers that the basalt of the Giant's Causeway and other places had originated by deposition from water.[24] On 2 August

20. Samuel Philip Sheppard (1766–1832) was Rector of Eaton-Constantine, Salop, (1823–32). Venn, *Alumni Cantabrigienses (1752–1900)* vol. 5, p. 492.

21. C. Lyell, "Memorandums 1794–1795." Kinnordy mss., pp. 15 ms., 34 ms.

22. Ibid., p. 35 ms.

23. Apparently Daniel Richard Warrington. See Venn, *Alumni Cantabrigienses, (1752–1900)* vol. 6, p. 359.

24. William Richardson (1740–1820) between 1802 and 1808 published a series of papers in which he attacked the view of Nicholas Desmarest, James Hutton and others that basalt was a volcanic rock. *D.N.B.* Cf. Sir Gavin de Beer, "The Volcanoes of Auvergne."

Lyell visited the Causeway. The next day, Sunday, he recorded:

> Dr. Richardson convoyed us as far as the turning to Port
> Rush. — He pointed out several places by the roadside where the
> stones & rock bear a resemblance to the columns of the Cause-
> way. — In opposition to the system of the causeway & adjacent
> rocks being the production of a volcano,—he observes that there
> is a rapid descent inland from the top of those rocks—the volcano
> must therefore have been in the Sea.

Lyell added heretically, "Why not."[25]

On 22 October 1795 he arrived back in London where he mused
in this journal, "Everything has conspired to make this last Tour
(which has been of 2,000 miles) most agreeable; delightful weather,
an interesting route, the travelling companion I could have wished
for, and while in Ireland, society the most agreeable & obliging I
have ever met with, & perfect health to crown every other advantage." In this contented mood he installed himself in his new lodgings at No. 2 New Square, Lincoln's Inn, and went to dine at St.
Martin's Lane where he found Mr. and Mrs. Smith and Miss Smith
all in perfect health.

Charles Lyell had engaged his new lodgings for three years, expecting to continue his pleasant, busy, and comfortable life as a
young lawyer in London for at least that time. On 15 December,
however, he was summoned to Kinnordy:

> My Brother [John] having been long in a dangerous state of
> health I received with joy the news that he had gained sufficient
> strength to travel, that the Physician had advised a milder cli-
> mate & that it was wished I should attend him.—
>
> The call arrived yesterday. I took leave of my Sisters,—dined
> in St. Martin's lane today, and at 7 o'clk. went to the Bull &
> Mouth to take the York Mail.[26]

On his arrival at Kinnordy on 19 December he found his brother
"much recovered & quite able to travel. But my Father alarmingly
ill of Bile and Rheumatism." A month later, on 19 January 1796,
the elder Lyell died at the age of sixty-two in great pain apparently from an abdominal cancer.

Thus ended for the first Charles Lyell a life which had been far-
ranging and of remarkable accomplishment. From an apprentice

25. C. Lyell, "Journal in Ireland and Wales, 1795." Kinnordy mss.
26. C. Lyell, "Diary 1794–1796," Kinnordy mss., p. 45 ms.

merchant and humble captain's clerk he had risen to be a great Scottish laird. His years in the navy must have involved hardship and possibly adventure. In his portraits there is a hint of humor in his slight smile and this suggestion is borne out in his surviving letters. Whatever Lyell's merits as an executive officer and naval supplier, he must have been intelligent and enterprising. He enjoyed the trust and sometimes the friendship of distinguished officers including, in addition to Admiral Byron, Sir William Fairfax, who supported Admiral Duncan in the suppression of the mutiny of the Nore and at the battle of Camperdown. The fortune with which Lyell endowed his family was to be of inestimable benefit to the development of science in the nineteenth century.

At the age of twenty-six his son, the erstwhile carefree law student and traveler, became Charles Lyell, Esq. of Kinnordy, head of his family and responsible for a large estate. On 4 October that year he married Miss Frances Smith, aged twenty-two, at Sidmouth, Devonshire, where her father may have been residing temporarily in connection with the business of the navy. Soon after they went to live at Kinnordy, and there on 14 November 1797 Frances Lyell gave birth to a son who, like his father and grandfather, was named Charles.

CHAPTER 2

Boyhood of the Third Charles Lyell, 1797–1816

THROUGH the mild winter of 1797–98 which followed the birth of his son, Mr. Lyell of Kinnordy must have given some serious thought to the kind of life he wished to lead and the place where he wished to bring up his children. He possessed a handsome estate in Scotland. His fertile fields stretched for miles along the gently sloping northern side of the vale of Strathmore. The house, which his father had improved and renovated, was comfortable and pleasantly situated, being protected by a grove of fir trees from the cold winds off the Grampians. His neighbors were friendly and even congenial, and the market town of Kirriemuir, of which he was the heritor, was prosperous. It bustled not only with farmers' markets but with shoemaking and linen weaving. According to the *Statistical Account* of 1792 some 1,200 pairs of shoes were made there annually to be exported, and between September 1791 and September 1792 the town had also manufactured about £38,000 worth of "osnaburgh," "scrim," and "bindy," different forms of coarse linen goods.[1]

But Scotland was not for Mr. Lyell, as it had been for his father, his native home. Both he and his wife had been born at London within sound of Bow Bells and had spent most of their lives there. Charles Lyell had probably not even visited Scotland many times before he matriculated at St. Andrews in 1787 when he was already eighteen years old. He therefore lacked that intuitive understanding of and sympathy for his Scottish tenants which his father seems to have possessed. Though generous to a fault, he may have found the duties and responsibilities of a resident laird irksome. Then, too, Kinnordy was two days' journey from Edinburgh and there were in the quiet countryside no theaters, concerts, or picture galleries; no exciting trials at the Old Bailey; none of that steady hum of gossip and flow of people in which he had delighted while at London. Moreover, the scenery of Scotland, though beautiful beyond compare to modern eyes, was, in its severer aspects, only

1. J. Sinclair, *The Statistical Account of Scotland* ... (1791–99) vol. 12, p. 194.

beginning to be appreciated at the end of the eighteenth century. Certainly it was much more barren of trees in 1798 than it is to-day. Mr. Lyell may have longed for the gentler and more luxuriant landscapes of the south of England.

At any rate in the winter of 1798 he made the decision to leave Kinnordy and began to pack books, pictures, and linen to go by sea from Dundee to London. On 14 January he noted, observing the development of his young son: "Charles 2 months old, a thriving infant but plaguey cross. Blue eyes, light hair. Thought to be amazingly like Grandfather Smith. A month later Mr. Douglas of Kirriemuir inoculated the baby with smallpox to give him immunity to the disease—a drastic and dangerous procedure widely used before Jenner's discovery of vaccination. For the next two weeks the child was severely ill with smallpox and his arm was still excessively sore on 4 March.[2]

On Monday 4 June Mr. Lyell departed with his wife and infant son from Kinnordy and traveled south to Ilfracombe in Devonshire. At the end of August they were at Lymington in Hampshire "where they intend passing some time."[3] In the meantime Mr. Lyell's mother and his sisters Mary and Ann had also left Kinnordy and were at Edinburgh. Mr. Lyell seems in the course of these ramblings to have been looking for a suitable place to settle in the south, and this search may have begun to assume some urgency becuuse Frances was now expecting her second child. To continue to live in lodgings would not be a pleasant prospect. From Lymington they went to Southampton where on 24 February 1799 their second son, Tom, was born.

About the middle of the eighteenth century, Southampton, which had been a very quiet little town, became fashionable as a watering place (Map 1). The opportunity for sea bathing was at first its principal attraction, but as members of the royal family began to come, as noblemen and men of wealth began to build villas and to make annual visits, it became like Bath and Tunbridge Wells, and later Brighton, a center which possessed its own power of attraction. There were balls and concerts, libraries and theaters and, perhaps most important, many persons of consequence. Officers of the army and navy frequently retired there or purchased country houses in the vicinity. The combination of pleasant company with every facility for pleasure was a powerful

2. Charles Lyell, "Diary 1798," Kinnordy mss.
3. Mary Lyell to Charles Wedderburn. 1 Sept. 1798. Wedderburn mss.

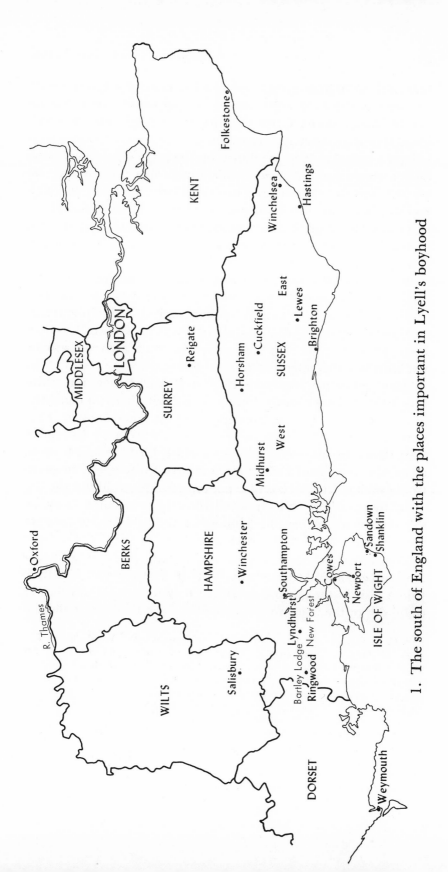

1. The south of England with the places important in Lyell's boyhood

lure and must have greatly attracted a man of Charles Lyell's temperament. So, with the need for a permanent home for his family now apparent, in the autumn of 1798 he took a fourteen years' lease on Bartley Lodge, a substantial house with eighty acres of land attached to it, at Lyndhurst on the edge of the New Forest, only a short distance from Southampton. He was always very pleased with this decision and two years later, writing from Weymouth to his former neighbor in Scotland, Charles Wedderburn of Pearsie, he said: "I am more convinced than ever that for a permanent residence the New Forest combines more advantages than any other spot in England."[4]

In October 1801 Mr. Lyell took Mrs. Lyell to Weymouth because sea bathing had been recommended for her health. Her trouble may have been the too frequent arrival of children, for on 14 March 1800 her third child and first daughter, Frances, had been born and on 16 June 1801 the fourth, Marianne, arrived. Caroline was born on 7 November 1802.

Shortly after her son had settled at Bartley Lodge, the senior Mrs. Lyell had come down from Scotland with her two daughters Mary and Ann, and had taken a house in Southampton. They were thus able to visit frequently at Bartley. On 14 November 1802 they came to celebrate Charles's fifth birthday and brought toys and sweetmeats for him.[5] Mr. and Mrs. Smith also came down from London. Charles was now not only five years old but the eldest of five children, and Mr. Lyell ruefully commented "may, on this rate of proceeding, the Kinnordy acres yield famous crops or the rents will never keep pace with us."[6]

The summer of 1802 was unusually warm, and the autumn a long succession of bright warm days. On 29 December Mr. Lyell paid a visit in the gig and remarked how unusual it was that he could do so; the roads would ordinarily have been too muddy. It

4. C. L. to C. W. 5 Nov. 1801. Wedderburn mss. Charles Wedderburn (1748–1829) was born at Pearsie in Glen Prosen, near Kirriemuir and entered St. Andrews University. He studied medicine, visited Paris in 1765 and then entered the military service of the East India Company. He retired in 1785 with the rank of Captain and returned sometime thereafter to Pearsie which he had purchased from his father in 1779. He freed the estate from debt and built a new house which he completed in 1805, and where Lyell visited very often. See Alexander Wedderburn, *The Wedderburn Book, a history of the Wedderburns in the counties of Berwick and Forfar* . . . 1296–1896, 2 vols., privately printed, 1898, I, pp. 325–327.

5. K. Lyell, *Life and Letters* I, 3. Cf. C. L. to C. W., 13 Nov. 1802. Wedderburn mss.

6. C. L. to C. W., 13 Nov. 1802. Wedderburn mss.

was also a year of peace brought by the treaty of Amiens. But early in 1803 new signs of war developed and on 18 May Great Britain declared war on France. Almost immediately Napoleon began to plan a great invasion of England. He ordered the construction of hundreds of invasion barges and gunboats and mobilized every French seaport. Addington, Prime Minister of England, alarmed at these preparations, sought to create a force to contain Bonaparte's invading army in the south of England. Since an army of regular soldiers was not available, he called for an army of militia or volunteers.

By considering Napoleon's invasion army as an actual possibility, Addington created both alarm and rage throughout the country. In Hampshire Mr. Lyell undertook the command of a company of volunteers. In June he thought that "notwithstanding this plaguey war" he might go to Kinnordy by himself in August, but as the threat of invasion loomed larger he abandoned this idea.[7] He explained his decision to Wedderburn:

> When it came near the time to set off I must confess that I found it no easy matter to volunteer so long a journey & long an absence from my family & my hesitation was put an end to by the necessity there was of turning Soldier, & the propriety of taking a Company in the Corps of this Parish under Major Serle.

He enclosed a copy of Cobbett's *Weekly Register* which was severely critical of the volunteer corps, and he expressed his own doubts as to the effectiveness of these companies.

> Would it not have been wiser in Government to have reserved a power during invasion to annex any Company of Volunteers to any Reg.[ts] of Regulars or Militia? I know I should have felt much more confident of steadiness in my ragamuffins, if they were to have had good men on either hand of them, than I shall when I see them flanked by just such doubtful characters as themselves.[8]

In the summer of 1804 Mr. Lyell was able again to make his visit to Kinnordy and returned south by post chaise, covering the 535 miles to Bartley in eight days. By this time the threat of inva-

7. C. L. to C. W., 19 June 1803. Wedderburn mss.
8. C. L. to C. W., 10 Nov. 1803. Wedderburn mss.

sion was diminishing, but a bad harvest had greatly raised the price of bread in England. Fortunately the harvest in Scotland had been bountiful so that his tenants were in a position to benefit from the high prices.[9]

In the spring of 1805 Mr. Lyell sent his two small boys, Charles and Tom, to the Reverend R. S. Davies' school at Ringwood where about fifty boys were enrolled. Charles, now seven and a half years old, had been kept back nearly a year so that Tom could go with him.[10] They were there for only about ten weeks before the summer holidays. From school Charles wrote his first letter in a large, clear hand:

Spring Gardens, March 12, 1805

Dear Papa and Mama

As we have not seen you for some time I flatter myself a few lines from me will not be unacceptable, to say that we are very well. My Brother received his Cake on the day expected. We gave a piece to everyone in the house and it lasted till the Saturday following with our having a piece every day. We drank tea with Mrs. Davies on Thomas's birthday. We are still rich in cash as your good supply of oranges etc. lasted so long, and sav'd our money. I like dancing very much. My Brother gets on very well in his writings so you may expect a letter from him. We beg our love to Grandmammas, Grandpapa and Aunts. Thomas unites with me in love to you and thanks for the cake.

I am Dear Papa and Mama
Your Affectionate Son
Charles Lyell

P.S. Mr. Mrs. & Miss Davies desire their Compliments to you.[11]

A few weeks later a great battle occurred between the boys of the school and those of the town—an introduction to the savagery of English school life which Charles never forgot even though he was not directly involved. Another and more pleasant interval occurred when his father came to Ringwood in October with his company of volunteers.[12] They had originally expected to come in

9. C. L. to C. W., 18 Oct. 1804, 3 Dec. 1804. Wedderburn mss.
10. In his autobiography written for his fiancée Mary Horner in 1831 Lyell's memory seems to have deceived him. He must have gone to Ringwood in the early spring, rather than the late summer of 1805. See *L. & L.* I, 3.
11. C. L., Jr., to his parents. 12 March 1805. Kinnordy mss.
12. *L. & L.* I, 3–4.

July, a prospect which did not please Mr. Lyell who wrote to his friend Wedderburn,

> I hope the crops look well in the North. . . . Here they look admirably but are late owing to a succession of cold weather.— Very little clover is stacked but much is cut. As this and the meadow hay form a very principal crop in this country and as our Volunteer Corps is composed entirely of Agriculturalists you will wonder that those who are set in authority over us should have fixed on this particular time to order us into Quarters for three weeks![13]

Since all of Bartley's eighty acres were in hay, the haymaking was a matter of no small consequence to him. By virtue of the volunteers' not coming till the autumn, they were at Ringwood when the news of Trafalgar came early in November. Charles recalled the event in his reminiscences.

> There were bonfires on the summit of every hill round Ringwood, which had a grand effect at night: an illumination in the town, where almost every candle was blackened on the outside in mourning for Nelson. The band of the volunteers played "Rule Britannia" and "Battle of the Nile," while the people sang standing round a great bonfire in the market-place. . . . I remember participating perfectly in the mixed feeling of sorrow for the death of Nelson and triumph for the great victory.[14]

Trafalgar removed permanently the threat of invasion which had haunted Englishmen for several years.

Shortly after Charles and Tom returned from school for the Christmas holiday Mrs. Lyell gave birth to her seventh child, Eleanor, on 21 December, exactly a year after the birth of Henry. Mr. and Mrs. Smith came from London for Christmas and early in January Charles's grandmother and his aunts came from Southampton for Twelfth Night.[15] These large family parties were characteristic of life at Bartley and were happy and interesting times for the children. It was a spacious place. The grassland surrounding the house was unenclosed so as to make a park which contained many large oak trees. The owner of the property, Major

13. C. L. to C. W. 27 June 1805. Wedderburn mss.
14. *L. & L.* I, 4.
15. C. L. to C. W. 6 Jan. 1806. Wedderburn mss.

Gilbert, cut some of these from time to time to supply the navy, a fact regretted by Charles.

> I knew every tree, great and small, and used to miss them as you might a piece of old furniture in a room. To every clump and single tree in the park I gave a name. One was "Ringwood," another "Salisbury," or "London," or "Paris" etc. Single trees were named after flowers, an odd fancy: thus one was called "Geranium." These names were afterwards adopted by the rest of the young ones.
>
> We were now allowed to roam about a good deal by ourselves, and I always contrived to learn where the trees were to be cut within reach of a walk, which was very frequent, for the demand for the navy was then most pressing; and besides the thousands of oaks cut near Lyndhurst, a great number of beech trees were also consumed, for every house has a certain share of firewood, by old custom from the king's forests.[16]

Wonderful as the New Forest was as a playground for an imaginative child, it was also of interest to Mr. Lyell. On 14 February 1806 he wrote to James Sowerby, "They have been cutting many fine old Beeches in the Forest lately which has enabled me to increase my acquaintance with the crustaceous lichens. Many have puzzled me having only the meagre descriptions of Withering to refer to except as to those which have been described by Dillenius or in E. B."[17] Mr. Lyell was thus devoting his leisure as a country gentleman to the study of botany and he had already begun to add botanical books to his library. He seems to have been especially interested in the mosses, liverworts, lichens, and fungi—obscure plants which often require the help of a microscope to examine. On March 30 he again wrote to Sowerby, "Your favour of the 24th incited me to explore the sides of a favourite Forest Brook on Friday in search of *J. [ungermannia] ciliaris* which I found in three different places, but sparingly & without any appearance of fructification. I have marked the places and shall revisit them." He sent specimens to Sowerby and searched for rare species on re-

16. *L. & L.* I, 8.
17. C. L. to J. Sowerby. 14 Feb. 1806. Eyles mss. James Sowerby (1757–1822), botanist of Lambeth is known for his thirty-six volume *English Botany* (1790–1814), which included 2,592 colored plates. It is probably the "E.B." which Lyell refers to. The "Withering" was W. Withering, *A Botanical Arrangement of all the Vegetables Naturally growing in Great Britain. . . .* (1776). Dillenius was John James Dillenius, M.D. (1687–1747), professor of botany at Oxford. His greatest botanical work was his *Historia muscorum . . .* (1741).

quest, frequently protesting his desire to be useful in scientific work. On 3 April he wrote again, "I have been guilty of Botanical extravagance you will say in giving a coverlid to the box of *H.[ypnum] molluscum* in fruit. In riding through Ravens Nest Inclosure in a dry elevated part of the Forest near Fritham I found it in as great abundance as the commonest Moss whatever, filling every vacancy left by the Furze & Heath." Sowerby appreciated his efforts and named a lichen after him.[18]

The Lyell children were all ill that spring, so at the end of May Mr. Lyell took them to Cowes on the Isle of Wight for a month and brought Charles and Tom over a few days later when they came from school. It was not a long excursion. "We are but 8 miles from South[amp]ton where we step into a boat & land almost at our door."[19] The Wedderburns, who had been in Devonshire for Mr. Wedderburn's health, came to visit them there, and were followed by their Hampshire friends, the Heathcotes, so they remained much longer than they expected and were still there on 19 July. They went sailing frequently, especially since the Heathcotes had a sailboat of their own in which to take them. Mr. Lyell collected seaweeds and lichens to send to Sowerby. He also looked for fossil plants.

> We were on an excursion by water to the Needles on Tuesday, & I made them land me at Yarmouth that I might employ the evening in searching for the petrified tree, which I did by prowling along the Beach from Cary's Sconce to Weston Point, without ever finding a vestige of an incrustation. I must blame my ill fortune, as I must have passed the spot your friend describes; though it is possible the stump may be buried, as the cliff is of a mouldering clay which is brought down by the landsprings in great masses every Winter. The ramble however was a delightful one & afforded some grand specimens of *Inula helenium.*
>
> The next morning was most agreeably passed in Alum Bay, a spot but little visited though more interesting as a picture than any other in the island. It is very deep, about a mile in diameter, & surrounded by cliffs 500 or 600 feet high, the westernmost side of these is chalk & terminates in the Needles, the easternmost is of clay striped in the most singular and brilliant manner with perpendicular veins of green, yellow, purple & black. The last

18. C. L. to J. Sowerby. 16 April 1806. Eyles mss.
19. C. L. to C. W. 28 May 1806. Wedderburn mss.

is Alum & Coal, the former ochres; though I perceive I neglected to bring away any of a greenish tinge. The chalk cliffs are
unbroken, but the clay ones are rent into vast chasms which
would allow a Mineralogist to explore them to great advantage.
I loaded myself with as many of the treasures as a Boy and I
could well carry on Horseback to Yarmouth.[20]

Mr. Lyell was gradually teaching himself botany. He apologized
to Sowerby for his mistakes in identification and requested a copy
of the list of new plants observed in Hampshire by Dawson Turner
and William Borrer.[21] He shared this botanical interest with a
neighbor in Southampton, Miss Constance Biddulph, for whom
Sir James Edward Smith named *Conferva biddulphiana*.[22] One
of the charms of botany for him was that it was a year-round interest. He wrote to J. E. Smith, "I had scarcely discovered that
Botany could be pursued in Winter when I met with Lichen pollinarius in fruit, & the immediate notice you took of it encouraged me to give my attention to the rich store of mosses and Lichens in our Forest, which has proved an inexhaustible source of
amusement. I have never since wanted a most captivating pursuit
to draw me into the open air."[23]

In the summer of 1807 all of the children were sick with scarlet
fever and measles and Mrs. Lyell, worn out with taking care of
them, became ill herself. In the autumn Mr. Lyell went north to
Kinnordy taking Mrs. Lyell and his sisters by post chaise. They
returned early in December.

The summer of 1808 was particularly fine and when Charles
and Tom were home in July for the holidays, they greatly enjoyed
the haymaking then in progress:[24]

We (Tom and I) used to attend the mowers all day, and learnt
to mow a little, and used to tumble about with Marianne and
Fanny in the hay-cocks, and ride in the loaded waggons to the
haystack.[25]

20. C. L. to J. Sowerby. 19 July 1806. Eyles mss.
21. Dawson Turner (1775–1858), banker of Yarmouth, Norfolk, was a botanist
and antiquary by avocation and published many works in both fields. William
Borrer (1781–1862) was a gentleman of private means who studied botany. Together
with Dawson Turner he published *Lichenographia Britannica,* 1839.
22. C. L. to C. W. 21 July 1807. Wedderburn mss.
23. C. L. to J. E. Smith. 18 April 1808. Linnean Soc. mss.
24. C. L. to C. W. 3 Dec. 1807, 7 July 1808. Wedderburn mss.
25. *L. & L.* I, 7.

On the first of August they returned to school and shortly afterward Mr. and Mrs. Lyell set off for Kinnordy, traveling by post
chaise because Mr. Lyell had been suffering from fits of dizziness
which seemed to preclude his going alone by mail coach. While
they were still at Kinnordy in November, they received the news
of Mr. Lyell's younger sister Ann's engagement to marry Captain
Gilbert Heathcote.[26] This event was also noted by Jane Austen
who, then living at Southampton, was acquainted with Mrs. Lyell,
Sr., and her daughters.[27]

When Mr. and Mrs. Lyell and Frances reached London on their
return from Scotland they found there a letter from Tom which
gave them disturbing news of Charles's health. The boys were now
at Dr. Radcliffe's school at Salisbury to which they had been transferred the previous year. They did not like it so well because it
was in the middle of a town instead of on the borders of the country as Dr. Davies' school at Ringwood had been. Charles recalled
"we had now a small yard surrounded by walls, and only walked
out twice or three times a week, when it did not rain and were
obliged to keep in ranks along the endless streets and dusty roads
of the suburbs of a city. It seemed a kind of prison by comparison,
especially to me, accustomed to liberty in such a wild place as the
New Forest."

Their chief walk was to the rotten borough of Old Sarum where
there was an ancient fortified hill with a deep triple trench and a
deep long sloping tunnel "said to have been used by the garrison
to get water from a river in the plain below."[28] Some of the older
boys knocked off their hats which rolled down this tunnel, so they
had to climb down after them. Charles did not recall this incident
with particular pleasure and his whole period at Salisbury seems
to have been unhappy. He started to study Latin, but since the
teaching was dull, he learned little. They had great bolster fights
at night, but these seem to have been more a symptom of disorder
and anarchy in the school than entirely joyous occasions. In 1808
Charles had measles while at school and was for a time delirious.
He recovered but in late autumn again became seriously ill.

He had complained of a pain in his chest and Dr. Radcliffe had

26. Captain Gilbert Heathcote, R.N. (1779–1831) was the fifth son of Sir William
Heathcote, M.P. (1746–1819) third baronet of Hursley near Winchester.
27. Jane Austen to Cassandra Austen. 21 Nov. 1808. R. W. Chapman, *Jane
Austen's Letters . . .* (1952), pp. 231–33.
28. *L. & L.* I, 9.

called an apothecary who had given the boy a cathartic "which
brought away a quantity of Ascarides." The apothecary thought
this was the cause of his trouble and did nothing more. Mr. Lyell
asked Dr. Radcliffe to consult Dr. Fowler, "a very eminent physician at Salisbury" who pronounced that Charles's disease was in
his lungs. Mr. Lyell then brought the boys home from Salisbury
on 17 December in the midst of severe frosty weather.

> We were almost heartbroken for several days with seeing the
> woeful alteration in Charles, his thinness, paleness, difficulty of
> breathing, severe cough, acute pains in the breast & side & fever-
> ishness; but by giving him milk immediately from the Cow as
> soon as it is light, keeping him on a bread and milk diet (with
> no meat or fermented liquor) giving Oxymel, squill for the
> cough, & regulating the bowels with Castor Oil & using every
> precaution against cold, the amendment is astonishing.[29]

Mr. Lyell sent this full account of their treatment to Charles Wedderburn so that if they were omitting anything, Wedderburn,
who had himself had medical training, could warn them of it. Mr.
Lyell was really worried, and with reason, for Charles's complete
recovery was very slow and he did not return to school until early
in April. "An able medical man expressed his belief that an affliction of the liver was the primary cause of his complaints" but the
symptoms which Mr. Lyell described are those of acute pleurisy.[30]
Exposure, malnutrition, and a chaotic school environment, conditions which the English fondly believe are good for children,
probably contributed to the severity of his illness.[31] During
Charles' illness, Mrs. Lyell had given birth on 22 November
1808 to her eighth child and fifth daughter, Maria.

While he was home with no studies to occupy him, Charles became interested in collecting insects. His father had bought some
books on the subject a short while before, including Donovan's
Insects[32] whose colored plates Charles found very attractive. From
these he was able to identify a number of species of butterflies and
moths which attracted him by their beauty.

29. C. L. to C. W. 26 Dec. 1808. Wedderburn mss.

30. C. L. to C. W. 19 March 1809. Wedderburn mss. Charles Wedderburn had
replied promptly and kindly to Mr. Lyell's request for medical advice, on January
3, but evidently approved the course they were pursuing.

31. In his autobiography written for Mary Horner, Lyell later made light of this
illness but since acute pleurisy often led to consumption his parents were more than
justified in removing him from the school.

32. E. Donovan, *The Natural History of British Insects* . . . (1793–1813) vol. 1–10.

... besides the procuring the chrysalis and seeing its transformation; and the feeding and breeding of caterpillars was another reason for preferring this numerous and showy class. I soon, however, learnt to prefer the rare to the brilliant species, and was not long in discovering by the comparison of one season with another, that each species had its peculiar time for appearing, some twice, some once only in the year, some by day, some in the evening, and others at distant hours of the night.[33]

However, he soon became interested in aquatic insects

and used to sit whole mornings by a pond, feeding them with flies and catching them if I could. . . . I was greatly surprised to find every pond tenanted by water-beetles of different sizes and shapes, and to observe them row themselves along by the broad row of bristles attached to their legs. I threw flies and moths into the water and observed them rise, and learnt their relative strength, seeing some species relinquish the booty on the appearance of others. The long spider-like flies which run on the surface, the glimmer chafers which thread the surface, in what we called a figure-of-eight movement, the beetles which swim on their backs, and many others, such as the red tick, used to be caught and brought in a basin into my bedroom, and there kept, to the annoyance of the housemaids when the water was none of the sweetest; and then the whole were fed with window-flies until some died and others took wing in the night and flew back to their native waters.[34]

Charles began by knocking down butterflies with his hat but as this was good neither for the butterflies nor the hat, Miss Newlands, the governess, made him a small string net.

In March 1809 Ann Lyell and Captain Gilbert Heathcote were married and went to live at Aldborough in Suffolk. During holidays Charles and Tom were thereafter sometimes invited to visit Embley, the seat of Captain Gilbert Heathcote's father, Mr. William Heathcote, M.P. (later Sir William Heathcote). Charles seems to have returned to Dr. Radcliffe's school early in April and to have continued there, apart from the summer holidays, until Christmas 1809. Thereafter Mr. Lyell, being dissatisfied with this school, apparently taught Charles and Tom at home during the first half of 1810. They read Virgil's *Eclogues,* and a French

33. *L. & L.* I, 14.
34. Ibid., pp. 14–15.

master came twice a week.[35] Mr. Lyell intended to send them to
Winchester, but found on inquiry that their names would have
to be on the college lists for two years to give them a chance to get
in. He therefore sent them to Mr. Bayley's school at Midhurst,
Sussex, apparently intending to transfer them, for he had no illusions about it. "The school is upon the absurd English System of
consuming 4/5 of a boy's time on Latin and Greek, and is a good
preparative for Winchester, which mine will probably have taste
of."[36] But it was the best he could find, and at the same time he
renewed his lease on Bartley for seven more years in order to remain in the south of England for the education of his children.
His original lease for fourteen years had been at £100 per year,
but the inflation during the Napoleonic wars had been so great
that the owner had been offered £10,500 for the property if he
would sell and 350 guineas a year if he would rent.[37] Mr. Lyell
seems to have been able to renew his lease well below the latter
figure but his expenses had nonetheless increased greatly.

In 1811 he renegotiated the lease for another fourteen years
and, with tenure assured for this period, made extensive additions
and improvements to Bartley, "the two wings having been gutted
& raised" and "3 servants' bedrooms, a servants' Hall, large Store-
room and a beautiful Library . . . together with a pleasure ground
and flower garden" added.[38] To offset this expense he was undoubtedly also benefiting from both higher rents at Kinnordy and
the increased value of the hay crop at Bartley.

In 1812 Mr. Lyell began to correspond about botanical matters
with Dawson Turner, the banker of Yarmouth, Norfolk.[39] His
correspondence with Turner also introduced him to Turner's
son-in-law, William Jackson Hooker, who then lived at Hales-
worth in Suffolk. Mr. Lyell's earlier correspondence with James
Sowerby had tended to lapse because Sowerby had become more
interested in mineralogy than botany as his *English botany* neared

35. Ibid., p. 18.
36. C. L. to C. W. 30 Dec. 1810. Wedderburn mss.
37. C. L. to C. W. 5 July 1810. Wedderburn mss.
38. C. L. to C. W. 14 July 1811. Wedderburn mss.
39. Dawson Turner (1775–1858) had attended Pembroke College, Cambridge,
1793–96, but then, on account of his father's death, took over the latter's resident
partnership in Gurney's bank at Yarmouth. As a young man he devoted his leisure
to botany, but gradually shifted his interest to the antiquities of Norfolk. About
1815 he began to gather what became a very large collection of manuscripts and
autograph letters. He possessed a magnificent library of botanical books which in
1815 Lyell, after a visit to Turner, said had cost £8,000. C. L. to C. W. 18 Dec. 1815.
Wedderburn mss.

completion. Mr. Lyell also corresponded with James Edward Smith, William Borrer, and Robert Brown about botanical matters. His searches for mosses and liverworts in the New Forest proved very fruitful and he discovered several new species. Robert Brown named the genus *Lyellia* for him and his name was likewise attached by Hooker to a species of moss, *Orthotrichum lyelli*, which he discovered growing on trees in the New Forest. On his trips to Scotland Mr. Lyell seized the opportunity to observe and collect plants on the bogs and moorlands of the Grampians. As he wrote to Charles Wedderburn, "I look back with more pleasure to the mornings I spent on Catlaw with you & the quiet evenings at Pearsie than all the other events of my journey."[40] The pursuit of this quiet hobby brought him in 1813 the honor of being elected a fellow of the Linnean Society.

These trips to Scotland, besides being long and arduous, were in 1812 and 1813 made particularly unpleasant by his having to deal with a situation created by an untrustworthy factor. His extensive alterations to Bartley in 1811 had apparently run low his reserves of cash, so that in order to build a new farmstead at Kinnordy he was obliged in 1813 to borrow £4,000 and an additional £3,000 to put into what he called "the sinking fund."[41] Because of earlier borrowing to finance improvements, the indebtedness standing against the Kinnordy estate now amounted to £12,000. But the need for borrowing seems not to have restrained Mr. Lyell much in his spending. His building at Bartley seems extravagant, especially as he did not own the property and had no means of recovering his investment when he came to leave there. In justifying his expenditures he frequently referred to the shortness of life. But, apart from his love of travel and of expensive books, his mode of life was quiet and economical. He was upright and, by the standards of the day, a remarkably temperate man.

MIDHURST 1810–15

Midhurst, to which Charles and Tom were sent in 1810, was very different from the schools at Ringwood and at Salisbury. It was larger, the boys older, and it was run on the principles of a great public school, being modeled especially on Winchester where the headmaster, Mr. Bayley, had formerly taught. The government of the boys, such as it was, was in the hands of the seniors who acted as prefects. There were seven classes; the seventh was the

40. C. L. to C. W. 30 Nov. 1812. Wedderburn mss.
41. C. L. to Mrs. Lyell. 10 Nov. 1813. Kinnordy mss.

lowest, while the first, taught by Mr. Bayley himself, was the highest and its members enjoyed great distinction as seniors. Charles entered at the fifth class, and during his five years at Midhurst passed successively from the fifth class to the first.

He found the atmosphere of Midhurst intimidating.[42] "I felt for the first time that I had to fight my own way in a rough world and must depend entirely on my own resources." During his first half year one of the senior boys took him under his protection, but at the end of that time he told Charles that he was "old enough and had been there long enough" to stand up for himself. Immediately, Charles began to be attacked by other boys and suffered endless insult and abuse because he was reluctant to fight back. At length, having been knocked down by a boy a year younger than himself, he resolved to fight. The resulting battle, which consisted of a series of one-minute rounds, lasted two days, five or six hours each day, and left both boys badly battered. By a narrow margin Charles seems to have been considered the victor, establishing his position in the primitive pecking order of the school and thereby saving him from being bothered further, at least by his contemporaries. He continued to suffer abuse from those above him, perhaps the more because he was a retiring boy.

Promotion from one class to the next was not by any means automatic at Midhurst but depended on a boy's score on the "Classicus Paper" week by week throughout the term. By this method the boys were ranked in a class according to their ability to translate Latin. As Charles described it:

> Thus suppose there were eight boys in the class. Their names would be arranged according to the number which they had got the week before, when Forbes being least was Classicus and had the fag of keeping the Classicus paper. But as he obtained the mark of 13 during that week and topped Lyell Senior, the last mentioned dunce would take his place, and be Classicus for the ensuing week. The great satisfaction with which the said paper is handed over to another to keep, may be conceived, for it is considered as a place of some reproach. Every boy is put on to translate a passage in his turn and as often as he fails, the word is passed on to the next below: if he knows it he takes the other's place.

Charles thought this competition for places in an order of prece-

42. *L. & L.* I, 18–31. Unless otherwise noted, all recollections of the time at Midhurst are from this source.

dence did much to overcome his "natural antipathy to work and extreme absence of mind." But this forced attention he found "very painful" and it may not have been the best method to awaken a dreamy and sensitive mind. Yet he found in study some refuge from the brutality of the school, and toward the end of his first year began to rise in his class. His score was helped by an incident in which he profited from the erudition of his father. During holidays Mr. Lyell required him and Tom to read during part of the day some of the books which they were going to study during the ensuing half year. With his philosophic outlook Mr. Lyell went beyond the simple translation of the Latin and Greek to consider ancient mythology and the geography of the Mediterranean. Thus when Mr. Bayley once asked the class what the Aegean Sea was now called, Charles was the only boy in the class who could answer "The Grecian Archipelago," and by this happy chance his Classicus Paper score rose from two to fifteen.

At the end of his first year, when the annual exercises of the school were held, he won first place for reciting English poetry and received a prize, a copy of Milton's *Paradise Lost*. Every year thereafter he won a prize for speaking until he rose high enough in the school to take prizes in Latin and English composition. He seems to have had a real feeling for poetry, particularly English poetry, although he could also appreciate to some extent Virgil and Ovid. His favorite English poets were Milton, Thomson,[43] and Gray, but during his holidays he also read Scott's *Lady of the Lake*.

Poetry was to exert a strong influence on the development of Charles's mind. He continued for many years to read Milton for pleasure and now and then would introduce a brief quotation from Milton into his geological writing and more frequently into his private notebooks. Milton's poetry is remarkable for its rich imagery and dramatic action—action which ranges through the whole cosmos from heaven to hell to earth. Milton treats the cosmos as a single theater of action for the battle between God and Satan for the soul of man. The sense of the unity of the universe, implicit in Milton, was to be for Charles Lyell one of his most fundamental and unshakable assumptions.

His reading of Thomson's *Seasons* was also to color Charles's attitude to the natural world. This long poem in four parts—

43. James Thomson (1700–48), a Scottish poet who lived at London where he wrote *The Seasons, Liberty,* and *Rule Britannia.* His poetry is considered to mark the beginning of the English romantic movement.

Spring, Summer, Autumn, and Winter—describes the changing aspects of nature through the course of the year. Thomson, as Mr. Jack Lindsay has pointed out, was deeply influenced by such sixteenth- and seventeenth-century painters as Claude, Poussin, and Salvator Rosa and was led thereby to introduce into his poetry a series of brilliant and ever-changing visual images.

> Nature ceases to be a static pattern, of which the parts are separately described, and is realized as something in ceaseless movement and change, with violent clashes and overriding harmonies. This inner movement of nature involves continual contrasts and collisions of opposites: here stark cliff and softening light, desert and fertility, horror and joy, nearness and distance. Light itself is not a mere incident . . .; it becomes an active principle linking the parts, not something spread passively over the scene.[44]

Lindsay is discussing the influence of Thomson's *Seasons* on the painter J. M. W. Turner. Thomson's *Seasons* must have exerted a similar though less conscious influence on the perceptions of the schoolboy Charles Lyell. His view of nature, inevitably tinged by contemporary romanticism, was infused with light, color, and movement. He became sensitive to change and continuity of process.

The feature of Bartley which thus seems to have influenced Charles most profoundly throughout his boyhood was that it was richly provided with books. The "beautiful library" which Mr. Lyell had incorporated into his renovation in 1811 was very well stocked and he ordered new books regularly from London.

Toward the end of his first year at Midhurst, Charles recalled, a mania for gambling swept over the school, and boys who had lost all their other belongings finally staked their breakfasts. Charles, who had gambled away his breakfast for several days, became so ravenously hungry that he entered the dining hall beforehand to steal some food. Being surprised there by the return of Mr. Budd, the purveyor, he "had nothing left for it but to disguise my face and rush out, knocking him over, with half his milk streaming in the gutter." This desperate act had the good effect of causing the seniors to investigate and to make a rule "That no boy should pay away more than half his breakfast in one morning." This rage for gambling was followed by a rage for chess

44. J. Lindsay, *J. M. W. Turner* . . . (1966) p. 58.

which consumed his hours for play and sometimes a portion of his school time as well.

During his second year in the autumn of 1811, Lady Ramsay of Banff, a Scottish friend, on Mr. Lyell's advice entered her two sons James and George at Midhurst. At the same time she took lodgings in the town in order that she might have her children "always under her observation."[45] This made a pleasant change for the Lyell boys too because once a fortnight she invited them out on Sunday. They were thus able to escape one church service and to walk in the country, where they hunted for eggs of partridges and pheasants. They also went bird-nesting and Charles became particularly adept at climbing trees. "I remember in particular an owl's nest, which could only be taken by a long-legged and long-armed boy, who could stretch up from one bough to the next." We catch here a glimpse of a long-limbed agile fifteen-year-old boy with brown hair and gray-blue eyes who is beginning to gain some confidence in himself as he finds he can do some things which other boys cannot.

At the end of his second year he became interested in music and began to play a small octavo flute. When he went home for the summer holidays his father, who had also once been a flute player, gave him one of his large flutes. Charles worked hard to learn to play this instrument and when he returned to school in August 1812 he, together with several other boys, tuned their flutes in unison and began to play together. "Some theatricals having been got up, we had a regular orchestra to play between the acts—three flutes, two octaves, a tambourine, and, by way of melodious accompaniment, a triangle. Charles seems to have been the leader of this orchestra because the following year, when it had expanded to eight flutes, it was referred to as "Lyell's band." He even added further instruments:

> One day I happened to observe that one of the hall tables, when set in a particular way, gave a sound very like a kettle-drum, the middle boards, which were long, vibrating, and producing a fine mellow drum-like sound. I accordingly got my band into the dining-hall, to the great delight of the boys, but it attracted a crowd in the street every evening and gave the Doctor an excuse for putting a stop to it.

Christmas in 1812 was celebrated quietly at Bartley because

45. C. L. to C. W. 5 Nov. 1811. Wedderburn mss.

Charles's grandmother Lyell was obliged by her failing health to remain in her house at Southampton and his aunt Ann was at Sir William Heathcote's. On 10 September 1812 Mrs. Lyell had given birth to yet another daughter who was named Sophia Georgina. In January Mr. Lyell took Charles and Tom to London to have their teeth fixed. They each had to have several fillings and one tooth pulled. He wrote to Mrs. Lyell:

> I showed the Boys St. Paul's & Westminster Abbey & took them by water to see the New Bridge.—Today we go to the Exhibition panoramas etc. & Coriolanus & afterwards to a Masquerade! The last amusement, you may believe, is not of my seeking.[46]

In 1813 at the end of the first half year Mr. Lyell allowed Tom, now fourteen, to leave Midhurst to join the navy as a gentleman volunteer or midshipman. This step was in the hope of providing a naval career for Tom who, as a younger son, would have to fend for himself. In mid-July Mr. Lyell took him to Plymouth to sail with Captain Otway in the *Ajax*. Because Great Britain was now at war with the United States as well as with France, the fleet was very active. The pattern of family life was further altered by the death in May at Southampton of Charles's grandmother who had suffered from progressive heart disease for more than a year.[47]

At the beginning of August Charles returned alone to Midhurst. He was about to begin his fourth year. During this year he wrote a Latin composition of which he was rather proud. He was later to describe it to his fiancée, Mary Horner:

> I wrote a Latin copy of verses (a weekly exercise required of all) on the fight between the land-rats and the water-rats, suggested by reading Homer's battle of the frogs and mice—a mock heroic. Dr. Bayley had just drained a pond much infested by water-rats, which was on one side of our playground, and they used to forage on not only our cakes and bread and cheese in the night, but literally on our clothes and books.

He had the good fortune to have the Latin in this fantasy corrected by the second master, Mr. Ayling, who pointed out "all the gramatical errors and one false quantity." Having then recopied it he

---

46. C. L. to Mrs. Lyell. 21 Jan. 1813. Kinnordy mss.
47. C. L. to C. W. 26 April 1812, 11 July 1813, and intervening letters. Wedderburn mss.

submitted it to Mr. Bayley who, Charles thought, was surprised both at the correctness of the Latin and at the imaginative ingenuity there displayed.

On 19 October 1814 the tenth and last child was born at Bartley Lodge to Mrs. Lyell, a seventh daughter; she was named Elizabeth. In the meantime Charles seems to have been creating a favorable impression on both his teachers and his father because at the beginning of 1815, when Charles was soon to go to Midhurst for his final year, Mr. Lyell wrote to Dawson Turner, "Charles makes me proud of his scholarship. He will return to Midhurst till Midsummer."[48]

Interlude in Scotland

At the end of June 1815 Charles left Midhurst. He was seventeen years old and might have been expected to go to university at the beginning of the Michaelmas term in October. For some reason, perhaps because there was still doubt whether he should go to a Scottish or an English university, perhaps because he had not applied to Oxford soon enough (he evidently applied first to Christ Church and then to Oriel before being admitted to Exeter College), or possibly because his father wished to take him north to see Kinnordy, he did not go to Oxford until the beginning of February 1816.

Early in August Mr. Lyell, Mrs. Lyell, Charles, and Fanny set forth in the family carriage for Scotland. The journey took them eight or nine days but they arrived without mishap. During September and October William Hooker and his bride Maria, daughter of Dawson Turner, came from Carlisle to Kinnordy to pay them a visit. During their stay Mr. Hooker, Mr. Lyell, and Charles went on expeditions in the Highlands to collect plants. On one occasion Mr. Hooker and Charles seem to have gone by themselves, for Mr. Lyell wrote to Dawson Turner, "Charles was enraptured with the excursion to Dunkeld, and exulted like a young Botanist in bringing me a store of *Eucalypta streptocarpa*."[49] Both Charles and Fanny seemed to have liked Kinnordy so well that Mr. Lyell thought if they did have to return there, it would be no hardship to them.[50]

On 14 November, Charles's birthday, they left Kinnordy and

48. C. L. to D. Turner. 13 Jan. 1815. Dawson Turner mss.
49. C. L. to D. T. 16 Oct. 1815. Dawson Turner mss.
50. C. L. to D. T. 14 Nov. 1815. Dawson Turner mss.

set off southward, sending Mr. Lyell's servant with their luggage by sea from Dundee to London. Despite snow on the eighteenth, between Dunbar and Balford they stopped to see Durham cathedral and went out of their way via Cambridge to Yarmouth to visit Dawson Turner. Mr. Lyell described the journey to Charles Wedderburn:

> Dry cold weather attended us and Charles bore his outside Berth without flinching.—We never started before 7 in the morning after fortifying ourselves with a stout breakfast, took a luncheon at about 2, and tea at night.—Till we entered Norfolk there were little signs of a milder climate than that of Angus. We staid at Mr. Turner's the 24th, 25th, 26th, 27th a visit that would have repaid any extent of journey. . . You have heard me speak with astonishment of the acquirements and good spirits of Mr. T.—his whole family partake of them, and my admiration of them is greater than ever. . . . . On Tuesday the 28th we took leave of our warmhearted friends, and went to Mr. and Mrs. Hooker's at Halesworth in Suffolk, spirits of a similar cast. (Mrs. H. is Mr. Turner's eldest daughter). Botany is Mr. H's hobby. His library is magnificent, though not of half the value of Mr. T's which has cost above £8,000!—We were not suffered to leave Halesworth till Saturday the 2ᵈ Dec.ʳ—Slept at Witham in Essex. 3ᵈ Dined at the beautiful parsonage at Bovinger[51] and slept at Flading's Hotel London.—It was the pleasantest journey from Kinnordy I ever made and my fellow Travellers were equally delighted with it.[52]

They spent two days at London, attended *Richard III* and *The Orphan* at the theater, and then went on to Bartley. Since Charles did not have to go to Oxford until 2 February his father set him to reading Horace so as to occupy his time profitably. He wrote to Turner, "You have done him inestimable benefit in enforcing the learning by heart."[53]

51. Where his brother-in-law and old friend Richard Smith was rector.
52. C. L. to C. W. 18 Dec. 1815. Wedderburn mss.
53. C. L. to D. T. 13 Dec. 1815. Dawson Turner mss.

CHAPTER 3

Oxford and First Travels, 1816–1819

We spoke of our happy life, of Universities, of what they
might be; of what they were. How powerfully they might
stimulate the student, how much valuable instruction they
might impart! We agreed that, although the least possible
benefit was conferred upon us in this respect at Oxford, we
were deeply indebted, nevertheless, to the great and good
men of former days, who founded those glorious institutions,
for devising a scheme of life, which, however deflected from
its original direction, still tended to study . . .

Thomas Hogg, *Life of Shelley*[1]

THE OXFORD to which Charles Lyell went in February 1816 was
very different from the modern Oxford and very different from
what is today comprehended by the term university. History, economics, and political science were neither taught nor studied.
Natural science had been established in a very small way and was
represented by short courses of lectures in chemistry and mineralogy. However, because students never were examined in the
subjects taught in lectures, these were unimportant in the scheme
of Oxford life. Teaching was confined to the colleges, where it
was carried on by a rudimentary process of tutoring. All the great
intellectual currents of the eighteenth century had swept by Oxford leaving it undisturbed. Edinburgh, London, and Paris had
been shaken by a new revolution in chemistry, violent controversy
in geology, new economic, social, and political theories, but these
had barely touched Oxford. Certainly none of these movements
had originated there. Of all the work done in England in pneu-
matic chemistry in the eighteenth century none was carried out at
Oxford. Adam Smith and David Hume taught at Edinburgh;
William Paley and Thomas Malthus studied at Cambridge. Young
men of ability, such as Thomas Gray and Edward Gibbon, left
Oxford with feelings of bitterness and did their creative work
elsewhere.

1. T. J. Hogg. *The Life of Percy Bysshe Shelley* (1906) p. 65.

During the eighteenth century Oxford had become principally a training school for clergymen, and for country clergymen at that—the population of eighteenth century England being overwhelmingly rural. Since the intellectual demands upon country clergymen were not then very exacting and yet at the same time represented all that the average country gentleman would expect in the way of education for his son, Oxford comfortably adjusted itself to their level. It had begun as "the chief grammar school in England" and was still largely that.

Within the colleges themselves there was no incentive to aspire to excellence. In the very nature of their organization the colleges at Oxford and Cambridge had a built-in inertia. Since the fellows of a college controlled its finances, their interest in educating students was at war with their interest in their own comfort and luxury. Because they were themselves the arbiters of this conflict, it is not difficult to see in which direction their decisions tended to be made. As a result, the colleges had rarely been able to reform themselves without external compulsion.[2]

But in the years just before Lyell's arrival, Oxford had begun to stir with new life. In 1800 it had passed a new statute which established examinations for a degree. These examinations had the effect of requiring both the tutors to teach and the students to study, so that the tendency toward complete idleness on the part of both groups was counteracted. In 1801 John Kidd had been appointed reader in chemistry and in 1803 he became the first Aldrichian professor of chemistry.[3] He was accustomed to give lectures in chemistry and, for several years before 1813, in mineralogy. Shelley had attended one of his mineralogy lectures in 1810 but had been greatly disappointed at the contents.[4] In 1813 Kidd had resigned his chair of mineralogy and William Buckland had been appointed to it. Buckland infused his lectures in mineralogy with the excitement and fascination to be found in scientific research. If Shelley could have heard them he might have found therein a counterpart to his own vision of the possibilities of sci-

2. *Oxford University Commission Report*. London: H.M. Stationery Office, 1852, XXVIII, 387 pp. *passim*.

3. John Kidd (1775–1851) was professor of chemistry at Oxford from 1803 until 1822 when he resigned in favor of Charles Daubeny. He also took a leading part in establishing the teaching of medicine at Oxford.

4. He talked "About stones!—stones, stones, stones!—nothing but stones!—and so drily. It was wonderfully tiresome—and stones are not interesting things in themselves." Hogg, *Shelley*, p. 47.

ence. However, these few scientific lectures were as yet an isolated and very minor part of the Oxford scene. The whole program of study for the undergraduate consisted of the reading of Latin and Greek authors, and the study of the philosophy of Aristotle and disputations over it.

At the end of January 1816 Mr. Lyell described his son to Dawson Turner:

> Tomorrow I am to take Charles to Oxford, an event full of interest to both of us, from which he is promising himself a rich harvest of fame as well as pleasure, and I (though M.A. of the Sister Alma Mater, and fully aware of his desultory habits) am not without hopes that even the former may be realized. There is more judgment, taste and imagination in him than you have an idea of, but without some powerful excitement he never brings them into play.—His late Master understood him perfectly and is well deserving of my gratitude for his perseverance and address in making him a scholar.[5]

On 2 February Mr. Lyell entered Charles at Exeter College as a gentleman commoner, then a highly privileged student who lived quite apart from the poor students or scholars. He had wanted to get Charles into Christ Church, but had not been able to obtain a place for him there. On visiting Exeter, however, Mr. Lyell was favorably impressed by the quality of the tutors and felt that he could not have placed Charles better. He also thinned his own bookshelves to provide Charles "with the best library of any undergraduate at Oxford"[6] (Figs. 3, 4).

The education of his eldest son was a matter of intimate and almost agonizing concern to Mr. Lyell. He did not feel he could support the boy as a gentleman commoner but determined to do so anyway, despite the catastrophic fall in rents after the peace of 1815. He wanted Charles to excel in scholarship and urged him to compete for a prize to be given for fifty lines of verse on "the horses of Lysippus." Dawson Turner was consulted for some historical information about these horses, which had supposedly been sculpted by Lysippus from horses belonging to Alexander the Great. He also encouraged Charles to write to him fully about university life, and we have a portion of the series of letters which he wrote—letters which seem remarkably mature for a young man

5. C. L. to D. Turner. 31 Jan. 1816. Dawson Turner mss.
6. C. L. to C. W. 25 Feb. 1816. Wedderburn mss.

of nineteen. On 29 February 1816 Charles described some of his new acquaintances:

> I mentioned to you in my last letter that I had met with two pleasant men in Corpus, but extremely dissipated, their names were Creek & Eckersall. The latter, accompanied with Stirling of Baliol formerly a Midhurst man under Dr. Wool, and Torr of New College ran away from their respective colleges the day before yesterday, taking places in the London coach, after having made a sale of their furniture, etc. and packing up their books and clothes.

Stirling, it appears, was an "old stager" and Eckersall was "mad for Theatricals" so Charles expected to hear of them next on the stage. But if the escapades of these characters provided news, university life was actually much more serious.

> There is full as much necessary business here as I had at Midhurst the last year and a half. But at Corpus it is beyond every thing. Although Norris has been diligent lately, fagging in the evenings and refusing invitations, yet yesterday he and Richards during a holiday which they had, sat five whole hours from breakfast till dinner working.

Charles thought this was too much, especially considering that Norris got through work quickly. It was not then thought fashionable at Oxford to work hard, as is possibly still true, and Charles noted that Norris tried to maintain and did maintain "the highly honorable and fashionable title of a complete idle fellow."

Charles liked his rooms, which were "almost the best, it seems, in College," and was rapidly making new acquaintances. He had subscribed to the concert series at the Music Room under the impression, which proved wrong, that many men at Exeter would be subscribing. He also commented on the effort which university officials were making to combat extravagant habits among the students:

> They have begun a reform at Trinity. At least as far as the enormous expense. Everything which goes in there is inspected and one of their Gentlemen Commoners told Norris yesterday that he should take his name off positively "for the principal has declared that not an *ice* or a *pine-apple* shall enter the College!" Dreadful Extremity!![7]

7. C. L., Jr. to his father. 29 Feb. 1816. Kinnordy mss.

The idea of ices and pineapples as symbols of extravagant luxury may seem strange today; the extravagant tendencies of university students are not.

Somewhat later in the term Charles gave his father a further account of the social life at Exeter College, which traditionally had been the home of students from Devonshire:

> I have now seen a great deal of the society here and like it very much. We are very much divided into sets. The first division consisting of about ten of the Gentleman Commoners and 15 or 20 Commoners, certainly the genteelest chosen out of the whole. The remaining 7 of the Gentlemen Commoners are not in any other party, but the greater part are in a short time to take their degrees and are consequently reading; the others never go into any society. As for the rest of the college I don't exactly know whether there are any such decided divisions but there is certainly an immense herd of Devonshire men who are almost all great raffs in their appearance and complete provincialists in their language. Nevertheless they seem pretty good scholars.

He remarks that both the rector of Exeter, Dr. Cole, and the sub-rector, Mr. Jones, had been chaplains in the navy.

> The latter is a good scholar, as for the former this anecdote will be sufficient.
>
> When he as Vice-Chancellor was escorting the Duchess of Oldenburg to the Bodleian Library, and her Highness was prying into everything, she took down some books and asked the Dr. what languages they were & what was the meaning of something in the title page of a Greek book. The Head of Exeter was not only obliged to confess that he could not assist her in the translation of any passage but that he was even totally ignorant of the names of the languages! . . . If she had asked the Doctor how to make an Oxford sausage he would have given her as good a receipt as any one as he is famed for his dinners.

He had also had time to compare notes with students in other colleges. At Christ Church, for instance, "Their Gentlemen Commoners seem to have very little intercourse with the Scholars but a large acquaintance of Out-College men. They are kept desperately to the reading, and I think in the extreme."[8]

At the end of March Charles went home for spring vacation and

8. C. L., Jr. to his father. 5 March 1816. Kinnordy mss.

took with him an Oxford calendar so that he would not have to answer his sisters' questions about the university. During the vacation he wrote his verses on the horses of Lysippus and studied Herodotus. The poem, his father thought, was "not above mediocrity and certainly ought not to gain a prize, but is not destitute of *estro poetico*."[9] He did not get the prize and while he seems to have anticipated this result it was still a disappointment to him. He was finding himself backward in classics and regretted that he had not read more since he had left Midhurst.

> As for Logic I have had nothing to do with it this term but have made a determination to get up in the Long Vacation the 4 first books of Euclid. My Little Go comes after the Vacation about a week from the time I come up. Mathematics will therefore be preferable in every respect. I cannot learn logic without an assistant and there will be no time after I return.[10]

On 31 May he wrote to his father, "The men here have taken a good deal of interest about Christabel, as the Author is an uncle of our Coleridge." Our coleridge was John Taylor Coleridge, later a judge, but then a fellow of Exeter and a few years earlier a student at Corpus. The *Times* had just published a severe criticism of *Christabel,* but Charles was inclined to be favorable to the poem, especially towards its style. "I lay so much stress on the style" he wrote, "because it strikes me in that consists all the Originality. In the story there is no clue, nothing to interest you but *Singularity*."[11]

During the summer of 1816 Mr. Lyell went north to Kinnordy alone, while Charles remained at Bartley to read because in October he had to face his first examination.

In contrast to Charles's academic interests and the buoyant life of undergraduates, whose chief concerns were social relationships, Mr. Lyell encountered in Scotland much grimmer problems. The weather had been very wet and every crop except oats had failed. On 12 October, the first day of sunshine since his arrival at Kinnordy, he wrote to Dawson Turner:

> Such a season is most unfortunate for this poor country and must compleat the ruin of those Farmers who are on the totter.

9. C. L. to D. T. 24 April 1816. Dawson Turner mss.
10. C. L., Jr. to his father. 14 May 1816. Kinnordy mss.
11. C. L. Jr. to his father. 31 May 1816. Kinnordy mss.

—Scarcely one of mine is solvent. I can get no money but by sequestration (rouping [i.e. auctioning] stock and crop) and am obliged to be merciful where there is a chance of the Tenant's keeping on his legs as there are few applications for Farms that are vacant. Three of my largest are thrown on my hands and at Martinmas, which is our collection, I have not a chance of receiving as much as will pay the year's property tax still due, the expenses of management, lawyers etc. . . .

The population of our Parish is 5,000, chiefly brown linen manufacturers, of whom 1500 are in the Town. The poor fund arising from a Sunday collection at the Kirk and small contributions, is about £200 and this is sufficient even now, when the manufacture is at its lowest, and there are some orphans and one insane person maintained out of it. The cheapness of their diet, the practice of relations, though very distant, assisting each other, and a noble Scotch pride are the principal causes that the applications for relief from the poor's fund are so trifling. The energy of character here has been remarkably shown this summer. The Weavers were unable to dispose of their works in Dundee, Glasgow or any of the usual channels, and in their distress resolved to try the hawking of them which answered sufficiently well to have induced three hundred to leave Kirriemuir at different times. Some of the young and strong took upon their back 130 yds., 3/4 wide, weight above 60 lb.; others went by sea and with carriers; they have been all over the Hebrides, in Hull, London, perhaps in Yarmouth. The fabric is called Osnaburghs, is chiefly used in the West Indies for the Negroes' dresses and is from 5 d. to 9 d. the yard at Kirriemuir.[12]

On 31 October Charles wrote to his father that the examination was over "and much to my satisfaction." His tutors had been offended by his decision to take the examination in mathematics, especially the mathematics tutor, because the previous term Charles had refused to attend his lectures in mathematics. On examining him, however, he found that Charles knew the propositions of Euclid individually very well, but did not understand the relations among them. "I worked most perseveringly all the week," Charles wrote, "and when he examined me afterwards the day before I went up, he declared me marvellously improved." The examination itself was a triumph.

12. C. L. to D. T. 12 Oct. 1816. Dawson Turner mss.

> I was the last on the list, that is of the 8 who were examined this same day, and they gave me to employ the time 3 propositions to prove on paper which were not in Euclid, which, as some of my companions who took up 6 books could neither make head or tail of, they gave me great kudos for doing correctly, and gave me another stiffener the proof of which I got at, to their surprise, tho' they said it was neither by the shortest road, nor by the way they intended.

Charles was also studying hard at Aristotle whom he found "an astonishing stiff author." He found the other students ahead of him in this regard and had to work hard to keep up. He also found the social competition occasionally harsh.

> As to what you said of T. T.—I have introduced him to many here. They have always behaved pleasantly to him in company and then cut him when they met him afterwards. The mischief of continuing this is that you are yourself offended with your friends, you feel for the man and he is also hurt. The cause of this illiberality is, that Oxford is in the first place immensely full. The society in your own college must be large and if men have out-college acquaintances they wish them to be such as would reflect some credit and dash on them.

Whether this was sufficient justification for the rudeness of a set of young snobs is doubtful. Charles himself seemed to think so. He went on:

> As for myself I should feel less reproach on my conscience for not warring more stoutly with these groundless prejudices of the World from the consciousness, that, as it is I am so great a sufferer. An unfortunate instance of which occurred the other day. Mr. Bayley came up here to take his *Doctor's degree*. He dined with me in our Hall, and in return I went with him to New College. . . Tragitt was with us. In the common room after dinner we met a Mr. Williams brother to the 2nd master of Winchester. Mr. B. had been speaking of Lady Rivers and Mr. W. immediately gave a long History of Lady Holland's protegée, addressed to Tragitt whom he called Lyell mistaking him for me. After drawing the parallel dreadfully exact and lengthened as if for the purpose of torture, he ended by raising his voice, and fixing the attention of the whole room "And I myself, Sir, have dined there when the girl has come in after dinner to

the dessert & her Father the *Butler* waiting at the table at the same time."!!

Such pointed things can happen but seldom, but when they do come they are more cutting and painful both to the person concerned and his friends than if (by way of a *summum malum*) the examining Master in the Schools was to give you to understand that you were a pluck'd man.

This incident reveals a ruthless snobbery in English university life at that time which one would rather not see, but which goes far to explain both the timorousness and the cruelty in social matters of which Charles complained. Mr. Lyell had evidently been urging on him the need to cultivate the abilities required by a barrister.

As for the confidence and quickness which you were speaking of as one of the chief requisites of the Bar, I don't know whether intercourse with the world will supply it, but God knows I have little enough of it now in company, and I was surprised at feeling so much unconcern as I did in the Schools.[13]

However Mr. Lyell who was facing cold wet weather and a crop failure at Kinnordy was cheered by Charles's letter and wrote to Dawson Turner, "I have great hopes of him [Charles] because he is very unlike me in many of my failings."[14] Several months later he again referred to Charles in writing to Turner, "He has as gentlemanly right minded ideas as could be wished, and talents above mediocrity, and more industry than most men of his age."[15]

In the spring of 1817 Charles again submitted verses, this time with the Farnese Hercules as subject, and again failed to win. The disappointment was perhaps softened by the fact that his enthusiasm had now been kindled by a new interest. During one of his vacations, possibly that of the previous summer or the Christmas vacation, he had read in his father's library Robert Bakewell's *Introduction to Geology*. Mr. Lyell had bought and read this book as early as March 1816, for he mentions it to Dawson Turner as "An interesting and popular volume, notwithstanding a peevish preface."[16] Charles later said this book first "gave him an idea of

13. C. L., Jr. to his father. 31 Oct. 1816. Kinnordy mss. *L. & L.* I, 38 (printed in part).

14. C. L. to D. T. 6 Nov. 1816. Dawson Turner mss.

15. C. L. to D. T. 20 March 1817. Dawson Turner mss.

16. C. L. to D. T. 21 March 1816. Dawson Turner mss. Mr. Lyell seems to have read the 2nd edition of this book.

the existence of such a science as geology," and he seems to have been particularly excited by what Bakewell had to say about the antiquity of the earth.[17] Bakewell, who had adopted the geological theories of Dr. James Hutton of Edinburgh, believed that the earth was immensely old—much older than the six thousand years allowed by the chronology of the Old Testament. A vast and indefinite age for the earth was in fact the single most distinguishing feature of the Huttonian theory. The reasons Dr. Hutton adopted this view require some explanation, but it gave his geological theory a startling significance for religion.

After he returned from the spring vacation Charles enrolled on 13 May 1817 in a course of lectures in mineralogy given by one of the younger fellows of Corpus, the college where his friend Norris studied so hard. This lecturer was the Reverend William Buckland, who had been reader in Mineralogy at Oxford since 1813. Buckland (Fig. 5), one of his later students tells us, "was a wonderful lecturer, clear, fluent, rapid, overflowing with witty illustrations, dashing down amongst us, ever and anon to enforce an intricate point with Samsonic wielding of a cave-bear jaw or a hyena thigh bone."[18] The cave bear and the hyena were to come later, but Buckland had already made an important collection of fossils, particularly from the strata of southwestern England.

Born in 1784 at Axminster in Devonshire, Buckland had while still a child become interested in the Ammonite fossils of the surrounding rock strata. In 1801 he had come from school at Winchester to Corpus Christi College, Oxford and in 1808 was ordained and elected a fellow of his college. From 1808 to 1812 he had ridden on horseback over a large part of southwestern England tracing out the geology of the country, with maps and directions given him by the geological genius of England, William Smith.[19] Smith, a land surveyor and civil engineer by profession, had worked out the succession of strata in the south of England and had determined the principles on which geological maps should be made. Although Smith did not publish his Geological Map of England until 1815, he had for years given his knowledge

17. *L. & L.* I, 32.

18. W. Tuckwell. *Reminiscences of Oxford* (1901) p. 38.

19. William Smith (1769–1839) was born at Churchill, Oxfordshire and educated at his village school. He became an assistant to a land surveyor and thereby became acquainted with the soil and underlying rocks of a wide area of Oxfordshire. In 1793 while surveying for a canal in Somersetshire he came to understand the regular order of the English strata and their uniform dip to the southeast. He identified strata always by their characteristic fossils.

and the use of his hand-drawn maps freely to such men as Buckland.

Smith had recognized the continuity of stratified rock formations across southwestern England on the basis of their physical characteristics. Then when he examined the Reverend Benjamin Richardson's fossil collection at Bath he found that he was able to tell the rock formation from which the different fossils had come. He realized that each formation contained characteristic fossils and that he could use the fossils to identify the rock. Smith's method therefore of distinguishing between otherwise similar rock strata, and of identifying a particular stratum when he came across it in a different part of the country depended on identification of its characteristic fossils. Smith thus added scientific significance to the interest which fossils had long possessed as natural curiosities and thereby gave particular point to Buckland's efforts to form a collection of fossils. From 1812 to 1815 Buckland had made extensive tours with George Bellas Greenough[20] to assist Greenough in compiling data for the geological map of England which was to be published by the Geological Society of London in 1819. In 1816 Buckland, Greenough, and John Conybeare[21] had made a long tour on the Continent, passing through Silesia to Poland, Austria, and Italy. On this expedition Buckland made a collection of fossil shells from the sub-Apennine hills of Italy and noted that many of them resembled shells from the strata of Hampshire and Sheppey Island.[22] This kind of observation may have appealed to Charles Lyell, brought up in Hampshire as he was, but perhaps the contact with a young and energetic man, already widely traveled, who was developing a new and exciting science with much force and drive, was by itself a sufficient stimulus.

Another stimulus to interest in geology at Oxford was that each June, during Whitsun week, several members of the Geological Society of London were accustomed to visit Dr. Buckland and accompany him on geological excursions. In this way Charles may have met William Daniel Conybeare, an Oxford graduate and

20. George Bellas Greenough (1778–1855) was one of the founders and first president of the Geological Society of London. He possessed private means which enabled him to devote his leisure to geology.

21. John Josias Conybeare (1779–1824), who had been a student of Christ Church, Oxford, was vicar of Batheaston, Somerset and a prebendary of York Cathedral. He published a number of geological papers.

22. A. Gordon. *The Life and Correspondence of William Buckland, D.D., F. R. S.* (1894) pp. 14–16.

friend of Buckland, who in 1817 was appointed curate of Chal-combe.[23] Conybeare was at this time studying the skeletons of species of large fossil marine reptiles first discovered in 1814 at Lyme Regis in Dorsetshire which in 1820 Conybeare was to name *Ichthyosaurus. Ichthyosaurus* was the first large fossil reptile to be found in the secondary strata of England, but since the 1790s Georges Cuvier had been astonishing the world with his recon-structions of fossil animals both from the superficial gravel and alluvium of the Seine valley and from the gypsum quarries of Montmartre. In 1812 Cuvier had drawn together the results of his work in the four volumes of his *Recherches sur les ossemens fos-siles.*

The whole subject so fired Charles's imagination that on 4 June 1817 Mr. Lyell wrote to Dawson Turner of his son: "Buckland's Mineralogical lectures are engaging him heart and soul at pres-ent." Neither Mr. Lyell nor Dawson Turner was entirely happy about his shift of interest from classical studies but Mr. Lyell thought that geology was at least "rational and gentlemanlike . . . though lighter than Aristotle or the Law" and would not inter-fere.[24]

During the long summer vacation of 1817 Mr. Lyell had de-cided that Charles should accompany him to Scotland. His ten-ants were still in a bad way as a result of the harvest failure the previous year and the low prices and stagnation of trade resulting from the peace. Mr. Lyell thought it was time that Charles should see something of the problems with which the estate was faced. But first he was to be allowed to pay a visit to the Turners at Yarmouth. Dawson Turner took a great interest in the young man and had some thought of making a short trip to Holland with his family and taking Charles along. They did not go but Charles found the Turner household itself entertaining and pleasant enough. Charles left Bartley on 16 July and traveled by stage-coach overnight to London.[25] He found it difficult to sleep in the coach because his legs were too long for him to stretch them out,

23. William Daniel Conybeare (1787–1857), a younger brother of John Josias Conybeare, had entered Christchurch, Oxford in 1805 and was graduated B.A. in November 1808. Between 1807 and 1812 he worked to compile geological maps of Hampshire, Somersetshire, Gloucestershire, and South Wales. See W. D. Conybeare, *Letters and Exercises of the Elizabethan Schoolmaster John Conybeare . . .* (1905).

24. C. L. to D. T. 4 June 1817. Dawson Turner mss.

25. He wrote the account of this journey to his father 20 July 1817. Kinnordy mss.

but after he had reached the Gloucester Coffee House, had dressed, breakfasted, and posted his letters, he was ready for a day of visiting and sight-seeing in the metropolis. He first went to call upon his father's old botanical correspondent, James Sowerby, who was now working at the description and illustration of British fossils for his *Mineral Conchology*.[26] Sowerby, who described and illustrated fossils for various workers, including Buckland, lived at 4 Meade Place, Lambeth, which Charles had a little difficulty in finding:

> When searching about the Row for his house behold the *very identical Ammonites Bucklandi* was lying on the steps![27] I went in and introduced myself, telling him by what means I had discovered his house. "Ah!" said he, "little I believe did they think at Oxford what advantage I should take of that joke. I hear Buckland was perfectly astonished when he read it." I exclaimed involuntarily "Well he might be," which he took in good part, laughing heartily, indeed the very remembrance of such an exquisite specimen of Wit set the whole family to laugh, in which I joined with equal glee & satisfaction.
>
> His eldest son [James de Carle Sowerby] appeared that morning to great advantage. I had no conception from his ordinary appearance at Bartley that he was so well entitled to form a part of a collection of Curiosities. He was dirty in the extreme in person & his coat was ornamented with a splash of white paint, for he had been assisting a painter who is now painting their Cabinets. He put me in mind of the Echinus which you will find on my mantlepiece, still retaining some of the clay in which it had been imbedded and with that paint on it which Reynold's child has thought fit to add. I was much amused there, but lost much from the confusion.

Young Sowerby may have been grimy simply because he had been working. Charles is perhaps a shade supercilious, but he was obviously delighted with his visit.

Charles also visited his relations in London, went to see "the

26. J. Sowerby. *The Mineral Conchology of Great Britain* . . . (1812–46).

27. *Ammonites bucklandi* is a large Ammonite which frequently has lost its inner whorls. On one occasion Buckland had found an extraordinarily large specimen with its inner whorls gone and carried it home over his shoulder in the manner of a French horn. Since he was riding horseback his friends in amusement called him an "Ammon Knight." Sowerby later named the species for him.

Elephant at Exeter Change," Bullock's museum,[28] and Francillion's collection of foreign and British insects at the British Museum. The next day he boarded the coach for Norwich, but recorded only "Journey from London uninteresting. Except proving Phillips' egregiously & unpardonably wrong in his direction of the Chalk line in the Map." This indicates, however, that he had with him a copy of Phillips' *Outlines of Mineralogy and Geology*, the second edition of which, published the year before, had included a geological map of England.[29] Charles was using it to try to follow the geology of the country as he went. He visited Sir James Smith at Norwich and looked at the Linnean collection of insects. He also visited the cathedral where he climbed the spire to see the view, and looked for fossils in a chalk pit where he found "an immense number of Belemnites, Echinites and bivalves." In the afternoon he went on by stagecoach to Yarmouth where he found everyone well at Mr. Turner's and some interesting guests present. Charles became friendly there with Dr. Joseph Arnold, a very quiet man who had served for a number of years as a naval surgeon and who had travelled in Java.[30] On his return voyage from Java in 1815 the ship burned and his journals and collections of insects from South America, Australia, and Java were destroyed. Arnold had a large collection of fossils from the strata of Norfolk and Suffolk. When alone he was very willing to talk about fossils and went over the whole of his collection with Charles. He also allowed Charles to copy for Dr. Buckland part of a paper which he had written.

Charles enjoyed the pleasant, busy life of the Turner household. Mr. Turner was usually at the bank during the day or occupied with writing letters and other concerns. His family was equally industrious. On 28 July Charles wrote to his father, "What I see going on every hour in this family makes me ashamed of the most active day I ever spent at Midhurst. Mrs. Turner has been etching with her daughters in the parlour every morning this week at half-past six!! Harriet has as much talent as all the others united, and her knowledge of Latin is astonishing." Since everyone was thus employed, Charles was left free to explore

28. William Bullock (fl. 1827) had in 1812 established a miscellaneous collection including much natural history at the Egyptian Hall, Piccadilly and it remained there as the London Museum till 1819.

29. W. Phillips, *Outlines of Mineralogy and Geology* . . . (1816).

30. Joseph Arnold (1782–1818) who accompanied Sir Stamford Raffles to Sumatra and died there during their first tour into the interior.

the countryside. Already he had become interested in the way in which landscape was formed by the forces of rain and rivers, wind and sea acting upon it.

Dr. Arnold returned on Saturday after being away four days. I was very glad of it for as Mr. T. has been much employed in the Bank I have had time to examine and consider the Geological wonders of this country. The Dr. says my conclusions are exactly like his which no body ever before he had made, and has become in consequence very communicative & quite another person.

Yarmouth is a Delta formed at the mouth of the Yare. When first these sands rose by the opposition of the sea tide & river, Norwich was a great seaport (as we find records of) the violence of the tide being kept off by this bank the estuary filled up with "fluviatile detritus," the Yare then wound thro' the present marshes and entered the sea North of Yarmouth. (Mr. T. says "no") The reason that it then turned off at right angles, was that the mouth being stopped up by the sea it was obliged to find a new course & the North river meeting it there, it flowed with it, southward & entered a little south of the town, then two miles farther off, then 4 miles at Gorleston where the Pier is which you saw.

All these ancient channels I found & the Dr. confirmed them, tho' Mr. T. laughs in spite of facts & tradition. I believe he does not like that he should not have seen it before.

The last movement of the river threw inland at least a mile of perpendicular sand cliff, 15 feet high, on which the village of Gorleston stands. The terrace or platform on top of this cliff is on a level with the marsh land reaching to Norwich. A friend of Mr. T's told us yesterday that 35 years ago he could stand by the river and see the hulks of the ships over the deens, which rise now six feet & more too high on the sea-side for such a prospect & yet the sea has not been over them all that time.

Dr. Arnold & I examined yesterday the pit which is dug out for the foundation of the Nelson Monument & found that the first bed of shingle is 8 feet down. Now this was the last stratum brought by the Sea. All since was driven up by wind & kept there by the "Restharrow" & other plants. It is mere sand. Therefore, 35 years ago the dunes were nearly as low as the last stratum left by the sea, & as the wind would naturally have begun adding from the very first, it is clear that within 50 years the sea flowed over that part. This even Mr. T. allows is a strong argument in favour of the recency of the changes.[31]

Here at the age of nineteen Charles was observing geological processes at work and was interpreting a complex pattern of phenomena with the insight which was to emerge as characteristically his own. He shows the ability to link together diverse facts and to see in his mind's eye both what must have been, and what will be, as a result of forces presently at work. This rare imaginative grasp of the meaning of landscape, this ability to see the earth's surface as a plastic, shifting thing, steadily and relentlessly molded throughout the long course of time by the slow action of ordinary processes, was to enable him to alter the whole science of geology.

In Lyell's reconstruction of the recent history of geological processes at Yarmouth he exercised a quality of dynamic pictorial imagination similar to that present in a Turner painting and perhaps derived from the same influences—their common reading of Thomson's *Seasons* and of Milton. In place of a swirling pattern of wind and water there is a pattern of shifting river mouths, gravel bars, and sand dunes, but the sense of both movement and unity in the landscape is similar.

Charles was delighted to find that Dr. Arnold agreed with him that Great Britain had formerly been connected with France by a land bridge which had since been eroded away to form the straits of Dover. Dr. Arnold thought it was "the meeting of the great North current with that of the English Channel that burst open the straits of Dover" and Charles was delighted with this opinion because it agreed with what Abraham Werner (1749–1817), Alexander von Humboldt (1769–1859), and William Buckland all thought. But his whole time was not taken up with geology. He had found in his rambles some species of beetles which were rare at Bartley. He was also memorizing Greek poetry and playing chess with Mr. Turner or his daughter Elizabeth in the evenings. He was satisfied with the work he was doing. "Between Dr. Arnold's long Catalogue of Norfolk fossils & a map which I think I shall be able to make of this country I flatter myself I shall compile some interesting information for Buckland, who is quite of White's opinion 'Local information from actual observation tends more to promote Natural History & Science than all that is

31. C. L., Jr. to his father. 28 July 1817. Kinnordy mss.

Fig. 1. The first Charles Lyell and his family ca. 1780; Charles Lyell, Mary Lyell (née Beale), Mary, and Charles. Painted by Thomas Hickey (1741–1824). Courtesy of Lord Lyell of Kinnordy.

Fig. 2. Kinnordy House as it was before reconstruction in 1880. Charles Lyell was born 14 November 1797 in the room with the two large windows in the wing on the right. Courtesy of Lord Lyell of Kinnordy.

Fig. 3. Silhouette of Mr. Lyell of Kinnordy. Courtesy of Lord Lyell of Kinnordy.

Fig. 4. Silhouette of Charles Lyell: The Oxford undergraduate. Courtesy of Lord Lyell of Kinnordy.

Fig. 5. The Reverend William Buckland lecturing at Oxford in 1823; *Ammonites bucklandi* and *Ichthyosaurus* skull in the foreground. Courtesy of Devon County Record Office, Exeter, England.

Fig. 6. Thomas Pennant's illustration of Fingal's Cave, Staffa.

Fig. 7. The Lyell brothers in 1819; Henry (aged 14), Charles (aged 21), Thomas (aged 20). Painted by Thomas Phillips R.A. Courtesy of Lord Lyell of Kinnordy.

Fig. 8. Dr. James Hutton (1726–96) by Sir Henry Raeburn R.A. Courtesy of Lord Bruntisfield.

Fig. 9. The Reverend John Playfair (1748–1819) by Sir Henry Raeburn R.A. Courtesy of the National Portrait Gallery, London.

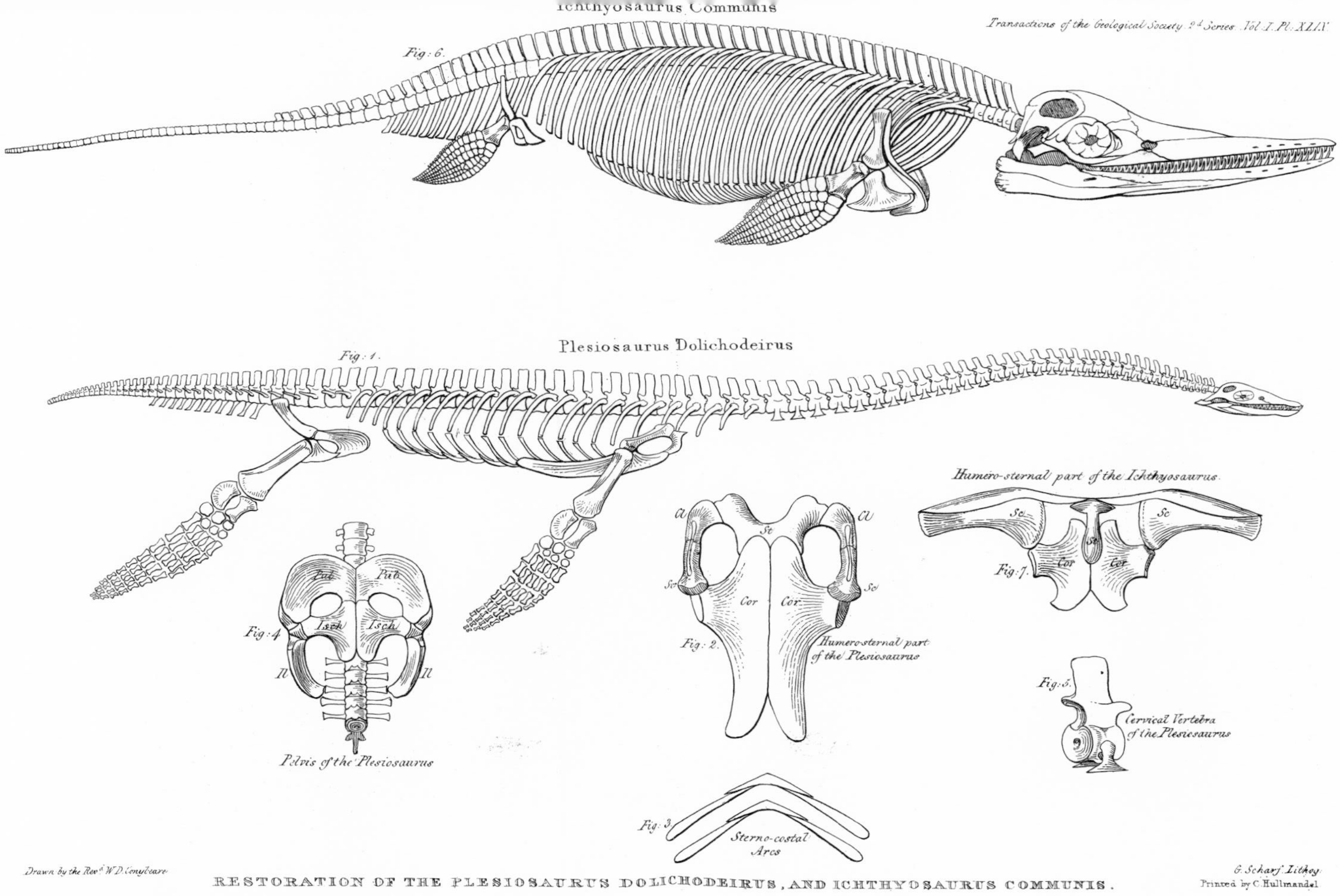

Ichthyosaurus Communis

Fig. 6.

Plesiosaurus Dolichodeirus

Fig. 1.

Humero-sternal part of the Ichthyosaurus

Sc
Co
Cor
St
Fig. 7.

Cervical Vertebra of the Plesiosaurus

Fig. 5.

Humero-sternal part of the Plesiosaurus

Cl
Sc
Cor
Cor
a
Fig. 2.

Sterno-costal Arcs

Fig. 3.

Pelvis of the Plesiosaurus

Pub
Isch
Il
Il
Costa
Fig. 4.

Drawn by the Rev.d W.d Conybeare.   Printed by C.Hullmandel.   G.Scharf. Lithog.

RESTORATION OF THE PLESIOSAURUS DOLICHODEIRUS, AND ICHTHYOSAURUS COMMUNIS.

Fig. 10. W. D. Conybeare's reconstruction of *Ichthyosaurus* and *Plesiosaurus*.

Fig. 11. Gideon Mantell (1790–1852) in 1837. Engraved by Samuel Stepney from the portrait by J. J. Masquerier. Courtesy of the Alexander Turnbull Library, Wellington, New Zealand.

Fig. 12. Vertical chalk strata at Handfast Point, Dorsetshire from Englefield's Isle of Wight. Drawn by Thomas Webster.

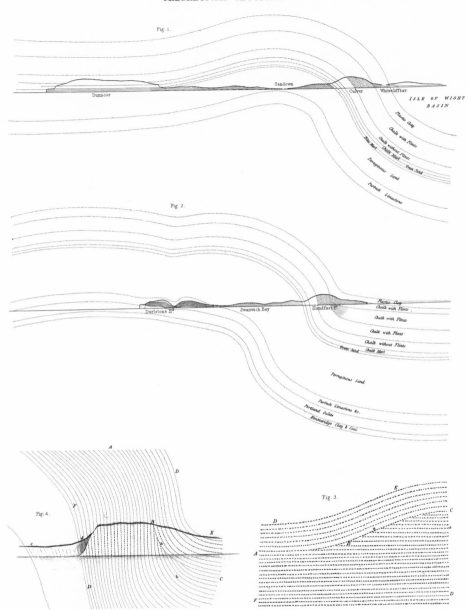

Fig. 13. Thomas Webster's theoretical sections: (upper) of the Isle of Wight; (lower) of the adjacent part of Dorsetshire to the west.

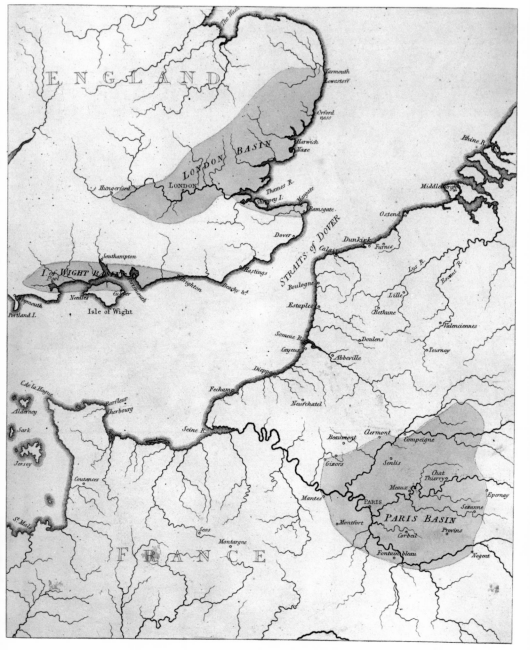

Fig. 14. Thomas Webster's geological map of the Paris, London, and Isle of Wight basins.

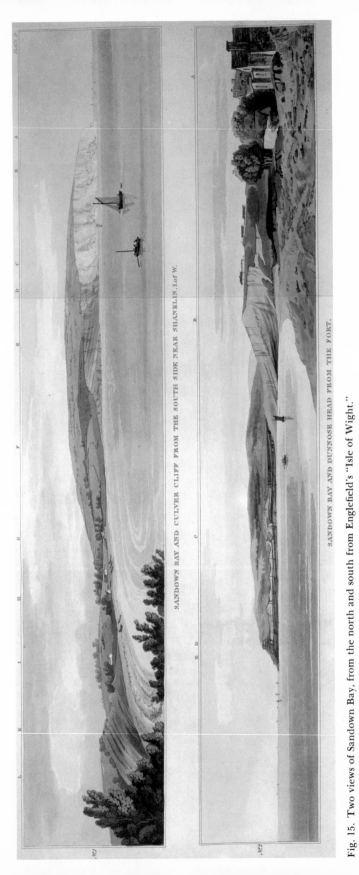

SANDOWN BAY AND CULVER CLIFF FROM THE SOUTH SIDE NEAR SHANKLIN. I. of W.

SANDOWN BAY AND DUNNOSE HEAD FROM THE FORT.

Fig. 15. Two views of Sandown Bay, from the north and south from Englefield's "Isle of Wight."

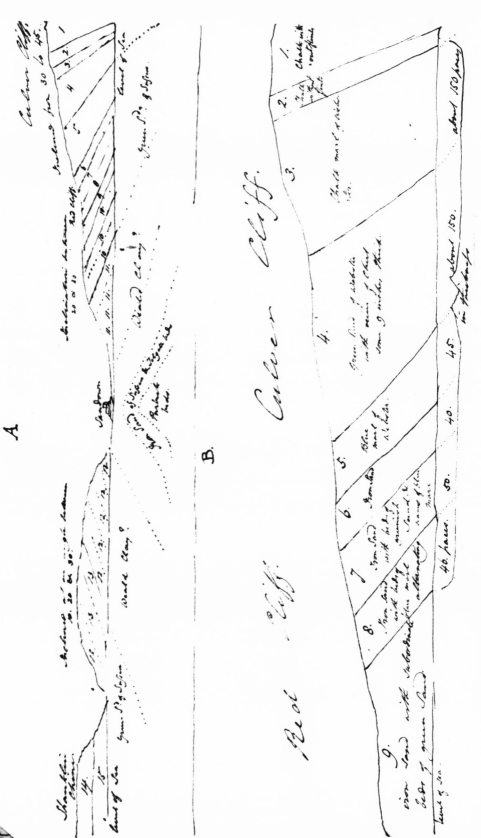

Fig. 16. Lyell's section of Sandown Bay, 1822.

done by the speculation and compilations of voluminous Authors.' "[32]

Charles spent some three weeks at Yarmouth before returning to Bartley early in August. His visit had been thoroughly enjoyable. In writing on 29 August to Mr. Turner from Kinnordy of this visit and the subsequent trip, he mentioned "that Dr. Arnold and I parted the garden keys. He is to carry one to Sumatra and I have hung up the other in my study here as a remembrance of happy days." The Turners wanted him to come back.

Charles and his father set out on 20 August for Scotland. As far as York they traveled by stagecoach, but there they hired a post chaise to make an excursion across the Black Hambleton hills to Helmesley. They passed through Duncombe Park and visited Rivaulx Abbey "the scenery about which is as romantic as the ruin is beautiful and extensive." Charles noted the geology of the hills and the depth of a supposedly bottomless lake as well as the beauty of the scenery.

At Newcastle they gave up their post chaise and stayed overnight. They had dinner with a cousin of Mrs. Lyell, Dr. Headlam, at whose house they heard considerable discussion of the controversy over the priority for the discovery of the Miner's safety lamp between Sir Humphry Davy (1778–1829) and George Stephenson (1781–1848), who had at this time not yet become famous as the builder of the rocket, so that Charles referred to him as "an obscure man." They also went to see Mr. Winch,[33] who walked with them about Newcastle. From Newcastle they went on to Edinburgh by stagecoach.

Edinburgh then was still one of the most important intellectual centers in Great Britain. Its grandeur had faded from what it had been at the end of the eighteenth century but the city was still vigorous. John Playfair (1748–1819), the great exponent of Dr. James Hutton's geological theories, was professor of mathematics at the university where his chief antagonist in the fierce Huttonian–Wernerian controversy, Robert Jameson (1774–1854), was professor of natural history. After graduating in medicine from Edinburgh in 1792, Jameson had taken up mineralogy and in 1800 went to Freiburg to study under Werner, then at the height

32. Ibid.
33. Nathaniel John Winch (1769?–1838) studied the botany and geology of the north of England. He was a fellow of the Linnean Society and of the Geological Society of London.

of his powers as a teacher. In 1804 he returned from Germany to Edinburgh and was immediately appointed regius professor of natural history and keeper of the university museum. He also became immediately the chief advocate of Werner's theories in opposition to those of Dr. Hutton. Jameson's role as a spokesman for Werner and thus for a false theory has perhaps tended to overshadow his solid contributions to science. He wrote important works on the mineralogy of Scotland and gathered together an enormous collection of rocks and minerals for the museum. As a result of his period of study in Germany he also tried to keep British scientists informed of developments in German science and partly for this purpose had in 1808 established the Wernerian Natural History Society.

On their arrival at Edinburgh, Mr. Lyell and Charles went to call upon Professor Jameson in the hope of being taken through the museum, but were disappointed because the collections were packed up on account of the building of the new college. Charles thought him "completely the gentleman and his physiognomy is very prepossessing." They dined at the house of a Forfarshire neighbor, Mr. Laing Mason, where they discussed architecture. Charles was impressed by the new building at Edinburgh. Continuing his account of their trip to Dawson Turner:

> I was more struck with Edinburgh this year than I ever was with any place in my life. I could scarcely have thought it possible that in these times we should ever have to admire public works so arduous and so truly worthy of the Romans. The grand double terrass which they have made round the Carlton Hill through solid basalt would have alone immortalized them had not the new passage thro' the rock lower down made the former, grand and beautiful as it is, shrink to nothing. Every inch they are obliged to blow with gunpowder. . . .
>
> Besides this, two new Churches are built, both immense works in these days and very leading features in views of the New-Town from the new walk around the Carlton-Hill. They are going on with the College again actively, the building of which was at a stand for some time . . . They have just finished a Presbyterian church with a dome. In short since the two years which have expired since I last was here the town seems to have grown doubly magnificent tho' I am inclined to think it was before unrivalled for its natural advantages.[34]

34. C. L., Jr. to D. T. 29 Aug. 1817. Dawson Turner mss.

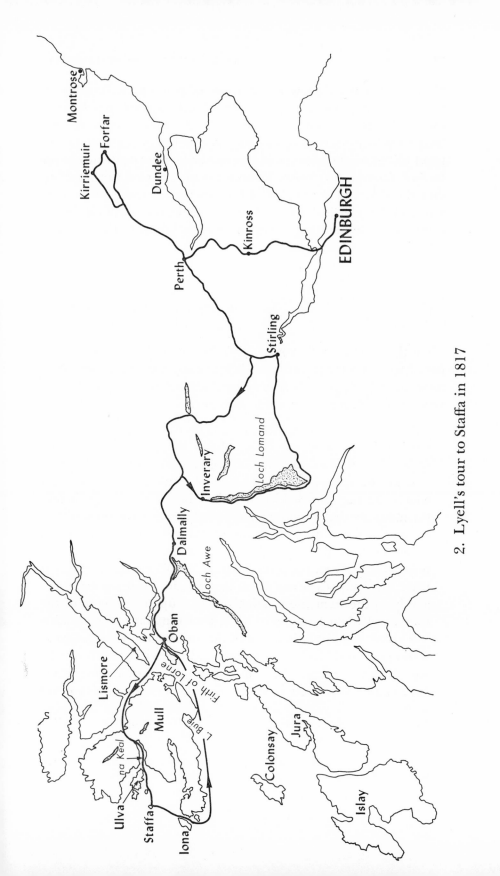

2. Lyell's tour to Staffa in 1817

On 28 August they went on from Edinburgh to Dundee by stagecoach and thence to Kinnordy. While at Kinnordy Charles occupied himself in long rambles on which he collected rock specimens, visited quarries, and climbed to the top of the ancient fortified hill of Finhaven. In mid-September he went with two of his Oxford friends, Sir James Ramsay[35] and Thomas Corbett,[36] to visit the island of Staffa (Map 2) which lies off the west coast of Scotland. Charles had ridden to Ramsay's house, Banff, in Perthshire and together they rode on horseback north through the Highlands. Charles recorded:

> We were very much struck with the North-West end of Loch Awe where the cliffs rise on each side very precipitously and shortly afterward had a beautiful mountain view down Gelk-Ay, where Cruachan and Ben Lewis come into view finely.

On the fourth day they reached Oban where they found a number of wild Highland smugglers being tried. There they left their horses, and hired a small cutter-rigged sailing vessel to proceed by water. Charles then had a minor adventure.

> We were a long time even in getting past Kerrera. I grew so tired of being there motionless that I got into the small boat which was attached to the vessel and amused myself with rowing, my companions by way of a joke untied the rope with which the skiff was held and I then began to row on before them. Seeing that Lismore appeared quite close I determined to endeavour to get to it, and leaving the vessel unable to move, I went on towards it. The distance over the water had deceived me surprisingly and it turned out to be full 2 miles and a half what I had supposed was about half a mile. I lost some time in admiring the immense number of shells upon the rocks of the shore, and when I returned to the boat the Sun had set, and it was growing so dark that I could but just see the vessel.—Before I had got a mile it became cloudy and the wind began to rise, and there was no possibility of seeing the cutter. I exerted myself as much as possible in persevering in the same direction but

35. Sir James Ramsay, 8th Bt. of Banff (1797–1859) was a student at Christ Church, Oxford and graduated in 1819. *Burke's Peerage*, London, 1963, p. 2017.

36. Thomas George Corbett (1796–1889) was also a student at Christ Church and like Ramsay and Lyell, graduated in 1819. In 1832 he succeeded to the estate of Elsham in Lincolnshire and was later M. P. for the northern division of Lincolnshire. B. Burke, *Landed Gentry of Great Britain and Ireland*, p. 400.

the waves prevented my making way, and I at last was in such alarm and despair, that after having hallooed as loud as I could several times, and received no answer, I began to debate whether I should attempt to get back to Oban, or turn round and land at Lismore. I was in such a mere cockle shell of a skiff that every wave seemed to threaten a wreck.

After about ten minutes of this suspense to my great surprise and joy I saw the vessel close to me, they had heard me call but the wind prevented them from getting up quickly and from making an answer heard.

After having been thus severely punished for my rash enterprise, I of course thought nothing of sleeping on board, which to my companions was no small inconvenience.

They had intended to sail around the island of Mull to Staffa but found the wind too much against them so landed at Arrow on Mull, where the innkeeper rented them a boat which he had on Loch Nalgael, a long inlet on the opposite side of Mull which nearly divides the island in two. After a short walk across the island they boarded this craft and sailed on to Staffa.

As an island, Staffa is famous for its magnificent array of basalt pillars capped with a layer of igneous rock solidified from former lava. At several points there are openings between the pillars forming caves into which the sea extends. The largest and most famous of these is Fingal's cave. Staffa first became well known to Europeans when Sir Joseph Banks visited it on his way to Iceland in 1772 and his description was published in 1776 in Thomas Pennant's *Tour in Scotland*.[37] From that time it was a place which travelers to Scotland had tried to include in their itineraries and it had been visited by both William Buckland and Dawson Turner.

Only a few weeks before Leopold von Buch[38] had been at Staffa in the course of a tour of Scotland. On his return to England he had visited Buckland at Oxford and had suggested a theory to account for the origin of Fingal's cave. He had supposed that an

37. T. Pennant. *A Tour in Scotland and Voyage to the Hebrides*. 2nd ed. In this 2nd edition there is an "Account of Staffa" by Joseph Banks Esq., vol. I, pp. 299–309.

38. Christian Leopold von Buch (1774–1853) was a Prussian who had studied under Werner at Freiburg. Having inherited wealth he devoted himself to geology and traveled widely for that purpose. Quite early he abandoned Werner's neptunian theories.

intrusive dyke of softer lava had invaded the basalt and had later been eroded away to leave the opening which was Fingal's Cave (Fig. 6). To support his theory von Buch asserted that there were no broken ends of columns appearing in the roof of the cave as there should have been if the space occupied by the cave had once been filled with basalt columns. Buckland had been surprised by this assertion because he thought he remembered having seen broken ends of columns appearing in the roof when he had visited Staffa, but since it had been long before, he was not certain. Pennant's illustration of the cave also showed the broken ends of columns in the roof. Buckland therefore had asked Charles to check this particular point and Charles found that von Buch was wrong. They first landed opposite the Clam-shell cave and climbed to the top of the island. From there they went round the cliff till they reached Fingal's cave. Continuing his account of this tour, Charles described his impressions:

All representations of Staffa must fall short in expressing the bold and regular swell or semicircle in which the pillars are ranged on each side [of] the entrance. In a front view this of course is foreshortened and becomes nearly a flat wall. When we had walked in as far as we could by climbing along the side we returned to the boat and enjoyed a much more delightful view of it from the water. Fortunately the wind was northerly and the waves were therefore exhausting themselves on the other side of the island which must otherwise have prevented our getting in. When we had just past the entrance a large swelling wave sucked us in suddenly a considerable way, the boat sinking at the same time five or six feet. There we were left motionless for some time and heard the wave slowly winding up the cave, then dash against the end of it. It then returned and carried us completely out again raising us up at the same time.

The boatmen shewed great address with their oars in preventing the boat from striking against the sides of the cave. After repeating this experiment several times one wave (I suppose a *ninth*) threw us back so suddenly that we were afraid to try it again.—The boatmen however would willingly have gone in again.

The echo in the cave is very loud. We had no bagpipes unluckily. The roof is ornamented with the broken tops of pillars.

From Staffa they went on to Iona where they planned to stay overnight. The Inn, a small two-roomed cottage or *But and Ben,* was not very attractive. The one door led into *But,* "a miserable apartment indeed, of a conical shape open at the top and a large fire in the middle of the floor. All round were hung immense store of fishes, which were seen in every direction where the smoke permitted." They were hungry, cold, and very tired. When the landlord arrived, they were shown into *Ben,* the best parlour, but when the fire was lit there, the smoke drove Charles outside. There he saw "the Aurora Borealis in great splendour, which made the old ruins look fine and interesting." Their supper was sparse:

> Milk and bannock was all we could get to eat but the Landlady recommended some of her haddocks. After waiting about half an hour for these a Lassey came in and before she could tell us her errand she burst into a fit of laughter. Upon going into But we found the haddock when just roasted had fallen into the tub of oatmeal. We lost nothing but our time and patience for when another couple were roasted we found them uneatable.

Next morning, after examining the ruins on Iona and procuring a keg of whiskey for their crew, they sailed around the south side of Mull in order to return to Oban. As they went they observed magnificent cliffs of red granite along the south shore of Mull, which in McLeod's bay became columnar. With a good breeze they sailed onward and reached Oban at midnight. There they retrieved their horses and returned southward. On their last day Charles and Sir James Ramsay rode forty miles in order to attend a county ball at Forfar. They arrived in the evening "before the first dance was fairly over and finished our delightful tour of 10 days by a night's dancing."[39]

On this tour Charles emerges as an eager, active young man of contagious gaiety. He sought to collect the kind of local information which Dr. Buckland had said was important for the further development of geology but he was also observant and appreciative of human peculiarity and foible. He returned southward alone because estate affairs kept Mr. Lyell at Kinnordy. Instead of going by stagecoach he sailed from Dundee in a coastal smack. In his voyage to London the smack passed so close to Yarmouth

39. C. L., Jr., Ms. Diary, sent to D. T. 21 Dec. 1817. Dawson Turner mss.

that he could see Mr. Turner's house and count the people on the jetty. Charles thought of sending a note to Mr. Turner if a boat came out "but the wind carried us thro' the roads like an arrow, & no boat could come out."[40] The remainder of his passage to London was particularly pleasant.[41] "The sail we enjoyed up the Thames at the rate of 12 knots an hour with generally 300 vessels near us moving rapidly in all directions was delightful beyond description. A side wind shows off every vessel in the most picturesque view." From London Charles went home to Bartley for a few days, in the course of which he visited his sister Caroline who was staying at Muddiford on the Hampshire coast. Eagerly observing geological detail, he noted that the cliffs there were composed of what must be the green sand of Werner. Shortly he returned to Oxford.

The experiences of this long, eventful summer had had a profound effect upon Charles. His growing preoccupation with geology is evident. He had made observations which later were to give rise to two of his early scientific papers. At the bridge of Cortachy in Angus he had noted a peculiar greenish rock which, on his return to London, he was to identify in William Bullock's museum as serpentine. Several years later he was to trace this serpentine for many miles from the bridge of Cortachy and to show that it constituted a well-defined dyke.[42] Later he was also to make extensive studies of the strata of Hampshire and the Isle of Wight which resulted in another paper.[43]

Charles felt a sense of strangeness after his return to Oxford. He wrote to Dawson Turner:

It would have required some time and study . . . to imagine a more complete change from one extreme to another, than after a rambling vacation of nearly 4 months over pleasant scenes and in pleasant society to be set down to make ones way . . . over treatises of barren and abstract Science, a world of terms in themselves unmeaning, & the most fanciful and laborious analysations & divisions of immaterial things which exist but in the mind. The very intensity of the change itself has some charms.

---

40. C. L., Jr. to D. T. 25 Oct. 1817. Dawson Turner mss.

41. C. L., Jr. to his father. 21 Oct. 1817. Kinnordy mss. *L. & L.* I, 53–54.

42. "On a Dike of Serpentine cutting through Sandstone, in the County of Forfar" (1825).

43. "On the Strata of the Plastic Clay Formation exhibited in the Cliffs between Christchurch Head, Hampshire and Studland Bay, Dorsetshire" (1826).

Aristotle is, I think, the most wonderful of Authors for with even Genius, Imagination & invention beyond most of the Ancients, he has plunged into the most quibbling & mechanical refinements. He divides and subdivides all his subjects as infinitely as Horace proposes to do the horses's tail "deme atque etiam unam" till at least it requires an effort & stretch of the mind to keep up with him, and a still greater one of the Memory, to answer an examination of all these niceties thro' several books & treatises. His style is so Elliptical that when you attempt in English an analysis of a Chapter, after you have lopped off the Examples & illustrations, you will generally find that your writing exceeds the Text in length.

I feel however some pleasure in it, greater than I ever thought I should, arising, I suppose, from the Emulation or Vanity of doing what some fail in & many do not dare attempt: if from the latter feeling it is some comfort to bring good from Evil. There certainly is nothing in the subject that warms me.[44]

One could hardly ask for a more heartfelt declaration of the bankruptcy of the Oxford system of education of that time.

Despite his lack of illusions Charles settled down to hard work. Many of his former acquaintances had not returned to Oxford so he had fewer distractions. Dawson Turner invited him to Yarmouth for Christmas but he declined. On 11 November he sat in the schools to listen to the examination of another student, Baring of Christ Church, in preparation for his own. Charles feared the examinations were to be "unusually severe." He wrote a poem about Staffa which he sent to his father.[45] At Christmas he went home where his father said he was "the life and soul of us."[46] He spent the vacation in part preparing Latin verses on a new prize subject, "Titus Hiero solymam expugnans" and sent a copy of his Staffa diary to Dawson Turner.[47] At Christmas time his father thought that Charles was "applying almost too closely to Aristotle, it was becoming meat, drink and exercise to him."[48] Certainly he made a valiant effort to master Aristotle's philosophy and this not because he was fond of it, but because such studies represented the one avenue toward academic distinction at Oxford.

44. C. L., Jr. to D. T. 25 Oct. 1817. Dawson Turner mss.
45. C. L., Jr. to his father. 11 Nov. 1817. Kinnordy mss. *L. & L.* I, 54–56.
46. C. L. to C. W. 14 Dec. 1817. Wedderburn mss.
47. C. L., Jr. to D. T. 21 Dec. 1817. Dawson Turner mss.
48. C. L. to D. T. 3 Jan. 1818. Dawson Turner mss.

Charles clearly wanted such distinction very much, perhaps in part to please his father but also to satisfy his own ambitions. Since he was to study law, he attended the assizes when they met at Oxford. He wrote to Dawson Turner:

> I can scarcely conceive the study of the Law more dry and abstruse than the long treatises of Aristotle I am now buried in, and they have been already the source of much pleasure to me in increasing my taste for light reading and making me take up many things for recreation, which I should before have considered subjects of study.[49]

This is backhanded praise. In May he submitted his Latin verses and his lines on the Coliseum for prizes, but as a matter of form. Both prizes were awarded to a friend of his at New College. Charles was not surprised but wrote to Dawson Turner with slight bitterness:

> The Tutors to whom my Coliseum was shown pronounced them to stand a very good chance, whereas my Latin they thought stood none. This and your contrary judgment has served to convince me how little I was in either. But you are not aware of the very peculiar style requisite to please the Examiners here for the English verse. It has been well described in a publication of infinite merit which has appeared from some young Oxonian, we know not whom, within the last fortnight. A spirited Satire on the follies of Oxford, called the "Oxford Spy." . . . But the sooner I forget the business the better.[50]

It must have been with a sense of pleasant relief, therefore, that Charles turned to his second course of Buckland's lectures which were this year on mineralogy and geology and began on 18 April. He also visited London where he heard Henry Brougham deliver an "eloquent speech" on the education of the poor in the House of Commons.[51]

While Charles was pursuing his studies with mixed feelings, his father had been hesitating whether to take his family abroad for the summer. Early in May he made up his mind to go and went to London to obtain a traveling Landau. They left London on 6 June as soon as Charles was free from Oxford. On the eighth they crossed from Dover to Calais and on the twelfth were at Paris

49. C. L., Jr. to D. T. 8 March 1818. Dawson Turner mss.
50. C. L., Jr. to D. T. 21 May 1818. Dawson Turner mss.
51. Ibid. Cf. C. W. New, *The Life of Henry Brougham to 1830* (1961) pp. 213–14.

where they spent nearly two weeks in sightseeing. The Duke of
Wellington was there and on one day they saw all of the fountains
at Versailles play in his honor.[52]

Charles was particularly interested by the fossils, anatomical
displays, and living animals at the Jardin des Plantes. He could
not meet Cuvier, who was absent in England, but he did go to
the Royal Library to read his book on fossil remains.[53] He also
read Cuvier's paper on the geology of the Paris basin.[54] Two
days later he returned to the Jardin des Plantes "where I again
looked over Cuvier's lecture-room filled with fossil remains,
among which are three glorious relics of a former world, which
have added several new genera to the Mammalia." The phrase
"relics of a former world" is revealing, for it expresses concisely
the assumptions contained in the geology which Charles had
learned while attending Buckland's lectures at Oxford, and which
were taken for granted by Cuvier. The present world, whose creation is described in the book of Genesis in the Old Testament,
was thought to be quite recent—not more than six thousand years
old. It was in fact the only world which had been known until
the study of fossils had revealed whole populations of once-living
things. Since these former creatures were not mentioned in the
account of creation given in Genesis, nor did the Bible mention
the extinction of any living creature, it was thought that fossil
forms must have belonged to a *former world* whose existence
preceded the creation described in Genesis and which had been
utterly destroyed before that creation took place. This theme of a
succession of worlds each terminated by a great holocaust or catastrophe, to be replaced by a new world and a new creation, had
been expounded in the cosmogonies of Burnet and Woodward
in the seventeenth century, and at the beginning of the nineteenth century had been reinforced by the catastrophic theories of
Cuvier. It was a necessary assumption if the findings of geology
were not to come into immediate conflict with the Bible. By its
means the findings of geology were at least temporarily separated
from having any significance for religion and the geologist could
pursue his work undisturbed.

After visits to the theater, the opera, the Louvre, the Royal

52. The account of this trip is found in *L. & L.* I, 62–77, 98, unless otherwise
noted.

53. G. Cuvier. *Recherches sur les ossemens fossiles de quadrupèdes* (1812).

54. G. Cuvier and A. Brongniart. *Essai sur la géographie minéralogique des
environs de Paris* . . . (1811).

Observatory and other places of interest, Mr. Lyell and his
family left Paris on 26 June on the road to Geneva. Charles noted
the limestone outcrops in the forest of Fontainebleau, and the succession of chalk, limestone, and other strata along the road. Near
Avallon "we came upon a blue limestone abounding in Ammonites, some as large as the crown of my hat, some considerably
larger, with many gryphites and other shells, continuing to Rou-
vray." After passing over granite they again came upon this limestone. Near Dôle "I saw gravel strewed in large hillocks over the
plain as it is in Scotland."[55] Of his observations during this part of
the journey Charles wrote later to Dawson Turner:

> I exercised myself in noting down the Geological strata among
> other things in hopes of getting on by having my mistakes criti-
> cized and corrected at Oxford by abler hands who have already
> examined carefully the same ground.[56]

On the summit of the Jura he noted the influence of climate
upon mountain scenery.

> Now that we had gained the height of the loftiest mountains in
> Scotland, we could not help reflecting with astonishment on the
> contrast between the Grampians and the Jura. Instead of a cold
> piercing wind we were here glad of an umbrella to screen us
> from the heat of the sun; instead of a desolate waste, the dwell-
> ing of moor-game alone, here were towns and houses scattered
> about and cattle; in place of a boundless expanse of heath, here
> were tall forests of fir, with the Alpine rose and a thousand
> beautiful flowers.

From Geneva they went up the valley of the Arve to Chamonix
where Charles was able to observe the effects of glaciers (Map 3).
The glacier of Bosson was of particular interest because it had advanced markedly in the preceding three years:

> Marching on with its enormous bulk, it has trodden down the
> tallest pines with as much ease as an elephant could the herbage
> of a meadow. Some trunks still are seen projecting from the
> rock of ice, all the heads being embodied in this mass, which
> shoots out at the top into tall pyramids and pinnacles of ice of
> beautiful shapes and of a very pure white, which is finely set off

55. *L. & L.* I, 66. In both cases these hillocks are the result of glacial action.
56. C. L., Jr. to D. T. 10 July 1818. Dawson Turner mss.

3. Lyell's tour in Switzerland with his family, 1818

by a background of dark fir. This lower part of the glacier is urged on by an enormous precipice of ice above, descending from the upper parts of the mountain, and which increases in weight every year. It has been pressed on not only through the forest but over some cultivated fields which are utterly lost.

While at Chamonix Charles went on hikes up the mountains with the son of one of the guides who had accompanied Saussure in his ascent of Mont Blanc. He climbed *l'Aiguille de Brevent* and went part way up Mont Blanc on to the great glacier, the *Mer de Glace,* walking as much as forty-eight miles in one day.

From Chamonix they returned to Geneva and went on by way of Lausanne to Neuchâtel and thence to Basel. The mountain scenery was a source of unceasing wonder:

> We were obliged to have six horses to mount a long and steep hill from which we enjoyed again a grand view of the distant Alps. A fine mist between us and the base of the chain had exactly the appearance of a second atmosphere, and the gigantic summits of the Alps seemed cut off and unconnected with the earth.

From Basel they went along the banks of the Rhine to the falls at Schaffhausen. Charles found some fossil shells in the limestone rock at the falls. They then turned back southward toward Zurich and from there to Zug. At Zug the rest of the party went on with the carriage to Lucerne while Charles took a guide to climb the Rigi, where he met Sir John Wrottesley and his three sons, the oldest of whom was a student at Christ Church, Oxford.[57] They climbed to the Rigi-Culm where they slept until three, rising to see the sunrise.

From Lucerne the Lyells' route took them to Meyringen, Berne, Vevey, Martigny, and thence across the pass of the Simplon into Italy. Charles did much walking as they went, traveling on foot sometimes as much as thirty-five to forty miles a day. He was somewhat proud of this performance and boasted of it to his guide who commented, "Oui, c'est assez pour un monsieur," a reproof which he took in good part since the guide walked the same distance and carried his bags. On the Martigny road they saw a vast quantity of

57. Sir John Wrottesley, first Baron Wrottesley (1771–1841). His eldest son Sir John Wrottesley, second Baron Wrottesley (1798–1867) F.R.S. became a very distinguished astronomer.

sand which had been brought down by the river in flood. In Switzerland Charles thus had an opportunity to see what great and continual changes were brought about by the action of glaciers, floods, and mountain torrents. He would always be aware that the occasional recurrence of such violent events as floods was part of the regular order of nature and helped to produce geological change.

Charles was impressed by the magnificence of the scenery and the excellence of the road on their descent in to Italy.

> The difference of the Italian side of the Alps is as remarkable as that of the southern side of a garden wall. Houses and fruit-trees reach to an extraordinary height up the mountains, and the crops of tall maize and hemp make a great show in the valley.

In Italy they went to Milan, across the plains of Lombardy to Venice, southward to Bologna and Florence, and then back to Milan by way of Parma. At each city they looked at pictures, churches, and statues. Charles had little opportunity to make geological observations and concentrated instead upon art and architecture. By 22 September they were at Lyons, having crossed the Alps from Turin, and early in October they reached Paris whence Charles departed directly for Oxford via Calais and Dover. Mr. Lyell and the rest of the family went at a leisurely pace from Paris to Le Havre, stopping at Caen to see Mr. Lyell's old Irish friend Heyland who was living there. From Le Havre they crossed in a sailing packet to Southampton and so home.

At Oxford Charles settled into his third year and was soon "reading most laudably" which his father thought very creditable considering all the distractions to which he had been exposed through the summer.[58] Mr. Lyell went north to Kinnordy where he found his tenants so much more prosperous and able to pay their rents that on his return to London he arranged to have his three sons painted together (Fig. 7) by Thomas Phillips R.A.[59] In this handsome portrait done at the end of January 1819 we see Charles at the age of twenty-one. At this time Mr. Lyell also entered Charles at Lincoln's Inn to study law there, instead of at the Scotch bar at Edinburgh.[60]

During the spring of 1819 Charles worked very hard, hoping to get a first in his degree examination. He managed to achieve only

58. C. L. to D. T. 22 Nov. 1818. Dawson Turner mss.
59. C. L. to D. T. 26 Dec. 1818. Dawson Turner mss.
60. C. L. to C. W. 9 March 1819. Wedderburn mss.

a second which, considering the nature of Oxford examinations at that time, was possibly more creditable than a first. In March he was elected a fellow of the Geological Society of London. His father was well satisfied with him and was especially proud too because in this year when Charles was also elected a fellow of the Linnean Society, Mr. Lyell went to London to be present on 1 June when he should attend his first meeting. Mr. Lyell congratulated himself that he had sent Charles to Oxford as a gentleman commoner "as it gave the command of his society; and the best is not within a man's reach at that Tory University unless he is *well born,* or has been educated at a public School, or is a Gentleman Commoner."[61] At least the avenues to distinction were various.

Charles's struggles to prepare for his examination had however exacted a painful price. His eyes had begun to bother him seriously and he had had to study with a wet towel around his head to ease the pain. Even during the summer holiday after he had stopped reading he found they were very weak and easily inflamed.[62] This perhaps minor affliction was ultimately to determine his career.

61. C. L. to C. W. 25 May 1819. Wedderburn mss.
62. C. L. to C. W. 18 July 1819. Wedderburn mss.

CHAPTER 4

The State of Geology in 1819

WHEN LYELL was elected to the Geological Society of London in 1819 he joined a society composed essentially of enthusiastic amateur geologists. The society had been formed in 1807 and from the beginning it had actively encouraged geological investigations by its members and had solicited geological information from anyone able to contribute it either in Great Britain or abroad.[1] In 1811 it had published the first large quarto volume of its *Transactions* and in 1820 the fifth volume appeared. These early volumes of the *Transactions* contained many important papers. In addition to descriptions of the geology of particular localities and districts, the fifth volume contained descriptions of important new fossils.

Although the Geological Society promoted the gathering of geological facts and observations, it did not encourage the discussion of theoretical questions. In 1807 when the Society was formed, geologists in Great Britain had been sharply divided into two opposing schools of thought—the Wernerians and the Huttonians.

The Wernerians supported the doctrines of Abraham Gottlob Werner (1749–1817) who had begun teaching at the School of Mines at Freiburg, Germany in 1776. His fame as a teacher had grown so great by 1800 that he attracted students from other European countries including France and the British Isles. Werner had been impressed by the fact that the rock strata of northern Germany always overlay each other in the same order and tended to lie in a horizontal position in level country whereas in the vicinity of mountains they were inclined and bent. He developed a theory of the history of the earth which seemed to him to accord with these facts. Werner was primarily a mineralogist and the value of the training he gave his students was that he made them familiar with many different minerals and enabled them to

1. M.J.S. Rudwick, "The foundation of the Geological Society of London . . ." (1963). Cf. H. B. Woodward, *The History of the Geological Society of London*, pp. 6–67.

identify minerals by particular and well-defined characteristics. But he was also aware that a knowledge of minerals was only the foundation on which must be constructed our general knowledge of the crust of the earth and its history. To this broader concept of knowledge of the earth Werner gave the name geognosy. Geognosy was to him a positive science because it was concerned with what was known about rocks and minerals and not with speculations concerning the origin of the earth. When Werner himself put forward a theory of the earth, he believed that it was in every respect founded on factual observation and was, therefore, merely the expression of the meaning of the facts themselves, rather than a theoretical construction. In this he sadly deceived himself.

In 1786 Werner published his *Brief Classification and Description of the Various Kinds of Mountains* in which he distinguished four kinds of rocks in order of age: the primitive rocks, stratified rocks (floetz gebirge), volcanic rocks, and alluvial or water-washed deposits. In 1796 he added a fifth category, the transitional rocks, which were intermediate between the primitive and stratified rocks. His classification was slightly different from that of his contemporary geologists who tended to classify rocks as *primitive* or *secondary*.

The fundamental classification of stratified rocks had originally been based upon observations made in northern Italy by Giovanni Arduino (1713–95), who wrote about the mountains in the vicinity of Padua, Vicenza, and Verona. In them he found that there was a fundamental group of greatly altered schistose strata containing no fossils and interspersed with numerous veins of quartz. Since they seemed very ancient, dating from before the existence of living forms, and when the world was still in a formative state, he called them primitive mountains. The presence of crystalline rocks among these strata made it difficult to assume that they could have originated as sediments like the younger strata. Another group of strata which, where they were adjacent to the primitive strata, lay above them, consisted of limestones, marls, and clays containing many marine fossils; to the hills formed of these, Arduino gave the name secondary mountains. To yet a third and younger group of strata, commonly containing pebbles derived from the secondary strata and especially rich in marine fossils of kinds quite different from the secondary, Arduino gave the name of Tertiary.

In the mid-eighteenth century the distinction between primitive and secondary strata had also been drawn in Germany by Johann Gottlob Lehman. Lehman and Arduino both considered the primitive rocks to underlie the lowest series of stratified rocks and thought that they never contained traces of fossil plants or animals and therefore were composed entirely of chemical materials as opposed to organic. Lehman and Arduino thought that the primitive strata represented the materials of the earth's surface at its first creation before life had appeared. The secondary strata lay above the primitive series and were sharply distinguished from them by the fact that they contained many fossil remains of plants and animals. In Germany the primitive strata were usually found in the higher mountains where they were in highly inclined or vertical positions, whereas the secondary strata usually occurred in lower country where they lay horizontally or nearly so. Werner, therefore, designated the secondary strata as the flat-lying or floetz formations. However, there was a third series of strata in which crystalline strata lacking fossils were interspersed with limestones, sandstones, and conglomerates containing fossils. In position these strata were usually inclined, but less so than those of the primitive series. Since in these different respects they tended to be intermediate between the secondary and the primitive series, Werner called them transition rocks. In the existing definition of "secondary" the transition series would be included in the secondary class. Werner, therefore, decided to subdivide the secondary into the floetz and transition series and to omit the term "secondary" from his classification.

In 1793 Peter Simon Pallas decided from his study of mountain ranges in Siberia that the characteristic structure of mountain ranges was a central core of granite with schistose rocks, containing no fossils, along the flanks of the granite, and with fossil-bearing limestone strata lying outside and above the schistose. Pallas' observations on the structure of mountain ranges and those of Horace-Bénédict de Saussure on the Alps seem to have been used by Werner in the later development of his theory of the earth.

Werner assumed, in accord with the nebular hypothesis of the origin of the earth and the general thinking of eighteenth-century cosmogonists, that the earth had been first formed as a hot incandescent molten mass which had gradually cooled. As it cooled, its surface did not remain perfectly smooth, but formed minor ridges and furrows which gave rise to mountain ranges, valleys, and ocean basins. Traces of this original surface of the earth could be seen in the masses of granite and gneiss found in the heart of mountain ranges. After the earth had cooled it became covered with an ocean which extended over its whole surface, even to the top of the mountains. The depth of this universal ocean was demonstrated, Werner thought, by the fact that even on the tops of mountains there were rock strata proved to have been laid down beneath the sea by the fact that they contained marine fossils. So long as he assumed that the earth's crust was stable and unmoving, an assumption which seemed natural and reasonable, Werner was also obliged to assume that the ocean had previously covered the earth to the height of the mountain tops.

Because Werner's primitive rocks, which included granite, gneiss, porphyry, and serpentine, consisted almost entirely of crystalline rocks, Werner thought that they had crystallized out of the primitive ocean. He considered them therefore to be chemical deposits, as opposed to the limestones, sandstones, and shales of the stratified rocks which were mechanical deposits. In later geological ages the level of the universal ocean had receded, it ceased to form chemical deposits, and instead deposited the stratified rocks. As the universal ocean dropped to still lower levels, it deposited loose gravel, sand, and clay as alluvial sediments which never became consolidated into rock.

The disappearance of the universal ocean remained a mystery unexplained in Werner's theory, but the limitations of the theory are of less historical importance than the sense of organization it gave to geological data. In the districts he examined Werner found the various formations always superposed one upon another in the same order. Because these formations occurred throughout the geographical area with which he was familiar, Werner thought that they must occur throughout the world and were, therefore, "universal formations." Although Werner's belief that the succession of rocks in Germany occurred universally throughout the world was mistaken, his concept of universal formations did lead geologists to attempt to correlate the formations of different countries.

In contrast to Werner, the teacher at Freiburg of many eager and enthusiastic students whose imaginations were caught up in the comprehensive sweep of his theories, Dr. James Hutton of Edinburgh was a much more solitary figure (Fig. 8). Born at Edinburgh in 1726 Hutton studied medicine there for three years and then chemistry and anatomy at Paris for two years before he was graduated M.D. at Leyden in 1749. He did not practice medicine long, for in 1752 he began to study farming in Norfolk and after two years began to farm his own estate in Berwickshire, Scotland. In 1768 he retired from farming to return to Edinburgh, where he devoted himself to scientific pursuits and became a close friend of Dr. Joseph Black, professor of chemistry at the University of Edinburgh.

Hutton first presented his theory of the earth to the newly formed Royal Society of Edinburgh in 1785.[2] Like Werner, Hutton was impressed by the fact that sedimentary rocks had been formed from sediments laid down beneath the sea. In the seventeenth century the Danish anatomist Nicolaus Steno had also demonstrated that since stratified rocks originated from sediments laid down on the sea bottom, the strata must have been formed in a horizontal position. Therefore, when strata were found in inclined or vertical positions, they must have been subjected to upheaval and displacement after the time of their first formation. Hutton was interested particularly in two questions: first, how had the loose sediments been consolidated into solid rock, and second, what series of changes had brought the rock strata from the horizontal position, in which they had been first formed, to those inclined or vertical positions in which he so often found them. At the same time he realized that sediments deposited on the sea bottom must be formed of materials worn away and carried down from some pre-existing land.

In his consideration of stratified rocks Hutton began to see that geological processes were cyclical. Rock was broken down by the action of wind, rain, and frost to form soil. The soil was in turn removed by the action of rain and running water and carried along by streams and rivers to the sea where it was spread out over the sea bottom as layers of sand, clay, or chalky ooze. As these layers accumulated more and more deeply on the sea bottom they were subject first to compression by the weight of overlying sediments and then to heat which consolidated them into solid rock. The force of the internal heat of the earth also served ultimately to uplift the consolidated rock strata from the sea bottom to form new areas of land. As soon, however, as the new land was raised

2. J. Hutton, "Theory of the Earth . . ." See also V. A. Eyles, "A bibliographical note on the earliest printed version of James Hutton's Theory of the Earth, its form and date of publication" (1955).

above the water it became subject to the disintegrative action of
the atmosphere and to erosion by rain and running water. Thus
rock strata were no sooner elevated into land than the process of
reconverting them into loose sediments to be deposited ultimately
on the sea bottom was again begun.

To Hutton the endless cycle of changes involved in the uplift
of the land, its weathering, and its ultimate wearing away was an
illustration of divine providence because it maintained, over the
surface of the land, a soil fit for the growth of plants. This view reflected his experience as a farmer, but the whole of his theory was
the product of his reflection on the geological features of Scotland.

In the vicinity of Edinburgh there were many indications of
earlier volcanic disturbance marked by large masses of rock known
in Sweden as trap rock and in Scotland as whinstone. Hutton
found that where a vein of whinstone passed through stratified
rock, the strata were visibly altered, as if by great heat, adjacent to
the vein. He concluded that the whinstone had originally pene-
trated through the layers of stratified rock in a molten condition
and that this was a manifestation of the interior heat of the earth.
If water were the sole agent by which rocks were formed, all the
components of rocks, Hutton thought, should be water soluble.
Instead he found in certain crystalline rocks crystals of pyrites,
galena, fluorspar, calcareous spar, and quartz, all water insoluble
substances, intimately mixed together. The only way that so many
distinct substances could be brought together so closely was to be
melted together by heat.

Hutton read an account of his theory to the Royal Society of
Edinburgh in March and April 1785. During the summer of 1785,
when he went as a guest of the Duke of Athol on a hunting expedition to Glen Tilt in the Grampians, Hutton discovered veins of
granite in the stream bed of the Tilt and found that where the
granite veins passed through the surrounding strata of white schist,
the schist was greatly darkened and altered as if by heat. He was
able to trace these veins to a large mass of granite on the north side
of the Glen and to show that they were offshoots of this larger
body. The meaning of Hutton's discovery in Glen Tilt was that
granite must be considered an igneous rock. It could no longer
be considered the first rock to have crystallized out of the primitive ocean. Instead veins and masses of granite were actually
younger than the stratified rocks which surrounded or overlay
them. The reason masses of granite occurred in the center of

mountain ranges might then be that the granite had been the agent which had helped to uplift the mountains to their present height by forcing its way in from below in a molten condition. Hutton seems to have had a keen appreciation of the revolutionary significance of his discovery at Glen Tilt because "the guides who accompanied him were convinced that it must be nothing less than the discovery of a vein of silver or gold which could call forth such strong marks of joy and exultation."[3]

Hutton was particularly impressed by unconformities between strata. In 1787 he discovered a spot on the sea shore at the northern end of the isle of Arran where strata of a secondary red sandstone overlay the edges of nearly vertical strata of primitive schist and at one point, just below the high-tide level, he discovered the junction between them. That autumn he also found in the bed of the river Jed at Jedburgh horizontal beds of red sandstone resting on the edges of a series of vertical beds of primitive schist.

In 1788 Hutton, in company with his friends John Playfair (Fig. 9) and Sir James Hall of Dunglass, visited St. Abb's Head on the east coast of Scotland to search for the junction between the primitive micaceous schist of the Lammermuir hills and the secondary strata. On a fine day they sailed along the coast and landed at the headland known as the Siccar point. It was low tide and at their landing place at low water they found themselves standing on the edges of the nearly vertical strata of primitive schist. Near the high-water mark they found horizontal strata of red sandstone resting on the edges of the schist and rising behind into a high cliff. John Playfair described the impression which Hutton's explanation of the junction of these two distinct sets of strata made on the minds of his friends:

> We felt ourselves necessarily carried back to the time when the schistus on which we stood was yet at the bottom of the sea, and when the sandstone before us was only beginning to be deposited, in the shape of sand or mud, from the waters of a superincumbent ocean. An epocha still more remote presented itself, when even the most ancient of these rocks, instead of standing upright in vertical beds, lay in horizontal planes at the bottom of the sea and was not yet disturbed by that immeasurable force

3. J. Playfair, "Biographical Account of the late Dr. James Hutton, F.R.S. Edin." (1805).

which has burst asunder the solid pavement of the globe. Revolutions still more remote appeared in the distance of this extraordinary perspective. The mind seemed to grow giddy by looking so far into the abyss of time.[4]

Because Hutton's discovery of the intrusive nature of granite had shown that the oldest rocks must be sedimentary rocks and because the oldest sedimentary strata required the pre-existence of still older land areas from which they had been worn down, Hutton saw the long cycle of geological changes as extending indefinitely into the past. At the end of his paper of 1785 he expressed this idea succinctly: "In the economy of the world I can find no trace of a beginning, no prospect of an end."[5] He had shown that the history of the earth could be read from the rocks and that this history was the result of a succession of great geological cycles still visibly in progress today.

Hutton's theory was criticized by Jean André Deluc in 1790 and 1791 and by Richard Kirwan in 1793. Kirwan's criticisms in particular spurred Hutton to write a more complete account of his theory and in 1795 he published it as a large work in two volumes.[6] However, this work contains many long untranslated quotations from French authors. It is consequently difficult to read and to follow Hutton's arguments. His friend John Playfair, recognizing the deficiencies of Hutton's book, in 1802 presented Hutton's ideas more concisely and simply in his *Illustrations of the Huttonian Theory.*[7]

The publication of these books provoked a prolonged controversy. Part of the objection to the Huttonian theory was religious because Hutton made the earth so very old that it was effectively eternal. His theory therefore contradicted the Biblical account of creation. As one of his criticisms of Hutton, Richard Kirwan wrote: "I have been led into this detail by observing how fatal the suspicion of the high antiquity of the globe has been to the credit of the Mosaic history and consequently to religion and morality."[8] The danger to religion and morality seemed particularly serious to Kirwan because the French revolution had severely shaken the whole basis of social order in Europe. The church was

4. Ibid., pp. 72–73.
5. J. Hutton, "Theory of the Earth . . ." (1785), p. 304.
6. J. Hutton, *Theory of the Earth* . . . (1795).
7. J. Playfair, *Illustrations of the Huttonian Theory of The Earth* (1802).
8. R. Kirwan, "On the primitive state of the globe and its subsequent catastrophe" (1797) p. 307.

central to the social order in Great Britain and any idea which undermined its doctrines seemed to endanger society itself and threatened the interests of the governing and landowning classes. In the early 1790s there were abundant signs of revolutionary Jacobinism in the British Isles but by 1800 the wars with France had produced a sharp reaction. The Tory government took energetic repressive measures against political radicals and conservative attitudes dominated society and religion. Although Hutton himself believed in divine providence his whole temper of mind reflected the calmly rational and philosophical spirit of the eighteenth-century enlightenment, an outlook similar to that of the French philosophes who had prepared the way for the French revolution.

The followers of Hutton at Edinburgh tended to be young men of liberal thought; the advocates of the Wernerian theory were usually Tories. These political associations intensified the scientific dispute and attached to the Huttonian theory the stigma of political radicalism. The leading Wernerian was Robert Jameson, who returned to Edinburgh in 1804 from two years of study under Werner at Freiburg and two years of travel on the Continent. He was immediately appointed professor of natural history at the University of Edinburgh. Jameson had already published his *Mineralogy of the Scottish Isles* in 1800 and he now proceeded to develop a large collection of minerals in the university museum.

The chief point at issue between the Wernerians and Huttonians was the question of the origin of crystalline rocks. According to Werner such rocks as granite, porphyry, gneiss, basalt, and whinstone had crystallized out of the primitive ocean; according to Hutton they had cooled from a hot, molten condition. In the case of veins, whether of granite, whinstone, or other crystalline rock which traversed sedimentary strata, the Wernerians said that these were special deposits which had settled out of the universal ocean from above into cracks in previously deposited strata of sandstone, limestone, or shale. Hutton had asserted to the contrary that these veins had intruded from below in a molten condition and had then cooled. He was able to point to signs of alteration in the stratified rock along the margins of the veins. Where a vein traversed a stratum of limestone, a band of the limestone on either side had been converted to crystalline marble; where it traversed a bed of coal, the coal had been converted to coke.

The question of the origin of basalt was especially important.

This rock occurs in broad sheets, often of considerable thickness, and such layers of basalt are common in Saxony. Werner had become convinced of the aqueous origin of basalt by his visit to a hill near Scheibenberg in Germany where he found a thick layer of basalt overlying sand and clay on one side of the hill and strata of a primitive rock called "wacke" on the other. Because the sand and clay and wacke had been deposited from water, he decided that the basalt must have been likewise. However, from the mid-eighteenth century French geologists had published descriptions of the Auvergne district where thick sheets of basalt lay in such a clear and close relationship to extinct volcanoes that every visitor to the district became convinced that basalt was a volcanic rock. When Werner's own student Leopold von Buch visited Vesuvius in 1798, he found both basalt and feldspar porphyry occurring undeniably as former lava flows. In 1802 he visited Auvergne where he was convinced that the basalt formations were of volcanic origin. However, he continued to believe that the German basalts had been formed under water. Similarly when Jean François D'Aubuisson de Voisins (1769–1819), who had studied with Werner for four years, visited Auvergne in 1803, he was rapidly convinced of the volcanic origin of the basalt sheets he saw there. Later he concluded that the basalts of Saxony, which he had studied while with Werner, were also volcanic.

Although the origin of basalt had been warmly disputed at Edinburgh between 1800 and 1810, in 1814 it seems to have been settled for most British geologists by the 1813 visit of William Buckland and William Daniel Conybeare to the Giant's Causeway in Ireland. After a detailed and dispassionate examination of this particularly famous basalt formation, Conybeare had concluded that the basalt was volcanic in origin and that associated trap dikes had intruded the sedimentary strata in a molten condition.[9] Yet Conybeare, who was a very competent and serious geologist, did not go beyond the particular question of the origin of basalt to make a judgment between the Huttonian and Wernerian theories. In this he represented well the attitude of members of the Geological Society of London; the Society wished deliberately to prevent its meetings from becoming a forum for the continuance of the increasingly sterile Huttonian–Wernerian debate. They were fed up with geological theories at a time when geologists

9. W. D. Conybeare, "Descriptive notes referring to the outline of sections presented by a part of the coasts of Antrim and Derry" (1816).

were discovering many new and exciting fossils and when the land surveyor and engineer William Smith (1769–1839) had recently shown that fossils might be used to identify stratified formations in their different outcrops across England. In 1807 Smith had not yet published his map nor any extensive account of his work, but about 1790 he had recognized that in southwestern England various strata succeeded each other in regular order, all dipping slightly to the southeast and passing under one another, and that each formation could be recognized by its characteristic fossils. In the course of his work Smith traveled extensively throughout the English countryside and came to know it intimately. From the early 1790s he devoted all his spare time to the gathering of geological observations and in 1799 marked out and colored outcrops of formations on a county survey map of Somersetshire. He kept his hand-drawn maps and his fossil collection available for the examination by visitors in a room at his house in Buckingham Street, London.

In March 1808 George Bellas Greenough, president of the Geological Society, and a few other members of the society, visited William Smith at his London house to examine his collections. One of the purposes of the society at its first formation was to collect from many observers a large number of geological facts and to give to this otherwise scattered information a coherent arrangement. The society thus wished to function as an organization for cooperative research; Dr. Martin Rudwick has suggested that when the leaders of the society visited Smith at his house in March 1808 their purpose was to obtain his help. Dr. Rudwick also suggests that Smith refused to cooperate because his work of compiling a geological map of England was already so far advanced and was so exclusively the product of his own efforts that he did not wish to share it.[10]

In 1815 William Smith's geological map of England, which had been long in preparation, was finally published in fifteen sheets. The number of copies was small and each was hand colored.[11] To accompany the map he published a *Memoir* to explain the principles on which it was drawn and to elucidate many of its details.[12]

10. M. J. S. Rudwick, "The foundation of the Geological Society of London . . ." (1963), pp. 339–40.

11. W. Smith, *A delineation of the strata of England and Wales, with part of Scotland* . . . (1815).

12. W. Smith, *A memoir to the map and delineation of the strata of England and Wales with part of Scotland* (1815).

Smith's map continued to appear in successive issues from 1815 until 1819 and Mr. and Mrs. Eyles have shown that later issues were corrected and amplified in many details.[13] The further publication of Smith's map stopped in 1819, evidently as a consequence of the publication in that year of the Geological Society's geological map of England prepared under the direction of G. B. Greenough.

Smith worked out the order of succession of the English strata and showed that each stratified formation contained certain fossils with such regularity that the fossils could be used to recognize the strata. In 1816 he published a short work to illustrate and explain this principle.[14] He had also formed a collection of the fossils represented most commonly in the English strata and in 1817 published illustrations and descriptions of them.[15] He had identified the fossils as well as he could from the scientific literature then available, and had prepared his descriptions for the clearer exhibition of his collection at the British Museum. However, after his collection was purchased by the British government for the museum it was not unpacked, and the value which Smith's specimens might have had for the development of English geology in the early nineteenth century was lost.[16]

Yet the publication of Smith's map and studies of fossils between 1815 and 1817 exerted a profound influence on geology. Smith had named and described a set of fossils characteristic of every stratified formation in England from the mountain limestone beneath the coal to the chalk and this included a nearly complete sequence of the secondary formations. Moreover, his method of identifying strata by means of the fossils they contained, particularly the fossil shells, was one which Georges Cuvier and Alexandre Brongniart had also used successfully in their study of the Tertiary strata of the Paris basin.[17] Werner and his students had assumed that they could identify strata of the same formation in different countries by the characters of the rock, that is, by whether it was a limestone, sandstone, or shale, granite, gneiss, or porphyry, whether hard or

13. V. A. Eyles and J. M. Eyles, "On the different issues of the first geological map of England and Wales" (1938).

14. W. Smith, *Strata identified by organized fossils* (1816).

15. W. Smith, *Stratigraphical system of organized fossils . . .* (1817).

16. J. M. Eyles, "William Smith: the sale of his geological collection to the British Museum" (1967).

17. G. Cuvier and A. Brongniart, *Essai sur la géographie minéralogique des environs de Paris . . .* (1811).

soft, by its color, texture, consistency, and so forth. In 1809 William MacLure had attempted to classify the strata of North America in terms of Werner's four groups of primitive rocks, transition rocks, floetz or secondary rocks, and alluvial rocks, and had sought to identify these formations on the basis of the character of their rocks.[18] In 1814 Robert Bakewell attempted similarly to correlate the strata of England with those which Werner had described for Germany.[19] Both MacLure and Bakewell assumed without question that there was a single overall series of rock strata existing throughout the world and representing the successive formations laid down in successive geological epochs. The character of each formation was determined, according to Werner's theory, by the conditions existing in the universal ocean at the particular period in the earth's history when the formation had been deposited. As a consequence of this view, therefore, it seemed reasonable to expect that one could correlate the strata of different countries by the characteristics of the rocks forming them. As late as 1824 the American geologist Amos Eaton attempted to apply this principle to the identification of the strata of New York state. For instance, Eaton decided that a grey sandstone occurring at Starch Factory Creek near Utica, New York (actually a Cambrian formation) was the "mill-stone grit" described by Bakewell as lying immediately beneath the coal formation in Derbyshire, England.[20] His reason for so identifying it was that the rock seemed to have the physical characteristics which Bakewell gave for the millstone grit. In terms of the classification then in use however, the grey sandstone near Utica, New York ought to have been placed early in the series of primitive formations, whereas the millstone grit in England was a secondary formation.

The use of fossils to identify strata of corresponding age in different localities, different countries, and even different continents thus made a radical difference to the determination of the geological succession. Whereas William Smith established this succession for the secondary strata of England, his work was made more universal in its application by the fact that when he prepared his *Stratigraphical system of organized fossils* in 1817 he attempted to

18. W. MacLure, "Observations on the geology of the United States" (1809).

19. R. Bakewell, *An Introduction to Geology* ... (1815).

20. A. Eaton, *A Geological and Agricultural Survey of the District adjoining the Erie Canal, in the State of New York* (1824). For a fuller discussion of the effort to correlate North American with European strata see L. G. Wilson, "The emergence of geology as a science in the United States" (1967).

identify and describe the different species of fossil shells in terms of Lamarck's classification.[21] Lamarck's descriptions of shell species and classification of the Mollusca was also essential to Georges Cuvier and Alexandre Brongniart in their earlier study of the Tertiary strata of the Paris basin.

The Paris basin is a basin in the chalk formation; that is, the country surrounding the basin and forming its rim is everywhere composed of chalk strata. Cuvier and Brongniart noted that the chalk was composed of horizontal beds with very little separation between them, but in places containing beds of flints. However, the essential characteristic was the fossil content. Although not all the fossils had been classified, there were significant differences both in genus and species from those of the Paris limestone.[22] The formation immediately overlying the chalk in the Paris basin was the plastic clay. In contrast to the chalk, it contained so little calcium carbonate that normally it would not effervesce with acids. As its name implied it was a soft, sticky clay from which the porcelain of Sèvres was made. Fossils were rare and one found in it none of the fossils which occurred in the chalk. Cuvier and Brongniart concluded that the fluid from which the plastic clay had been deposited was very different from that which had formed in the chalk. Furthermore, they presented evidence that the chalk had already solidified into solid rock before the plastic clay had been deposited on it.

Above the plastic clay was the Paris limestone, called by Cuvier and Brongniart "le calcaire grossier." It did not always overlie the clay directly for there was sometimes an intervening layer of sand of variable thickness. Cuvier and Brongniart were not sure whether this sand was part of the limestone or part of the clay formation. The limestone formation itself consisted of alternating layers of coarse limestone, argillaceous marl, marl parting in very thin layers, and calcareous marl, but these numerous thin beds always appeared in the same order of superposition throughout the Paris basin. It was in their study of so many different beds of limestone that Cuvier and Brongniart discovered that they could always recognize a bed which they had studied previously by the nature of its fossils, even though the difference between the fossils of one bed and another was much less than that between the Paris

21. J. B. de Lamarck had worked out a classification for the Mollusca in a series of papers in the *Annales du Muséum d'Histoire Naturelle*, Paris.

22. G. Cuvier and A. Brongniart, *Géographie minéralogique . . . Paris* (1811) pp. 11, 17, 20–21, 42–43.

limestone taken as a whole and the chalk. The marked feature of the whole system of beds making up the Paris limestone was the enormous number of fossil shells it contained. The species of shells in the lower beds tended to differ more from corresponding living species than the fossil shells in the upper ones.

Cuvier and Brongniart distinguished three successive systems of beds in the Paris limestone. Their general conclusions concerning this formation were: (1) That the fossils of the Paris limestone had been deposited slowly in a calm sea because the fossils occurred in regular layers; they were not confused together and most were perfectly preserved despite the fact that their structure might be delicate. For instance, even the spiny points of the shells were usually intact. (2) That the fossils were entirely different from those of the chalk. (3) That as successive beds had been deposited the species changed; some disappeared while new ones appeared. This fact suggested a long series of generations of marine animals, and that the number of shell species has always been diminishing. Their final conclusion was that conditions in the sea from which the beds of the Paris limestone had been deposited, must have been very different from those in modern seas, because in modern seas there are no longer any solid layers formed and the same species of shells are always found in the same localities. In the same position as the calcaire grossier, that is, immediately overlying the plastic clay, there was in the forest of Fontainebleau another formation the calcaire siliceux, or siliceous limestone, which was remarkable for containing no fossils at all, an indication again perhaps of the distinctive character of the ancient seas.

Above the beds of the calcaire grossier was another quite different formation, the gypsum formation, composed of beds of gypsum alternating with beds of marl and limestone. Like the beds of the coarse limestone the beds of the gypsum formation always occurred in the same order of superposition, represented most completely at Montmartre where large gypsum quarries were worked. The formation contained three series of beds. In the first and lowest series were alternating thin beds of gypsum, lime marl, and thinly foliated clay marls. The lower beds of this series rested in places on the marine calcareous sandstone containing fossil shells, and in these localities, the gypsum beds also contained marine shells. At other places the gypsum beds rested on a bed of white marl containing many freshwater shells, which covered the beds of marine limestone.

In the first mass of marl there occurred the scattered skeletons and bones of birds and mammals. To the north of Paris these fossil bones occurred in the gypsum beds themselves and were very solid; south of the city the bones occurred more often in the layers of marl between the gypsum beds and there the fossil bones were very fragile and easily crumbled into dust. Freshwater shells sometimes occurred with these bones. They were rare, but were sufficient to suggest that the gypsum had been deposited in a freshwater lake. Above the gypsum, the beds of marl also contain freshwater shells which indicated that they too had been laid down in a freshwater lake.

These beds of gypsum and marl together formed the older freshwater formation of the Paris basin. Above the uppermost marl bed was a thin but very extensive bed containing marine shells. It represented the beginning of the marine formation, a series of yellowish marls containing marine shells. Thus the strata of the Paris basin showed an alternation from the plastic clay and calcaire grossier which were both marine formations, to the freshwater gypsum formation, and back to the upper marine formation. The gypsum formation was particularly remarkable because, as Brongniart pointed out, it had no counterpart in the series of formations described by Werner and his pupils. In a separate paper Brongniart in 1810 had also shown that freshwater formations were not restricted to the gypsum beds of the Paris basin, but that a thick series of freshwater marls occurred throughout an extensive area in the volcanic districts in Auvergne and Cantal in south-central France.[23]

The discovery of a freshwater formation in the Paris basin and of an even more widespread and thick series of freshwater strata in Auvergne and Cantal was startling to scientists who shared broadly the same assumptions as Werner; namely, that strata had been deposited in an ocean which had once covered the presently existing land areas. While it was one thing to say that the ocean had formerly stood at a higher level in relation to the land, it was quite another to imagine the changes which would be necessary to convert either the Paris basin or a large area in south-central France into great freshwater lakes. Even more startling was the fact that the freshwater gypsum formation of the Paris basin was overlain again by a series of marine sediments, so the sea had not only retreated from the land at the beginning of the deposition

23. A. Brongniart, "Sur les terrains qui paroissent avoir été formés sous l'eau douce" (1810).

of the gypseous beds but returned after their deposition was completed again to occupy the Paris basin. At a still later period a second freshwater formation was deposited over the upper series of marine sediment. These successive retreats and incursions of the sea suggested to Georges Cuvier the occurrence of great catastrophes any of which would have been disastrous for the animals and plants then living on the earth. According to this theory, the numerous species of mammals and other animals whose fossil remains were found in the gypsum beds must have been made extinct by the invasion of the sea in which the marine beds overlying the gypsum had been formed.

Since the presence of a freshwater formation in the series of Paris beds was startling to previous assumptions, the evidence for it was questioned. Brongniart argued that as in former geological periods it had been possible for such rocks as marble and schist to be formed in the sea, it may also have been possible for fresh waters then to form rock strata which would contain remains of the animals and plants which lived on their banks or in their depths. In this seemingly naïve comparison we see how bewildering geological phenomena might be in the absence of any adequate knowledge of the effects of heat and igneous action, because schists and marbles are sedimentary rocks which have been altered by heat and pressure after they have been deposited.

But what convinced Brongniart that the strata had been laid down in freshwater was the presence in them of shells of genera which today live only in freshwater. These included representatives of the genera *Lymnea, Planorbis, Potamides, Cyclostoma, Bulimus,* and *Helix.* He also found "gyrogonites," bodies not then understood, but which were actually the reproductive bodies of the green alga *Chara,* and remains of other water plants. In the vicinity of Clermont in Auvergne, Brongniart found a limestone made up of myriads of short, straight tubular structures each about 3 centimeters in length and a half centimeter in diameter. Each tube consisted of grains of sand and small shells all held together by a calcareous cement. Bosc, who had first discovered these peculiar structures, considered them correctly to be fossil larval cases of the caddis fly, *Phryganea,* and called them indusia tubulata.[24] Brongniart thought this interpretation correct, but wrote that some naturalists considered them simply to be calcareous concre-

24. L. Bosc, "Note sur un fossile . . ." (1804–5).

tions which happened to enclose bits of plant debris. Yet the whole assemblage of fossils, taken together, suggested overwhelmingly that the sediments had been laid down in fresh waters, and gave a corresponding certainty to the alternation of freshwater with marine sediments in the Paris basin.

In his study of the fossil vertebrates of the Paris basin, which he carried on during the years of his collaboration with Brongniart on the strata of the Paris basin, Cuvier had studied primarily two fossil faunas. A number of fossil skeletons had been found in the superficial gravel and alluvium near Paris. Cuvier showed that these bones included those of a daman (or hyrax), rhinoceros, hippopotamus, tapir, elephant, and mastodon, all extinct in France and found living only in the tropical regions of Africa and Asia. They all belonged to one family, the *Pachydermata*. Cuvier began his studies in comparative anatomy with the pachyderms because they are large animals with genera so distinct from each other that he could identify a fossil pachyderm skeleton even when he had only a fragment of the jaw, skull, or extremities. In his comparative studies he demonstrated his principle of the correlation of parts; namely, that the different parts of an animal must be formed in such a way that they may function effectively together and in relation to the animal's way of life.

In the gypsum quarries of Montmartre the workers frequently came across fossil bones. In 1804 Cuvier examined a fossil skeleton, the skull of which contained 28 molars, 12 incisors, and 4 canine teeth. This was an arrangement of teeth similar to that of the living tapir, but the shape of the molars was more like that of a modern rhinoceros. The species did not belong to either genus, and Cuvier, therefore, placed it in a new genus, *Palaeotherium*. Later he examined a skeleton very similar to that of *Palaeotherium*, but different in that it lacked canine teeth; to this fossil animal he gave the name *Anoplotherium*.[25]

Ultimately from the gypsum beds of Montmartre Cuvier described four species of *Palaeotherium* and three of *Anoplotherium*, with two additional uncertain species. These nine species of fossil pachyderms together with a fossil tortoise and other vertebrates made up a considerable fossil fauna, all of which had evidently disappeared with the incursion of the sea which had deposited the marine beds overlying the freshwater gypsum forma-

25. W. Coleman, *Georges Cuvier, zoologist* . . . (1964), pp. 123–24. Cf. G. Cuvier, "Sur les espèces d'animaux dont proviennent les os fossiles . . ." (1804).

tion of the Paris basin. Thus the geological changes, which Cuvier and Brongniart had detected in the history of the Paris basin, seemed to have resulted in the wholesale destruction of animal populations. When in a later geological period a new assemblage of animals appeared, they belonged to different species, or even different genera, and were adapted to different conditions. Such changes seemed to Cuvier to have occurred so suddenly and completely as to have been catastrophic. He developed this view in 1812 in his preliminary discussion to his *Recherches,* a collection of his memoirs on vertebrate paleontology.[26]

Cuvier's descriptions of so many large and sometimes bizarre fossil animals, belonging to extinct species and genera, drew widespread attention. They revealed to the scientific world a variety of genera of fossil animals, sometimes larger and more numerous in species than their modern counterparts. Moreover, even in 1812, a pattern of fossil succession was beginning to emerge. In Werner's transition strata there were only the fossils of marine invertebrates: corals, echinoderms, molluscs, and the like. Fossil crocodiles and other fossil reptiles had been discovered in the chalk and in the Maestricht beds, but so far no fossil mammals had been reported either from the chalk or from any of the secondary strata below the chalk. However in the gypsum beds, a Tertiary formation above the chalk, Cuvier had found many different species of mammals and these were succeeded by a still different set of species in the gravel and alluvial deposits of the Seine valley.

In 1814, as if to reinforce the significance of Cuvier's work, a remarkable fossil was discovered in the soft clay of the blue lias beds, a secondary formation, at Lyme Regis on the coast of Dorsetshire in England. The skeleton was about seventeen feet long. Its teeth were reptilian and it had four well-defined feet, but the vertebrae had fish-like characteristics. Because the fossil combined some of the features of a fish with those of a large lizard, Charles König of the British Museum called it *Ichthyosaurus.* It had been a very large marine reptile with paddle-like limbs and other features to adapt it for life in the sea.

In 1820 W. D. Conybeare confirmed the appropriateness of the name *Ichthyosaurus* and described another large fossil reptile found in the blue lias formation in the same localities where

26. G. Cuvier, *Recherches sur les ossemens fossiles de quadrupèdes* (1812).

Ichthyosaurus bones were found.[27] This reptile was also adapted for marine life and appeared intermediate in structure between the *Ichthyosaurus* and the crocodile. Conybeare named it *Plesiosaurus* (Fig. 10). In his discussion of the different fossil reptiles that had been discovered in the British strata, Conybeare also mentioned that Dr. John Kidd and the Reverend William Buckland had for some time been studying the remains of a still larger unknown reptile found in a quarry at Stonesfield near Oxford.

The discovery of these large fossil reptiles in the secondary strata of England lent a new interest and excitement to the study of geology and emphasized the overriding importance of the study of organic remains. While naturalists had known since the seventeenth century that the British secondary strata contained marine shells, it was only in 1817 that William Smith had published his *Stratigraphical system of organized fossils* which showed that different stratified formations each had a distinctive and characteristic group of fossil species. His work, together with the discovery of *Ichthyosaurus* and *Plesiosaurus,* showed that the secondary strata contained the records of a number of living creatures which had existed on the earth's surface during successive ages of the secondary period. Werner and earlier mineralogists had assumed that the secondary rocks represented essentially a single epoch in the history of the earth. Now it was clear that the secondary period represented a long succession of epochs each with its characteristic plants and animals.

At the same time the emphasis in geological investigations shifted markedly from the study of the mineralogical characteristics of rocks to the study of fossils.

27. H. T. de la Beche and W. D. Conybeare, "Notice of the discovery of a new fossil animal . . ." (1820).

CHAPTER 5

Law Student and Amateur Geologist, 1819–1824

WEEKS of perfect weather followed Charles's return to Bartley from Oxford. The foliage on the oaks about the house was more luxuriant than ever and a fine crop of hay ripened in the meadows. "Time," Mr. Lyell wrote, "slips away amusingly if not profitably with us, in the interchange of dinners in this wealthy & somewhat elegant neighbourhood, & in travels to Southhampton and Hursley."[1] The rest was proving very necessary to Charles because his eyes continued to bother him all summer long. In mid-September Mr. Lyell took Marianne and Caroline and went to Kinnordy by post chaise while Charles traveled northward independently along a route of his own in order to study the geology of the country.

Lyell went first to Oxford and on 9 September, apparently in company with Dr. Buckland, he left there by stagecoach for Woodstock and Stratford-on-Avon. He kept a travel journal:

Sept. 9th 1819. Between Oxford & Woodstock passed numbers of Gypsies. The country between Woodstock & Euston much resembles that between Fontainebleau & Avallon in France from the shape of the Oolite hills. But the winding of the road in England prevents its being so tedious as the same country is in the straight roads of France.

We met a man driving mules which, the Coachman informed us, were going to the West Indies.

. . . At Stratford the red sandstone formation has succeeded to the Oolite & continues to Birmingham.

Friday 10 Sept. Sutton. Observed numbers of rounded pebbles in red sandstone. Litchfield cathedral with 3 spires. Here we began to get out of the red sandstone which had afforded a rich & well-wooded country from Stratford to this place. Coal now began & a poorer soil. Large brick kilns.

Macclesfield — many idle people about the streets. Not a great many hands out of employ, but wages exceedingly low.

1. C. L. to D. T. 18 July 1819. Dawson Turner mss.

Stockport — met [illeg.] Hunt entering, drawn in a coach, [on] the top of which was a flag & some people. The mob immense, above 3,000. Our coach obliged to stop, hooted us — soldiers mixed with them. . . .

Three days later they were in the Lake District:

Monday 13 Sept. Tour by Loughrig Tarn, weather so misty that we gave up climbing the pikes, but went up as far as waterfall called Dungeon Gill, in a large chasm, with stone suspended in mid-air, & forming bridge, over the top [of] which I crossed . . . returned to Langdale Chapel thence to Grasmere — this lake beautiful, day quite cleared up. Rydal & its wooded islands, pretty scene . . . went into Wordsworth's garden, Rydal Mount — from thence a very pleasing view of the lake.
Tuesday 14 Sept. Went to Potterdale on foot with boy to carry my sac-de-nuit — schistose trap mountains from which are procured fine slates.
Wednesday 15 Sept. 1819. Took a guide for Helvellyn — a gentleman accompanied me up Griesdale — drank water at Red Tarn — fine ridge on north shoulder of Helvellyn whence we looked down two precipices into two basins with tarns at the bottom of each. Could get no stones to roll down into water, owing to the separation of lamina of the schist, cut my fingers with them badly . . . descended & got into coach 6 miles to Keswick. Poor boy who had been shipwrecked by Holyhead up behind.
Thursday 16th Sept. Went from Keswick along the side of Derwent water . . . up Borrowdale, thought nothing in the scenery here striking. Shower. Stopped at farm house, library of dissenter's books. Crossed over into Borrowdale. Lakes of Buttermere & Crumnoch in view. The former viewed from the Inn with Horister Crag is very beautiful. Shakespeare in the parlour of the Inn. In the first page a reprimand from Mr. Wilberforce in his own handwriting, written when he was here last year to the Landlady "for having such ungodly books in the house"! Notwithstanding I was glad to have this profane book to read & found in it what at the time applied well to myself, for I was lame from a hurt in my foot & unwell & had a very stupid, dull guide, a poor Inn & no traveller there but myself. Touchstone: "Ay — now I am in Arden. The more fool I. When I was at home I was in a better place, but travellers must be content."

Friday 17 Septr. Was rowed in a boat to Seale Force, over the Crumnoch, waterfall fine height. Cleft in the rock magnificent. Rock red syenite. Back to the Inn. Returned to Keswick by Newlands. Grasmere rather fine mountain. Found the Inn very much overcrowded by travellers. Much amused with an offended gentleman pedestrian from Porley.

The next day, Saturday, Lyell returned to Penrith where he took the mail coach to Carlisle and thence to Edinburgh where on Monday 20 September he arrived at Walkers' Hotel just as his father and sisters were setting off for Kinnordy. He remained at Edinburgh for the next few days and called on Professor Robert Jameson. Possibly influenced by his observations in the lake district, he wrote in his journal after this visit, "Inclined now to think most of the formations chemical deposits."[2] On Saturday 25 September he reached Kinnordy, having come by coach through Stirling and Perth and walked the last few miles from Glamis.

The Lyells had reached Kinnordy "Just at the conclusion of a golden harvest & the weather still warm & dry" and spent a happy month there. They visited many of their neighbours in whose houses Mr. Lyell found "an absence of stiffness rarely found in the south" which was especially pleasant for Marianne and Caroline.[3] Lyell too had a good time. He went riding with Mr. Blackadder of Glamis and they discussed the origin of the deposits of marl which occurred in a number of the small freshwater lakes in the vale of Strathmore. Several of these shallow lakes had been drained, as had been the loch of Kinnordy, to enable their beds of marl to be dug up to spread upon the land. Mr. Blackadder thought that the marl had not formed from shells, at least not principally, and must have had some other source. The question interested Lyell because the marl deposits were clearly post-diluvian, that is, they had been deposited since the time when the principal features of the surface of the country had been established.

Mr. Lyell wrote to his wife, "The young Boy staid at Balamary to take a farming lesson of David Millar, intends to pass a few days with some Oxford friends here in Edinbro' & perhaps to visit Oxford before Bartley. He & I have never had even a momentary difference since we left you, the best proof I can give you that he has

2. C. L., Jr., "Notes from Journal of Tour with Dr. Buckland" [copied by K. M. Lyell], Kinnordy mss.
3. C. L. to D. T. 13 Oct. 1819. Dawson Turner mss.

behaved amiably."[4] Apparently because of the trouble given him
by his eyes, Lyell did not begin his legal studies until the first of
February 1820, when he entered the office of John Patteson, the
Pleader,[5] then a young lawyer of thirty, where he was "with three
gentlemanlike very clever young men, who are not slaves to the
desk and yet look to the law for fame and independent circumstances."[6] At the same time Mr. Lyell congratulated himself because Tom passed as a lieutenant in the navy and his youngest son
Henry entered the Royal Military College at Sandhurst.[7]

When Lyell took up concentrated study again, the pain and in-
flammation of his eyes returned. On 9 May Mr. Lyell wrote to
Dawson Turner:

> If time had allowed you to beat up Charles's quarters 29 Nor-
> folk Street you would have found him nursing eyes which
> threaten to be permanently so weak & painful that the possi-
> bility of intense application & consequently of pursuing the law
> with effect becomes very doubtful.—The plan of life, however is
> not to be changed suddenly, & the terms are to be kept, but a
> temporary cessation from hard reading is indispensable & there-
> fore I propose making him my companion (& one of my daugh-
> ters) in a flight to Rome![8]

In fact, he did not take one of his daughters and it was August before he and Lyell left England.

On their way to London on 4 August they saw George IV returning from a review of the troops on Bagshot heath. Lyell describes
the scene in a letter to his sister Fanny:

> As the King past about 10 dirty fellows & as many women
> shouted 'Queen Caroline for ever.' We then drove on & found
> the whole road to London covered with carriages coming too
> late to the Review & among others the *Queen herself* at Brent-
> ford with a gay equipage. This is not the way to court her own
> friends the *Mob* for she does away with their commiseration by
> the gaiety of her appearance. She is as vulgar a woman as was
> ever seen. It was an open carriage.

4. C. L. to his wife. 30 Oct. 1819. Kinnordy mss.
5. C. L. to D. T. 20 Jan. 1820. Dawson Turner mss. John Patteson (1790–
1861) was educated at King's College, Cambridge (B.A. 1813, M.A. 1816). In 1815
he went on the Midland circuit as marshal to Mr. Justice Champre.
6. C. L. to C. W. 30 March 1820. Wedderburn of Pearsie mss.
7. C. L. to C. W. 13 Feb. 1820. Wedderburn of Pearsie mss.
8. C. L. to D. T. 9 May 1820. Dawson Turner mss.

Two days later they were at Dover, but had to wait there a day for the wind to die down to allow the packet to cross to Calais. Even so the crossing was rigorous.

> We crossed in 3 hours without tacking once—almost everyone dreadfully sick—I for one but not very bad. Papa very ill. Vessel heeled much. Sea came in on lower side so that the ladies who sat there were *up to their middle* in salt water, yet they were so ill they w^d not be moved. Many ladies screamed the whole way & some of the men groaned horribly. A pretty frontispiece to a Tour on the Continent![9]

But after this the discomforts of continental travel would seem minor. However, even while touring Lyell's eyes continued to bother him so much as to prevent him from keeping his journal. From Calais they went into Flanders to St. Omer and Lille. At Baisieu they entered Belgium. Lyell wrote to his sister Marianne:

> To give you an idea of these 80 miles which we went thro' France I must first beg you to suppose everything as different as possible to what you saw between Calais & Paris. The road not an endless straight line but winding like England & when it formed an avenue instead of small pear trees, enormous white poplars & elms forming a complete screen from the heat of the sun. No want of hedges nor of wood which abounds everywhere & in fine masses together. No want of villages, nor of people, carts & waggons on the road which are all as numerous as in England.[10]

He noted too the abundance of poppies in the fields of Flanders. While at Brussels they made the customary pilgrimage to the field of Waterloo, and then went on to Louvain and thence to Liège, Spa, Aix-la-Chapelle, and Cologne. From here they went up the Rhine to Bonn. Lyell admired the ruined castles "but I am sorry to add to these the wreck & ruin of the French Revolution, rich convents without number & churches pillaged & deserted everywhere. The churches unroofed often—in one immense one at Andernach we saw more than a hundred horses of the Prussian Cavalry feeding!"[11] They continued along Napoleon's military road up the west side of the Rhine to Mainz where they crossed the river to Frankfort. From Frankfort they traveled south to Stuttgart, thence to Munich, and then for 300 miles south through the

9. C. L., Jr. to his sister Fanny. 8 Aug. 1820. Kinnordy mss.
10. C. L., Jr. to his sister Marianne. 17 Aug. 1820. Kinnordy mss.
11. C. L., Jr. to his sister Fanny. 29 Aug. 1820. Kinnordy mss.

Tyrol to Verona in Italy. This was steady traveling and sight-seeing. On 15 September they reached Ravenna and there for the first time Lyell mentions the geological features of the country.

> After seeing the Antiquities of Ravenna in which that city is very rich, but which I dare say you will excuse me for passing over, we took a drive to an immense plain which has been left along this coast by the sea, which retires before two rivers that bring down from the Apennines great quantities of debris. There were 3 cities in the time of the Romans which stood close together here—Cesarea, Ravenna & Classis. The two last were sea ports & at Classis 150 galleys of the Roman Emperors were constantly stationed. Yet the sea is now five miles distant from these! 3 Roman Towers which once stood on or near the shore as sea-marks are now far inland & a Church has been built (& a convent now destroyed) on to one of them in the midst of the plain.

Lyell noted the pine forests and herds of cattle on these sandy plains and the richness of their wildlife:

> Here and there on these plains there are small lakes which abound in fish and wild-fowl, the latter, in winter chiefly, of many varieties & some rare ones. We saw many, even in this month, enough to add to the wildness of the scene. Saw many curious insects & plants. The Tamarisk in particular gave a character to these sands.

At Rome they found the malaria only recently abated and in the Campagna "the Post-boys & every peasant look like ghosts."[12]

Mr. Lyell had intended to travel southward as far as Naples, but Italy was in a state of political disturbance and the banditti were reported to be active on the road between Rome and Naples. Naples itself was considered unsafe and many English families had already left there. Lyell and his father, therefore, contented themselves with examining the sculpture and painting and ancient ruins of Rome. Except for the coliseum, the ruins failed to live up to Lyell's expectations and he thought they were a positive detriment to the historical imagination.

At the end of September they left Rome for the north, going first to Florence where they renewed their acquaintance with the

12. C. L., Jr. to his sister Caroline. 21 Sept. 1820. Kinnordy mss.

art galleries, and then to Lerice on the coast where they took passage on a small sailing ship or felucca to Genoa. From Italy they crossed the pass of Mt. Cenis to Geneva where "A Yorkshire family of the name of Marshal with whom Charles [through a College friend] was intimate and the civilities of the famous botanical Professor [Decandolle] made a short sojourn of four days one of the pleasantest incidents of our tour."[13] They passed thence directly home and, when they landed at Dover, found the people rejoicing in drunkenness over the acquittal of Queen Caroline. On 12 November they reached Bartley.

After this long tour abroad Lyell returned to his lodgings at 29 Norfolk Street in London, coming home only for a brief visit at Christmas time. He pursued his legal studies as diligently as his eyes would allow. Meanwhile he was learning to order his own life. When Dawson Turner wrote to inquire whether he should invite him to Yarmouth at Easter, Mr. Lyell replied:

> I persuade myself that I do best by interfering as little as possible with Charles's movements. He does not always think or act as my feelings prompt me to do; but as he is thoroughly right minded and far from idle I do not think it wise to discourage the spirit of independence which is part of his character.[14]

Evidently his eyes were considerably better because on 18 April 1821 he wrote to his father that he intended to remain steadily reading in town for some months if he continued as well as he was then.[15] He did stick at it until mid-July and then after a short holiday at Bartley attended the judges on part of the western circuit as an amateur. He was thus acting as a serious law student. Yet once at Bartley he remained there through September and got his sisters to read his law books to him. His father was concerned about his health. Late in September he wrote to Dawson Turner:

> I almost despair of Charles's ever having strength of constitution to bear the sedentary life which is unavoidable at the bar; nothing else is wanting to secure his following the profession with ardour & perseverance, and therefore I who have no other line

13. C. L. to C. W. 2 Dec. 1820. Wedderburn mss.
14. C. L. to D. T. 8 March 1821. Dawson Turner mss.
15. C. L., to D. T. 22 April 1821. Dawson Turner mss.

of life to propose to him have every reason to be pleased with him. He came from town thin & pale, but country air & strong exercise on horseback have given him a complexion fit for an idle foxhunter. Still the eyes protest against reading & writing.[16]

One of Lyell's excursions on horseback was to his old school at Midhurst on 2 October. While there, he did some casual geologizing in a neighboring stone quarry where the quarry men told him that the stone they were working was "whin." Since this is the Scottish term for traprock, a volcanic product, Lyell wondered what such a rock was doing in the southeast of England. The stone actually consisted of irregular masses of quartz embedded in sandstone and was used for repairing roads.[17] When he asked the laborers further why they called it "whin," one of them referred him to "a monstrous clever man, as lived in Lewes, a doctor who knowed all about them things and got curiosities out of the chalk pits to make physic with."[18] His curiosity aroused by this description and being alone with nothing to do, Lyell rode at a leisurely pace over the South Downs, a distance of about twenty-five miles, to Lewes, which he reached in the evening. He immediately called at Castle Place, the house of Gideon Mantell, to whom he had been sent (Fig. 11). Mantell was then a successful country surgeon, thirty-one years old, who had been carrying on his own practice at Lewes for about three years; he had also been born, brought up, and apprenticed to a surgeon there. He had become interested in the study of fossils partly by having spent his boyhood on the South Downs where they abound in the rock strata, and partly by having been influenced while he was a medical student at London by the friendship of James Parkinson (1755–1824), a surgeon and medical practitioner in Hoxton Square, the third volume of whose *Organic Remains of a Former World* had been published in 1811, the year in which Mantell received his diploma from the Royal College of Surgeons.[19] This great work was the first attempt to give a systematic, scientific description of the fossils of the British strata. When he settled at Lewes, Mantell seems to have determined to devote himself to furthering the work which Parkinson had begun by collecting and studying in greater detail the fossils of the strata in the neighborhood of Lewes.

16. C. L. to D. T. 23 Sept. 1821. Dawson Turner mss.
17. G. Mantell, *The Fossils of the South Downs* ... (1822) p. 71.
18. S. Spokes. *Gideon Algernon Mantell* ... (1927) p. 125.
19. Ibid., p. 8.

Lyell introduced himself as a pupil of Buckland and the two young men took to each other at once. Mantell, a tall, handsome, extraordinarily intelligent and ambitious man, was tormented by loneliness and intellectual isolation at Lewes. He seized upon the opportunity to talk about geology, for his imagination had recently been set on fire by the fossils which he was finding not only in the chalk of the Downs but in the clay and sandstone strata of the Weald which lay beneath the chalk. At one place on the Weald, in the Tilgate forest, he had been excited to find the remains of land plants, the bones of vertebrate land animals, and freshwater shells, which suggested to him that these strata had been laid down in freshwater and represented possibly the delta of a once great river. Lyell, though tending to be shy and reserved, after rusticating in the country for many weeks was delighted to find someone with interests akin to his own. They looked over Mantell's collection, which at that time still amounted to only a few drawers of fossils, and then talked enthusiastically until the early morning. Mantell seems at this time to have confided to Lyell his discovery of the freshwater nature of the Weald strata and to have asked him about the strata of Stonesfield near Oxford. Mantell's curiosity about these strata had been aroused by the fact that Dr. John Kidd mentioned briefly in his *Geological Essay* that they contained the bones of various land animals.[20] As Kidd pointed out, the only fossil bones known apart from these, except for those in very recent river deposits, were those described by Cuvier and Brongniart in the Paris basin. However, the strata of the Paris basin lay above and were younger than the chalk. The strata of the Weald and those of Stonesfield were beneath and older than the chalk. Fortunately Lyell had at Bartley some fossils from Stonesfield and these he promised to send to Mantell so that Mantell could compare them.

Next morning, since Lyell intended to go to Brighton and thence along the coast to Bognor, as Mantell wrote in his Journal:

> I accompanied him on horseback to Ditchling Beacon, to shew him the general features of the country. He was quite enchanted with the beautiful and magnificent coup d'oeil from that ele-

20. "Again there is reason to think, that besides the remains of crabs and birds and tortoises, which are usually characteristic of the newest strata, the Oolite of Stonesfield contains also the remains of one or more large quadrupeds; which, with the exception in favour of the Paris beds, have only been found in depositions formed above all the regular strata." J. Kidd, *A Geological Essay* ... (1815) p. 38.

vated spot; we parted at that place, M. L. taking the road to Patcham.[21]

It was the beginning of a long and close friendship that was to result in vigorous cooperation in scientific work.

After his return to Bartley from his Sussex tour about 10 October, Lyell sent off to Mantell a parcel of fossils including those from the Stonesfield shale. Then on the twenty-first he left Bartley for Oxford to take his M.A. degree.[22] During the week he spent at Oxford he also visited the quarry at Stonesfield, a small village near Woodstock about twelve miles northwest of Oxford. This quarry had long been famous for the fossils found in its shaly limestone and some of them had been described and drawn long before by Edward Lhuyd. Lyell, therefore, collected a box of specimens and, when he got to London, wished he had got more, because he found waiting for him a letter from Mantell who had been much struck by the resemblance between the fossils of Stonesfield and those from the Tilgate forest near Lewes. The noteworthy fossils were those of vertebrates, but some species were different and this fact worried Mantell. Lyell protested in a letter to Mantell:

> What weight of evidence do you require to identify beds? You say you detect decided differences in many of these organic remains. How is it possible it sh.^{d} not be so if they sh.^{d} really contain each the same? Put 2 alphabets each in separate box & then take out at random 6 letters from each, would you expect half of them to be the same? And how do the odds increase ag'st us, when there may be 5 or 50 thousand in each. Consider they are both *slates*,[23] both calcareous, both sometimes inclining to sandy slates, both contain Amphibia, Aves, Pisces, testacea, vegetables, mixed together. How few have you compared & yet how many of these few again exactly. Why sh.^{d} there not be many kinds of Monitors in each?

Once in London, Lyell settled again to the study of law. He seems to have tried sincerely to comply with his father's wish that he make a career for himself as a barrister, but for more than two

---

21. G. Mantell, *The Journal of Gideon Mantell* ... (1940) pp. 41–42.

22. C. L. to C. W. 21 Oct. 1821. Wedderburn mss.

23. Lyell uses the term "slate" for shale. In modern geological terminology the term "slate" is restricted to metamorphic laminated rocks.

years now his eyes had been impeding him. Clearly he enjoyed field excursions, and his interest in geology seems to have been steadily increasing. In the same letter to Mantell he continued:

> Let me know what Hawkins says of the Whin, but do not write to me before Xmas unless I can be of use to your work by getting you any information, for I am buried in the study of Law here & am too fond of Geology to do both. It is not so compatible with my profession as with yours.[24]

He did keep at the law until the beginning of Christmas vacation in mid-December and then went to Bartley where he remained until near the end of January. While he was there he received a gift of fossil specimens from Mantell. He also ranged the surrounding country to see whether the freshwater formations of the Isle of Wight extended into that part of Hampshire but failed to find them.[25]

Soon after Lyell's return to London he attended the annual dinner of the Geological Society. In a letter to Mantell describing its highlights, the chief of which were the fossil bones and dung of hyaenas which William Buckland had found the previous summer in a cave at Kirkdale in Yorkshire, Lyell wrote:

> Buckland in his usual style enlarged on the marvel with such a strange mixture of the humorous and the serious that we could none of us discern how far he believed himself what he said, take the following as an example of the whole.
>
> 'The hyaenas, gentlemen, preferred the flesh of elephants, rhinoceros, deer, cows, horses etc., but sometimes unable to procure these & half starved they used to come out of the narrow entrance of their cave *in the evening* down to the water's edge of a lake which must once have been there, & so helped themselves to some of the innumerable water-rats in which the lake abounded—thus you see the whole stalactite & the other bones stuck over with the teeth of water rats.[26]

As winter wore into spring Lyell devoted himself less to law and more to geology. In March he went on an excursion again with the purpose of finding in the southeast of England beds which would correspond to those of the Isle of Wight.

24. C. L., Jr. to G. A. M. 3 Nov. 1821. Mantell mss.
25. C. L., Jr. to G. A. M. 8 Feb. 1822. Mantell mss. *L. & L.* I, p. 115.
26. Ibid. (previously unpublished)

The geology of the Isle of Wight is in itself very interesting and proved an important key for unlocking the geology of southeastern England. The history of its geological exploration is worth considering.

In 1799 Sir Henry Englefield (1752–1822), an antiquary and amateur scientist, spent the summer months in the Isle of Wight where he passed his time in the study of the topography, the beauties, and antiquities of the island. In the course of his rambles over the island Sir Henry noted that the central range of hills, which runs almost due east and west across the island and forms its backbone, was composed of chalk. The beds of chalk, far from being horizontal or gently inclined, were so steeply inclined in places as to be almost vertical and their dip was always to the north. The inclination was indicated by the beds of flints which mark their boundaries. These flints, which must originally have been deposited in horizontal layers, were now steeply inclined and when he examined them, Sir Henry was confronted with an astonishing phenomenon: ". . . every flint though lying in its place and retaining perfectly its original shape, was more or less burst and shattered." Some of the flints had even been reduced to powder but this powder had not become at all mixed with the chalk. Sir Henry concluded that because the chalk strata must have been laid down originally in a horizontal position, "when the tremendous convulsion took place" which shifted them into their present steeply inclined position, the strata of chalk must have tended to slide one upon another, and the tremendous strain thus imposed on the intervening flints would have tended to shatter them.[27]

Englefield had planned to publish his description and sketches of the Isle of Wight shortly after his final summer there in 1801 but for personal reasons this plan was delayed for a number of years and when he took it up again, he thought he ought to give a much more complete account of the geology of the island. Because he felt unable to do this himself, he asked a young architect, artist, and traveler, Thomas Webster, to do it for him. Webster had been born in the Orkney islands in 1773 and after attending the University of Aberdeen had come to London where he studied architecture and agriculture. He made his living by traveling through England and France to make sketches for illustrated

27. H. C. Englefield, "Observations on some remarkable Strata of Flint in a Chalk-pit in the Isle of Wight . . ." (1802) pp. 107–08.

books, but in 1799, he was also employed by Benjamin Thompson, Count Rumford, as clerk of the works to design the building for the Royal Institution in Albermarle Street, London.[28]

Webster went to the Isle of Wight in May 1811 (Map 4), and reported his observations to Englefield in a series of letters,[29] the first of which is dated from Shanklin, 21 May. After landing at Cowes he went to Parkhurst Barracks and thence through Newport to St. Helens near the eastern tip of the island. There he hired a boat to take him round the eastern tip into Sandown Bay and in this way he was able to examine Culver Cliff from the water. There he noted how the horizontal strata which are characteristic of the north side of the island curve upward as they approach the vertical clay and chalk of the central east–west ridge. He noted that the dip of the strata in Culver Cliff lessened toward the south side. Beyond the cliff in Sandown Bay he found a regular succession of the strata beneath the chalk and therefore took care to determine their order. All of these beds dipped to the northeast but farther south in the hills behind Shanklin he found that the sandstone strata and the chalk above them were horizontal. On the south shore of the island, by contrast, the strata dipped "gently to the south." At Western Lines on the south shore he observed the lines of sandstone cliffs which he thought to be the green sand of Sussex and Surrey.

> The stratum to which I allude, is that, which, in the English series, is situated immediately under the chalk marl, and which, from its frequently containing a considerable quantity of green earth has been called the green sand bed or green sandstone. In the Isle of Wight it is about seventy feet thick, and is subdivided by subordinate beds of other substances. [p. 140]

In this rock he found a great abundance of branched corals which later turned out to be a species of *Alcyonium*. Wherever he found the lower edge of the chalk along the whole line of the downs in the island, he found this sandstone beneath it. At Freshwater Gate he crossed back over the central chalk ridge again and there found it dipping to the northwest at an angle of about 70°.

After visiting Alum Bay and the Needles at the extreme western tip of the Isle of Wight, Webster hired a small sailing cutter

28. D. N. B.

29. H. C. Englefield, *A Description . . . of the Isle of Wight. With additional observations . . . By Thomas Webster Esq.* (1816) pp. 117–207.

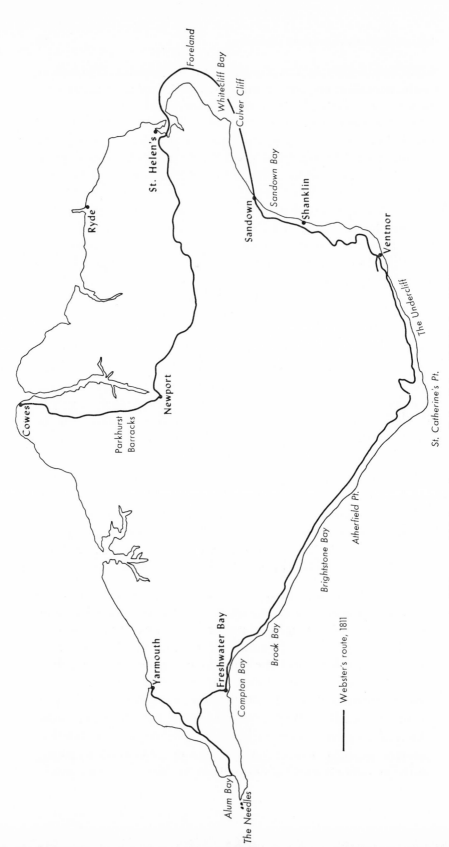

4. Thomas Webster's tour of the Isle of Wight, 1811

to take him along the Dorset coast where he was astonished to find the chalk strata of Handfast Point quite vertical (Fig. 12).

This was not even the most striking circumstance, for the greatest part of the cliff towards the north consisted of horizontal strata of chalk, which, when they approached the vertical chalk, turned upwards into a curve, forming nearly the quarter of a circle; and the vertical layers of flints met the bent part of the chalk, as so many ordinates would meet a curve, decreasing in height as they got more under it. [p. 165]

He noted too that the curved strata adjacent to the vertical ones were much hardened.

A year later, in June 1812, Webster returned to the Isle of Wight to examine further the central ridge of hills and the Dorsetshire coast. He found that the vertical and curved chalk strata of Durdle Cove had been hardened in the same way as those at Handfast Point whereas the adjacent horizontal strata were still soft. The agreement seemed "to point out some connexion between the hardness of the chalk and its vertical position." [p. 195]

After his return to London from this second tour Webster summarized the results of his observations in a number of conclusions and speculations which he sent to Englefield in a letter of 2 August 1812. He noted first, as the most striking feature of the Isle of Wight, the series of vertical, or highly inclined, strata which extended across it in the middle from east to west with less inclined or horizontal strata on either side. Between this middle range of hills and the range of hills on the south side of the island the chalk and green sand strata were completely lacking. He concluded that they had once been there but had been eroded away.

In connecting together, and, as it were, restoring (to use the language of the antiquary) this series of strata, which now in ruins, was probably much more entire in some former condition of the earth, a singular conclusion presents itself to the imagination, and which would seem to force itself upon our conviction, with nearly the same certainty which we feel in putting together the fragments of an ancient temple.

The conclusion to which I allude is, that the chalk of the middle range, together with the clay of Alum bay and the inferior strata, once formed a sort of arch or vault, by which it joined to the horizontal strata of the hills of St. Catherine and Shanklin and that the present abrupt ending of the vertical and highly inclined strata, is owing to the action of the same denudating causes which have swept away such large portions of the earth in other places. [p. 201]

With these words Webster announced his discovery of the anticline, or fold, which forms the basic structure of the Isle of Wight. Possibly his architectural training had helped to give him insight into geological structure. Although Webster's work is very little known today, his discovery of the folding of strata was completely new and original and anticipated by some thirty years the description of folded strata in the Appalachians by William Barton Rogers and Henry Darwin Rogers. On further reflection, he decided that the various outcrops of chalk in England—in the Isle of Wight, the South Downs, the North Downs, the Chiltern hills, etc.—were but remnants of what had once been a continuous sheet of chalk which had stretched across England from Flamborough Head in Yorkshire to a little beyond Lyme Regis in Somersetshire and which had extended completely over the Isle of Wight (Fig. 13).

In a paper published in 1814 Webster set forth his theory of the chalk strata:

> The chalk of England, although it appears upon the surface only in detached hills and patches, is actually continuous through considerable tracts of country, where it exists at great depths, as is now ascertained by numerous wells and other sinkings. In the order of position which the strata of the chalk itself, and those which lie above and below it, bear severally to one another, there has been observed in distant places a remarkable agreement. . . .
>
> This agreement renders it extremely probable that the corresponding strata, found in different parts of the same country, arose from the same cause and at the same time; and favours the idea that many of these although now broken and unconnected, were originally continuous.[30]

The idea of the general continuity of the chalk implied that, because the chalk of the middle hills of the Isle of Wight dipped to the north and that of the South Downs dipped to the south, the

30. T. Webster, "On the Freshwater Formations in the Isle of Wight . . ." (1814).

chalk probably "might pass under the channel called the solent, thus forming a basin." The fact that the bottom of the Solent was composed of the same kind of clay as lay immediately above the chalk further confirmed this idea. In this way Webster defined the boundaries of what he then called the Isle of Wight basin. All of the strata contained within this basin were younger than the chalk and probably could be compared in age with strata in other similar basins or depressions in the chalk sheet. Another such basin in England, Webster suggested, lay in the area around London between the North Downs of Surrey on the south and the Chiltern hills on the north. This he called the London basin and he suggested further that the strata in both the London and the Isle of Wight basins would be comparable with those of the Paris basin which was also a depression rimmed and underlain by the chalk. By comparing fossils from the strata of all three he was able to confirm these inferences. In the English basins Webster was able to distinguish three principal groups of strata above the chalk. They included (1) a marine formation lying immediately over the chalk, (2) a lower freshwater formation, (3) an upper marine formation, (4) an upper freshwater formation.

Websters' delineation of the Isle of Wight basin and the London basin and his study of the strata contained in them were particularly important because he thereby pointed out groups of English strata analogous to those of the Paris basin which had been studied by Cuvier and Brongniart (Fig. 14). Because Cuvier and Brongniart had identified the various strata primarily on the basis of the fossils they contained, Webster's work gave further impetus to the study of the fossils of the English Tertiary strata even though he himself was able to make only rudimentary use of fossils to identify particular strata and correlate them with others.

In his *Letters to Englefield* Webster had also described the strata below the chalk in the Isle of Wight. These he had identified respectively as (1) chalk without flints, (2) chalk marl, (3) green sand, (4) blue marl and (5) iron sand. The term green sand which he applied to the strata under the chalk marl was that which had already been given to strata similarly located with respect to the chalk in England and represented particularly by outcrops in the vale of Pewsey.[31] The term green sand was used by the Reverend Joseph Townsend, Rector of Pewsey, to describe the beds in the

31. T. Webster, "Reply to Dr. Fitton's Paper . . ." (1825) p. 37.

Vale of Pewsey in his book *The character of Moses established for veracity as an historian* and Townsend acknowledged in the preface to his book that he was indebted to William Smith for his knowledge of the strata.[32] Thus the term green sand appears to have been one used quite early by William Smith. Smith considered its characteristic fossils to be corals and several genera of univalve and bivalve shells and of echinoderms.[33] Webster correlated his green sand of the Isle of Wight with strata which were found in the wealds of Kent and Sussex at the foot of the chalk downs and which were dug at Merstham and Reigate for firestone.[34] There must have been some question raised concerning this correlation because Webster discussed it further in a paper which he read to the Geological Society of London on 1 May 1819.[35] He had visited the quarry at Merstham from which this stone was being removed and found the stone very similar to that which he had called green sand in the Isle of Wight. Furthermore, its position below the chalk was the same and it was underlain by beds of "chert and hard rag" similar to those of the Isle of Wight beds.

Webster's view was nevertheless challenged in 1822 by W. D. Conybeare in his contribution to Conybeare and Phillips's *Outlines of the Geology of England and Wales.* Conybeare believed that the firestone bed of Merstham should be assigned to the chalk marl rather than to the green sand. Webster, he said, "has pronounced the firestone beds which we assign to the chalk marl formation, to belong to that of green sand, and the range which we consider as the true green sand to be iron sand."[36]

Son of the rector of St. Botolphs, Bishopsgate, London, William Daniel Conybeare had begun to study geology when he was an undergraduate at Christ Church, Oxford from 1805 to 1808. His grandmother at this time bequeathed him an annual income of £500 which allowed him to collect books and manuscripts on

32. Ibid., p. 39. Cf. J. Townsend, *The character of Moses* . . . (1815).
33. W. Smith, *Stratigraphical System of Organized Fossils* . . . (1817) pp. 24–35.
34. Englefield, *Isle of Wight*, p. 237.
35. T. Webster, "On the Geognostical Situation of the Reigate Stone and of the Fuller's Earth at Nutfield" (1819).
36. This book had first appeared as W. Phillips, *A Selection of Facts . . . to form an Outline of the Geology of England and Wales . . .* (1818). Appended is *Order of Superposition of Strata in the British Islands* by W. Buckland. The second edition was W. D. Conybeare and W. Phillips, *Outlines of the Geology of England and Wales . . .* (1822) p. 150.

English antiquities and to travel about England. As a guide he used William Stukeley's *Itinerary Curiosities* which pointed out the principal physical features of the English landscape including the line of chalk hills from Flamborough Head in Yorkshire to the Chiltern hills and to Dorsetshire in the south, and the line of sandstones underlying the chalk formation as well as other geological formations. In his tours, Conybeare became familiar with the distinct kinds of fossils characteristic of the different formations and was thus prepared to appreciate the ideas of William Smith when he became aware of them about 1809. From 1809 to 1812 Conybeare made a series of excursions through the counties of southwest England and Wales with the intention of compiling geological maps of these areas. In 1814 he married and left Oxford and after taking orders in 1817, settled in 1819 at Brislington near Bristol in Somersetshire where he held the curacy of Banbury and the lectureship of Brislington. At Brislington Conybeare collected and studied the fossils of the blue lias formation which crop out in the neighborhood of Bristol.

This was the state of knowledge in the spring of 1822, when Charles Lyell began to investigate actively the geology of southeast England. His friendship with Gideon Mantell had aroused his curiosity concerning the stratification of that large triangular area lying between the North and South Downs in Kent and Sussex. The geological structure of this area has resulted from the erosion of a great anticlinal fold of the chalk and underlying strata. As a result of the wearing away of the chalk from the upper surface of the fold the underlying strata have been exposed and the edges of the eroded chalk strata are represented by the North and South Downs. The axis of this anticline extends roughly northwest-southeast and intersects the English Channel near Winchelsea. Thus it is that at Winchelsea one finds the lowest, and therefore the oldest, strata represented in this fold, cropping out in cliffs along the sea coast and from there, whether one goes eastward towards the chalk cliffs of Folkestone and Dover, or westward towards those of Beachy Head, one will find in the succession of strata exposed in the sea cliffs the same orderly series proceeding upwards towards the chalk. Because Mantell was just completing for the press his *Fossils of the South Downs,* in which he described the position of the strata of Tilgate Forest, containing his exciting fossil reptiles, as between the iron sand and the Weald clay, he was anxious to determine accurately the succession of beds in this region.[37]

Lyell, who was trying to obtain subscribers for Mantell's book, wrote that:

> I have spent some days lately in investigating the country from Godstone to Merstham—Reigate, Bucland, Betchworth & Dorking & feel sure that the green sand is there exactly as the I. of Wight— & I traced a bed of black blue marl or clay 200 ft. upwards in thickness, between the bed in which the firestone is & the ferruginous sand, the whole way from Godstone to Dorking ... if the green sand of Folkestone c.ᵈ be traced in a continuous bed to the Reigate bed of firestone I feel sure that Greenough c.ᵈ no longer continue to paint in his Map the iron sand as green sand & nothing was ever more exact in resemblance &c. than that country I went over & the I. of W. as far as those four
> beds—   1. Hard grey chalk marl
>   2. green sand
>   3. blue marl or black earth
>   4. iron sand
> But I am aware what great difficulties there may be in reconciling this with other parts of your country.[38]

On 11 April 1822, Lyell wrote to Mantell that he was about to start for Winchelsea to spend a week visiting a friend and studying the geology of the country there. He asked if he could ascertain any fact for Mantell or obtain any specimens and added:

> In several short expeditions which I have made into Surrey I have examined very carefully the junction of the chalk with the beds below, about Reigate, Dorking, and Guildford. I have brought specimens from what Webster would have us call the ferruginous sand, exactly like some brought from the green sand of other parts, which certainly creates a great difficulty.[39]

37. G. Mantell. *The Fossils of the South Downs* . . . (1822). (The work was published in May, 1822.) Of the Tilgate limestone he wrote, "As these strata are of inconsiderable extent, and hold an intermediate situation between the Iron Sand and the Weald clay, appearing to repose upon the former, it seems probable, that they are either a local deposition, formed in an excavation, or basin, of that deposit; or a protrusion of the Purbeck beds, which lie beneath it. Without however, deciding in favour of either supposition, it has been thought expedient to describe these strata in a separate section" (p. 37).
38. C. L., Jr. to G. A. M. 7 March 1822. Mantell mss.
39. C. L., Jr. to G. A. M. 11 April 1822. Mantell mss. *L. & L.* I, 116.

He reserved judgment on this question until he could examine beds further east on his visit to Winchelsea. Five days later he wrote to his father from Winchelsea:

> Among other things I have found the Hastings and Battle lime-stone rock, with its peculiar fossils in the cliff of that isolated hill on which this borough stands, which I believe is the most east-ernmost point in which it has been seen, and I hope will settle Mantell's doubts about its position, as I have here found in the perpendicular cliff the bed of sandstone which is above and below it.[40]

Lyell also communicated these observations to Mantell on 19 April.[41] During a subsequent visit to Mantell at Lewes they went over the ground in the Tilgate forest. On his way back to London Lyell also studied the quarries at Horsham and Sedgwick in Kent. In his geological studies Lyell had the great advantage of being able to use the collections of fossils and rock specimens assembled by the members of the Geological Society at the society's rooms in London and of consulting its experienced curator, Thomas Webster. Writing to Mantell on 5 June he said:

> When I took my specimens to compare them with those from Battle & Winchelsea Webster shewed me a set from Hastings which he had collected 8 years since but had published nothing concerning them save that in his "Order of Superposition" in Sir H. Englefield's I. of Wight. He tells me he included those beds in [the] Iron Sand formation. If so he was the first who assigned a proper position to beds, which, from the series which he presented to the Geological Society, are strictly identical with those of Cuckfield, but if he lays claim to more, you have nothing to do with what he knew if he did not publish it to the world.
>
> He said he should himself communicate with you on that subject.
>
> I am sorry I have given all my Winchelsea specimens to the society but they are *all the same rock* & you had better lose no time in declaring this to be your opinion.[42]

Mantell was prompt to take this advice because in June 1822, he

40. C. L., Jr. to his father. 16 April 1822. Kinnordy mss. *L. & L.* I, 117.
41. C. L., Jr. to G. A. M. 19 April 1822. Mantell mss. *L. & L.* I, 119–20.
42. C. L., Jr. to G. A. M. 5 June 1822. Mantell mss.

sent to the Geological Society a letter[43] in which he recalled the difficulty in determining the stratigraphic position of the Tilgate beds described in his *Fossils of the South Downs* and his reasons for considering them related to the Purbeck limestone, a relationship which he had stressed just at the end of the book. He had again examined the strata of Tilgate forest in company with Charles Lyell who had also given him a further description of a section of the quarry at Horsham.[44] Mantell added:

> From the preceding observations we may, I think, fairly conclude that the calciferous sandstone of Rye, Winchelsea, Hastings, Tilgate Forest and Horsham are but different portions of the same series of deposits, belonging to the iron-sand deposits formation: the Ashburnham beds being situated beneath them.[45]

While he was at Horsham Lyell was fascinated by the ribbed surface of the paving stones in the street and was told that the underside of these stones was ribbed even more strongly. He then went to the quarry at Sedgwick from which this stone came. There he found that the ribs on the upper surface of a slab of stone were sometimes at right angles to those on the lower surface. For this reason he at first doubted that they could have been scooped out by the waves of the ocean as he and Mantell had previously believed they were. "I will add too," he wrote to Mantell, "I was greatly disappointed, as I hope every Geologist is when he finds himself compelled to abandon a theory which refers not without probability to the agency of known causes some of the many obscure phaenomena which his investigations daily disclose." However, he had developed a somewhat more detailed hypothesis to account for them.

> Most of the slabs I found would cleave into thinner laminae & the inner faces were also furrowed & fitted exactly into each other. If this last fact should prove on further examination as invariable as I found it, I should entertain little doubt that the under side of each layer merely presents a cast of that on which it has been deposited. And when many thin layers suc-

43. This letter was eventually published. See G. Mantell, "On the Iron-Sand Formation of Sussex. . . ." (1829).

44. C. L., Jr. to G. A. M. 6 June 1822. Mantell mss.

45. G. Mantell. "On the Iron-Sand Formation of Sussex . . ." Cf. Spokes, *Mantell,* p. 13.

ceed each other, we have only to suppose the lowermost to have been deeply worn by the waves & that it then formed a mould into which the next layer was cast, & the others successively into those which preceded them. . . .

That the most indurated of these rocks was in a perfectly soft state when first formed, no one will dispute who observes the manner in which the organic remains are imbedded in them.

The sandstone of which the town hall of Horsham was built was also furrowed "and presents so striking a resemblance to a sea-beach worn by the waves that it has not escaped the observation of many of the common labourers."[46]

At the meeting of the Geological Society held in June 1822, shortly after Lyell's return from Horsham, there was so much business that Mantell's letter could not be read. However, Lyell was able to discuss the question of the position of the Tilgate beds with G. B. Greenough who thought that if they corresponded to the Battle beds, the latter were indeed the lowest in the series of strata in the Weald and were "fast approaching to the character of the Purbeck." Lyell also reported that:

Webster was highly delighted with the marm rock of W.S. [West Sussex] but regretted you had given no precise locality. It proves identical with his green sand of the I. of Wight so that no one could distinguish them, & the fossil body contained in the specimen you sent was the same as occurs in all his I. of W. specimens in our Collection. It also is [in] the Reigate firestone. He observes not without reason that he is right because his *type* of the Greensand is that of the I. of W. Your's & Phillips' & Greenough's may be that of other parts as Wilts, Cambridge etc. Of the Bletchingley fossils he says he should like a section of all the beds there, & that the Galt of Cambridgeshire has never been accurately made out as to its position & relation with other parts.

Lyell also announced in this letter that he would shortly be going to Scotland. "I have set up blow-pipe, magnetic needle etc.," he added, "and am working away at primitive formations. Conybeare's is a delightful book. It will make Geology as fashionable as Botany was & I hope more so. His style is perfection."[47] Conybeare's book was Conybeare and Phillips, *Outlines of the Geology*

46. C. L., Jr. to G. A. M. 6 June 1822. Mantell mss.
47. C. L., Jr. to G. A. M. 16 June 1822. Mantell mss.

of England and Wales. Lyell's enthusiastic reception of this book indicates that it was a powerful stimulus to his already vigorous interest in geology.

The *Outlines* reflects the many excursions and studies made by members of the Geological Society. To William Phillips' original text W. D. Conybeare had added and interpolated long notes and essays on particular formations. He also added observations taken from Greenough's notes because Greenough had collected many observations for the geological map of England which the Geological Society had issued in 1819. The accumulated geological data naturally had a bearing on geological theory and Conybeare expressed his understanding of their meaning in a sixty-one page introduction.[48]

From the borders of Wales eastward the English strata overlay one another in a regular and undisturbed order from the lias through the great oolite formation of the Cotswold hills and a series of clays and sandstones to the chalk. The outcrops of these strata lay in narrow bands extending from Yorkshire on the northeast coast of England to Somerset and Dorset on the southwest coast. This series of strata, succeeding one another in regular order and all nearly horizontal, with only a slight dip to the southeast, suggested a long period of calm and uninterrupted deposition in the history of the earth. Yet these strata had been, for the most part, laid down beneath the sea and they had somehow changed their position in relation to sea level to form ranges of hills and elevated land. As Conybeare wrote:

> The great and fundamental problem, therefore, of theoretical geology is obviously to assign adequate causes for the change of level in this ocean which has permitted these masses which once formed the bottom of its channel to rise in hills and mountains above its waves. [p. xv]

There were three possible explanations. First, the amount of water on the earth's surface may have been diminished by its chemical transformation into some other substance, or second, the volume of the water may have been diminished either by absorption into a central cavity in the earth or by its contraction on cooling. The third possibility was that the present continents may have been upheaved by "violent convulsions."

48. Conybeare and Phillips, *Outlines.* Page numbers given in the text are specific references to this work.

> . . . if the violent elevation of the continents . . . supposed in the last mentioned hypothesis really took place, it must have left traces in the disturbed, contorted and highly inclined position of the strata, and these disturbances must be the greatest where the change of level has been the greatest, i.e. in the neighbourhood of the loftiest mountains. [p. xvi]

This was in fact the way strata were usually found in the vicinity of mountains. However, in other respects the order of the strata of Great Britain did conform to that suggested by Werner's theory. The oldest strata occurred in the mountains of Scotland, at lower levels lay the transition strata of southern Scotland, Cumberland, and Wales, still younger strata outcropped at successively lower levels. Yet when one compared the level of a single formation in different parts of Europe, one found the oolite, never above 1,200 feet in England, at 4,000 feet in the Jura chain and at the top of some of the highest Alps in the Tyrol. Moreover, the counterparts of the English secondary strata in the Jura were highly inclined and disturbed as well as greatly elevated.

The only force which Conybeare saw as capable of producing the kind of convulsion he thought was required to produce the elevation, inclination, and bending of the strata, was volcanic action. He thought too that volcanic activity had once been far more violent and extensive than at present.

> . . . the extinct volcanoes of the Rhine, Hungary and Auvergne, as well as those which occupy so large a portion of Italy, where one only now remains in activity, concur in proving that we now experience only the expiring efforts, as it were, of those gigantic powers which have once ravaged the face of nature. [p. xviii]

He did not believe that "causes now in action" were capable of producing any very significant change on the earth's surface, and he condemned as "crude and hasty speculations" the view "which would refer to these alone, acting under their present conditions, and with only their present forces, the mighty operations which have formed and modified our continents" (p. xxxiii).

When Conybeare referred to "mighty operations" or to "the last great convulsion of the Earth's surface" he had in mind such disturbances as had produced the anticlinal fold of the Isle of Wight, where the chalk strata stood vertical in the central range of

hills, or the great anticline formed by the Mendip hills and surrounding coal strata in the coal district of Somersetshire.

> . . . no one can have attentively considered the monuments of
> the great changes with which Geology makes us acquainted
> without at once perceiving that they prove the existence of an
> order of things in which such convulsions not only might, but
> actually did, take place. [p. lvi]

Conybeare thought that the whole character of the strata
formed in the "former and different order of things" which had
preceded the last great convulsion was different from that of more
modern sediments. Since he seems to have thought that the most
recent convulsion had been the one which had elevated the chalk
and had produced the two great anticlinal folds, that of Sussex and
Kent in southeast England and that of the Isle of Wight, he supposed that this convulsion marked a change in the order of things
which was reflected in the Tertiary strata deposited after the elevation of the chalk. The Tertiary beds were usually loose and not
consolidated into hard rock, they contained many fossil shells,
usually well preserved and unchanged except for some loss of
color "and might be mistaken for recent shells" (p. 8). In the
secondary strata, however, the shells were not merely preserved
as in the Tertiary strata, but had actually been converted into
stone; that is, their substance had become thoroughly impreg-
nated with stony matter. In other instances the fossil itself had
disappeared completely and only a mold of it remained in the
rock. Furthermore, while many of the fossils of Tertiary strata
belonged to extinct species, those of secondary strata belonged entirely not only to extinct species but even to extinct genera (p. 60).
They seemed, therefore, to Conybeare to belong to a natural order quite different from that of the modern world. Then too the
fossil shells of the secondary beds differed not only from those of
the strata above the chalk, but also from those of the strata of the
coal formation. However, Conybeare saw the epoch of the coal formation as separated from that of the upper secondary beds by the
convulsion which had produced the anticline represented by the
Mendip hills. Thus this difference between the fossils of two earlier periods tended to confirm his view that great convulsions of
the earth's surface in the past had brought about a drastic
change in the whole natural order.

Conybeare's broad outlook on geology seems to have influenced

Lyell deeply because it was based upon such extensive geological experience and was so soberly reasoned. Lyell had probably met Conybeare at Oxford because the latter was a close friend and associate of William Buckland whose lectures on mineralogy and geology Lyell had attended. He certainly accepted Conybeare's opinion that the fossils of secondary rocks were to be distinguished from those of Tertiary beds by their greater mineralization and continued to hold this view until the crisis which altered his whole outlook on geological history.

In late June Lyell went to Bartley and while there paid a visit to the Isle of Wight. This proved an exciting excursion, as is indicated by a long letter which he wrote to Mantell on his return.[49] In the Isle of Wight he found that Webster's green sand was indeed identical with the firestone of Reigate and the marm rock of western Sussex, all of them strata lying immediately beneath the chalk marl. But the green sand of Greenough and Conybeare was identical with a lower series of beds which Webster had called the ferruginous sand in the Isle of Wight.

Early in July 1822 Lyell went with his parents and his sisters Fanny and Eleanor to Scotland to spend three months at Kinnordy. During this time Lyell presumably studied the geology of Forfarshire, making use of the blow-pipe and magnetic needle bought in London. With the beginning of the shooting season on 12 August he spent some of his time on the grouse moors and on the twentieth went shooting with Lord Airlie's party.[50] At this time also, the Lyells had as a guest at Kinnordy, William Hooker, Dawson Turner's son-in-law, who was now professor of botany at the University of Glasgow. There were dances and whist parties, and the time passed very pleasantly. At the beginning of November they returned south by sea, taking passage in a sailing smack from Dundee to London. On the way their small ship encountered a fierce gale which prevented them a whole day from getting round St. Abb's Head. "Every soul was sick as death," Mr. Lyell

49. C. L., Jr. to G. A. M. 4 July 1822. Mantell mss. Lyell never published his discovery of the resolution of this question. William Fitton, who had read a copy of Lyell's letter to Mantell before his visit to the Isle of Wight, published the first correct correlation of these strata in 1824. W. H. Fitton, "Inquiries respecting the Geological Relations of the Beds between the Chalk and the Purbeck Limestone in the South-east of England" (1824). In this paper Fitton also correlated Webster's blue marl lying between Webster's green sand and ferruginous sand (upper and lower green sands) with the gault of Cambridgeshire.

50. C. L. to D. T. 20 Aug. 1822. Dawson Turner mss.

wrote from London. "Some were a little frightened but had too much spirit to own it, & all must have been indebted to my consolatory reflection, that if the mode of travelling were neither safe nor pleasant it was at least cheap."[51] When they reached London, the ladies went shopping and spent all the money that had been saved.

After a long summer of "shooting and geologizing" and being "most strenuously and rationally idle" Lyell settled down in his old quarters at 29 Norfolk Street where he resumed the study of law with his reading clerk.[52] In the midst of his geological activities in the spring he had been called to the bar at Lincoln's Inn on 15 May so that he was now an accredited barrister. At the beginning of February 1823, he wrote a letter of general news to his sister Marianne in which he said, "I am spending my time very luxuriously in reading, my old Clerk not having as yet deserted me."[53] He was also writing a paper on the geology of some rivers near Kinnordy which he later read to the Geological Society although it was never published. At this time he was elected one of the two secretaries of the Geological Society of London, in which position he helped to read and edit the papers to be published in the society's *Transactions*.

Meanwhile his eyes remained so troublesome that he not only used a clerk to read to him but on 12 February had to have an amanuensis write one of his letters to Gideon Mantell. Mantell and Lyell had evidently written a paper together on the geology of Sussex and had submitted it to the Geological Society to be considered for publication. The referee was G. B. Greenough and Lyell went to his house to go over the paper with him. "I can assure you," Lyell wrote to Mantell, "that he has not only travelled over the greater part of Sussex & examined the geological features of the limestone & the iron sand, but has taken very extensive views which he still retains in his memory of the general bearings of these strata thro' the County; of their various relations with each other there & with similar beds which appear in the Isle of Purbeck." Greenough counselled that they should defer publication until they had more thoroughly worked out the relationships of the strata. Lyell accepted this advice with good grace at the time but later was to question its wisdom. (In fact, this paper was never published by the Geological Society.) Possibly Greenough was

51. C. L. to C. W. 7 Nov. 1822. Wedderburn mss.
52. C. L. to D. T. 17 Nov. 1822. Dawson Turner mss.
53. C. L., Jr. to his sister Marianne. 2 Feb. 1823. Kinnordy mss.

anxious that a paper which differed from him in geological interpretation should not be published. He also suggested that Lyell
write a separate memoir on his hypothesis to account for the furrowed surfaces of the sandstone at Sedgwick "as it is a phenomenon of very general occurrence & presenting difficulties in some
countries beyond those of Sedgwick." Because Lyell had also observed these ripple marks in the old red sandstone of Scotland he
was inclined to take up the subject but offered to defer to Mantell
who eventually published a brief paper on it.[54]

In June Lyell paid a second visit to the Isle of Wight in company with William Buckland. The cause of the confusion that
existed concerning the identity of the green sand beds in the Isle of
Wight and Sussex was that the beds of blue marl, described by
Thomas Webster in the Isle of Wight, had been considered identical with those of the Weald clay in Kent and Sussex, whereas
actually they corresponded to the beds of the gault of Cambridgeshire. The gault was a marine formation whereas the Weald clay
had been deposited in fresh water or in an estuary, and the gault
formation lay above the greensand whereas the Weald clay lay
below it. Consequently the beds above the blue marl in the Isle of
Wight which Webster had called greensand, corresponded to those
which Conybeare, Greenough, and other geologists had described
as chalk marl in Kent and Sussex. This confusion had continued
to exist because the geologists concerned had attempted to identify
beds by their apparent rank in the order of superposition. They
could, therefore, be misled if they happened to use different reference points and they had so far used fossils only to a limited degree to correlate the beds of these localities.

When he had visited the Isle of Wight the year before (in June
1822) Lyell had discovered some of the nature of this discrepancy from examination of the strata revealed in the cliffs of Sandown Bay on the eastern side of the island. Even before his visit
he had written to Mantell "But if W's blue marl . . . sh.d prove to
be galt, as I think possible, it w.d certainly be difficult enough."[55]
After his two-day visit to the island he had sent Mantell a section
and description of the beds of Sandown Bay (Figs. 15, 16), from
the chalk down through Webster's green sand, blue marl and iron
sand to a series of underlying beds which he could not identify,

54. C. L., Jr. to G. A. M. 12 Feb. 1823. Mantell mss. Cf. G. A. Mantell, "On the
ripple marks made by the waves observable in the sandstone strata of Sussex,"
(1831).

55. C. L., Jr. to G. A. M. 16 June 1822. Mantell mss.

but which he suspected belonged to the Weald clay. From his examination of these beds Lyell had been certain of three points:

(1) that Webster's green sand corresponded to the firestone of
    Reigate in Surrey.
(2) that Webster's blue marl was not the Weald clay.
(3) that Webster's iron sand corresponded to the green sand for-
    mation described by G. B. Greenough, and in Conybeare
    and Phillips' *Outlines,* in Sussex and Surrey.

Now on his second visit to the Isle of Wight in June 1823
Lyell found in the cliffs of Compton Bay on the western side of
the island a more complete series of strata which included a full
exposure of the beds of the Weald clay and of the beds of iron
sands (corresponding to the Hastings sandstone) beneath them.
He also identified Webster's blue marl tentatively as identical
with the gault. He wrote to Mantell:

> You are aware that Webster never found in his blue marl any
> fossils, except 2 ammonites.—At Compton Chine [Figs. 17, 18]
> however I found several *Inocerami, I. sulcatus* I believe, & altho'
> I was only there 5 minutes, I saw so many fragments of shells in
> this same blue marl, that I am inclined to believe the identity
> of this bed with the blue marl of Folkestone & the Gault might
> be made out by a further search for the organic remains which it
> contains.
>
> The section from Compton Chine to Brook is superb, & we
> see there at one view the whole geology of your part of the
> world, from the chalk with flints down to the Battle beds, all
> within an hour's walk, & yet neither are any of the beds absent,
> nor do I believe they are of less thickness than with you.—This
> is so beautiful a key that I should have been at a loss to con-
> ceive how so much blundering could have arisen if I had not
> witnessed the hurried manner in which Buckland galloped over
> the ground.—He would have entirely overlooked the Weald
> clay if I had not taken him back to see it. This clay however is
> only partly exposed, the softness of it having caused a ruin of
> the cliff just at the point where the Petworth marble[56] ought

56. Conybeare and Phillips, *Outlines,* p. 134: "[The Weald clay] . . . contains
occasionally layers of argillo-calcareous concretions replete with shells of the genus
Vivipara fluviorum. The interior of these is usually filled by calcareous spar; and as
the cement has firmness enough to admit a slight polish, masses of this description
are occasionally wrought for ornamental purposes, and form what is well known in
many of our gothic buildings by the name of Petworth marble."

to be looked for.—Soon after this Sandstone containing layers of limestone with Bivalves appears, then some mottled beds purple & white, then pyritous coal like that at Bex Hill I suppose.— The white sands at Winchelsea & Fairlight are magnificently exposed [Fig. 19].[57]

In this same letter Lyell announced that he was planning to go to Paris at the end of the month and offered to take any books or presents which Mantell cared to send with him to Parisian scientists, at the same time explaining that such gifts would have the advantage of introducing him to the recipients. He was going to Paris primarily to learn French, but by this time it was clear that he was not pursuing his career as a barrister in such a way as to make his fortune at it. His father accepted the situation regretfully, but philosophically, and took comfort in the fact that Lyell was at least spending his time "rationally" and "like a gentleman."[58] On 21 June Lyell reported to his father that he had been at dinner at Judge Richardson's where he "met Mr. Eyre's young friend Spedding."[59] This was apparently his first meeting with Thomas Story Spedding, then twenty-two years old, who was to be a lifelong friend and correspondent. Lyell was also reading works on political economy, for he gave his father a reference to Adam Smith's *Wealth of Nations*. He was going to Paris well prepared with letters of introduction to the leading French naturalists including Alexander von Humboldt, Georges Cuvier, Alexandre Brongniart, and Constant Prevost. He took with him copies of Buckland's recently published *Reliquiae diluvianae*[60] as presents from Buckland to various of the French scientists and some of his own rock specimens from both Scotland and the Isle of Wight to give away.

In 1823 Paris was still the scientific capital of the world. Since the seventeenth century the books and memoirs published by the members of the Académie des Sciences, each of whom was a full-time professional scientist, had set world standards for thorough and exact scientific work. Of particular importance was the work of the Paris Observatory and of the Museum of Natural History. French explorers and travelers and French government expeditions had regularly deposited their natural history collections at

57. C. L., Jr. to G. A. M. 11 June 1823. Mantell mss.
58. C. L. to D. T. 14 March 1823. Dawson Turner mss.
59. C. L., Jr. to his father. 21 June 1823. Kinnordy mss. *L. & L.* I, 122.
60. W. Buckland, *Reliquiae Diluvianae* ... (1823).

the museum. The museum's collections were further increased by the systematic efforts of its staff which included such eminent naturalists as Georges Cuvier, Jean-Baptiste Lamarck, and Pierre André Latreille. The presence of the great natural history collections at Paris meant that Paris was the leading center for the description and classification of new species or the identification of obscure specimens. Lamarck's great systematic study of invertebrate zoology for instance, had been the indispensable foundation for the study of invertebrate fossils and their use in the identification of strata.

Lyell's trip to Paris in 1823 was much swifter than that which he had taken with his father three years before when they had gone with their carriage to Dover and crossed to Calais in a sailing packet and when the journey had required three days, partly because of the need to wait for a fair wind at Dover.[61] This time Lyell sailed directly from London in a steam-packet, the *Earl of Liverpool* ("engines 80-horse power, for 240 tons") and passed the 120 miles to Calais in 11 hours. After doing some geologizing near Abbeville, where he also visited the "manufactures of cloth, carpets, glass etc." and saw "an *English* steam-engine of 18-horse power, which enables them to dispense with 1,000 workmen," Lyell went on by diligence to Paris where he arrived 25 June.[62]

In Paris he was immediately very busy. Through a young Englishman at the British Embassy he obtained an introduction to a French family with whom he could board, if he wished, or else dine occasionally in order to learn French conversation. M. Duvan called on him at his hotel and arranged to take him to Cuvier's soirée on Saturday. Every Saturday evening Cuvier received guests in the great drawing room of his library, a social gathering at which foreign scientists and naturalists were often present. Cuvier gave Lyell a pleasant welcome and invited him to come to his soirées every week and to come to the Institute on Monday. They were served a collation of fruit and discussed Sir Walter Scott's most recent novel, *Quentin Durward,* which Lyell had not read, but with which Cuvier and the ladies were delighted.[63] Lyell called on Cuvier at the museum to show him some specimens of a peculiar fossil tooth from the Tilgate forest beds which Mantell had sent to see if Cuvier might be able to

61. C. L., Jr. to his sister Fanny. 8 Aug. 1820. Kinnordy mss.
62. C. L., Jr. to his father. 28 June 1823. Kinnordy mss. *L. & L.* I, 123.
63. C. L., Jr. to his father. 3 July 1823. Kinnordy mss. *L. & L.* I, 125.

identify it. Cuvier immediately pronounced it to be the upper incisor of a rhinoceros.[64]

Lyell also left his letters of introduction and a copy of Buckland's *Reliquae Diluvianae* at Alexander von Humboldt's apartment. When he later met this great man, he described his reception to his father:

> Humboldt addressed me, as Duvan had done, with "I have the honour of being familiar with your name, as your father has laboured with no small success in botany, particularly the *Cryptogamae*. I suppose when he was in Paris I was absent, or of course I should have met him somewhere. But I hope, if he comes again, to be more fortunate."
>
> He was not a little interested in hearing me detail the critiques which our geologists have made on his last geological work, a work which would give him a rank in science if he had never published aught besides.[65] He made me a present of his work, and I was surprised to find how much he has investigated the details of our English strata. I am going to him this morning with some specimens to make him master of the last point which was cleared up in my Isle of Wight tour with Buckland and afterwards he takes me and Sir J. Croft to the Observatory to show it to us. He appears to work hard at astronomy, and lives in a garret for the sake of that study.[66]

Lyell also mentioned that he was attending lectures on mining, geology, chemistry, and zoology at the Jardin du Roi free of charge.

On the following Saturday (4 July) Humboldt escorted Lyell and Sir John Croft (1778–1862) to the Paris Observatory. On the way he entertained them with conversation and opinions, which were both original and acute, though Lyell suspected that his opinion of Cuvier was influenced by jealousy.[67] At the observatory they met the great French astronomer, La Place, and the mathematician, François Arago, who was Humboldt's particular friend.

64. Spokes, *Mantell,* p. 20.
65. A. von Humboldt. *Essai géognostique* . . . (1823). It was immediately translated into English as *A Geognostical Essay on the Superposition of Rocks in both hemispheres* (1823).
66. C. L., Jr. to his father. 3 July 1823. Kinnordy mss., *L. & L.* I, 125–26.
67. C. L., Jr. to his father. 8 July 1823. Kinnordy mss. *L. & L.* I, 126–28.

Paris was at this time in the grip of a political reactionary movement. The freedom of the press had been severely curtailed, letters were even being opened, so that Lyell took the opportunity of sending letters home with the British embassy dispatches. He had little sympathy with these political tendencies and was persuaded by an Oxford friend, who arrived in Paris, to contribute two guineas to the cause of the Greeks who were then rebelling against Turkey.

During his stay at Paris Lyell was invited by Alexandre Brongniart to visit the pottery manufacture at Sèvres. He had observed earlier that among English geologists Brongniart had "the highest reputation both for knowledge & agreeable manners of all the French sçavans."[68] At Sèvres he met Brongniart's father-in-law, the Baron Coquebert de Montret, who later took Lyell to see a fine section of the Tertiary formations of the Paris basin near his country house at Bas Meudon on the Seine. Lyell "was much gratified at the analogy between this section and the same beds in the Isle of Wight."[69]

Near the end of July Lyell settled in two rooms at 51, Rue Richelieu. From time to time he saw Sir John Croft, with whom he had become friends; he attended Cuvier's soirées and met and talked with various geologists. Occasionally he complained about his eyes for their soreness limited even the amount of letter writing he could do. He also visited art galleries.

Towards the end of July Lyell spent a day with Louis Constant Prevost (1787–1856), whom he describes as "a friend of Dr. Fitton's," at his country house at Montmorency. Prevost, a distinguished geologist, had been a pupil of Alexandre Brongniart and of Lamarck. Lyell wrote of his visit with Prevost at Montmorency:

A long walk wh. we took gave me a great knowledge of the geol.^{y} of the environs wh. is very interesting. Prevost has travelled much in Europe, is a man of good fortune & an excellent Geologue. He has come to Paris since & I dined with him yesterday at his house here, a pleasant party consisting chiefly of his wife's relations who have a good deal of land in the neighbourhood of Paris. I have promised to spend the whole of next week in different geolog.^{l} excursions with him chiefly in the neigh-

68. C. L., Jr. to his father. 28 June 1823. Kinnordy mss. *L. & L.* I, 123.
69. C. L., Jr. to his father. 20 July 1823. Kinnordy mss. *L. & L.* I, 132–33. Lyell is referring to the Tertiary beds of the Isle of Wight on the north side of the island.

bourhood of Fontainebleau at his own Mother's. We are to visit the millstone quarries wh. supply nearly all Europe & North America.[70]

They went to Fontainebleau during the first week of August. They studied the geology of the Fontainebleau sandstone and of beds of the upper freshwater formation which overlay it. In a quarry near Les Basses Loges, Lyell collected from a thin bed of greenish sand of the upper freshwater formation some fossil fruiting bodies (fertilized eggs) of the aquatic plant *Chara*. Before their identity as *Chara* fruiting bodies had been recognized, these peculiar fossils had been named gyrogonites for their spiral markings. Lyell was able to extract the gyrogonite entire from the soft sand and he later compared the features of this peculiar fossil with similar ones from the Isle of Wight, and with living forms in Scottish lakes. On 10 August Lyell wrote to his father, "I am going with Prevost this week to see those parts of the Paris basin wh. I have not yet seen."[71]

In 1809 Prevost and Anselme Desmarest had discovered in the lower beds of the gypsum formation of Montmartre layers containing a mixture of marine shells with freshwater shells.[72] Their conclusion was that gypsum deposits, which had previously been thought to be laid down exclusively in fresh water, might also be formed in the sea. In 1821 Prevost by himself had described a new instance of the intermixture of freshwater and marine shells in the same strata and had discussed its significance.[73] He showed that the mixture of freshwater and marine fossils occurred in a boundary area between a freshwater and marine formation. The discovery did not invalidate the distinction between the two kinds of formations but it did suggest that the change from marine to freshwater conditions and vice versa had been gradual rather than abrupt. He raised the question of the conditions under which this blending of the organisms of two different kinds of environment might occur.

In 1822 Prevost had published a more detailed description of the

70. C. L., Jr. to his father. 28 July 1823. Kinnordy mss. *L. & L.* I, 134.

71. C. L., Jr. to his father. 10 August 1823. Kinnordy mss. *L. & L.* I, 137–40, p. 140.

72. C. Prevost and A. Desmarest, "Sur des empreintes de corps marins . . ." (1809).

73. C. Prevost, "Sur un nouvel exemple de la réunion de Coquilles marines et de Coquilles fluviatiles . . ." (1821).

mixtures of freshwater and marine shells occurring in the sandstones of Beauchamp, a series of beds lying between the calcaire
grossier (coarse limestone) of Paris basin and the gypsum of
Montmartre. He found that in passing upward from the calcaire
grossier, a purely marine formation, to the gypsum, a purely
freshwater formation there were several alternating layers of marine and freshwater deposits. He suggested that during the period
of the calcaire grossier, the Paris basin had been a great inlet of the
sea. Later it had gradually become cut off from the sea and converted into a freshwater lake. As it did so the areas of the basin
around the mouths of rivers flowing into it would be converted to
fresh water first while other parts of the basin might remain salty.

> I suppose now that the great lake, having been formed by the
> retreat of the sea, its waters having become fresh, begin to pro-
> duce deposits in their turn and to nourish new animals; that
> then by a circumstance whose cause can easily be appreciated,
> a great flood of water occurred in the rivers which cross the lake.
> These waters, overflowing their banks, wash the higher ground.
> They pick up the former productions of the sea that they en-
> counter. They carry them with the mud and deposit them with
> it when the current slows.[74]

The importance of this explanation, suggested by Prevost to
account for the intermixture of beds of freshwater and marine
shells, was that it offered a natural explanation for the change
from marine to freshwater deposition and back again. Cuvier had
interpreted these alternating formations as the result of successive
retreats and incursions of the sea of unknown cause and on a catastrophic scale. In contrast, Prevost showed how these deposits
might have been formed by the ordinary course of geological processes. This explanation was part of a consistent attitude which
Prevost had developed towards the interpretation of geological
history. In a paper on the importance of the study of fossils,
written perhaps not long before Lyell's visit to Paris, Prevost
said:

> It is with these [facts] given, that the observer can be led by
> induction to deduce what has been *from what is,* to distinguish

74. C. Prevost, "Observations sur les grès coquillers . . . et sur les mélanges de
coquilles marines et fluviatiles . . ." (1822) p. 16.

accidental complications from general rules and finally to learn with some confidence even the nature of the causes which have presided at the formation of the most recent strata of the earth.[75]

He then used the principle of examining "what is" to study the mixture of freshwater and marine fossils. Prevost noted that in these thin alternating layers of freshwater and marine shells the layers containing the freshwater shells usually contained complete and perfect shells with the various shell species associated together and spaced in the same way as they might be distributed over the bottom of a modern lake. The thin beds containing freshwater shells, therefore, appeared in every respect as if they had been formed in calm, clear fresh water. The layers containing marine shells were very different. Instead of whole shells they contained mostly broken fragments of shells and the various marine species were jumbled together. Fragments of species from various marine habitats occurred indiscriminately together instead of in natural associations. These facts taken together suggested to Prevost that the layers containing marine shells had been disturbed after their first deposition in salt water and transported by currents to be deposited a second time on the bottom of the freshwater lake then occupying the Paris basin.[76]

By the time of Lyell's visit to Paris in 1823 Prevost had developed a highly individual point of view toward the study of geological formations, especially those of the Paris basin. He thought that such features as the alternation of freshwater and marine strata, the state of preservation of fossils whether broken or entire, the distribution of fossils within the rock matrix and their relation to the matrix, or the associations of fossil species, all were to be understood by means of detailed comparison with what went on in modern lakes, rivers, and seas. In 1825 Prevost wrote that his observations had

. . . led him to this basic idea; that around us, whether it be on the earth, under the waters, whether it be in the depths and in the vicinity of volcanoes, it produces phenomena whose causes do not differ essentially from those which, in times more or less

75. C. Prevost, "De l'importance de l'étude des corps organisés vivans . . ." (1823) p. 262 [translation mine].
76. Ibid., pp. 266–67.

remote, have given rise successively to the different geological states of the globe.[77]

He thought that geologists who believed that the whole order of nature had been different during the past history of the earth had formed their opinion "before having observed all the effects of the causes still acting and of having compared them step by step to the effects formerly produced."

Therefore when Lyell went with Prevost on a geological expedition to the forest of Fontainebleau, he went with a geologist who could draw a multitude of new meanings from detailed examination of the strata of the Paris basin. The idea of analogies to be drawn between present and past conditions became permanently imprinted on Lyell's mind. It was possibly as a result of Prevost's influence that in 1824 Lyell was to begin his own detailed study of the geological processes going on in freshwater lakes in Scotland.

Lyell was also steadily enlarging his circle of friends, one of whom he described to his father:

I have made acquaintance with Le Baron de Ferussac, a colonel on the staff of the French army, who went through Napoleon's Spanish campaigns. [André Étienne d'Audebard de Ferussac (1786–1836), French naturalist.] He is a lively young man of very pleasant manners, of an old family and in the first society. He is engaged in publishing a work on the Molluscae, and has studied much those branches which relate to Geology. He has the finest collection by far of land and freshwater shells in the world. I spent two mornings with him, and he is certainly the most brilliant builder of theories I have ever met with. I fought hard with him for Buckland's notion of the Diluvian formation, in which Ferussac is not orthodox. A cabinet geologist can account for everything much more easily than one who takes the field, and looks all the difficulties in the face; but he is very ingenious, and his knowledge of shells gives him a powerful clue.

As you have almost said enough to provoke a geological letter from me, I will endeavour to state in a few words an outline of Ferussac's cosmogony. He says geology yields ample proofs, both that the ocean was at a much higher level than at present, and that the general temperature of the earth has decreased.

77. C. Prevost, "De la formation des terrains des environs de Paris," (1825) p. 74 [my translation].

That from chemical reasons the diminution of heat would naturally be attended by a subsidence of the waters. That from the organisation of the molluscae, some can only live at great, others at slight depths. On the shores and shallows of the Mediterranean different species now exist from those in the deep parts, and that we may conclude totally different ones again dwell in the fathomless sea.

In this manner he accounts for the oldest and lowest beds presenting us such totally different fossils from the superior ones, and the reason that, as we ascend in the series the productions resemble more and more those which now live, is merely because the ocean, as it became shallower, contained animals more and more analogous to those which alone we have now access to. At length the chalk was deposited, and covered with its analogous formations almost all the continents we know anything about.

Much land was then left bare, and freshwater formations began. The present system of valleys did not then exist, of which there is proof, and instead of the waters being carried off, as they are so beautifully at present, the whole was nearly covered with great lakes of which we know thirteen, those of the London and Hants and Paris basins being three. All these thirteen present similar phenomena of alternating fresh and salt water formations and mixtures of both. As the ocean was then still nearly on a level with the chalk, it often broke down a dyke, as in Holland, and deposited oysters, etc. once more. Analogous phenomena may now be seen in progress in the Caspian and other inland lakes etc.[78]

While Lyell did not accept all this, he was clearly fascinated by the idea of drawing up geological theories to account for the various phenomena. Moreover, Ferussac had drawn his attention to two points, which were to figure largely in Lyell's later thinking: first, that the earth's climate had been warmer during the geological past so that tropical conditions had existed at such high latitudes as that of Britain; second, that as one rises in the geological series towards more recent strata, the fossil forms tend to resemble more closely those of species now living in the sea.

Towards the end of August Lyell made another excursion of several days with Constant Prevost down the Seine to Triel, traveling by both land and water. The purpose of this expedition

78. C. L., Jr. to his father. 10 Aug. 1823. Kinnordy mss. *L. & L.* I, 139–40.

seems principally to have been to complete Lyell's picture of the
geology of the Paris basin, although they also visited the palace of
Versailles. At the end of the trip Lyell agreed to accompany
Prevost on a geological expedition to the district around Bristol
in England, which he himself wished to see, and to get Dr. Fitton
to go with Prevost to the Isle of Wight. Lyell did not wish to spend
time going over the geology of a district with which he was already thoroughly familiar.

Lyell also spent several afternoons with Humboldt helping him
with the correlation of the strata of England with those of France
for a new edition of his book. "There are few Heroes," he wrote
to his father, "who lose so little by being approached as Humboldt."[79]

Early in September Lyell left Paris to tour through Belgium
and the Low Countries. At Cambrai the wheel of a diligence ran
over his foot while he was getting into a cabriolet. It became infected and, until it healed, he was obliged to spend three weeks
with his father's old friend, Col. Heyland, now British consul at
Ostend.[80] He enjoyed the pleasant society of their house and his
convalescence gave him time to reflect on his French experiences.
On 4 October he went on to Ghent, Antwerp, and Rotterdam
from which place he sailed to England about the end of the month.

All the time that he was at Paris Lyell's eyes had continued to
trouble him; he had to restrict both his reading and letter-writing.
When he first returned to London he did not have a reading clerk
and consequently "a few hours reading per day have made my
eyes so weak that they are quite painful."[81] He made his usual visit
to Bartley at Christmas time and returned to London in January.

On 17 February Lyell wrote to Mantell to thank him for a copy
of his new book,[82] and to give him geological news. Among other
items, he wrote:

> W. D. Conybeare is in Town and has been with us for some
> time. He is waiting for the arrival of the new Lyme Regis Plesio-
> saurus of which he has an excellent drawing. The Duke of Buck-
> ingham has bought it, but it will be exhibited for some time at
> our rooms 20 Bedf.ᵈ St. It affords a great anatomical triumph to

79. C. L., Jr. to his father. 28 Aug. 1823. Kinnordy mss. *L. & L.* I, 146.
80. C. L., Jr. to his mother. 23 Sept. 1823. Kinnordy mss.
81. C. L., Jr. to his sister Marianne. 12 Nov. 1823. Kinnordy mss.
82. G. A. Mantell, *Outlines of the natural history of the environs of Lewes* (1824).

W. D. C. as most of his hypothetical restorations in his former memoirs turn out true to nature. The new animal is a very perfect skeleton and a prodigy for it has 40 cervical vertebrae whereas existing quadrupeds range from 7 to 9, reptiles from 3 to 9, Aves reach no higher than 20, the Swan being the maximum. What a leap have we here and how many links in the chain will Geology have to supply.[83]

In 1821, in collaboration with Henry de la Beche, Conybeare published his first paper on the fossil reptiles of the blue lias.[84] In this paper he gave the definitive description of *Ichthyosaurus,* and then described a series of vertebrae which he thought must belong to a new fossil animal to which he gave the name *Plesiosaurus. Plesiosaurus* seemed especially remarkable because of its large number of cervical and dorsal vertebrae, which Conybeare estimated at forty-six, "a number almost double that of any recent Saurian animal." In 1821 he had not yet found any bones of the head, and those which he had of the front limbs were detached; accordingly he had been forced to reconstruct the front limb using conjecture. He had reasoned from the features of the bones that they had formed a paddle-like forelimb, similar to that of *Ichthyosaurus,* and used for swimming. In 1822 Conybeare had been able to announce the discovery of additional bones of *Plesiosaurus,* but sustained search had failed to bring to light a complete skeleton.[85] Therefore, when a nearly complete skeleton of *Plesiosaurus* was discovered in 1823 at Lyme Regis on the coast of Dorsetshire (Fig. 20), Conybeare's excitement must have been very great. The new specimen confirmed almost all of his earlier conclusions but it revealed further the enormous length of the neck which exceeded that of the body and tail combined.[86] The new specimen of *Plesiosaurus* also stirred Lyell's interest in the significance of the gigantic fossil reptiles.

As the spring of 1824 drew on Lyell became even more fully occupied with geology. As one of the secretaries of the Geological

83. C. L., Jr. to G. A. M. 17 Feb. 1824. Mantell mss. Published in part in *L. & L.* I, 151.

84. H. T. de la Beche and W. D. Conybeare, "Notice of the discovery of a new fossil animal . . ." (1821).

85. W. D. Conybeare, "Additional notices on . . . Ichthyosaurus and Plesiosaurus" (1824).

86. W. D. Conybeare, "On the discovery of an almost perfect skeleton of the Plesiosaurus" (1824).

Society, he was seeing through the press the first volume of the
new series of its *Transactions*. In April he sent to Mantell two sets
of fossils, one from Thiers in France, the other from the Isle of
Wight. In commenting on the freshwater formations of the Isle
of Wight he said, "I ought to observe that there is a remarkable
and somewhat unaccountable discrepancy between the beds of
the lower freshwater formation at Headon Hill and the same beds
at the eastern side of the island between Bembridge ledge and
Culver Cliff."[87] Nearly thirty years later, as a result of his study of
the Isle of Wight for the Geological Survey, Edward Forbes was
to show that the Bembridge beds did not correspond to those of
Headon Hill, but constituted a younger series which ought to be
placed above them.[88]

In May Dawson Turner invited him to come to Yarmouth but
Lyell was unable to come. In declining he explained that:

> besides an engagement of long standing to Mr. Greenough on
> Wednesday I am to receive here on Friday Monsieur Constant
> Prevost, an eminent French Geologist who received me last
> year in France with great hospitality. In a fortnight I am to
> commence a tour with him from Purbeck along the coast of
> Dorset & Devon to Cornwall to return by Wales, Bristol, Oxon
> —etc. The moment I return I start for Scotland where I am
> preparing two papers, one on the geology of the district between
> the rivers Dee & Tay which Dr. Macculloch has assigned to me,
> as being a blank on his grand map. Besides I am in part Editor
> of a vol. of the G.Soc.ʸ's Trans. not yet quite out.—I am making
> for my two tours no inconsiderable outfit of Geological &
> Geographical maps, not to mention Laminae etc. etc.—in short
> you will readily imagine that the work which I have cut out for
> this summer is fully as much as my weak, tho' improving *eyes,*
> my *time,* & my *exchequer* can afford.[89]

In their tour Prevost and Lyell went first to Oxford (Map 5). He
described their further progress to his father:

> We left Oxford May 29 for Birmingham & slept same night at
> Dudley. We spent a day & a half there as it is a remarkable Ge-
> ological station. All the Manufacturers have full employment

87. C. L., Jr. to G. A. M. 20 April 1824. Mantell mss.
88. E. Forbes, *On the Tertiary fluvio-marine formation of the Isle of Wight*
(1856).
89. C. L., Jr. to D. T. 8 May 1824. Dawson Turner mss.

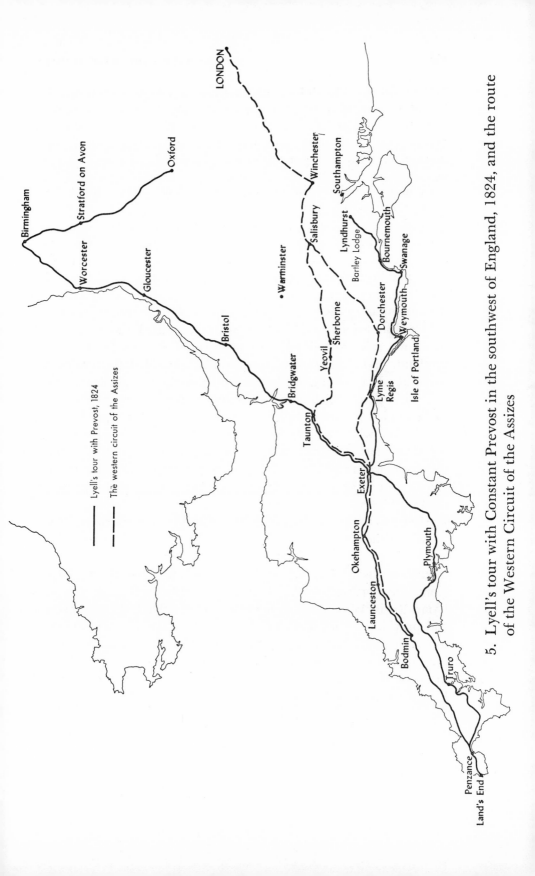

LONDON

Oxford

Stratford on Avon

Birmingham

Worcester

Gloucester

Bristol

Warminster

Winchester

Salisbury

Southampton

Lyndhurst
Bartley Lodge

Bournemouth

Swanage

Sherborne

Yeovil

Dorchester

Weymouth

Isle of Portland

Lyme Regis

Bridgwater

Taunton

Exeter

Okehampton

Plymouth

Launceston

Bodmin

Truro

Penzance

Land's End

——— Lyell's tour with Prevost, 1824

– – – The western circuit of the Assizes

5. Lyell's tour with Constant Prevost in the southwest of England, 1824, and the route
of the Western Circuit of the Assizes

& some most splendid schemes are on foot, some already *in actual progress* for railways for *steam-carriage* by which canals are to be rendered of very secondary importance. The sections which the Geologists are getting from these lines will enrich the Science very much.[90]

From Birmingham they returned southward cross country toward Bristol. On 2 June Lyell called at Tortworth Rectory near Falfield where he hoped to find the rector, Dr. Cooke, whom he had met at Professor Buckland's. Instead he found Mr. Weaver, a member of the Geological Society, who was staying there temporarily and keeping house.[91] Weaver invited them to 'breakfast and dine" with him and gave them much geological information about the surrounding district. Lyell was particularly interested in the old red sandstone conglomerate which appeared there because this same stratum cropped out at Airlie Castle in Forfarshire, Scotland "and on proceeding northwards," he added, "all the beds which the Isla present, are formed in succession, in particular the Cortachie slate, which contains organic remains here, proving it to belong to the transition-limestone series."[92] He was thereby given a key with which to unlock the geology of his native country. Two years earlier, during the summer of 1822, he had begun the geological mapping of Forfarshire for Dr. John Macculloch who had in preparation a geological map of the whole of Scotland.[93]

After two days at Tortworth, Prevost and Lyell went on to Bristol where the Reverend W. D. Conybeare welcomed them to his house. From Bristol they went southwest through Somerset to Exeter, westward into Cornwall, to Plymouth, and thence back along the south coast visiting various classic geological sites at Lyme Regis, Weymouth, and the Isle of Portland. Since Prevost had previously worked on the oolites of France, he was anxious to see those of England. At Lyme Regis they saw "a magnificent specimen of an Ichthyosaurus" which had recently been discovered in the cliffs there "by the celebrated Mary Anning," of which Prevost made a sketch. They also actually "witnessed the discovery of a superb skeleton of Ichthyosaurus vulgaris, by Miss Anning.

90. C. L., Jr. to his father. 6 June 1824. Kinnordy mss.
91. Thomas Weaver (1773–1855), geologist, had been a pupil of Werner and wrote on the geology of the older rocks of southwest England and southern Ireland.
92. C. L., Jr. to his father. 6 June 1824. Kinnordy mss.
93. V. A. Eyles, "John Macculloch F.R.S., and his geological map . . ." (1937).

It was perfect save the tail, wh. a cart wheel had passed over."[94] Finally, after visiting the various points of geological interest along the coast, Prevost spent several days with the Lyells at Bartley. "Mons. Prevost is so sensible, unaffected, & quiet," Mr. Lyell wrote to his friend Turner, "that even my idle young ladies would have been pleased if he had made a longer visit though he could not speak a word of English."[95]

Early in July Prevost left for London and, after only a week at Bartley, Lyell set off for Scotland to spend the summer geologizing there. On his arrival at Kinnordy he went on a ten day's tour of the county of Forfarshire with Captain Ogilvy as part of the survey which he was making for Macculloch. This proved quite profitable:

> The Sidlaws are what Werner termed "a saddle" the stratification being this, the oldest beds in the centre, flanked by younger ones, but what is still more interesting the center beds are the same as appear on the Isla between Airly Castle & the Mill of Craig or between Kinnordy & Catlaw.
>
> The discovery of the New Red Sandstone explains many anomalies which Dr. Fleming[96] made by confounding it with the old. We went by Dundee, Arbroath, Lunan Bay. I drew the whole coast from boats & we examined it thoroughly, not stopped by rain a single day.[97]

Lyell had discovered that the Sidlaw hills represented an anticlinal ridge with its axis in a southwest–northeast direction and was thus comparable in structure, though not in the age of its strata, with the Weald of Kent. The broad vale of Strathmore, lying behind this line of hills, was a synclinal trough similar in its structure to the Isle of Wight and London basins. His quick success in unraveling this structure shows that his studies in southern England had already made him a very competent field geologist.

In September Lyell heard from the Reverend William Buckland, who had been exploring the geology of the Hebrides and who invited him to go on a tour via Aberdeen and Inverness and down the Great Glen to Sir George MacKenzie's at Cowl in Ross-

94 C. L., Jr. to G. A. M. 9 July 1824. Mantell mss. *L. & L.* I, 153.

95. C. L. to D. T. 15 July 1824. Dawson Turner mss.

96. The Reverend John Fleming (1785–1857) D.D., F.R.S.E., minister of Flisk, Fifeshire.

97. C. L., Jr. to his father. 10 Aug. 1824. Kinnordy mss.

shire. Buckland tended to pursue geology in an atmosphere of comic exuberance:

> I look forward to no small amusement in being ten days with him, when he is so full of new matter as he must be after a visit to the Western Isles, so interesting & disputed a field for geological enquiry.[98]

When Buckland arrived at Kinnordy, they first spent a couple of days studying the strata revealed on the banks of the Carity and the Isla and then went to Aberdeen where they were entertained by various gentlemen of the university, "& to say the truth," wrote Lyell, "the conversation was more agreeable & I may say clever than it would be if the same number of the efficient leading officers of Oxford were to meet on a similar occasion."[99] From Aberdeen they went directly to Cowl and after a few days spent pleasantly there, they went on into Sutherland to within a day's journey of John O'Groats before turning back southward to visit the parallel roads of Glen Roy, "one of the grandest natural phenomena in Great Britain."[100] Buckland was especially interested in these because he considered that they provided evidence for his diluvial theories. They came thence south on the main road through the highlands to Blair Athol where they visited the classic ground of Glen Tilt, first visited by Dr. Hutton in 1785.[101] It was there that Hutton found the granite intruding among the stratified rocks and altering them so much as to suggest that it had entered, in a molten condition, under great heat.

From Blair Athol Buckland and Lyell went to Edinburgh where they spent several days in the study of the geology of the neighborhood and of Professor Jameson's mineral collections. Since Buckland was already a considerable celebrity, on account of his geological discoveries, they met the different worthies of the university. After a geological excursion as far as Stirling they went to Dunglass to visit Sir James Hall who, though now an old man "far passed his prime," took them to see the geological unconformity at St. Abb's head which Dr. Hutton had discovered in 1788 and which had so impressed Playfair with the endless

98. Ibid.
99. C. L., Jr. to his father. 26 Sept. 1824. Kinnordy mss. *L. & L.* I, 156–57.
100. C. L., Jr. to his mother. 18 Oct. 1824. Kinnordy mss. *L. & L.* I, 158–59.
101. J. Playfair, "Biographical account of James Hutton M.D." in *Works* (1822) p. 74.

vista of past time which it opened up.[102] On their return to Edinburgh they dined with Francis Jeffrey, the famous editor of the *Edinburgh Review*, at his country home, Craigcrook. "He is a little man," Lyell reported, "of very gentlemanlike appearance & manner. Shines in conversation, whether on trifling or important topics."[103]

From Edinburgh Lyell returned to Kinnordy, where his father and brother were now staying, to spend several weeks; it was late in November before he was back in London. He had been away since the end of May but felt that the time had been well spent, for as he wrote to Mantell: "I have made a very detailed Geological map of 2 thirds of the county of Forfar this year besides many more labours on rock marl, serpentine etc."[104] On 17 December he began reading to the Geological Society a paper on the freshwater limestones and marl deposits of Forfarshire and this, when it appeared in the *Transactions* in 1826, was his first published paper.[105]

This paper was based on Lyell's geological work carried on at Kinnordy during the summer and autumn. He gave first a general account of the geology of Forfarshire accompanied by a geological map of the county and a geological section extending from the Grampians across the synclinal trough which formed the broad vale of Strathmore and the anticlinal fold of the Sidlaw hills separating Strathmore from the estuary of the Tay. The floor of the vale of Strathmore was formed by strata of old red sandstone, nearly horizontal in the middle of the valley, but curved upward along its margins. However, the old red sandstone strata were thickly overlain in places with deep deposits of gravel forming irregular hillocks and hollows. Many of the hollows lacked natural drainage and therefore were swampy and occupied by peat bogs or small lakes. The lochs of Bakie and Kinnordy were two such lakes. Both had been drained in the mid-eighteenth century to give access to the deposits of marl in their bottoms. The marl, composed largely of calcium carbonate, was of great value to farmers as a manure for making fertile the sour, often recently drained land of Angus (Figs. 21, 22).

102. Ibid., pp. 78–81.
103. C. L., Jr. to his mother. 18 Oct. 1824. Kinnordy mss.
104. C. L., Jr. to G. A. M. 24 Nov. 1824. Mantell mss.
105. "On a recent Formation of Freshwater Limestone in Forfarshire . . ." (1824). Specific page references in the text are to this article.

The Bakie loch, originally a sheet of water 200 acres in extent, had been completely drained about 1817 so that Lyell had been able to study its former bed completely. The lake had been fed by springs which still flowed unfailingly. When he had been at Kinnordy in October Lyell had examined a pit where workmen were digging marl south of the largest spring of the former Bakie loch. There the marl formed a layer nine feet thick. In other parts of the old lake bottom the marl was more than sixteen feet thick. In the neighborhood of the springs, on top of these thick deposits of soft marl, lay a thin layer of very hard limestone. When Lyell broke off a piece of this rock and examined it with a lens he found it crystalline in many places and blocks of the limestone which had been quarried to enclose the great spring at Bakie had not crumbled under the action of frost and weather. It had another remarkable characteristic:

> The rock is traversed vertically by numerous irregular tubular cavities, the sides of which are in general fretted with minute stems and fibres of fossilized vegetables in a very friable state, apparently Charae. Since clusters of these vegetables sometimes occupy the centres of the cavities, they possibly may have occasioned the cavities themselves. [p. 77]

Lyell also found in this limestone the valves of the small aquatic crustacean *Cypris ornata* (Lamarck), which impressed him because A. Brongniart had described the valves of a related species, *Cypris faba* from an ancient freshwater formation in the department of Allier in southern France (p. 78). In addition the Bakie limestone contained various species of freshwater shells. Lyell was particularly impressed by finding, in the Bakie limestone, plant remains which corresponded exactly to the fossil gyrogonites of the ancient freshwater limestones of the Paris basin, the Isle of Wight, and southern France, which Lyell knew were the fruiting bodies or, as he called them, the "seed-vessels" of the water plant *Chara*.

Lyell showed that the marl deposits of the Bakie loch, like those of similar lakes in the surrounding district, had been formed by an accumulation of freshwater shells even though most of the shells were broken and obliterated in the marl. He discovered that the source of the calcium carbonate (which permitted the accumulation of marl) was the spring water which rose from the underlying strata of old red sandstone, which were rich in lime.

The only lakes which contained marl were those which lay on top of the old red sandstone and were spring fed.

The thin layer of hard limestone overlying the marl in the Bakie loch required additional explanation. Lyell decided that because this limestone formed only after a considerable depth of marl had accumulated and because it had been formed in the lake only in the vicinity of the springs, the spring water, rich in carbonic acid and bubbling up through the depth of previously deposited marl, must have become heavily laden with carbonate of lime in solution. Then when it emerged into the lake it

> let fall a calcareous precipitate, which in some places falling alone, produced a pure crystalline limestone, and in others, mixing with the later deposits of shell-marl and the various lacustrine plants, had the effect of cementing them together into one tufaceous mass. [p. 82]

In the nearby loch of Forfar, Lyell was able to see the process he had postulated actually going on. Although Forfar loch had not been drained, its level had been lowered to lay bare a bed of shell marl on its southern bank. When the lake level rose or the wind was high, the water washed the edge of this marl bed and became milky. The lime later settled out of the turbid water and Lyell detected a thin layer of hard limestone forming as a result over the lake bottom.

In their study of the freshwater strata of the Paris basin Cuvier and Brongniart had thought that the homogeneous, compact freshwater limestones of the ancient deposits had no counterpart in modern lakes. They thought that in modern lakes the only deposit to be found on the bottom would be a friable mud. Lyell had now discovered a hard, compact freshwater limestone of modern formation occurring together with extensive deposits of calcareous marl. Furthermore, this limestone contained gyrogonites (fruiting bodies of *Chara* completely converted to stone), valves of the crustacean *Cypris*, and representatives of several genera of freshwater shells, all fossils characteristic of ancient freshwater limestones. Except for the absence of flint, these limestones possessed every characteristic which Cuvier and Brongniart had thought to be peculiar to ancient limestones.

Lyell was able to compare the limestone of the Bakie loch with those of the Paris basin and the Isle of Wight basin with assurance because he had himself visited the localities of these formations and collected and examined their fossils. Lyell's removal of the distinction between ancient and modern freshwater deposits exerted a profound but subtle influence on his thinking. When he came again to examine freshwater strata he would see in his mind's eye some ancient counterpart of those ponds in Scotland with which he was now so familiar. He would repeatedly interpret details of their structure and fossil contents by analogy with the plants and animals and the rhythm of seasonal change in a modern lake. He had begun to think in terms of geological processes still going on over the surface of the earth.

The writing of this paper marks Charles Lyell's coming of age as a geologist. It incorporated not only independent observation but also, and more importantly, originality in his reasoned deductions. Lyell had now explored the geology of Britain from the Isle of Wight and the Sussex coast at Winchelsea to the distant parts of Sutherland in the north of Scotland. He had thoroughly grasped the structure of the southeast of England and the Isle of Wight, first described by Webster, and had made his own contribution to the correct correlation of the green sand beds. This experience had undoubtedly prepared him to understand the similar structure manifested in the Sidlaw hills and the vale of Strathmore of eastern Scotland which he had mapped. He had become fully competent in the interpretation of geological structure. In France he had become acquainted with the classic formations of the Paris basin and the new currents of thought among French geologists. The enthusiastic amateur who had graduated from Oxford in 1819 was now a professional in all but name. Although, during the few years immediately to come, he was to give less, rather than more, of his time and thought to the science, geology had already claimed him for life. She could afford to hold him on a long leash.

CHAPTER 6

The Emerging Barrister, Scientist, and Writer
1825–1827

ON HIS RETURN to London in November 1824 Lyell's life acquired a new tempo of activity. On 19 November he wrote to his sister Frances:

> The Athenaeum, the new club of which I am a member, has now more than 900 members & an excellent list of names & I find is likely to become very pleasant.[1]

The Athenaeum had come into being early in 1824 under the leadership of John Wilson Croker, member of Parliament and secretary to the Admiralty, known for his contributions to the Quarterly Review, and Sir Humphry Davy, president of the Royal Society of London. It was intended as a club for "scientific and literary men and Artists" and the group of founders was largely made up of literary men who were accustomed to meet at the house of John Murray, the publisher in Albermarle Street.[2] Lyell seems to have been one of the original group of 200 persons invited to join the club by paying an entrance fee of ten guineas and an additional subscription of five guineas. He seems therefore already to have become a recognized figure in the literary and scientific world of London. The club took up temporary quarters at 12 Waterloo Place and its first secretary was Michael Faraday. During subsequent years it was one of Lyell's favorite resorts.

Lyell did not follow his usual custom of remaining at Bartley for an extended holiday during the Christmas season of 1824. Instead he was back in London to read the second half of his paper on the marl of the Forfarshire lochs at a meeting of the Geological Society on 7 January 1825. In the audience was a new member of the society, Roderick Murchison, a former army officer who had served in the Peninsular campaign and who had been until recently a country gentleman whose chief enthusiasm was fox-hunt-

1. C. L., Jr. to his sister Frances. 19 Nov. 1824. Kinnordy mss.
2. H. Ward, *History of the Athenaeum 1824–1925* (1926) pp. 9–10.

ing (Fig. 23). Prompted by his wife, however, he had moved to
London and had begun to study science by attending lectures at
the Royal Institution. Murchison, like Lyell, was a Scot. His father had established his fortune by service in India as a surgeon in
the eighteenth century. At the age of thirty-two he had leisure,
ability, and energy, all of which he was prepared to devote to the
study of geology. It was therefore natural that he and Lyell from
their first meeting should have become close friends and asso-
ciates.

Lyell's father, however, was not impressed by Lyell's scientific
work and when he visited Bartley in April urged him to pursue
the law. On 9 April Mr. Lyell wrote to Charles Wedderburn:

> Charles has just left us to resume his search for the philoso-
> pher's stone among the Geological, Athenaean and Linnaean
> sages of London acting in conformity with the beautiful prayer
> of Socrates, "Grant that I may consider wisdom Wealth," though
> between ourselves, I being a "parens de grege Epicuri"[3] am
> disposed to interpret Wisdom in a less spiritual manner than
> Charles and would fain persuade him that it comprehends the
> turning our talents to the acquisition of beef and mutton and
> a bottle of wine for a guest.[4]

Katherine Lyell, who possessed an intimate knowledge of the Lyell family, wrote that in 1825 Lyell "resumed the study of law at
his father's request" so that his father's urgings to take up the law
again during Lyell's visit to Bartley at the beginning of April may
have taken the form of a very firm request.[5] At any rate in 1825
Lyell's eyes showed so much improvement that he was able to work
at the law more steadily.

Mr. Lyell was perhaps unduly optimistic about the opportunities for financial success at the bar. Although they had an exclusive
right to be heard in all the higher courts, the functions of a barrister in England were restricted. They could not deal directly with
their clients, but had to do so through an attorney, who engaged
their services and presented them with a brief, a document setting
forth all points relevant to the case. The great bulk of legal business, including almost all of that which did not come into court,
was in the hands of attorneys, and the barristers were dependent

3. "parent from the company of Epicurus"
4. C. L. to C. W. 9 April 1825. Wedderburn mss.
5. *L. & L.* I, 160.

upon attorneys for briefs. Yet barristers were usually university graduates and were considered socially and professionally above the attorneys. Their fees were considered as gratuities given to gentlemen and as a result they were not entitled to sue for them.

Whereas the leaders of the bar might earn large incomes, junior barristers usually did not meet their expenses for a number of years. This had been the experience of such able men as Henry Brougham, Henry Cockburn, Francis Jeffrey, and Francis Horner practicing at the Scotch bar in Edinburgh at the beginning of the century. In the frustration of their inactivity they turned to literature and founded the *Edinburgh Review*.[6] In London it was the same. John Taylor Coleridge, who was called to the bar at the Middle Temple, recorded in his diary on 1 January 1820:

> In the former part of the year my profession languished. I had no pupil, and little to do: in June I was called to the bar, went the summer assizes and had no brief. On the circuit I was more successful, and at the Michaelmas sessions I reaped an uncommon harvest, and laid the ground, I trust, for future success.[7]

Like the Edinburgh group Coleridge turned to literature and supplemented his income by writing articles for the *Quarterly Review* and the *British Critic*. Even in 1824 his practice as a barrister was light enough that he could take on the editorship of the *Quarterly* for a year. He remained a poor man until he was appointed a judge.

Every barrister had to be a member of one of the Inns of Court, namely, Lincoln's Inn, the Inner Temple, or Gray's Inn. These were old societies for study of the law, corresponding in some features to the colleges of Oxford and Cambridge. Following the usual pattern Lyell had in 1819 entered Lincoln's Inn where he was required to keep twelve terms. There were four terms in the year, but the requirements for keeping a term were nominal in that they consisted merely of dining six times in the hall of Lincoln's Inn during each term. Despite his long absence on the continent in the summer of 1820 Lyell evidently fulfilled the dining requirement without difficulty because he was called to the bar at Lincoln's Inn on 15 May 1822,[8] which was about as early as it was

6. J. Clive, *Scotch Reviewers* . . . (1957) pp. 27–28.
7. E. H. Coleridge, *Life and Correspondence of John Duke* . . . (1904) p. 13.
8. Ms. copy of Lyell's call to the bar. Kinnordy mss.

possible for him to have kept his twelve terms. In order to be called he had to submit a certificate from a barrister attesting that he had read for twelve months in his chambers and Lyell had presumably fulfilled this requirement by his period in John Patteson's office. Patteson himself had been in practice as a special pleader, that is, as one who wrote arguments to be presented in court by a barrister, but who did not himself appear. However, he was called to the bar in 1821 and would, therefore, have been able to sign Lyell's certificate in 1822. The actual ceremony of the call to the bar was probably similar at Lincoln's Inn in 1822 to that experienced by William Ballentine at the Middle Temple about 1830. Ballantine recalled:

> The batch to be "turned off" were summoned to the bench table. We were each presented with a glass of wine, and a speech was made to us by the treasurer, giving us good advice and wishing us prosperity in our forthcoming career.[9]

After being called to the bar, the barrister remained a member of his inn for life and could use its library, dining hall, and common rooms. Lyell, therefore continued to be a member of Lincoln's Inn, but whether he used to dine or meet his friends there is not known.

When in 1825 Lyell decided to take up the law more seriously he chose the western circuit, which meant attending the courts as they moved from county town to county town throughout the southwest of England. Because the judges and barristers traveled together from town to town and were forbidden to use public transportation, they formed a natural community which by ancient custom had organized itself into a corporate body called a "Mess." The judges and leaders of the bar usually traveled in their own carriages while the junior barristers travelled in groups of two and three in post chaises. The Mess often arranged to transport the baggage and perhaps negotiated for board and lodging.

The judges of the various royal courts such as the Court of King's Bench and the Court of Common Pleas were accustomed to sit, either individually or together, at Westminster through two short terms of each year, the Michaelmas and Easter terms, and then during the summer to go on one of the six circuits to hold

9. Mr. S. [W.] Ballantine, *Some experiences of a barrister's life* (1882) vol. I, p. 16.

assizes in the county towns.[10] The western circuit began with the Hampshire assizes at Winchester and moved thence to Salisbury in Wiltshire, Dorchester in Dorsetshire, Taunton in Somerset, Exeter in Devon, and Bodmin in Cornwall. (See map, Fig. 25.) John Coleridge, who also attended the western circuit, recalled that the full number of barristers on the circuit usually assembled at Winchester and usually remained together as far as Taunton. When the circuit went into Devon and Cornwall the number dropped off.

> We met usually in high spirits and there was much excitement on the whole round. Those who were in full business were not the least merry or regular at the Circuit Mess. There were the aspirants, men who were beginning to rise into notice—full of hope and interest. There were the very young men . . . for whom the novelty of the life and the business in court, were in themselves a continual treat, who found in watching the proceedings, or the displays of eloquence and skill in the leaders, or of learning in the juniors both instruction and amusement. . .
>
> "Our circuit" was a somewhat stately affair. The judges did not post, but travelled with sober haste drawn by their own four in hand. The barristers posted or rode . . . The "leaders" always had their private carriages, and some of them their saddle horses also. Our mess was rather an expensive one, and we had our own cellar of wine at each circuit town. This was under the care of our "Wine treasurer" and a van, with four horses, attended us, under the superintendence of our Baggage master These were our two circuit officers.[11]

Coleridge also describes the social activities associated with the western circuit especially on "Grand day" at Dorchester when new members were formally introduced to the Mess and "an account generally given with much point and humour, of preferments, promotions, marriage and any other incidents which might have befallen any of the members since the last Circuit."[12]

10. My sources for this section have been B. Abel-Smith and R. Stevens, *Lawyers and the Courts* . . . (1967); W. Holdsworth, *A History of English Law* (1938), vol. 12; A. K. R. Kiralfy, *Potter's Historical Introduction to English Law and its Institutions* (1962).

11. J. T. Coleridge, *My recollections of the Circuit* . . . (1859) pp. 4–5.

12. Ibid. The legal and social customs associated with the bar on circuit in nineteenth century England are also described in the following articles: Anon., "On Circuit" (1856); J. Leys, "Going on Circuit" (1885); Anon, "Going on Circuit by 'One who goes'" (1890).

The circuit Mess served to maintain the group of barristers as a disciplined and cohesive professional body. Expulsion from the Mess was tantamount to disbarment and the Mess did not hesitate to expel one of their members whose conduct, whether strictly legal or not, was of a kind to bring discredit on the profession of barrister. Attendance on the circuit was often dull for the junior members because they had little business and often, therefore, nothing to do except listen to cases as they were tried. Yet the circuit offered an excellent education in the law. A large number of cases were tried in rapid succession at each assize. In the various trials the young barrister might witness the practical application of legal principles in a variety of circumstances. He saw the law at work. Lyell made notes of some of the trials he attended and of the legal principles he saw applied.

In England in the early nineteenth century criminal punishments were, by present standards, very harsh. Transportation to Australia and hanging were frequent penalties. But justice was fair and it was prompt. All cases awaiting trial at the assize had to be decided before the court rose.

As a barrister Lyell also attended some of the Quarter Sessions in county towns. The justices presiding over Quarter Sessions were justices of the peace of the county in which the sessions were held, and the purpose of Quarter Sessions, held quarterly as the name implies, was to try the more serious criminal cases referred from Petty Sessions. Petty Sessions consisted of two or more justices sitting without a jury while at Quarter Sessions the cases were tried with a jury. It was within this framework that Lyell began to practice as a barrister.

In 1825 Lyell devoted his spare time to writing up the work he had done in the field during the previous year. In February he prepared his paper on the marl lakes of Scotland for the press. He was still puzzled about the origin of marl because he could not understand why it formed in the lochs of Scotland lying among sandstone rocks which contained very little limestone and yet did not form in ponds in England where the underlying rock was chalk almost entirely composed of calcium carbonate.[13] In an appendix to this paper he gave descriptions and illustrations of various fossil and living species of *Chara* (Fig. 24). The drawings were made

13. C. L., Jr. to G. A. M. 8 Jan. and 14 Jan. 1825. Mantell mss.

for him by James de Carle Sowerby and were designed to illustrate "the identity between the ancient & modern Genus."[14]

In May Lyell began to write a paper on a dyke of serpentine which he had traced along a line running northeast and southwest, nearly parallel with the vale of Strathmore in Scotland and a few miles to the northwest of it. This dyke is now known to mark the line of the Highland fault. In writing about it Lyell consulted John F. W. Herschel who had discovered a somewhat similar outcrop of serpentine at Predazzo in the Tyrol.[15] This evidently was his first acquaintance with Herschel, the son of Sir William Herschel, the Astronomer Royal, who, now thirty-two years old, had been elected a fellow of the Royal Society at the age of twenty-one and had established his scientific reputation by a series of mathematical papers. Previously he had lived at his father's house at Slough but in November 1824, having been elected secretary of the Royal Society, he took lodgings at 56 Devonshire Street, Portland Place, London in order to carry out his duties. A few days after writing to ask about Herschel's Predazzo specimens Lyell wrote again with an invitation to accompany himself and Roderick Murchison on a jaunt down the Thames to see the construction of the new Thames tunnel which was being built by Isambard Brunel and his son.[16] Ultimately he persuaded Herschel to publish a short note on the Predazzo serpentine to accompany his own on the serpentine dyke of Forfarshire.[17]

Meanwhile, at Lewes, Gideon Mantell was discovering more fossil bones. In the summer of 1822, Mrs. Mantell had found in the Tilgate forest beds some fossil teeth which appeared to belong to an herbivorous reptile but with "characters so remarkable that the most superficial observer would have been struck with their appearance."[18] Because the teeth of crocodiles, *Megalosaurus,* and *Plesiosaurus* had already been found in these beds, the discovery of a new fossil reptile was not in itself surprising. However, all reptiles previously known were carnivorous and these teeth were so large that they must have belonged to a gigantic animal. Be-

14. C. L., Jr. to J. de C. Sowerby. 4 Feb. 1825. Eyles mss.
15. C. L., Jr. to J. F. W. Herschel. 9 May 1825. Kinnordy mss.
16. C. L., Jr. to J. F. W. Herschel. 14 May 1825. Kinnordy mss.
17. "On a dike of serpentine, cutting through sandstone, in the County of Forfar" (1825). J. F. W. Herschel, "Notice of a remarkable occurrence of serpentine at the junction of Sienite with the Dolomite of the Tyrol," (1825).
18. G. Mantell, "Notice on the *Iguanodon* ..." (1825) p. 180.

cause he wanted to get an expert opinion on them, Mantell entrusted some specimens to Lyell to take to Cuvier when he went to Paris in 1823. Cuvier had agreed that the teeth were reptilian and were those of an herbivore. To draw further conclusions he would have to have a portion of jaw-bone with some of the teeth attached. Encouraged by these remarks Mantell had made a further search and, when he had obtained additional specimens of individual teeth, had taken them during the summer of 1824 to the Hunterian museum at the Royal College of Surgeons where William Clift helped him to compare them with the skeletons of recent reptiles. The teeth resembled none of the living forms and they had almost given up hope when an assistant, Samuel Stutchbury, took Mantell to see the skeleton of an iguana from the West Indies which he had recently prepared. Its teeth, although much smaller, corresponded in detail to the fossil specimens. What Mantell had found, therefore, appeared to be the teeth of a giant fossil iguana which, at the suggestion of W. D. Conybeare, he named *Iguanodon*. Word of the *Iguanodon* soon got abroad so that Mantell records in his *Journal* for 28 November 1824 that he had "had numerous applications from different persons respecting . . . the Iguanodon."[19] He announced the discovery officially in a letter to Mr. Davies Gilbert, president of the Royal Society, and this letter was read to the society on 10 February 1825. Lyell was involved in each of the stages of Mantell's discoveries and in many ways acted as his volunteer agent and adviser in London. On 19 May 1825 he wrote to Mantell, "I have shewn your other new and interesting Tilgate fossils to Stokes, G. Sowerby, Dr. Wollaston, König & others.[20] All declare that it is new, remarkable & unintelligible & therefore may be what Mr. Mantell chooses & as I informed them that you wished it to be an insect Dr. W. says it shall be an insect!"[21] He had also written earlier in the year

19. G. Mantell, *Journal* (1940), p. 52.

20. Charles Stokes (1783–1853), a member of the Stock Exchange, collector and amateur naturalist and geologist; George Brettingham Sowerby (1788–1854), conchologist, assisted his father James Sowerby and his brother James de Carle Sowerby to publish illustrated works in natural history and was a dealer in shells and natural history objects; William Hyde Wollaston (1766–1828), M.D., F.R.S., physiologist, chemist, and physicist; Charles Dietrich Eberhard König (1774–1851), mineralogist, and a native of Brunswick. He came to England in 1800 to arrange the collections of Queen Charlotte and then became assistant to Dryander as librarian to Sir Joseph Banks. In 1807 he went to the British Museum first as assistant keeper and in 1813 as keeper of the department of mineralogy and natural history.

21. C. L., Jr. to G. A. M. 19 May 1825. Mantell mss.

with the news that "König tells me he has no fear of your not becoming F. R. S. What I can do I will."[22] This must have been welcome news to Mantell, who, living in the country, was hungry for recognition of his work in the great world.

In July Lyell went down to Bartley to spend a month in the country. He had some idea of going to Dresden to learn German but was undecided. He was undoubtedly uncertain about his future. Though keenly devoted to geology, he could see no opportunity to make his living at it, and his father, worried by a large family of unmarried daughters, frequently reminded Lyell of the desirability of his adding to the family fortune. The fact that these reminders did not come very well from Mr. Lyell, who himself had never followed a career nor been markedly economical, did not detract from their urgency for Lyell. During this year William Buckland was appointed a Canon of Christchurch Cathedral at Oxford, a position which carried with it a free house and an income of £1000 per year. On the strength of it he married and went on a long wedding trip through France and Italy. Lyell regretted to Mantell that no similar endowments were open to lay geologists. There were in fact very few paths open to a professional career in any science. The universities had no openings for outsiders, the government did not have scientific laboratories and the Geological Survey had not yet been established. Lyell mentions Buckland's good fortune with a trace of envy, but his own dilemma was very real.[23]

In September 1824 William Gifford, who had edited the *Quarterly Review* since its founding in 1809, resigned his editorship because of failing health and in December 1824 John Murray, publisher of the *Quarterly*, asked John Taylor Coleridge to assume the editorship.[24] Coleridge was a barrister at the Middle Temple, thirty-four years old, with strong literary interests. Educated at Eton and at Corpus Christi College, Oxford, he was handsome with a courtly manner, naturally a Tory in politics and, through his close friendship with the Reverend John Keble, formed while he was a student at Oxford, he tended to have Tractarian sympathies in religion.[25] But Coleridge was fair minded and had

22. C. L., Jr. to G. A. M. 14 Jan. 1825. Mantell mss.
23. C. L., Jr. to G. A. M. 20 July 1825. Mantell mss. *L. & L.* I, 160–61.
24. S. Smiles, *A publisher and his friends* ... (1891) vol. I, pp. 164–69.
25. Later he became Sir John Taylor Coleridge (1790–1876) a justice of the King's Bench.

broad interests. An immediate effect of his influence upon the *Quarterly Review* was a new emphasis upon the literature of science and medicine—an emphasis visible in the articles in the *Quarterly* in the latter part of 1825 and in 1826. Coleridge had been a fellow of Exeter College, Oxford during part of the time that Lyell was there as a student, but they seem not to have become acquainted then. At any rate, in 1825 Coleridge invited Lyell to write for the *Quarterly* and Lyell set to work. With his father's urgings in mind he may have been encouraged by the fact that the *Quarterly* paid for its articles.

Soon after Coleridge assumed the editorship of the *Quarterly* his professional work as a barrister on the western circuit increased so much that he saw he could not continue both, but he carried on until Murray could find a new editor. In November 1825 John Murray came to an agreement with John Gibson Lockhart, son-in-law to Sir Walter Scott, to take over the editorship. On 4 December Lyell wrote to Eleanor:

> Coleridge informed me yesterday that he has given up the Quarterly, and that Lockhart comes from Edinburgh in a week to take it. He could not get my paper into his last number, but would have put it into the next with certain parts abridged. These he recommends me to condense before I shew it to Lockhart (who you know is W. Scott's son-in-law). He shewed me how Gifford formerly cut to pieces his papers & thus encouraged me much. Indeed had I been aware how difficult a task even for such a man as Coleridge it had been to fit an article for the Review I sh.ᵈ never have presumed to write. I have at all events made Coleridge's acquaintance & tho' I expect to be wrecked in the attempt to Pilot myself into the graces of a new Editor I shall not be ashamed with such encouragement to run the gauntlet.[26]

This article, apparently his first, was a review of Thomas Campbell's *Letter to Mr. Brougham on the Subject of a London University*. It was published in the number for December 1825 and must have been written during the summer. The idea of a new university in London was under active discussion at the time. All dissenters were prevented by religious tests from taking degrees at Oxford and Cambridge. Thus, Quakers, Presbyterians, Method-

---

26. C. L., Jr. to his sister Eleanor. 4 Dec. 1825. Kinnordy mss. *L. & L.* I, 163.

ists, and Congregationalists, who now formed a large and prosperous segment of the population, had no means of education for their sons. The sons of many Anglican tradesmen were also well off enough to desire university education yet could not afford the extravagances of Oxford and Cambridge.

But their religious and social exclusiveness were not the only shortcomings of the older universities. Intellectually they had little to offer, nor was there much sign of their responding to the new and vigorous interest in the classics, history, political science, economics and the natural sciences which was widespread in England. Within their walls the existence of the broad and diverse range of studies that form the intellectual life of a modern university was barely acknowledged. At the same time, however, as the limitations of the older universities were becoming more painfully obvious, the whole question of what a university ought to be was involved in the launching of a new one. In discussing Campbell's *Plan*, therefore, Lyell surveyed the needs and aims of university education as a whole. He tended to doubt the practicality of a metropolitan university with no provision for residence in colleges. In order to see the older institutions in perspective he examined their history. Their original purpose, he said, was to train students for the professions of theology, law, and medicine and to provide "that common basis of liberal information which might exercise and enlarge the mind before its attention was confined to the particular business of those several callings." To this part of their function he saw that residence in colleges could make an essential contribution. The day-to-day association with other young men in a disciplined and orderly life seemed to him to be the means by which "a young man's character is gradually and almost imperceptibly formed."

It is by the cultivation of literature and science under such circumstances that a man may truly be said to have had the advantages of liberal *education;* advantages by no means confined to the degree of proficiency he may have reached in those studies, but which are exemplified in a thousand ways . . . in the opinions, the habits, the tastes and feelings of the individual so trained.

His ideal of a university education was still, therefore, very much that which he himself had experienced at Oxford. He believed that private lectures and tutorials were much superior to public lec-

tures by a professor to large open classes, and that the main reason for the transfer of students from the public lectures of the
university to the private classes of the colleges at Oxford and
Cambridge was the simple superiority of the latter method of instruction. On this point he was later to change his mind. At this
time he still verged on the extremely conservative for he thought
that all "disputable and untried doctrine" should be excluded
from university teaching, nor should students be encouraged to
acquire a taste for mere novelty. He was also afraid that university
education might actually unfit the sons of tradesmen for the mode
of life they must lead by making them dissatisfied with their day-
to-day work. The omission of religious instruction from Campbell's plan struck him as lamentable because it had traditionally
been "the parent of generous thought and well-regulated ambition."[27]

This is an interesting essay showing the initial stages of Lyell's
thought on university education. It contained several brilliant
passages but is marked by no single continued line of argument.
His affection for Oxford and respect for her greatness is in conflict with his awareness, as yet but half-formed, of how inadequate
she was to the conditions of the modern world.

Late in August 1825, after some geological rambles, Lyell returned to Bartley where he spent some six weeks. It was to be his
last long summer visit to his boyhood home, for Mr. Lyell had not
renewed the lease, and had decided, on its expiration the following year, to move himself and his family to Kinnordy. The difficulties of overseeing his Scottish acres from a distance of 500
miles were now, in his middle age, too great. He no longer felt up
to long journeys in a mail coach in winter. Because of his large
family of daughters he felt, too, the need for economy. At Bartley
Lyell occupied himself by collecting insects with his sisters and in
mounting and arranging their specimens.[28] Never, even in old
age, would he lose his delight in the beauty of rare moths and
butterflies. The time passed so pleasantly that after his return to
London he confessed himself homesick—a rare event with him.[29]

At the beginning of November Adolphe Brongniart came from
Paris to London and Lyell entertained him. When the Geological

27. "Art. X. *Letter to Mr. Brougham on the Subject of a London University*
...'' (1825).

28. C. L., Jr. to his sister Marianne. 20 Nov. 1825. Kinnordy mss. *L. & L.* I, 162.

29. C. L., Jr. to his sister Eleanor. 4 Dec. 1825. Kinnordy mss. *L. & L.* I, 163.

Society held its first meeting of the year on Friday 4 November, Lyell gave breakfast next morning to Buckland, Brongniart, Stokes, and Mantell at his rooms at 29 Norfolk Street.[30] Brongniart was able to confirm Lyell's and James Sowerby's conclusions concerning the identity of ancient and modern species of *Chara* contained in his paper in the volume of the *Transactions* which had just come out.[31]

At the end of 1825 Lyell resigned as secretary of the Geological Society. He had become weary of a long series of disputes between his fellow secretary, Thomas Webster, and the vice-president of the Society, G. B. Greenough. He planned to stay an extra week at Bartley during Christmas and wrote that "The more my eyes give me hopes of working for myself the more I am decided to cut the G.S."[32] Roderick Murchison was elected to replace him as secretary.[33] At this time too Gideon Mantell was elected a fellow of the Royal Society, and Lyell, who had promoted his election, wrote to congratulate him.[34] He also sent a parcel of books and specimens of English fossils to Adolphe Brongniart at Paris.[35]

At the first meeting of the Linnean Society in November Lyell showed some of the specimens of moths and butterflies which he and his sisters had collected the previous summer. One moth, a black *Noctua*, was a new species and Lyell traded it to the entomologist John Curtis[36] in return for several fine specimens of other rare butterflies and moths.[37]

On New Year's Day 1826, Mr. Lyell wrote a letter of general family news to Dawson Turner at the end of which he mentions that "Charles is here & tired of allowing his talents (which are certainly above mediocrity) to be merely employed on objects of amusement."[38] Whether Lyell would have agreed precisely with this diagnosis or not, it is evident that he felt the need for a new direction in his life. He had resigned as secretary of the Geological Society ostensibly because he needed to devote the time to his law

30. Mantell, *Journal*, p. 56.
31. C. L., Jr. to J. de C. Sowerby. 9 Nov. 1825. Eyles mss.
32. C. L., Jr. to his sister Eleanor. 4 Dec. 1825. Kinnordy mss. *L. & L.* I, 163.
33. Geikie, *Murchison*, I, p. 128.
34. C. L., Jr. to G. A. M. 10 Dec. 1825. Mantell mss.
35. C. L., Jr. to A. Brongniart. 22 Dec. 1825.
36. John Curtis (1791–1862) was the author of *British Entomology*. . . . The publication of Curtis's first two annual volumes in 1824 and 1825 may have been a factor in stimulating the younger Lyells to collect insects.
37. C. L., Jr. to his sister Marianne. 20 Nov. 1825. Kinnordy mss. *L. & L.* I, 162.
38. C. L. to D. T. 1 Jan. 1826. Dawson Turner mss.

practice but also because he was fed up with its affairs. His eyes were sufficiently improved to give him more hope of working for himself. After his return to London at the beginning of February he was elected F.R.S., an honor which he perhaps appreciated the more because he was temporarily discouraged with scientific work. His efforts to gain the approval of J. G. Lockhart, the new editor of the *Quarterly,* were successful and he was soon launched upon the writing of a new article. In March, despite his resolve to cut the Geological Society, he was also writing a paper on the plastic clay formation of the cliffs between Christchurch Head and Studland Bay in Hampshire.[39] This paper was a simple description of the strata exposed in these cliffs and was designed to complete the geological description of the southern coast of England of which so much had already been described by members of the Geological Society. Lyell ended the paper with an observation which related to the controversy then current over the manner of origin of river valleys. He noted that the small valleys, cut out of the clay loam and sand forming the cliffs, were proportional in size to the streams flowing in them and appeared to have been formed by the action of these streams over a long period of time.

> It is impossible not to draw this conclusion when we observe the power exerted at present by several small rills, which have divided the cliffs . . . by perpendicular fissures or narrow ravines, the sides of which still remain vertical, because the water constantly undermines them and removes the loose sand, clay, and gravel.[40]

At the beginning of April Lyell moved from his old quarters at 29 Norfolk Street to larger rooms at 9 Crown Office Row, Temple. "I have got rid of my cold at last," he wrote to Marianne "thanks to my *chambers* which really are comfortable enough now. As I attend the Courts in the morning now I have enough to do, but not more than I shall get thro' with pleasure if my eyes remain well."[41] To Mantell he described himself as "in chambers, *fixed in my own house*"[42] so that he seems to have felt himself lodged more independently than ever before. He said that he now spent the whole day in the courts at Westminster, and since he started

39. C. L., Jr. to G. A. M. 11 March 1826. Mantell mss.
40. "On the strata of the Plastic Clay Formation . . ." (1829) pp. 285–86.
41. C. L., Jr. to his sister Marianne. 18 April 1826. Kinnordy mss. Italics Lyell's.
42. C. L., Jr. to G. A. M. 16 May 1826. Mantell mss.

for the court sessions at seven o'clock in the morning, his days were long (Map 6). He also traveled with the court on circuit.

In May Lyell wrote a popular account of "Freshwater Formations" to form a chapter in a local guide to Christchurch, Hampshire which his friend William Stewart Rose was preparing.[43] He was at this time very much concerned with freshwater formations because he was writing his paper on the strata of Hordwell cliff on the Hampshire coast. In 1821 Thomas Webster had shown that the Hordwell strata were identical with the lower freshwater formation of the Isle of Wight, but at the same time he thought that the uppermost beds at the eastern end of Hordwell cliff might belong to the upper marine formation of the Isle of Wight.[44] Lyell now showed that although some of the beds contained a few shells belonging to marine genera such as *Mytilus* and *Serpula*, the entire Hordwell cliff consisted of freshwater strata. Lyell argued that these shells might live under essentially freshwater conditions in the estuary of a tidal river. He considered the presence of fossil *Cypris* and the fruiting bodies of *Chara* as clear evidence that the strata had been formed in fresh water and concluded that they had been laid down in a river, or at the mouth of a river. His closing sentence was that:

> Upon the whole, there are sound geological reasons, both in this and in other instances, for extending the term *Freshwater Formations* to deposits which may have been formed at the mouths of rivers, and for no longer restricting it to such as have originated in inland lakes.[45]

This opinion was in direct contradiction to that of Thomas Webster, who in 1825 had urged that the term "freshwater formations" be restricted to those deposited in lakes.[46] From his study of the fossils of freshwater lake deposits in Scotland, Lyell was confident

43. William Stewart Rose (1775–1843) was one of the clerks of the House of Lords. He was interested in Italian literature and was a friend of Sir Walter Scott and other literary men.

44. T. Webster, "On a fresh-water formation in Hordwell Cliff, Hampshire . . ." (1824).

45. "On the freshwater strata of Hordwell Cliff, Beacon Cliff and Barton Cliff, Hampshire" (1829).

46. T. Webster, "Reply to Dr. Fitton's paper . . ." (1825) p. 47. In speaking of the Hastings sands and Weald clay Webster wrote, "I do not go so far however as to consider these as freshwater formations, a term which I am accustomed to restrict to such beds only as have been probably formed in freshwater lakes." The point also touched the question whether the Tilgate forest beds, which had been laid down in a river delta, should be considered a freshwater formation.

Raymond Buildings

Gray's Inn

Gray's Inn Gardens

16 Hart Street

Bloomsbury Square

Russell Square

British Museum

Bedford Square

Lincoln's Inn

Lincoln's Inn Fields

High Holborn

Hart Street

The Temple

Fleet Street

Gardens

Norfolk Street

Somerset House

Strand

River Thames

Trafalgar Square

Pall Mall

Athenaeum

6. Lyell's London, with places where he lived and worked

that the discovery of such fossils as *Cypris* and gyrogonites (*Chara*) was decisive evidence in favor of the presence of fresh water, whether in ancient lakes or in rivers. To Mantell he wrote:

> I have pronounced, as Fitton stated (see Ann. Phil. Nov.ʳ 1824) that if a line be drawn between the Weald C.[lay] & Shanklin S.ᵈ, all above to Chalk and further is marine, all below to Portland freshw.ʳ . . .
>
> Do not conceal any evidence of marine in the Tilgate, indeed this you will not I know, but do not throw it in the shade. All will come right & it is a freshwater formation undoubtedly & the grandest discovery in Geology since Cuv. & Brongn.ᵗ came out. If in an estuary it must still have been above the mean level of the sea. How stupendous a conclusion with respect to beds below the chalk, so *widely extended* a formation![47]

He also offered to have James Sowerby give his opinion as to the freshwater character of any fossil shells which Mantell had gathered from the Tilgate forest beds. This offer was designed to aid Mantell in the preparation of his new book *Illustrations of the Geology of Sussex*.

Between 1822 when Mrs. Mantell had discovered the first *Iguanodon* teeth in a quarry at Cuckfield and 1827 when Mantell published the *Illustrations,* his understanding of the meaning of his discoveries in the Tilgate forest beds developed greatly. He had known in 1822 that the sediments had been deposited in fresh water but by 1827 he had developed a much clearer and more detailed conception of the conditions under which they had accumulated. He envisioned the beds as having been laid down in a river delta or estuary and created a vivid picture of the plants and animals which might have lived in the delta of a large river under tropical conditions and of the sediments in which they might become buried. He then showed that the fossils of the Tilgate forest beds corresponded precisely to such a picture.[48] In this imaginative reconstruction of the ecological environment represented by the Tilgate forest fossils, Mantell seems to have owed something to his exchanges of ideas with Lyell, and to Lyell's suggestions.

Since Mr. Lyell and his family were now packing their furniture and belongings at Bartley preparatory to their move to Scotland, Lyell sent detailed instructions to his sisters for the packing

47. C. L., Jr. to G. A. M. 16 May 1826. Mantell mss.
48. G. Mantell, *Illustrations of the Geology of Sussex* (1827) pp. 74–75.

and shipping of their joint insect collection. Their enthusiasm for collecting seems to have mounted to fever pitch during the preceding year and brother and sisters were all engrossed in the preoccupations of collectors—trading specimens, hunting for rarities, comparing the merits of various species for interest and beauty, etc. Lyell sent instructions for making a breeding cage for caterpillars using a garden flowerpot.[49]

In the same letter he mentioned that "Lockhart has taken up my offer of a review of the Geol. Trans. quite ardently." In the issue of the *Quarterly Review* for June 1826, Lyell published his second article, "On Scientific Institutions," a review of the current numbers of the proceedings of six provincial scientific societies.[50] He made this article an occasion to survey the libraries, museums, scientific societies, astronomical observatories, and botanical gardens of Great Britain as a whole.

The first quarter of the nineteenth century had seen a remarkable increase in the number of scientific societies in England. After the founding of the Royal Society of London in 1662 no other scientific societies had appeared in England until 1788 when the Linnean Society was founded, but after the founding of the Royal Institution in 1799 more than eleven societies for the promotion of one or other, or all, aspects of science and learning had been established in England. The 1820's had been a period of especially great activity in the founding of scientific societies, because in addition to the Astronomical Society founded at London in 1821, new scientific societies had appeared at Bristol, York, and other smaller provincial cities.

Lyell began with a survey of the libraries of England. The library of the British Museum he found smaller still than the *Bibliotheque du Roi* at Paris, but with its new reading room it would soon be much improved. Of the *Transactions of the Geological Society of London* he wrote:

. . . they contain a vast body of new and interesting matter; many memoirs, illustrated by maps and well executed plates, in

49. C. L., Jr. to his sister Marianne. 24 May 1826. Kinnordy mss.
50. "Art. VIII. 1. *Transactions of the Cambridge Philosophical Society.* vol. i. 2. *Memoirs of the Literary and Philosophical Society of Manchester.* 2nd series. vol. iv., London, 1824. 3. *Transactions of the Royal Geological Society of Cornwall, instituted February 11.* vol. i. and ii. Penzance. 4. *Report of the Liverpool Royal Institution.* 1822. 5. Bristol Institution. *Proceedings of the Second Annual Meeting held February 10, 1825* & c. 6. *Annual Report of the Council of the Yorkshire Philosophical Society for 1824.*" (1826).

which information is found concerning the mineral structure of some of the most distant quarters of the globe; but of the strata of England in particular, they supply us with details more ample than have as yet appeared respecting any tract of the same extent in the world.

The most interesting institutions, however, were the provincial institutions. In many cases they had museums, libraries, and reading rooms and employed lecturers to give scientific lectures. One point which greatly impressed Lyell was the large contribution which the members of the medical profession were making to all branches of science. This was the more remarkable because for the most part they had *not* been educated at the English universities. In general, Lyell rejoiced at the flourishing of the provincial institutions because he saw in them a counter-balance to the centripetal influence of London. In France he had seen how the cultural and intellectual life of Paris had been created at the expense of the provinces, which were drained of all cultural life of their own.

This article was evidently a success, for on 22 June he wrote to Mantell, "I am become a Quarterly Reviewer. You will see my article just out on 'Scientific Institutions' by which some of my friends here think I have carried the strong works of the enemy by storm." He added, "I am now far-gone with a 2d & hope to be delivered in less than 3 months." This was his review of the first volume of the second series of the *Transactions of the Geological Society* which he himself had helped to edit. In this article he planned to present the latest discoveries in paleontology and wrote to Mantell for pointers.[51]

On 2 July, however, Lyell had to leave London with his fellow barristers to travel with the judges on the western circuit which included Warminster sessions and Exeter assizes. While traveling from Exeter to Warminster he visited Longleat, Fonthill, and Wardour Castle, stopping to see the fossil collection of Miss Benett at Norton Baranther. He examined the geology of the country around Warminster with particular care to check whether the lower green sand in that area was a freshwater formation—a fact about which Gideon Mantell had become hesitant because of the mixture of both freshwater and marine fossils found in the Tilgate forest beds. Miss Benett's collection contained marine fossils

51. C. L., Jr. to G. A. M. 22 June 1826. Mantell mss. *L. & L.* I, 164–65.

but Lyell found that they were from the firestone lying above the gault. "The country is clear enough," he wrote to Mantell, *"& all right."*[52]

At the beginning of August Lyell returned from the circuit and went almost immediately to Scotland where the Lyell family were now settled at Kinnordy. He arranged with John Murray to have the proofs of his article on the *Transactions* sent to him there. While he was in Scotland, he did further work on his geological map of Forfarshire. It was the end of October before he returned to London. By then his *Quarterly* article had been published in the number for September 1826.[53]

This article not only included a review of the *Transactions* and of recently published geological books but it was also in effect a summary of the state of the science at that time. In writing it, Lyell was impressed first of all by the great strides which geology had made in the years immediately preceding. The impression which geology gave to the world was one of conflicting and unsettled views—a consequence of the long years of controversy between Vulcanists and Neptunists, Huttonians and Wernerians. But actually there was a broad area of agreement in the science. It was conceded that the strata were in a regular order which was never inverted, that they had been deposited at the bottom of the sea but "have been subject, at different, and often distant epochs, to violent convulsions" (p. 507). It was such convulsions which had produced, for instance, the vertical chalk strata in the Isle of Wight, but on the whole the strata were most remarkably dislocated and contorted near ranges of mountains. Geologists had shown "that certain series of strata are continuous over extensive districts, and often characterized throughout by peculiar assemblages of organic remains." In the oldest rocks, however, no remains of plants or animals had been found. The fossils found in older strata differed more widely from modern living forms than those in younger or more recent strata so "that as we ascend in the series, from the lowest towards more recent deposits an approximation may be traced in the characters of the fossil species to those of the species now in life" (p. 508). The remains of plants and animals were often preserved so well and so completely that the characteristics of fossil species could be defined almost as clearly as

52. C. L., Jr. to G. A. M. 19 July 1826. Mantell mss.
53. "Art IX. *Transactions of the Geological Society of London.* Vol. i, 2d Series. London, 1824." (1826). Specific page references are in the text.

those of living ones. The accurate determination of species had further confirmed what had been apparent almost from the beginning of the study of fossil plants and animals, namely, the striking fact that the fossil forms found in the strata of northern Europe corresponded to forms now found only in the tropics. The climate of Europe, and probably of the whole earth, must in past geological ages have been much warmer than at present.

Many of these broad conclusions had been drawn from the secondary strata—the series of strata extending from Werner's transitional strata upward through the chalk.

> Until within the last twenty years, the secondary strata were regarded with as much indifference as the sand and pebbles of Alpine torrents, or the muddy sediment of lowland rivers. It was never suspected that they contained the records of various and extensive revolutions in the condition of the land and ocean, as well as in the classes of organic beings with which our globe has been successively peopled. [p. 508]

Lyell then turned to a summary of fossil discoveries beginning with those found in most recent deposits. The horns of both the Scandinavian and the Irish elk had been found in the peat and marl deposits of Britain, while in superficial loam and gravel and in caves, the bones of the elephant, rhinoceros, hippopotamus, cave-bear and cave-hyena had been found. Many other tropical species had been found in similar locations on the continent. A large proportion of these fossils belonged to well-defined species which were now extinct. Yet they were closely related to species now living in tropical Africa and Asia and in some cases identical with these species. But this fauna, so different from the modern fauna of Europe, was in turn different from that which had preceded it, "a race of which most of the genera and all the species known to us in fossil remains have been since annihilated." The remains of these animals, which had perished so long before, were "found entombed in strata evidently deposited in the estuaries of rivers, and at the bottom of freshwater lakes, in a manner closely analogous to strata at present in the course of formation in our own lakes and rivers" (p. 511). Whatever "convulsions" may have intervened between the time when these animals had lived and the present, they had lived and died, and their remains had been preserved in a natural and orderly way. These facts, which Lyell had drawn largely from Georges Cuvier's *Discours sur les Revolutions*

de la Globe, tended to lead him to conclusions directly opposed
to those of Cuvier. He was struck more by the clear evidence for
the tranquil conditions which had persisted during the long period of time in which these animals had lived, and their remains
had been preserved, than by the changes which had brought these
periods to an end.

Yet great changes had occurred and they required explanation.
The freshwater formations, which contained the bones of all these
extinct animals, were overlain by marine deposits. Cuvier had consequently attributed the extinction of so many species to an invasion of the sea. The relative levels of sea and land must have altered, but it was a question whether the sea had risen or the land
had sunk. The Huttonian view, which had been argued by Playfair, was that it was the land which had moved. His chief evidence
was the dislocations of strata, not only the existence of inclined
and vertical strata but the presence of surfaces of unconformity,
such as those at Jedburgh and St. Abb's Head, where strata were
laid horizontally upon the edges of the underlying vertical or inclined strata. The vertical strata must have been laid down originally in a horizontal position under the sea. There they must have
been consolidated into rock and afterwards elevated and upturned
into their vertical position at which time they would form dry
land. Their edges had then been worn off to form a smooth surface. Afterwards they had sunk again beneath the sea and horizontal strata had been deposited over them. Then a second time they
had been raised into the position where they now lie and where
they again form dry land. In addition to this long history of depositions and earth movements, which Hutton had read from surfaces
of unconformity, the study of the succession of strata had provided
further evidence for the changes in level of the land. Lyell pointed
out that the coal-bearing strata were of freshwater origin. They
were overlain by the oolites, which were marine limestones, and
above the oolites was a series of a freshwater strata which included,
for instance, the Tilgate forest beds in which Mantell had found
so many land and freshwater reptiles. Above these again lay the
chalk. "The chalk," Lyell wrote, "is exclusively a marine deposit;
and from its great extent in Europe, and the absence of vegetable
matter, sand and transported materials, is considered to have been
formed at the bottom of a deep and tranquil sea. But above the
chalk, both in this island and on the continent, alternations of marine and freshwater strata occur" (p. 514).

If one were to attempt to explain these changes by alternations in the level of the ocean over the whole earth, insuperable difficulties would arise at once and it was in any case "an hypothesis unsupported by facts" (p. 515). Changes in the level of the land however were well known to accompany earthquakes, and an instance of this kind, in which 100 miles of the coast of Chile had been raised several feet had occurred during the great earthquake of 1822 and was described in this volume of the *Transactions*. Another paper described coral rocks on the hilltops in Sumatra, in which the coral species were identical with those in the surrounding sea—a fact which suggested that the island had, at a geologically recent period, been elevated out of the sea. All such facts seemed very suggestive to Lyell who wrote:

> No one can reflect on the above statements without being tempted to inquire whether the causes now in action are, as Dr. Buckland has supposed, 'the last expiring efforts of those mighty disturbing forces which once operated*' or as Hutton thought, they would still be sufficient in a long succession of ages to reproduce analogous results. . . . But in the present state of our knowledge, it appears premature to assume that existing agents could not in the lapse of ages, produce such effects as fall principally under the examination of the geologist. It is an assumption, moreover, directly calculated to repress the ardour of inquiry, by destroying all hope of interpreting what is obscure in the past by an accurate investigation of the present phenomena of nature. [pp. 517–18]

* *Vindiciae Geologicae* p. 5.

Lyell was ready with evidence that the assumption of a decrease in the energy of change was more than premature. The older strata had been laid down under long periods of tranquil and orderly conditions just as much as had the younger ones. The forces which had uplifted and contorted the chalk and plastic clay in the Isle of Wight were just as powerful as those which dislocated the much older "primary clay slate." In the Alps relatively recent Tertiary strata had been elevated to ten thousand feet. "Since then the disturbing force continued unimpaired even subsequently to the formation of some tertiary deposits," wrote Lyell. "Those geologists who contend it is now in the wane must reason from a very limited number of facts indeed" (pp. 518–19).

One change for which Lyell could suggest no cause now in action was that which had maintained a warmer and possibly more uniform climate on the earth's surface during previous geological epochs. He thought that the cause of climatic change would have to be found in astronomy, but for the present he could say nothing about it.

He concluded by taking up again what seemed to be for him the most significant fact which geology had already established: that successive races of distinct plants and animals have inhabited this earth.

> . . . none of these fossil plants or animals appear referable to species now in being, with the exception of a few imbedded in the most recent strata, yet they all belong to genera, families, or orders established for the classification of living organic productions. They even supply links in the chain, without which our knowledge of the existing systems would be comparatively imperfect. It is therefore clear to demonstration, that all, at whatever distance of time created, are parts of one connected plan. [p. 538]

Lyell saw the whole range of living things both past and present as part of that "great chain of being" which in the eighteenth century had come to form one of the common assumptions of educated men.[54]

> There is a gradation of animated beings, from those of the simplest to those of the most complicated organization; from the invertebrated to the vertebrated; and, ascending in the scale from the lowest of the vertebrated class to the most perfect, we find at length, in the mammalia, all the most striking characters of osteological structure, and all the leading features of the physiology of the human frame fully displayed. [pp. 538–39]

Moreover, he was led to quote Bishop Butler to the effect that this scheme is *"not a fixed but a progressive one"* (p. 539). Lyell did not suggest how it may progress although he did say that the succession of various groups of species may be as natural as the succession of generations in modern, living species.

This long review is a masterly essay and indicates the command which Lyell had acquired over a wide range of geological facts. It

54. A. O. Lovejoy, *The Great Chain of Being* (1933).

shows too that he had become aware of the need to reason about these facts. In those theoretical positions which he tentatively assumed, however, he was as yet uncommitted. It is as if he was aware of all those kinds of evidence which suggested the effectiveness of causes now in action and the continuity of the geological past with the present, but had not yet felt the inescapable force of conviction inherent in them. On his return to London at the end of October, Lyell went directly to Salisbury to attend the Wiltshire assizes, which continued for a week, so that it was not until early in November 1826 that he was again settled in his chambers at 9 Crown Office Row, Temple.

When he returned to London he found a check for forty guineas from Murray for his review. "Which," he wrote to Caroline, was a compliment I did not expect from him & his Editor & not to be measured by the quantum of cash. In fact, I find I have risen mightily in their opinion & Barrow[55] who abuses almost everyone & whom I cannot bear, has assured absolute John that I have shewn more *tact* in rendering a scientific Art. popular & intelligible to the uninitiated than any writer he could find in town."[56]

Lockhart now wanted him to write an article on the universities, "a fine subject," which he had agreed to do. There was at the moment a royal commission inquiring into the Scottish universities and since Sir Walter Scott was one of the commissioners for this inquiry, Lockhart invited Lyell to come to meet him at breakfast the following week, when Sir Walter would be in London after his return from Paris. The Bucklands had just returned from their long trip through France, Italy, and Sicily and were staying with Lyell at his chambers. Dr. Buckland "looks 5 years younger & is so full of health, spirits & information that to be with him is quite exhilarating."[57]

The breakfast at Lockhart's on 16 November went very well. Lyell wrote an account of it to his father the same day.[58] He was impressed with the genteel appearance of Sir Walter, but found his conversation forceful and down to earth. He was now going ahead with his article on the universities and early in December

55. John Barrow (1764–1848), traveler and author, was second secretary to the Admiralty and a frequent contributor to the *Quarterly Review*. In 1835, he became Sir John Barrow when he was created a baronet by William IV. A highly intelligent, self-made man, Barrow was probably insufferable.

56. C. L., Jr. to his sister Caroline. 9 Nov. 1826. Kinnordy mss.

57. Ibid.

58. C. L., Jr. to his father. 16 Nov. 1826. Kinnordy mss. *L. & L.* I, 165–66.

he asked Murray to let him have copies of various works on education.[59] "I am getting on with my University Art.," he wrote on December 15, "the reading for which is very instructive. I take a certain fixed portion of Law per day. Murray says the last number sold unusually well. I hope he thinks I helped it. He sends me all the books I want to read with the utmost promptitude."

Lyell also revealed some of the crosscurrents in the literary life of the period.

> The Bishop of Chester & his party cut the Quarterly. Archdeacon Lyell warned them that if they wrote for the British Critic the Public would not read it & then they would be worse off than by making the best of these radical times in the Q.R. They seceded. The British became more ultra. My friend Spedding, an old contributor, was astonished at a rejection of an Art. on "Phillips State Friends" accompanied by a *sermon* from the *Editor!* But it will not do. The sale fell off, & no more numbers are to appear! It is to merge into the "Theological Review." What an Euthanasion![60]

Over the Christmas holiday Lyell went for a week to Cambridge, where he stayed with his friend Thomas Story Spedding (1800–70) at Trinity College. The primary purpose of his visit was to gather information for his article but he had a gala time and won enough money at whist to pay his expenses. From J. S. Henslow, the professor of botany, and other men to whom Henslow introduced him, he learned much about the Cambridge system. The subject of universities now seemed so large that he thought he would have to divide his article in two with the first part devoted to the English universities.[61] On 24 January he wrote to Murray that his visit to Cambridge had caused him to change his plan for the article.[62]

Lyell was extremely busy during this winter both with his legal practice and with writing. His eyes had remained well and he was reading more briefs than ever before. He had entered the literary world and was enjoying it. At the same time he was continuing to collect and exchange insects in collaboration with his sisters. On 18 January he wrote to Caroline:

59. C. L., Jr. to John Murray. 6 Dec. 1826. Fitzwilliam Museum mss.
60. C. L., Jr. to his father. 15 Dec. 1826. Kinnordy mss.
61. C. L., Jr. to his sister Marianne. 5 Jan. 1827. Kinnordy mss. *L. & L.* I, 166–68.
62. C. L., Jr. to J. Murray. 24 Jan. 1827. Murray mss.

The best part of a foreign collect.[n] of Coleoptera is that a tropical sun acts as a magnifying glass in enlarging the same forms which we have here & teaches the generic distinctions without distressing the eyes.[63]

On 31 January he sent his sisters a box of Brazilian and African insect specimens which he had obtained by exchanges with collectors and dealers in London.[64] In February his father wrote to Charles Wedderburn, "We have a pleasant account of 'feasts of reason and flow of soul' at literary dinners in London from Charles today."[65] Lyell himself said in a letter to Mantell on 2 March, "half my time is now spent at Sessions, Circuits etc." While he was on the western circuit at Dorchester he received a copy of Lamarck's *Philosophie zoologique,*[66] a work which delighted him "more than any novel I ever read." If it were true, the theory of evolution by transmutation of species, which Lamarck elaborated in this work, would provide a solution to the problem of how that progress in creation, which the fossil record seemed to reveal, had actually occurred. "His theories," Lyell continued, "address themselves to the imagination at least of Geologists who know the mighty inferences which would be deducible were they established by observation." This was the difficulty, and Lyell considered that he read him as he would listen to an advocate on the wrong side of a legal case. He was glad to see that Lamarck admitted that if the theory were true, it "would prove that man may have come from the Ourangoutang." Yet the recent flood of geological discoveries had suggested so many new and startling possibilities previously unimagined that Lyell seems to have hesitated to reject even so fantastic a scheme.

But after all what changes species may really undergo! How impossible will it be to distinguish & lay down a line beyond which some of the so called extinct species have never passed into recent ones. That the earth is quite as old as he supposes has long been my creed & I will try before 6 months are over to convert the readers of the Quarterly to that heterodox opinion.

This last referred to a second geological article which he was preparing. In it he intended to give a more extended account of the

63. C. L., Jr. to his sister Caroline. 18 Jan. 1827. Kinnordy mss.
64. C. L., Jr. to his sister Eleanor. 31 Jan. 1827. Kinnordy mss.
65. C. L. to C. W. 25 Feb. 1827. Wedderburn mss.
66. J. B. A. P. Lamarck, *Philosophie zoologique*...(1809).

geological ideas which he had sketched in his review of the *Transactions*. He continued:

> I am going to write in confirmation of ancient causes having been the same as modern & to show that those plants & animals which we know are becoming preserved now are the same as were formerly, e.g. scarcely any insects now, no lichens, no mosses etc. ever get to places where they can become imbedded in strata. But quadrupeds do in lakes, reptiles in estuaries, corals in reefs, fish in sea, plants wherever there is water, salt or fresh etc etc.[67]

The argument which he was developing was that the absence of fossils of a particular group of animals in a stratum, was no evidence that they had not existed when the stratum was laid down, because they may have lived in places where their remains had no chance of being deposited in the stratum. Lyell had been deeply impressed by the absence of the bones of water birds from the marl of freshwater lakes in Scotland even though these same lakes swarmed with waterfowl. He realized that the factors that determine that certain animals will be preserved as fossils bear no necessary relation to the numbers or importance of those animals when alive. They depended instead on complex and little-understood factors in the ecological environment in which the sediment was formed. Lyell sustained this argument in future years more as a lawyer than as a scientist, because it failed to account for the absence of bony fishes, for instance, from the older marine strata, although such fish were preserved in abundance in younger strata, alongside invertebrate fossils belonging to groups also present in the older strata. But his original reasons for adopting it were scientific. Then, too, geologists were making new fossil discoveries so rapidly and they so regularly found fossils in strata older than any in which the fossils had previously been thought to occur, that the failure to find them in particular strata did not guarantee that the fossils were not there.

In April 1827, Leonard Horner came from Edinburgh to London to help with the founding of the new London University of which he was presently to be appointed warden. Although he was known chiefly as an educational reformer, Horner, at the age of forty-two, had long been interested in geology and had been one

67. C. L., Jr. to G. A. M. 2 March 1827. Mantell mss. *L. & L.* I, 168–69.

of the founding members of the Geological Society of London. In 1821 he had founded the School of Arts at Edinburgh, an institution organized for the education of "mechanics" (i.e. skilled workmen) and the forerunner of the "Mechanics Institutes" which would be established in many cities in both Britain and America during the nineteenth century. With his strong interest in education Horner also helped to found the Edinburgh Academy in 1824 — a school designed to provide for Scottish youth not only a good classical education, but instruction in mathematics, history, geography, and English literature. He was a man liberal in his attitudes to both science and education and Lyell, who met him at the Geological Society, found him friendly and stimulating. Horner approved strongly of Lyell's geological article in the *Quarterly Review* and gave him advice on his proposed article on the universities.

In describing his plans to his father, Lyell reveals something of the relationship of his work as a barrister to his literary work.

I have my doubts [he wrote] as to leaving sessions on the score of economy. I find the additional time of which I am master in consequence of ostensibly following a profession & perhaps the £30 that 4 sessions cost me might be annually returned by an additional art. which I might be thereby enabled to write. It is wonderful how little mercy one's friends have on one's time if one has no excuse deemed valid for declining unprofitable parties, or refereeships of papers, or secretaryships etc. The circuit costs under £50 everything included. My purse would not have required replenishing for some time, but I am much obliged to you for anticipating my wants as usual. I find them diminish monthly in proportion as I am more agreeably employed, & if with the willingness to work & industry which I now have I had any chance of earning what I require, by my own exertions I should be without a care as far as I am myself concerned. But to be willing without avail to work hard & almost for nothing is now the fate of many hundreds of barristers, & many millions of our labouring classes & we must congratulate ourselves at not being among the latter.[68]

It seems clear that Lyell derived very little income from his legal work and that part of the satisfaction that he derived from writ-

68. C. L., Jr. to his father. 10 April 1827. Kinnordy mss. *L. & L.* I, 169–71.

ing for the *Quarterly* came from his ability to earn part of his expenses in this way.

In this same month George Poulett Scrope published a new work, *On the Geology and Extinct Volcanoes of Central France.* Scrope's book of two years before, *On Volcanoes,* had been savagely attacked by Dr. John Macculloch in the *Westminister Review*[69] and Lyell and his geological friends had thought that this treatment of an original and valuable book had been very unjust. This time Lyell resolved that Scrope should get fair treatment and determined to review it himself in the *Quarterly.* In order to do so he decided to give up his idea of writing an original article on geology for the *Quarterly.* Such an article would require so much work that it ought to be published separately as a book. His model for a short illustrative work was Mrs. Marcet's *Conversations on Chemistry,* but he wanted anything that he published under his name to be serious and authoritative.[70]

In May Lyell was hard at work on his review of Scrope's book and wrote to Murray to ask for several books which he needed to consult for it. He had completed his article on the universities some time before and had sent it to a friend at Cambridge (probably Henslow) and to Dr. Buckland at Oxford. "Professor Buckland's censorship," he told Murray, "has been exercized as freely as by the new French Commission on the *Journal des Debats.* But barring the *unorthodox* parts he is pleased with it, & I shall take care under such correction not to frighten the nerves of the Q.R. readers which are only getting strength on these matters."[71]

A few weeks later he wrote again: "My university Art. is at length finished but the sensitiveness of Ox. & Camb. is amusingly great & the softening down of passages where the naked truth came out too clearly, some more of which a letter from Oxford this morning made necessary, *would* amuse you if you saw my correspondence."[72]

The article on the universities was published in the issue of the *Quarterly* for June 1827.[73] It represents a significant development of Lyell's views since he had written on the plan for a London university. Written with extraordinary skill, it was designed to be-

69. [J. Macculloch, M.D.] "Art. III. Considerations on Volcanoes . . . by G. Poulett Scrope," (1826).

70. C. L., Jr. to his father. 10 April 1827.

71. C. L., Jr. to J. M. 2 May 1827. Murray mss.

72. C. L., Jr. to J. M. 6 June 1827. Murray mss.

73. "Art. VIII. 'State of the Universities,'" (1827). Specific page references given in the text.

guile the orthodox conservative reader by presenting him with a series of propositions which were not only unobjectionable, but even appealed to his prejudices. Lyell then offered, as a further consequence of his propositions, the need for changes and reforms which, if presented by themselves to such a stout old English Tory as Lyell envisioned turning the pages of the *Quarterly*, would cause him to rear back violently.

The "State of the Universities" was ostensibly a review of five books, four dealing with various aspects of university education in Scotland, France, and Germany, and one on the philosophy of education in general, but in fifty-three pages Lyell included little actual critical analysis of the works supposedly under examination. Instead he used them to contrast university education in England with that in Scotland and on the continent of Europe.

The English universities gave a purely classical education while in Scotland and on the Continent the universities were concerned with professional training, leaving instruction in the classics to the schools. Oxford and Cambridge were peculiar in their exclusion of professional training in law and medicine. The whole time that a student spent at either place was taken up with studies preliminary to professional training. Lyell suggested that the omission of professional training might have meant that the courses of study were broader than those available at other European universities but, in fact, they were more restricted. Religious instruction, including compulsory attendance at chapel, was the single additional form of education offered at Oxford and Cambridge, but usually omitted elsewhere. Chapel attendance was considered by many as especially commendable,

> While others [Lyell wrote] are of opinion that as this attendance is compulsory, and sometimes repeated ten times a week, or oftener, and even occasionally inflicted in some colleges as a penalty for academical misdemeanours, its tendency upon too many dispositions is to weaken, rather than to exalt, the sentiment of true devotion.

This may have been one of the places "where the naked truth came out too clearly," because he then added, perhaps with tongue in cheek, a cautionary sentence:

> These last, perhaps, forget that religious observances, but slightly attended to at the moment, often exert a most deep and powerful influence afterwards. [p. 219]

The elimination of professional training in law and medicine in the English universities, however, had very serious consequences. It meant that almost all medical practitioners, all surgeons, and all attorneys-at-law in England lacked any university education whatsoever. If they had attended university before beginning their professional education, their total period of training would have been so long and so expensive that few could afford either the money or the years thus subtracted from their working careers. By this system England was deprived of a group of professional men with university education. At the same time the university students, who would in many instances become leaders in government and in national life, were deprived of an opportunity to become acquainted with those who would enter law and medicine.

> It should be the favourite aim, as it is the noblest end, of a university, to blend together the various elements of which the more enlightened portion of the community is composed—to soften down, by early associations, the prejudices springing out of distinct occupations, unequal worldly advantages, and discordant opinions—to form them into one harmonious whole, and to stamp upon the rising generation a character truly national. [p. 240]

In the existing circumstances the universities exerted precisely an opposite influence. Their tendency was to accentuate social differences. They failed to broaden the minds of their students, but often deepened their prejudices. One of their arguments for excluding professional studies was that they did so in defence of a liberal education, but by so doing, Lyell showed, they became in fact, more illiberal, rather than less. By contrast, the professions of law and medicine had to be carried on at a lower level in England than they ought to be because all but a few of the men who entered them were denied access to a liberal education.

Since, in order to persuade without startling, it was as much his purpose to camouflage as to reveal his true opinion, Lyell's argument tended to be oblique, circuitous, and sometimes delicately ironical. "Hence," he wrote in reference to the pattern of college teaching, "the superiority of the English nation in classical erudition has not been so marked as might have been expected, when it is recollected how great a sacrifice of other studies have been made to the branch of learning" (p. 249). Oxford and Cambridge did not make such an intellectual contribution as would offset their deficiencies as educational institutions. New critical editions of Greek and Latin classical works appeared frequently from the universities of Germany and in Germany classical scholarship was deeply cultivated. In England, however, there was almost no original scholarship in the Classics at this time, even though the Classics formed the principal subject of instruction. The reason for this anomaly, Lyell showed, was the fact that each tutor in a college had to teach the full range of subjects covered in the university examinations. Since the tutors, who were also fellows of the colleges, could not restrict their teaching to particular subjects, they could not develop their knowledge beyond an elementary level.

Lyell then traced the pattern of historical development which had led to the peculiar situation at Oxford and Cambridge. In earlier centuries a number of professorships had been established at both universities. In the sciences there were, for instance, chairs of anatomy, botany, chemistry, and medicine. In the seventeenth century Isaac Newton had held the Lucasian professorship of mathematics at Cambridge. But because the professors had no control over examinations for degrees, there was little incentive for students to attend the professors' lectures and corespondingly little incentive for the professors to deliver lectures. The professorships had therefore become positions of little influence or importance with duties which were only nominal, if performed at all.

When Lyell came to consider how Oxford and Cambridge might be reformed, he suggested that only modest changes were required and these would often constitute simply a return to earlier modes of proceeding which had been allowed to lapse. There was guile in his air of innocence as he suggested that the necessary reforms were really quite slight. He knew that they would strike at the heart of the vested interests of the fellows of colleges and particularly at the vested interest of the clergy in the universities. He suggested that examinations should be held "before competent boards, not only in the departments of science now encouraged, but in all those before enumerated by us under the faculties of theology, law, and medicine" (p. 249).

Lyell mentioned the success of Professor Smyth's[74] lectures on modern history at Cambridge and Mr. Cardwell's[75] lectures

74. William Smyth (1765–1849) was Regius professor of modern history at Cambridge from 1807 until his death.
75. Edward Cardwell (1787–1861) was elected Camden professor of ancient history at Oxford in 1825.

on ancient history at Oxford, and the great success of the lectures on geology given at Oxford by William Buckland and at Cambridge by Adam Sedgwick. He argued that if examinations for degrees might be taken in the subjects on which the professors lectured, and if these examinations were at a level which required specialized knowledge in each subject, then there would be no lack of students to attend the professors' lectures. However, the mere raising of standards in the existing examinations would only make the existing situation worse because it would require students to work ever more closely with their tutors.

> For, in proportion to the confidence felt in the impartiality and unquestionable competency of the examiners—in proportion also to the value generally set upon academical honours, and to the greater probability that these last will lead afterwards to more substantial and lucrative returns, in the shape of fellowships and livings—in the same degree must these inducements impel more irresistably the majority of the youth to restrict their thoughts exclusively to topics embraced within the university examinations. [p. 260]

As the examinations were stiffened the professors offering lectures in fields outside those of the examinations would have fewer and fewer listeners. Whatever might be the intrinsic value of his subject the professor could not hope for money, nor fame, nor "the proud consciousness of usefulness." The development of his subject would be stifled. Lyell concluded:

> The efficacy of the present system, therefore, *in so far as it depends on the stimulus supplied by the public examinations,* is inseparably connected with the imperfect cultivation of all sciences that cannot lead to academical distinction. [p. 260]

If, by contrast, the system of examinations were to be broadened to include the possibility of taking degrees in the different sciences on which the professors lectured, then the tutors in the colleges would be unable to prepare students for examinations unless they themselves first acquired specialized knowledge in particular subjects. Since there could not be enough fellows in any one college to provide tutors expert in a wide variety of fields, the colleges would necessarily lose the complete control of teaching they then exercised. But if such a broader range of subjects were taught in the universities, Lyell predicted that a larger number of students, including those who expected to earn their living in professions, would be attracted to them.

Lyell's analysis of English university education was original and comprehensive in its breadth of view. Many of the reforms he suggested would be implemented during the succeeding half century, although the process of reform has probably not even yet gone as far as Lyell wished and hoped for. Oxford and Cambridge may still have some distance to go before they will serve perfectly "to blend together the various elements of which the more enlightened portion of the community is composed."

In March 1827, shortly after he returned from the circuit at Dorchester and about the time he was reading Lamarck's *Philosophie Zoologique*, Lyell formed the idea of writing a book on geology. His success with his first articles in the *Quarterly Review* had shown him both that he could write and that he could earn money by writing. At the same time he knew the almost complete lack of books in English to present the results of recent geological work to the public. He had at first thought of writing a "Conversations on Geology" to be the counterpart of Mrs. Marcet's very successful *Conversations on Chemistry*,[76] but soon decided that any book he wrote must be at a level which serious geologists could respect. In March 1827 Lyell seems to have contemplated a series of geological essays on the correspondence between ancient and modern causes. In his notebook he sketched possible chapter headings:

Ch. 1. Modern causes same as ancient
2. Modern causes described as far as seen
3. Ancient described—Tertiary
4. Explained by modern & if not explicable by *seen* effects —by supposable unseen.
5. Ancient—secondary—Modern explanatory [causes] & possible.[77]

He did not proceed further with this plan then because he was still at work on his article on the universities, but he began to note books to read and the results of modern causes to observe.

76. [Marcet, Mrs. J. H. (1769–1858)] *Conversations on Chemistry* . . . (1806). The first edition of this work was published anonymously but later editions bore Mrs. Marcet's name. Its great success is indicated by the fact that in 1824 the ninth edition appeared.
77. Ms. Notebook 3, p. 121. Kinnordy mss.

Among the modern causes in which he was most interested were volcanoes and earthquakes because he suspected that they were involved in the elevation of the land. He had already made a note to himself to read von Hoff because Alexander von Humboldt had recommended it as the best book on volcanoes and earthquakes.[78] He made notes on the habits of the modern caddis fly larva from Kirby and Spence, *Introduction to Entomology*, probably to enable him to understand better the indusiae of ancient freshwater limestones.[79]

Lyell's intention to write a book on geology made him reflect continually upon the science and during leisure moments he jotted down some of his reflections. He had begun to doubt the reality of the difference, so readily assumed by geologists, between conditions in earlier geological epochs and those of the modern world. He noted:

Mod. Causes why unseen

As not being inhabitants of tropics we do not see corallines & madrepores & therefore there appears to us a greater difference between old & new world than there is.[80]

In June, when he had completed the article on the universities, Lyell broached the subject of a geological book to John Murray:

An intimate friend of Phillips[81] (George Good) told me what the sale of Conybeare's Introd.ⁿ to Geology has been, viz. above 3,000 copies & going on well. Considering how expensive an octavo vol. it is & how far beyond the generality of the unscientific, I am quite vexed that I did not set to work 2 yrs. ago & shall lose no time now.

Writing Geol. Arts. for the Q.R., at least reviews like the present,[82] not original Arts. like the last, helps to prepare me for

78. Ibid., p. 119. The work which Humboldt referred to must have been the first volume of K. E. A. von Hoff, *Geschichte der durch Ueberlieferung nachgewiesen natürlichen veränderungen der erdoberfläche* (1822–24).

79. Ibid., pp. 126–29. W. Kirby and W. Spence, *An introduction to entomology* . . . 4th ed., vol. 1, p. 468.

80. Ms. Notebook 4, p. 68. Kinnordy mss.

81. William Phillips F.R.S. (1775–1828), mineralogist and geologist carried on his father's business as printer and bookseller. In 1818 he wrote and published the first edition of the *Outlines of the Geology of England and Wales* which in 1822 was revised and enlarged by W.D. Conybeare. We have not been able to identify George Good further.

82. Lyell is referring to his review of Scrope's *Geology of Central France* on which he was then at work.

the work without exhausting my matter. I have ascertained that the only 4 or 5 English Geologists who are sufficiently up to the present state of the subject to anticipate me, are prevented from doing so by the necessity they are under of keeping their original information & ideas for their *lectures*.[83]

About this time (June 1827) Lyell began to visit the house of Dr. William Somerville, who had traveled extensively as a military surgeon in South Africa and had held posts in the Mediterranean and in Canada. In 1812 he had married Mrs. Mary Greig, then a widow, who had been born Mary Fairfax, and was Somerville's cousin. Mary Somerville was a beautiful and brilliant woman with a remarkable talent for mathematics (Fig. 25). Like Somerville, a native of Edinburgh, she had been helped as a girl in her mathematical studies by Professor John Playfair. Apart from his geological contributions, Playfair had also made an important effort to introduce the analytical methods and notation of the continental mathematicians such as Leibnitz, the Bernouillis, and Euler into Britain where the archaic synthetic methods of Newton were still taught. In 1816, having been appointed one of the inspectors of the army medical board in England, Dr. Somerville had moved to London. There Mary Somerville made her house a gathering place for scientists. She must have been at least slightly acquainted with the Lyell family for many years because her uncle William Charters was a friend of the Lyells of Kinnordy.[84] However, Lyell was now to become a frequent visitor at their house. He described to Marianne one visit:

> When last at the Somerville's Mrs. S. who is a delightful person promised to put by for you some recent Mediterranean shells when she next arranges her collection & made me promise to make you acquainted if [or] when you come to town. I am to go there next week to meet Prof.ʳ Amici of Modena & his lady, very agreeable Italians. We are to see some extraordinary botanical sights with Amici's microscope which magnifies a grain of sand to 27,000 times its magnitude!![85]

Lyell had already seen a "piece of the *dust* or feather from the wing of *Noctua sponsa*" magnified under Amici's microscope to

83. C. L., Jr. to J. M. 6 June 1827. Murray mss.
84. M. Somerville, *Personal Recollections . . .* (1873) pp. 43–44.
85. C. L., Jr. to his sister Marianne. 27 June 1827. Kinnordy mss.

reveal its elaborate and beautiful markings. "Every moth & but-
terfly," Lyell marvelled in the same letter, "has a particular form
of feather, but the number of fingers varies in the same." Amici
was also able to give Lyell new information about species of *Chara*.
He had used his microscope to study the fructification of *Chara* in
Italian lakes and had discovered seven new species.[86] One of them,
Chara ulvoides, occurring in the lake of Mantua, was very large,
almost equal in size to some of the fossil species and with a fruiting
body of similar shape. Lyell considered these observations important enough to mention them in a footnote to his review of Scrope.
They suggested that part of the apparent difference between fossil
and living species of *Chara* was simply the result of the incom-
pleteness of knowledge of the living species.

During June Lyell was writing his review of Scrope's *Geology
of Central France;* he completed it in July although he was out of
town a good deal that month on circuit. He attended the sessions
at Warminster in Somersetshire and at the end of this session he
seems to have become particularly discouraged with the prospects
for making a living as a barrister. In his notebook he wrote a brief
entry:

> Warminster Sess.ˢ 1827 July
> 13 barristers of whom no one makes £30. 8 only 5£ each or
> less.
> Expense £8 or more each?[87]

As a young barrister he must have been one of those who earned
£5 or less, so that he was still not even meeting his expenses while
on circuit. In these circumstances the idea of making money by
the far more congenial work of writing on geology must have
seemed ever more attractive. He continued to record his stray
geological thoughts and queries and while at Warminster entered
in his notes:

> Geology, objects of
> It is not cosmogony any more than is History of a nation an
> attempt to account for the origin of mankind.[88]

At the end of the court session Lyell went to Swanage on the
Dorsetshire coast. There he visited Durdlestone Point where he

---

86. G. B. Amici, "Descrizione di alcune specie nuove di Chara . . ." (1833).
87. Ms. Notebook 4, p. 133. Kinnordy mss.
88. Ibid., p. 138.

observed a white foliated marl "soft as that in our Angus lakes" which seemed to him very like some of the Tertiary marls of the Paris basin. He asked himself, "Can calcareous infiltration be cause of induration in some & not in *all* the beds of this series?"[89] He was continually thinking about the processes of geological change, their possible rates, and their effects over long periods of time.

While traveling during July he also corrected proofs of his review of Scrope and, even though the arguments in it ran directly counter to Buckland's opinions, had Dr. Buckland read it. Buckland must have been nothing if not magnanimous, because not only did he read it twice but, Lyell told Murray, "He has suggested a hit at the Penn school & the authors of the 'Scriptural Geology' last which I was happy to add, though it extended the Art. beyond 40 pages."[90] Early in August Lyell returned to London from the country and on 8 August left London by steamboat for Edinburgh taking the completed article with him to give to Lockhart then at Edinburgh. In the meantime Lyell had already heard some reaction to his article on the universities. He conveyed the news to Murray:

Altho' Campbell Ed.ʳ of the Brit. Critic says we have gone too far in the Univ.ʸ Art. & fears (*hopes* he shᵈ have said) that it will injure the Q.R. in the opinion of its old supporters, yet some news I have just learnt from Prof.ʳ Henslow (of Botany) Cambridge, convinces me that the bounds of prudence were not overstepped. He said "I have been in Paris so have not seen your Art. but the Prof.ʳ of Chemistry writes to me from Cambridge 'that a requisition is signing for the medical students to be required hereafter to attend the lectures on Chemistry & Botany —I suppose if it succeeds we may thank the Quarterly.' " Now the last drop makes the cup overflow, & if the seed vegetates so soon, the soil must have been prepared.[91]

Lyell did not return from Scotland until November. While he was away his review of Scrope was published in the October issue of the *Quarterly*.[92]

The district of Auvergne was then unfamiliar to Englishmen.

89. Ms. Notebook 5, p. 48. Kinnordy mss.

90. C. L., Jr. to J. M. 7 Aug. 1827. Murray mss.

91. Ibid.

92. "Art. IV. Memoir on the Geology of Central France . . . By G. P. Scrope . . . 1827." (1827).

The fact that it was an old volcanic region had been known since the travels of Jean-Étienne Guettard (1715–86) there in 1751.[93] In 1763 Nicholas Desmarest (1725–1815) had shown the connection of sheets of basalt with the extinct craters of the region so as to prove that basalt had originated as a solidified lava, and his observations had been published in 1774.[94] He had also shown that the former lava flows of Auvergne were of different ages and that there had been at least three successive periods of volcanic activity in the Auvergne separated by long periods of quiescence. The relative age of the various volcanic rocks was indicated by the degree to which they had been eroded away by running water. The youngest and most recent volcanoes still retained their conical form, with craters surrounded by scoriae much like a still active volcano. From these cones unbroken sheets of extrusive rock extended down into the present valleys. As Desmarest followed down the river valleys, however, he found that the rivers had cut through still older sheets of lava which had flowed from cones long since disappeared. The oldest eruptions were marked by outliers of basalt capping isolated hills. In 1778 a full and detailed description of these extinct volcanoes of the Vivarais and Velay regions, illustrated by numerous large copper plate engravings, was published by Faujas de Saint-Fond.[95]

The volcanic origin of basalt, discovered by Desmarest, had been denied by Werner, who asserted that basalt had been formed as a chemical precipitate from water.

The result of this dispute was a prolonged controversy over the origin of basalt; the two schools of thought came to be known as the Vulcanists on the one hand and the Neptunists on the other. Students who had studied with Werner at Freiburg invariably adopted his view of the origin of basalt as a chemical precipitate from water. However, by their visits to Auvergne, both Jean Francois D'Aubuisson and Leopold von Buch, two of Werner's pupils, were converted to belief in its volcanic origin. D'Aubuisson, in 1804, published a reversal of his former views.[96] Similarly, Leopold

---

93. See J. E. Guettard, "Mémoire sur quelques montagnes de la France qui ont été des volcans" (1752) p. 27. For a discussion of the early history of the study of the volcanic region of Auvergne see G. de Beer, "The Volcanoes of Auvergne" (1962).

94. N. Desmarest, "Mémoire sur l'origine et la nature du basalte" (1771).

95. B. Faujas de Saint-Fond, *Recherches sur les volcans éteints du Vivarais et du Velay* . . . (1778).

96. J. F. D'Aubuisson, "Extrait d'un mémoire sur les volcans et las basaltes de l'Auvergne" (1804).

von Buch (1774–1853), who had spent three years studying with Werner at Freiburg, visited the volcanic region of central France in the spring of 1802 and, once there, changed his view of the origin of basalt very quickly. His observations on Auvergne were published in the second volume of his *Geognostic Observations* in 1809.[97] The volcanic region of Auvergne was also described by one of its native residents, Count Reynaud de Montlosier (1755–1838).[98]

When Scrope first visited the Auvergne in 1821 he went to it as a region that was already classic and had been described with apparent completeness. Yet he found that there was still much to be said about both the geologic history of the region and its significance for the understanding of volcanic phenomena in general.

George Julius Poulett Scrope (Fig. 26) was born George Julius Poulett Thomson, but had changed his name in 1821 on his marriage to Emma Phipps Scrope, heiress of William Scrope of Castle Combe, Wiltshire. He had first observed volcanic activity when he had spent the winter of 1817–18 with his parents at Naples, where Vesuvius was then active. In 1819 he visited Etna and the Lipari Islands including Stromboli. After spending six months in the districts of Auvergne, Velay, and Vivarais in the summer of 1821, in May 1822 he visited the Ponza islands and in October returned to Naples just in time to witness the great eruption of Vesuvius.[99] On his way back to England he visited the volcanic districts of the Rhine, north Germany, and the Eiffel.[100]

When Scrope's first book, *Considerations on Volcanoes,* was attacked in the *Westminster Review,* although the review was anonymous its author was generally known to be Dr. John Macculloch.[101] Macculloch tended to be harsh in his attitude toward other geologists, but Scrope's book was especially vulnerable. He had tried to illustrate a relationship between the sites of volcanic activity and the lines of elevation of mountain chains over the entire surface of the earth. The startling scope of his generalizations tended to attract criticism. In the same year Dr. Charles

97. L. von Buch, *Geognostische beobachtungen auf reisen durch Deutschland und Italien* (1802–09); vol. II "Mineralogische Briefe aus Auvergne an Herrn Geh. Ober-Bergrath Karsten."

98. F. D. R. de Montlosier, *Essai sur la théorie des volcans d'Auvergne* (1802).

99. G. P. Scrope, "Notice on the Geology of the Ponza Isles" (1824) p. 197.

100. G. P. Scrope, *Considerations on Volcanoes* ... (1825) p. vii.

101. [J. Macculloch], "Art. III. Considerations on Volcanoes ... By G. Poulett Scrope, Esq." (1826).

Daubeny published *A Description of Active and Extinct Volcanoes,* which appeared shortly after Scrope's work.[102] In his "Introductory Remarks" Dr. Daubeny mentioned that prior to the publication of his own work the volcanoes of Auvergne were known to English readers chiefly through Montlosier's *Essai* and the second volume of von Buch's *Geognostische Beobachtungen* of 1809. He mentioned neither Desmarest nor D'Aubuisson, an omission which indicates that their work was as yet little known in England.[103] This may have been partly the fault of von Buch who failed to mention the earlier memoirs of Desmarest. Daubeny did explain that he was writing of what was known of Auvergne when he was a student at Edinburgh in the winter of 1816–17. He himself visited Auvergne in 1819 and published a short account of his observations in 1820. In that year Dr. Buckland visited the districts of Vicentin and Auvergne, and in 1823 Robert Bakewell gave a brief description of Auvergne in his *Travels in the Tarentaise.*[104]

Dr. Daubeny distinguished the volcanoes of Auvergne into two classes, "the one formed *before,* the latter *since* the vallies were excavated."[105] Because he adopted Buckland's view that valleys had been excavated by the waters of a great flood, he termed the two groups of volcanoes "ante-diluvial" and "post-diluvial" respectively. He described how the currents of lava from the most recent volcanoes had flowed down into the valleys and blocked up or altered the direction of their water courses in various ways.[106] Daubeny also drew attention to the discovery in 1824 that the limestone strata, which were distributed among the volcanic rocks and formed the floor of the plain of Limagne, were freshwater formations containing bones of extinct mammals and similar in age to those of the Paris basin.[107] Desmarest had thought that these strata were marine and pointed to an invasion of the sea.

Charles Daubeny's account of the volcanic district of central France in 1825 is, however, limited to a brief essay and is unaccompanied by maps or illustrations. Therefore the publication

102. C. Daubeny. *A description of active and extinct volcanoes . . .* (1825).

103. Ibid., pp. 4–5. In his bibliography, pp. 453–454, Daubeny lists the memoirs of Guettard of 1752 and 1759 and Desmarest's 1771 memoir, but not his later and more important writings.

104. R. Bakewell, *Travels . . .* (1823), vol. II, pp. 293–385.

105. Daubeny, *Active and Extinct Volcanoes,* p. 9.

106. Ibid., pp. 11–12.

107. Ibid., p. 34. Cf. L. Laizer, "Note sur l'existence d'ossemens fossiles dans le tuf volcanique ou peperino d'Auvergne" (1828).

Sections in the Wealden Beds, in Compton Bay, at Barnes High, and at Cowleaze Chine.

Scales : Horizontal, 8 in.=1 mile ; Vertical, twice the horizontal.

a   SECTION IN COMPTON BAY

b   SECTION AT BARNES HIGH

c   SECTION AT COWLEAZE CHINE

~~ Alluvium.   ≋ Gravel.   *S.B.* Sandstone of Barnes High.   *h.* Hypsilophodon Bed.   *l.* Principal lignite and bone beds.

. 18. A geological section of Compton Bay. From H. J. Osborne White, *A Short Account of the Geology of Isle of Wight*. Memoirs of the Geological Survey [Gt. Britain] London: H. M. Stationery Office, 1921, p. 12.

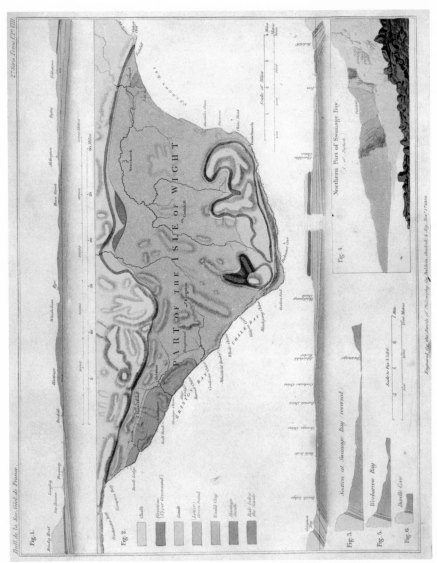

Fig. 19. W. H. Fitton's geological map of the Isle of Wight, 1824.

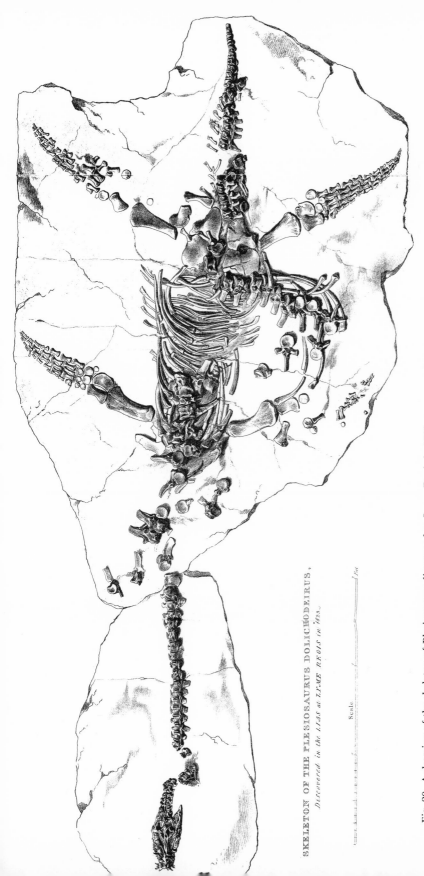

SKELETON OF THE PLESIOSAURUS DOLICHODEIRUS,

Discovered in the LIAS at LYME REGIS in 1823.

Scale

Fig. 20. A drawing of the skeleton of Plesiosaurus discovered at Lyme Regis in 1823.

SECTION OF PART OF FORFARSHIRE FROM N. TO S. THROUGH BAKIE LOCH.

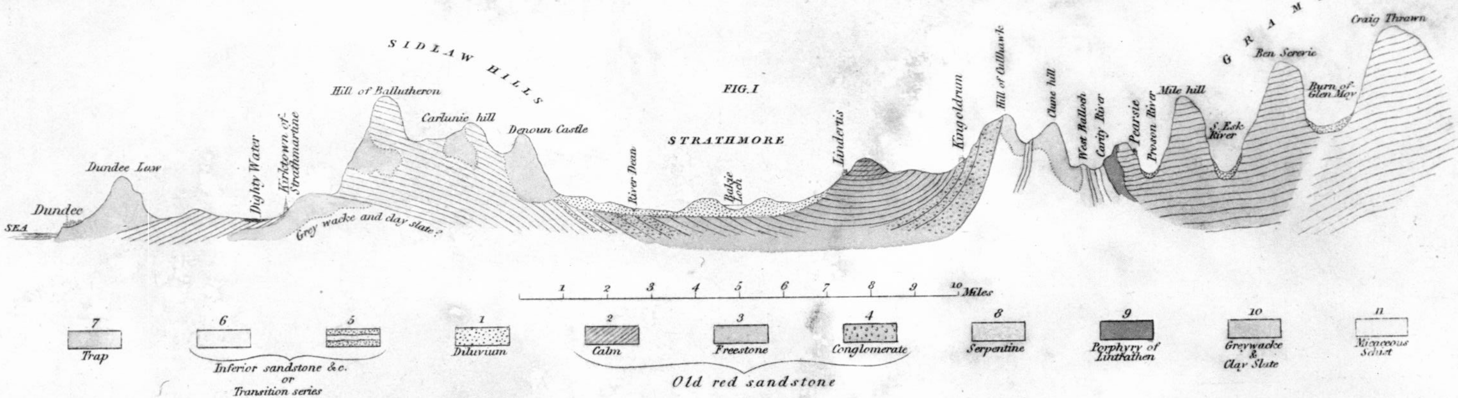

FIG. I

FIG. II

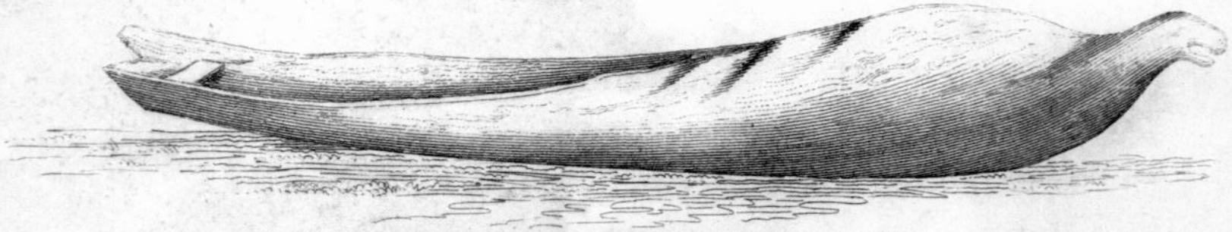

CANOE FOUND IN THE PEAT OF THE LOCH OF KINNORDY

FIG. III

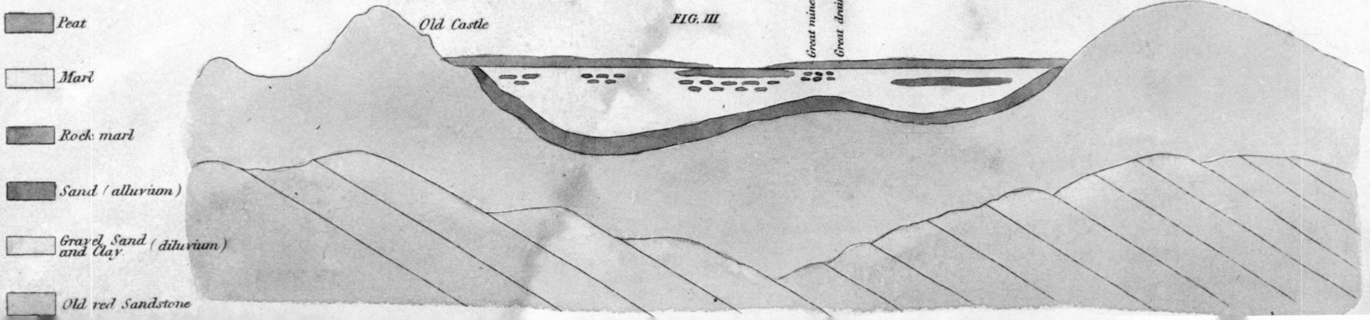

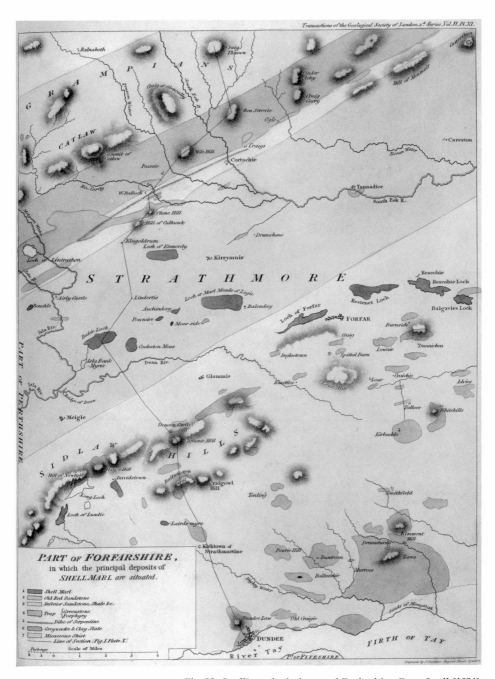

PART OF FORFARSHIRE,
in which the principal deposits of
SHELL MARL are situated.

1 Shell Marl
2 Old Red Sandstone
3 Inferior Sandstone, Shale &c.
4 Trap { Greenstone
         Porphyry
5 Dike of Serpentine
6 Greywacke & Clay Slate
7 Micaceous Shist
   Line of Section (Fig.1.Plate X)

Furlongs   Scale of Miles

Fig. 22. Lyell's geological map of Forfarshire. From Lyell [1824].

Fig. 23. Roderick Murchison (1792–1871). Courtesy of the National Portrait Gallery, London.

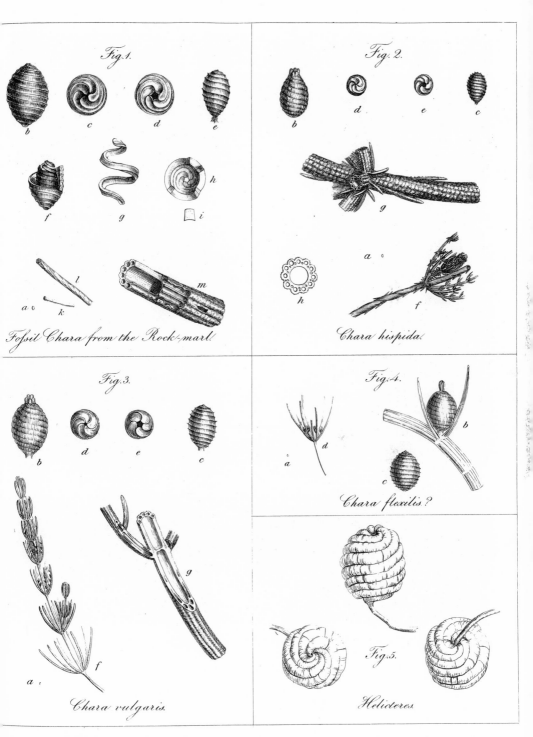

Fig. 24. Lyell's specimens of (1) Fossil *Chara* from the rock marl (2) living *Chara hispida*. From Lyell [1824].

Fig. 25. Mary Somerville (1780–1872). By Thomas Phillips R.A. Courtesy of National Galleries of Scotland, Edinburgh.

Fig. 26. George Poulett Scrope (1797–1876) Lithograph of a portrait by E. U. Eddis. Courtesy of the National Portrait Gallery, London.

Fig. 27. A river valley re-excavated through a basaltic lava current, France. (Drawing by Scrope, 1827)

Robert Roland

PLATE. III.

Volcanic cone called La Coupe d'Ayzae near Entraigues (Ardêche)

Fig. 28. A valley, filled by a current of basaltic lava, being re-excavated by the stream flowing in it. (Drawing by Scrope, 1827)

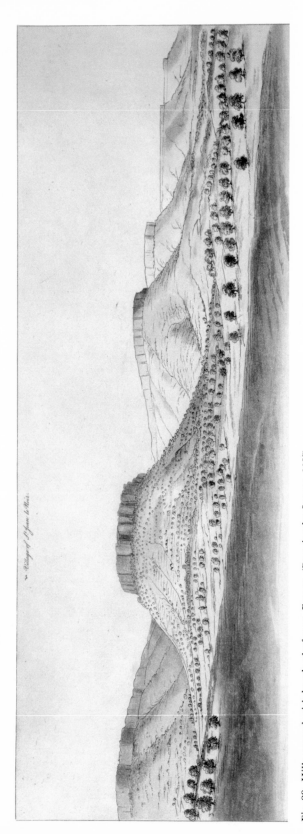

Fig. 29. Hills capped with basalt platforms, France. (Drawing by Scrope, 1827)

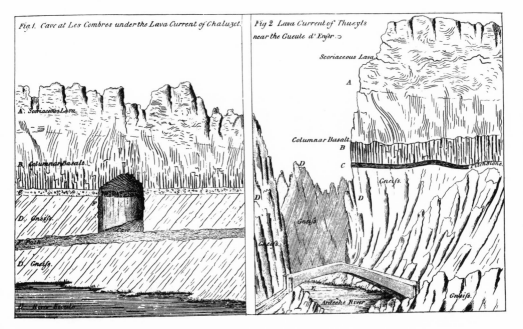

Fig. 30. The tunnel of a Roman lead mine under basalt in the bank of the Sioule river, near Pont Gibaud. From Lyell and Murchison, "Excavation of Valleys." [1829]

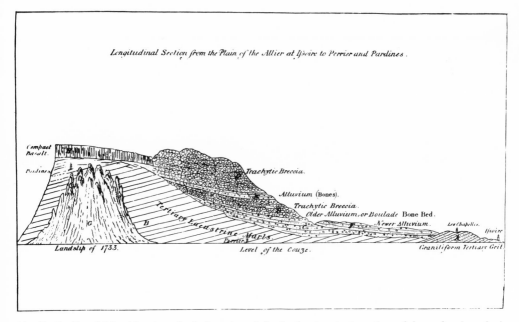

Fig. 31. Lyell and Murchison's geological section of the freshwater strata and overlying volcanic rocks in the valley of the Couze d'Issoire river, Auvergne.

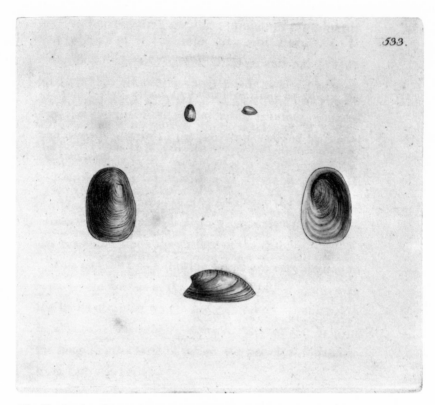

Fig. 32. *Ancylus elegans*, drawn by James Sowerby from specimens collected by Lyell. From Sowerby, *Mineral Conchology*, vol. VI, pl. 533.

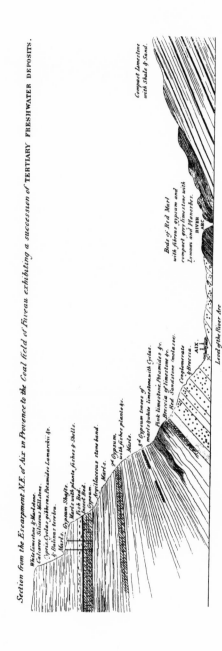

Fig. 33. Lyell and Murchison's geological section of freshwater strata at Aix-en-Provence.

Fig. 34. Ischia from the west (Illustration to G. P. Scrope, "Volcanic district of Naples").

of Scrope's memoir in 1827 had the effect of throwing a flood of light on a district about which English geologists had heard vaguely by rumour and report for a long time, but of which they had little detailed or accurate information. This effect was further reinforced by Lyell's review of the book in the *Quarterly*.

Lyell looked at the Auvergne, as described by Scrope, from the standpoint of English geology and was immediately struck by the contrast between the Auvergne and any region of similar age in England. The Auvergne presented a long history, stretching back to the beginning of the Tertiary period, of geological events which had involved the raising up of a succession of volcanic mountains and the subsequent wearing away of all but the most recent ones. But during all this time the Auvergne had remained a country of volcanic mountains and valleys, sometimes bordered by freshwater lakes, so that its geography during different periods of the past could be reconstructed in imagination. "Here, in a word, there has been an entire revolution in the species of plants and animals of a region which has nevertheless preserved its identity from first to last, and survived these extraordinary vicissitudes in organic life." England presented a far different set of circumstances:

> But there are strata in the Isle of Wight, and in Hampshire, still more recent, containing fresh-water animals and plants now unknown in these latitudes, and such as correspond, for the most part, with those in the interior of France. . . . Yet, although these strata were originally accumulated in the estuary of a river, or in an inland lake, and are among the most modern of the deposits termed tertiary, it is impossible to trace the least connexion between that distribution of land and sea which must have obtained when they were formed, and the present surface of the country. [p. 441][108]

The Auvergne therefore was important for geology because of the continuity of its history with the geological past. Then too the "alterations effected in the forms of the valleys and mountains, by rivers and floods, earthquakes and volcanoes, during so long a succession of ages, are the more instructive, because the various stages of their gradual operation can, in many instances, be pointed out" (p. 442).

The structure of Auvergne, Lyell showed, was essentially that of

108. "Art. IV. Memoire on the Geology of Central France . . . By G. P. Scrope . . . 1827." Specific page references are given in the text.

a granite plateau on which volcanic mountains of different ages rested, and which contained several depressions occupied by considerable thicknesses of freshwater strata. The secondary strata of conglomerate and sandstone, which surrounded the volcanic region, contained granite pebbles and sand but no trace of volcanic rocks. Therefore the volcanic activity of the Auvergne dated from the beginning of the Tertiary period, after the secondary strata had been laid down.

In the granite plateau are two broad and deep valleys running north and south—those of the Loire and Allier rivers. They are floored by horizontal beds of limestone and marl of freshwater origin. Like the sandstone and conglomerate which surround the borders of the Auvergne, they are older than the oldest volcanic eruptions, although the uppermost limestone strata were deposited after the oldest volcanoes became active. The plain of the Limagne, through which the Allier flows, showed signs of having been considerably eroded so that both Scrope and Ramond had concluded that it used to stand at a higher level (p. 445). Near the borders of the basin of the Allier the freshwater strata had been disturbed from their horizontal position and were found inclined or even almost vertical. The total thickness of these freshwater strata was more than nine hundred feet and a large part of it, Scrope showed, had been greatly elevated, some as much as fifteen hundred feet. In some places the strata contained fragments of volcanic rocks; in others they had clearly been disturbed and altered by volcanic action.

The freshwater strata in Auvergne, described by Scrope, were of particular interest to Lyell because of his own observations on freshwater deposits in the lakes of Forfarshire and at Hordwell cliff in Hampshire. Lyell noted that the freshwater formations of the Cantal contained gyrogonites or the seed pods of *Chara* just as did those of Britain. The freshwater strata of the Cantal, in contrast to those of the Limagne, had been buried under layers of volcanic rock and were revealed only where a river valley had cut through them. In age they corresponded with the upper freshwater formation of the Paris basin.

In the upper Loire valley Scrope described still other freshwater strata, where the borders of the lakes in which they had been deposited could still be traced even though these strata were now covered over with thick layers of volcanic rocks (Figs. 27, 28). These deposits were especially interesting because they showed three successive series of strata which appeared to correspond to the three principal series of freshwater strata in the Paris basin.

In discussing the actual volcanoes, described by Scrope, Lyell mentioned the perfect cones and craters of the Puys near Clermont with their well-marked lava streams which had, in several instances, flowed into the river valleys and caused the rivers to alter their courses. Scrope showed that these volcanoes varied greatly in age and that they could by no means be divided simply into two classes, ancient and modern.

Scrope demonstrated the enormous amount of denudation which had occurred in the Auvergne where what had once been continuous sheets of basalt had been eroded away to leave only fragments capping isolated hills (Fig. 29). A great volcano like that of Mont Dore had been dissected by broad and deep valleys on either side so that little was left of its original form. River valleys had been worn through the horizontal freshwater strata in Velay, had been filled with lava by a volcanic eruption, and the lava had again been cut through and removed by the force of running water. All of this was clear and, as Lyell showed, *critical* evidence to prove that river valleys in general were excavated by the rivers flowing in them (p. 479).

Lyell concluded his summary of Scrope's book with an eloquent appeal that all disputable questions which it might raise should be considered on the basis of geological evidence without recourse to religious writings of doubtful relevance.

The *Geology of Central France* undoubtedly exerted a powerful effect on Lyell's imagination. In a long rhetorical passage of his review he asked how modern geologists might think if they were able "to view the Tertiary lakes of Central France in all their original beauty and repose" (p. 472). He thought that every aspect of the natural world as it existed in Tertiary times would seem as calm and orderly, as little subject to change, as the modern world. Yet volcanic eruptions, earthquakes, and the slow deposition of sediments in lakes had been going on in Tertiary times just as they were going on in the modern world. The geology of Auvergne demonstrated the great effects which these changes, either intermittent or imperceptibly slow, could exert when continued over a very long period of time.

When Lyell left London on 8 August he stopped at Edinburgh to see Lockhart and probably reached Kinnordy by the eleventh or twelfth. He remained there nearly three months. Among the

books he had with him was Mantell's copy of Lamarck's *Philosophie Zoologique* and Lyell seems to have continued to read and
reflect on it. In his notes he records finding a very large mush-
room (*Agaricus campestris*) near the approach gate at Kinnordy
on 14 August and the occurrence of a remarkable aurora borealis
about 11 o'clock at night on 27 August. He made geological observations in Glen Prosen and further notes on the marl and
freshwater shells of Kinnordy loch. On 14 September he reflected
in his notebook:

Geol[ogical] Prej.[udices]

Any period in past history may be eventful or flat, warlike
or peaceful according as we extend the events over a wider or
less wide space, so in older rocks if we shorten time, we render
them marvellous.[109]

Somewhat later he observed:

Nature is not repose, but war. It is not rest, but change. It is
not preservation, but successive production & annihilation.[110]

And a little further on:

Uniformity of ancient strata must be due to the uniformity
of chemical and galvanic action prevailing over the local influence of organic life, of climate, of the separation of sea and land,
of the varying depth of the sea, of fresh water & salt, of vegetable & animal.[111]

In a series of memoranda to himself he observed:

Mem. Interior of the earth a great laboratory for the surface.
Mem. We sh.[d] speculate on what modern causes w.[d] produce.
Reason of our timidity in anticipating. Geol.[l] discov.[s] have
come upon us unexpectedly. Extinct animals are alone
rescued from an ancient system.[112]

He noted books to read and questions to ask his friends. These
three months seem to have been a quiet period of reading and reflection interspersed with geological rambles over the hills of Angus. He probably took part in the grouse shooting, parties, and
visits to neighbors, which were part of country life in Scotland.

109. Ms. notebook 6, p. 11. Kinnordy mss.
110. Ibid., p. 78.
111. Ibid., p. 89.
112. Ibid., 127.

During his long stay at Kinnordy Lyell had continued to mull over Lamarck's theory. He marked passages in Mantell's copy of the *Philosophie zoologique* with a pencil. The whole question of the relation of fossil forms to the living ones was central to geology if the natural order of past geological epochs was to be considered as having existed in a continuity through time with the present order. Amici had found large living species of *Chara* in the lake of Mantua similar to those large fossil *Chara* in the Tertiary strata of the Paris basin. Perhaps the changes in living forms since the early Tertiary period were much less than had been thought. Even if species could be modified, one into another, there still remained at some point in the history of the earth the question of how new living forms had arisen. Before he went to Scotland Lyell had written in his notebook on 3 August 1827:

Lamarck's theory

It is merely to prop the world on an elephant & the elephant on a tortoise to say that the higher animals came from the simpler, formed by gradual development. For it is as great an act of power to create an infant which shall in 20 years acquire the full powers of manhood as to create a full grown man in the perfection of his faculties. What is it but a vain attempt to push back into more remote obscurity that wh. we cannot account for? . . . However great the lapse of time we suppose to have passed away since first the simplest formed animals were created, that period is to eternity but a moment—therefore, unless we suppose that the first monad was self-created & with the power of creating us, we must suppose that we ourselves are self-created. We might as well suppose an infant to come into the world either by its own effort or by chance as an animalcule that was in process of time to develop itself into an infant & man.[113]

Lyell seems to have been both fascinated by Lamarck's theory and disturbed by the complex questions which it raised. It was, as it were, a specter which he put out of his mind whenever he could. When he returned to London he learned from his friend William Broderip that Broderip had found the fossil mammalian jawbone from Stonesfield which had been lost among Broderip's own belongings since 1814. Lyell wrote to his father:

113. Ms. Notebook 5, pp. 51–52. Kinnordy mss.

> The lost jaw of the Didelphis of the Stonesfield slate is found again!—a fine thing. This one seems a true opossum & in a beautiful state. It is another species. So much for the antiquity of terrestrial mammalia, & for the theories of a gradual progress to perfection! There was everything but Man even so far back as the Oolite.[114]

His relief seems almost palpable. The apparent continuity in mammalian life since the oolitic epoch early in the secondary period, was further, and to Lyell conclusive, evidence that the order of living nature as well as of the physical world had existed unchanged throughout geological time.

Lyell had matured greatly during the preceding three years. Although still financially dependent on his father, he had learned that he could write and could earn money by writing. He could hope to gain independence by authorship. Furthermore, he was becoming aware that he possessed a unique view of geology and of the history of the natural world to offer the public.

114. C. L., Jr. to his father. 14 Nov. 1827. Kinnordy mss.

CHAPTER 7

Travels through France, 1828

As a result of his review of Scrope's book, Lyell became aware of a multitude of questions which might be asked, and points which might be looked for, that he had never before noticed. He queried Mantell, "Are fissures & faults common in the Sussex beds, in chalk etc.? Are they more numerous where inclination greatest? Does one occur upon an average in every pit?"[1] While his interest in science was thus growing stronger he was, as a result of his now being a member of the Royal Society, tempted by the suggestion that he might serve as one of its secretaries for a year. He had the good sense to know that his time would be better spent in the pursuit of his own work for he now had a driving ambition to distinguish himself in science.[2] On 28 November 1827 he wrote to Gideon Mantell:

> I have often wished to be able to send you some good specimens from our Scotch recent freshwater formations but have never till this last year been able to procure any soft or rock marl with seed vessels of charae & stems which form the most perfect analogy to the Isle of Wight beds. I have now a few specimens but hope to add still more next spring if not before. In a small piece of the freshwater limestone you will see my modern gyrogonites & I believe the stem consisting of a tube surrounded by small tubes beautifully exemplified.
>
> I have put in several specimens of the rock. . . In the soft argillaceous marl you will find (if in luck) the elytra of coleopterous insects besides gyrogonites, a circumstance of the more interest because they occur low down in these recent deposits & afford an analogy to the 1st & 2^d. freshwater formation of M. de Serres in S. of France,[3] as also in the lignite beds of the Suffolk coast.

Lyell then drew for Mantell a section to show the successive layers

1. C. L., Jr. to G. A. M. 12 Nov. 1827. Mantell mss.
2. C. L., Jr. to his father. 14 Nov. 1827. Kinnordy mss.
3. M. de Serres, "Observations sur des terrains d'eau douce . . ." (1824).

of peat, shell marl, sand marl, and clay in the bottom of the drained loch of Kinnordy. He expressed the special meaning of these beds for himself when he asked Mantell, "Is not this a good modern analogy? All the organic remains are living Forfarshire creatures."[4]

In December 1827, Lyell went down to Lewes to pay a visit to Mantell, who had been seriously ill but was now recovered and back at work. Lyell went in the hope of cheering him up and giving him some diversion, because Mantell's wife had also been ill and his children all had whooping cough.[5] He also wanted to talk to him about the new work on geology which he was now planning. Lyell arrived on Friday 15 December, and after looking over all of Mantell's chalk fossils they "sat up very late, conversing on Geological subjects." He stayed over the week-end and left on Monday, "astonished," Mantell wrote, "at the immense additions I had made to my collection since he was last at Lewes."[6] It was probably during this visit that Lyell wrote the first pages of the work which would eventually become the *Principles*.

Lyell had by this time acquired enough experience to be confident of his own ability to write and to understand the mental obstacles to be overcome in writing. He described these to his father, who was then composing a review of Rossetti's *Dante* for the *Quarterly*.

> I have learnt enough of writing now never to put any rough copy in the fire. I am sure that the principal enemy to composition is fastidiousness, which much good reading & little practice in composition is sure to engender, but I am encouraged beyond measure in looking back to the first draughts of my last Article by seeing what miserable trash they are. You must not reckon after sowing a good many seeds that more than one in a page will turn out worth improving or grow up to anything very good at least until one has by practice enriched the mind with a multitude of ideas at command & acquired that courage & decisiveness in our opinions which writing gives in authorship & business in active life.

He mentioned that he had received a number of very favorable comments on his review of Scrope in the *Quarterly* and added:

4. C. L., Jr. to G. A. M. 28 Nov. 1827. Mantell mss.
5. C. L., Jr. to G. A. M. 10 Dec. 1827. Mantell mss. Cf. G. Mantell. *Journal* p. 66.
6. Mantell, *Journal* p. 67.

I find that for several days after such agreeable news I compose with greater rapidity & facility & as I believe the originality of a writer to depend mainly on a fearlessness of critics & the capability in giving pleasure or confidence in the ability to please, I live in hopes that I shall not always be as long in making anything good as I now am.[7]

At Christmas time 1827, Lyell went to his uncle Captain Gilbert Heathcote's at Southampton where his sisters Marianne and Caroline were, and where he was for a few days "in a continued round of dinners & balls."[8] At the beginning of January he returned to London.

On 17 January he wrote to Mantell to describe the fossils collected by John Crawfurd[9] in Burma, which had just arrived at the rooms of the Geological Society in Bedford Street. Crawfurd's party, returning from a diplomatic mission to Ava, had been descending the Irawaddi river in a steamboat when they became stranded by the river's drying up. On the surface of the sandy plain on either side of the river were many silicified fossils sticking up.

Crawfurd employed his servants & bribed the native to collect [Lyell wrote] & they filled 12 chests!! Almost entire jaws of a new species of Mastodon as big as an elephant! different from the 5 species described by Cuvier, smaller teeth of mastodon (Clift says may be young ones of same), silicified ivory tusk— teeth of rhinoceros (Qy. a new one?)—fragment of a bone of hippopotamus; jaws & teeth of an alligator—large scales etc. of Tortoises. Shells apparently freshwater—only one species Sowerby says a Cyrena. Wood, trunks of trees, monocotyledons & perhaps dicotyledons—no botanist has seen them, structure beautifully preserved as are all the teeth etc.

Lyell was struck by the resemblance in general appearance of these fossils to those which Mantell had collected from the Tilgate forest beds of Sussex.

7. C. L., Jr. to his father. 12 Dec. 1827. Kinnordy mss.

8. C. L., Jr. to G. A. M. 29 Dec. 1827. Mantell mss. *L. & L.* I, 173.

9. John Crawfurd (1783–1868) studied medicine at the University of Edinburgh and in 1803 went to India. In 1811 he accompanied Lord Minto on the conquest of Java and in 1823 was appointed governor of Singapore. In 1826 he was sent by Lord Amherst, governor general of India, on a diplomatic mission to the court of Ava in Burma. See J. Crawfurd, *Journal of an Embassy . . . With an appendix . . . by Professor Buckland and Mr. Clift* (1829).

The whole room & yard in Bedford St. looks as if it were filled with magnificent Tilgate fossils. They are of a yellow ferruginous colour. Saurians lying in all directions, here an immense femur, there a long stem like Clathraria Lyellii, here the scale of a large tortoise, there a shell & teeth of alligator etc. etc.[10]

Despite various distractions, including ten days of visiting with his sisters in Hampshire and at Dr. Buckland's house at Oxford, he continued to work on his geological book. At first he had planned a light popular treatment along the lines of Mrs. Marcet's *Conversations in Chemistry* but he soon found that his own intentions were more serious. He wrote to Mantell:

I felt that in a subject where so much is to be reformed & struck out anew & where one obtains new ideas & theories in the progress of one's task, where you have to controvert & to invent an argumentation, work is required & one like the Conversations in Chemistry & others would not do.[11]

He urged Mantell to write a popular book on geology in his place.

At the anniversary meeting of the Geological Society on 15 February the members discussed the new fossils from Ava. Lyell reported to Mantell:

The Evening discussion on the Ava bones was improving. Buckland reconciled all to his diluvian hypothesis, as what facts would he not? But be his theory wide of the mark or not, he is always worth hearing.

They think the remains thus hastily picked up belonged to from 10 to 20 individuals of the genus Mastodon, to begin with a pretty good haul. It was larger & quite different from the largest European Mastodon. The rest of the menagerie is rhinoceros, hippopotamus, ox . . . deer, several Alligators (very large), trionyx—turtle (gigantic), horse? doubtful—shells supposed to be a cyrene & very like a species now living in the estuaries of Indian rivers; nay in the Irawaddi. Buckland gets over the shells by saying that Crawfurd is not clear they were in the same continuous stratum . . .

The Mosaic deluge of course did all this. . . . The bones are never silicified. They are charged with hydrate of iron, not more

10. C. L., Jr. to G. A. M. 17 Jan. 1828. Mantell mss. *L. & L.* I, 176.
11. C. L., Jr. to G. A. M. 5 Feb. 1828. Mantell mss. *L. & L.* I, 177.

so it seems than some diluvial bones possessed by Buckland & Sedgwick. Be it so—then the modern post diluvian causes as you suggest can do everything, at least as far as mineralizing is concerned.[12]

In March 1828, Lyell decided to go with Roderick Murchison to the Auvergne to visit the volcanic country which Scrope had so vividly described. This decision, which, in effect, reversed his decision of two years before to devote himself more fully to law, brought forth a muffled cry of despair from his father. "Charles's life is an enviably happy one," he wrote to Turner, "and as it is a respectable one, I cease to bother either him or myself about pelf & futurity. He talks of exploring extinct volcanoes in Auvergne this summer."[13] Lyell sent to Kinnordy for his barometers and thermometers so as to be prepared to take measurements in Auvergne.

Scrope sent Murchison a letter of detailed advice on where to go and what to see in Auvergne, Cantal, and Ardeche. Murchison had evidently decided already to go on southward to explore either the Pyrenees or the Maritime Alps. Scrope advised:

I am a decided advocate for the latter as nearer to you, less explored and offering a much more agreeable *route de retour* than that across the tiresome *Landes* and the ugly & dull west of France. The Val di Fasso in itself is worth a whole summer's journey and would be all the better for a three month's examination. The Riviere di Genova offers a mine of geological wealth more especially as the road while freshly cut must give valuable sections.[14]

On 20 April Murchison set off for Paris where he planned to spend a fortnight and Lyell hoped to follow him by the first of May.[15] During these last few weeks he was working furiously on a review of Gabriele Rossetti's edition of Dante's *Divine Comedy* with an analytical commentary.[16] Rossetti, one of the group of Italian exiles in London, had formerly been an assistant curator of ancient marbles and bronzes in the Naples museum. He wrote

12. C. L., Jr. to G. A. M. 17 Feb. 1828. Mantell mss.
13. C. L. to D. T. 10 March 1828. Dawson Turner mss.
14. G. P. Scrope to R. Murchison. 30 March 1828. Murchison mss.
15. C. L., Jr. to G. A. M. 21 April 1828. Mantell mss.
16. G. Rossetti, *La Divina Comedia di Dante Alighieri con comento analitico* (1826–27).

poetry and in 1809 had become a Freemason and later a member of the Carbonari. As a result of his part in the constitutionalist revolt of 1820 at Naples, he had to go into hiding. He was rescued from there by that gay and intrepid commander, Admiral Sir Graham Moore, whose flagship, the *Rochfort,* happened to be lying in harbor at Naples, and who admired Rossetti's poetry. Moore took him to Malta and later to London.

On the publication of the first volume of Rossetti's *Comento Analitico,* Mr. Lyell, who had been studying Italian and reading Dante for many years, obtained a copy and almost immediately wrote a warm and friendly letter to him. Rossetti replied on 7 February 1826, and thus began a correspondence and friendship which was to continue until the end of Mr. Lyell's life in 1849.[17]

In his enthusiasm for Rossetti's commentary, which interpreted many passages in the *Divine Comedy* as being political in nature and having an anti-papal significance, Mr. Lyell decided that he would write a review of the work for the *Quarterly.* He soon found that he was not very well prepared for this task and therefore sought help from that experienced reviewer, his son Charles. It probably gave Lyell considerable pleasure to help his father with his own well-tried skill, but he was too proud to let others, except Murchison, know what he was doing. To Mantell he said only, "I am much pressed in completing some literary business which I had promised to assist a friend."[18] To Murchison he wrote on 29 April that he had written between thirty and forty pages "which I trust to providence will satisfy the editor."[19] In fact this article brought him nothing but trouble. At the same time as he submitted the final draft to Lockhart, the editor of the *Quarterly,* he sent a copy of it to his father who forwarded it on to Rossetti. The latter appears to have been outraged at the tone of the article although Lyell felt he had used his best legal skill in Rossetti's defense. From Clermont-Ferrand in the Auvergne Lyell wrote in protest to his father:

> I cannot express my surprise at finding that a review which I wrote so much against my conscience in part & which I felt confident would (from the place where it appeared) raise the author at last above the contempt into which his publication has

17. E. R. Vincent, *Gabriele Rossetti in England* (1936) pp. 14–15.
18. C. L., Jr. to G. A. M. 11 April 1828. Mantell mss.
19. C. L., Jr. to R. I. Murchison. 29 April 1828. Murchison mss. *L. & L.* I, 181–82.

thrown him amongst a large part of the literary world in town, should be deemed so injurious & severe. I assure you that never did counsel more earnestly endeavour to draw from a client all that could be advanced in support of a case & the strongest proofs in reserve were earnestly advanced by R. & submitted to Prandi[20] & appeared to him as to my judgment to make the matter not a bit better & therefore were not stated.

Since Rossetti felt the article to be injurious, Lyell had written to Lockhart to withdraw it. He had as a further reason for withdrawal,

> ... that the instant the Q.R. has made Rossetti worth attacking the Westminster will come down with a logical, the Edinburgh with a witty, & the Foreign Q.R. with a malign (Panizzi) Article against the work & they will annihilate it.

There was a further complication to this tangled situation in that Mr. Lyell seems to have been not only a subscriber to the second volume of the *Comento Analytico,* but to have given a subvention to assist its publication. Lyell thought this action less than wise, but he was nothing if not a loyal son. He added:

> If after cozing with R. & hearing his reserved corps of proofs ... you are convinced of its truth or even its *possibility* I will promise to make myself master of them & if I can bring myself to incline even to it I will tack on to the first part of my rejected Article a panegyrical peroration, but I hope you will go to the bottom of it before you recommend R. to go on, as I think Murray's advice as to Vol. 2 was that of a friend, & you might at least learn from John M. a fair estimate of the probable loss & be quite prepared to bear the whole before you were a party to R.'s doing himself farther injury in a pecuniary point of view.[21]

Lyell was both angry and travel-weary when he wrote this letter. It did not fail to wound his father who on 28 December 1828 complained bitterly to Rossetti of the "ill-natured sneers and sarcasms" of his son "whose contempt of my judgement and superior opinion of his own, put gall into my review, and then, because I would not allow it to be made bitter enough, persuaded Lockhart that the reputation of the *Quarterly* would be ruined if so mild a

20. Fortunato Prandi (?–?).
21. C. L., Jr. to his father. 6 June 1828. Kinnordy mss.

stricture of Rossetti's fancies were to appear in it."[22] Mr. Lyell's reply to Lyell's letter has not survived but it may have been hot enough. In the months that followed Lyell wrote seldom to his father. His letters home were usually addressed to his sisters or his mother. As is characteristic of quarrels between fathers and sons, it was perhaps of deeper significance than the mere point at issue between them. There is a suggestion of jealousy of his son's growing success on Mr. Lyell's part and of Lyell's resentment of his father's somewhat lavish generosity towards Rossetti. During the succeeding years of their friendship Mr. Lyell was to continue in his attitude of admiration of Rossetti's scholarship and to contribute money for the printing of his works.[23] These donations manifested a truly great generosity which was scarcely justified by the prosperity of the Kinnordy estate and contrasts oddly with his exhortations to Lyell to increase the family fortune.

It was on 3 May that Lyell finished writing this troublesome review and the next day left London by coach for Dover taking his clerk, Hall, with him. On the morning of Wednesday the seventh they reached Paris, where Lyell immediately had breakfast with Murchison and "had a grand day seeing people." In the evening he attended a lecture by Constant Prevost on geology and afterwards "cozed till midnight with him here & next morning again with him at breakfast."[24]

At half past six in the morning on Sunday 10 May, Murchison and Lyell left Paris in Murchison's light open carriage with the two men on the box and Mrs. Murchison and her Swiss maid inside. After a carriage breakdown in the streets of Paris and very bad roads from Fontainebleau to Moulins both "the roads & rate of posting improved & at last averaged 9 miles an hour & change of horses almost as quick as in England." Their trip southward proved enjoyable:

> We started every morning 6 o'clock—beautiful weather. I never did in my life so much real geology in as many days. . . . We have generally begun work at 6 o'clock & neither heat nor fatigue have stopped us an hour. Mrs. M. is very diligent, sketching, labelling specimens & making out shells in which last she is an invaluable assistant. She is so much interested in the affair as

22. C. L. to G. Rossetti. 28 Dec. 1828. Angeli mss. As quoted in Vincent, *Rossetti,* p. 55.

23. Vincent, *Rossetti,* pp. 56–66.

24. C. L., Jr. to his father. 9 May 1828. Kinnordy mss. *L. & L.* I, 183.

to be always desirous of keeping out of the way when she would interfere with the work, and as far as I yet see it would be impossible to form a better party.

They had decided to concentrate their work so as to cover thoroughly a limited range of country (Map 7). Lyell was delighted with the scenery:

Auvergne is beautiful—rich wooded plains, picturesque towns & the outline of the volcanic chain unlike any other I ever saw. The range of Mont Dor seen over the volcanic range from 50 miles to N. of this was covered with snow & looked like the Alps but they say it will soon melt.[25]

As an experienced campaigner Murchison did the bargaining at the inns, which saved them both time and money.

In the "valley-plain of the Allier" they made their first acquaintance with the freshwater formations of the Limagne which impressed them by their extent and great thickness. The ancient lake in which these strata had formed corresponded in its boundaries very closely to the present valley. They found deposits of gravel and sand such as had probably been brought down by streams into the old lake. The pebbles in the gravel were of granite and mica-schist but *never of volcanic rocks,* which indicated that the lake had existed before the period of the earliest volcanic eruptions on the plateau above. Later, after a considerable thickness of sandstone and marl had been deposited, volcanic eruptions began, and lava and tuff had been deposited in some places in alternate layers with the freshwater strata. The red sandstone and red marl which lay above the gravel struck Lyell by its resemblance to the much older new red sandstone of England which was in part a marine formation.

The deep valleys cut through the freshwater strata reminded Lyell of valleys in the oolite of the west of England and in general the physical appearance of these Tertiary freshwater formations was strikingly like that of the much older secondary formations of England. Perhaps most impressive were the marl strata which in some places were as much as 700 feet thick. They were usually thinly foliated, a characteristic given to them by "the innumerable thin plates or scales of that small animal called *cypris,* a genus which comprises several species, of which some are recent, and may

25. C. L., Jr. to his father. 16 May 1828. Kinnordy mss. *L. & L.* I, 183–85.

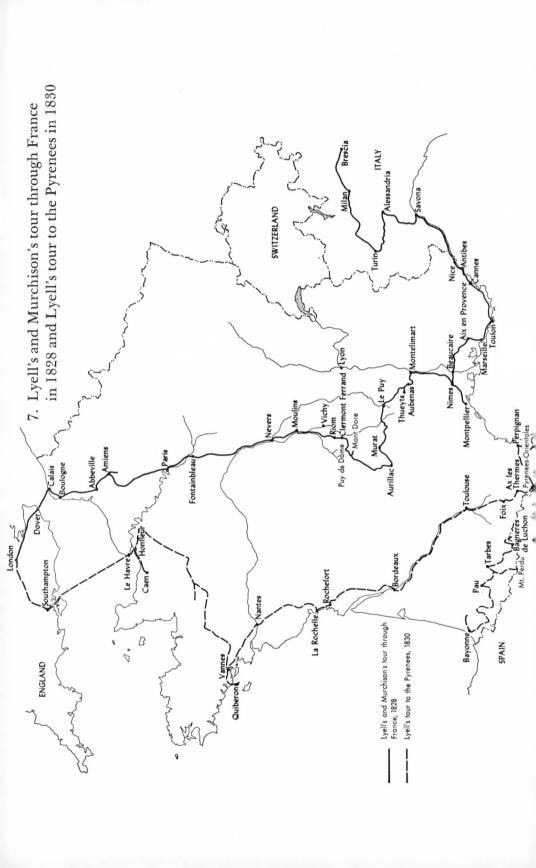

7. Lyell's and Murchison's tour through France in 1828 and Lyell's tour to the Pyrenees in 1830

ENGLAND

London
Dover
Southampton

Calais
Boulogne
Abbeville
Amiens

Paris
Fontainebleau

Le Havre
Honfleur
Caen

Nantes

Vannes
Quiberon

La Rochelle
Rochefort

Bordeaux

Toulouse

Bayonne
Pau
Tarbes
Foix
Ax les Thermes
Bagnères de Luchon
Mt. Perdu
Pyrenees-Orientales
Perpignan

SPAIN

Nevers
Moulins
Vichy
Riom
Clermont Ferrand
Puy de Dôme
Mont Dore
Murat
Aurillac
Le Puy

Thueyts
Aubenas

Montpellier

Nîmes
Beaucaire
Aix en Provence
Montelimart
Lyon

Marseille
Toulon
Cannes
Antibes
Nice

Savona
Alessandria
Turin
Milan
Brescia

ITALY

SWITZERLAND

Lyell's and Murchison's tour through
France, 1828

Lyell's tour to the Pyrenees, 1830

be seen swimming rapidly through the waters of our stagnant pools and ditches."[26] *Cypris* possesses two small valves, like the halves of a clam shell, which it casts off and renews each year. Lyell thought that it was the myriads of these shells cast off annually which gave rise to the paper-thin subdivisions of the marl even "in stratified masses several hundred feet thick. A more convincing proof," he wrote, "of the tranquillity and clearness of the waters and of the slow and gradual process by which the lake was filled up with fine mud, cannot be desired."[27] They also found in the Limagne thick strata of "indusial" limestone, characterized by *indusiae,* the tubular cases of the aquatic larva of the caddis fly (*Phryganea*) which is abundant in modern ponds. Both the ancient and modern caddis fly larval cases customarily have many small freshwater shells attached to them, and thereby suggested to Lyell a double analogy between past and present conditions.

The limestone resembled the English oolite in appearance, although its fossils were very different. This fact reminded Lyell that fossils were essential for determining the age and relationships of strata, an idea still new in the eighteen twenties. In his notebook he wrote, "Mineralogical writers have despised zoological characters. Oolite of Auvergne proves their importance."[28]

In a quarry in the Butte de Montpensier they found such a quantity of animal bones that Lyell thought it might be practicable to grind them up to make fertilizer for the land. They dug out part of the skeleton of a large animal and gathered up other bones lying about in the quarry.[29]

Upon their arrival at Clermont-Ferrand on 16 May they found Hall, Lyell's clerk, waiting. He had come from Paris a day earlier by diligence and had occupied his time in collecting insects. Lyell and Murchison made Clermont their base for expeditions to the nearby volcanic Puys. On 17 May they went toward Pradelle, where they examined the lava current of Pariou and then ascended the Puy-de-Dôme and Petit Puy on both of which they took barometric observations just as had Périer, the brother-in-law of Blaise Pascal, in 1646. However Lyell's barometric measurements were for the purpose of measuring the height of the Puy-de-Dôme; Périer's had been to demonstrate the reduction in air pressure at higher alti-

26. *Principles* III, p. 230.
27. Ibid., p. 231.
28. Ms. Notebook 8, p. 74. Kinnordy mss.
29. Ibid., pp. 86–87.

tudes. Mrs. Murchison accompanied them on their ascent of the Puys but on their return to Clermont remained there for the next several days employing herself "in making panoramic sketches, receiving several of the gentry & Professors to whom we had letters in the neighbourhood & collecting plants & shells etc."[30]

In the meantime Murchison, Lyell, and Hall set off on 21 May "in a Patache a one-horse machine on springs" (Map 8). They went first to see the spot near Pont Gibaud mentioned by both Desmarest and Scrope, where the Sioule river, having once been blocked by a lava current which had flowed down from the Puy de Dôme, had cut itself a new path. While they were there the natives surprised them by telling them of another puy, which was not marked on Desmarest's map nor mentioned by Scrope. On investigating they were surprised to find an unusual set of phenomena:

> We thought their account a mere fable, but their description of the cinders etc. was so curious that we had the courage to relinquish our day's scheme & proceed again down the river. You may imagine our surprise when we found within a ride of Clermont a set of volcanic phenomena entirely unknown to Buckland, Scrope etc. or the natives here. A volcanic cone with a stream of basaltic lava issuing out on both sides & flowing down to the gorge of the Sioule. This defile was flanked on both sides by precipitous cliffs of gneiss & the river's passage must have been entirely choked up for a long time. A lake was formed & the river wore a passage between the lava & the granitic schist, but the former was so excessively compact that the schist evidently suffered most. In the progress of ages the igneous rock 150 feet deep was cut thro' & the river went on to eat its way 35–45 & in one place 85 feet into the subjacent granitic beds; leaving on one bank a perpendicular wall of basaltic lava towering over the gneiss.

This place proved especially significant because it refuted decisively William Buckland's contention that river valleys in the Auvergne as elsewhere had been scoured out all at one time by the waters of a deluge. If this were so and the excavating power of the rivers themselves were inconsiderable, then rivers should flow now in the same valleys as they always had. Continuing in the same letter,

30. C. L., Jr. to his father. 26 May 1828. Kinnordy mss. *L. & L.* I, 185–88.

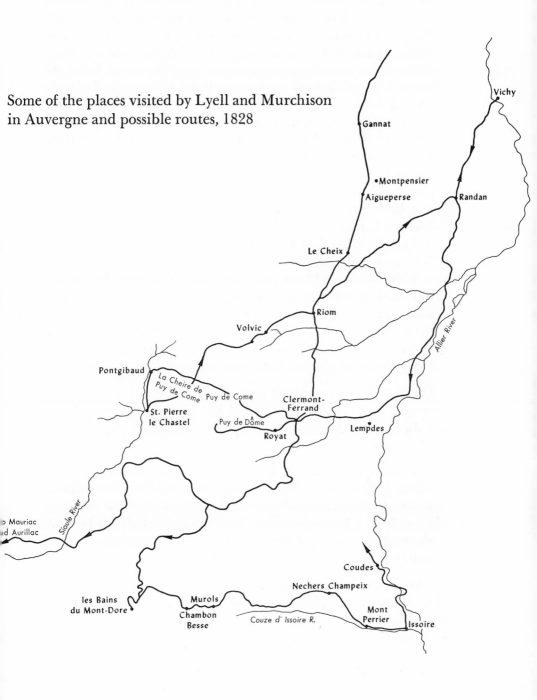

Some of the places visited by Lyell and Murchison
in Auvergne and possible routes, 1828

Vichy

Gannat

•Montpensier

Aigueperse

Randan

Le Cheix

Riom

Volvic

Allier River

Pontgibaud

La Cheire de
Puy de Come   Puy de Come

Clermont-
Ferrand

St. Pierre
le Chastel

Puy de Dôme

Lempdes

Royat

Sioule River

Mauriac
d Aurillac

Coudes

Nechers Champeix

les Bains
du Mont-Dore

Murols

Mont
Perrier

Chambon
Besse

Couze d' Issoire R.

Issoire

In the Vivarais where similar phenomena had been observed
Herschel[31] had remarked a bed of pebbles between the lava &
the gneiss marking the ancient river-bed, but Buckland endeavoured to get over this difficulty by saying that these pebbles
might have covered a sloping bank when the river filled the
valley & that this bank may have always been high above the
river bed, for if the sloping sides of a valley, said the Professor,
be covered with pebbles as they often are, & the valley is filled
with lava & then the lava cut thro' & partially removed there
will of course be a line of pebbles at the junction of the lava &
the rock beneath, but these pebbles will not mark an ancient
river bed. Now unluckily for the Doctor in this case he has no
loop-hole. An old lead mine said to have been worked by the
Romans happens to have exactly laid open the line of contact
& the pebbled bed of the old river is going in under the lava,
horizontally, for nearly 50 feet! [Fig. 30]

This is an astonishing proof of what a river can do in some
thousand or 100 thousand years by its continual wearing. No
deluge could have descended the valley without carrying away
the crater & ashes above. 600 or 700 feet higher is an old plateau
of basalt & if this flowed at the bottom of the then valley the
last work of the Sioule is but a unit in proportion to the other.[32]

On 22 May they continued from Pont Gibaud to Volvic, making
an ascent over the Cheire of Côme, but on the twenty-third they
left the volcanic hills to travel over the freshwater formations of
the Limagne to Vichy.

Vichy [Lyell noted] is built on a rock of indusial limestone
which is best exposed at the fountain where are the mineral
waters *des Celestines.* This spring is at the foot of the rock issuing only 3 or 4 feet above the Allier where the indusial beds are
elevated at an angle of from 80 to 90 degrees forming a vertical
wall.[33]

The change from volcanic rocks to limestone produced a startling change in the appearance of the towns. At Clermont and Volvic the buildings were made of dark grey or nearly black blocks of
quarried basalt which gave these towns a sombre and depressing

31. John F. W. Herschel (1792–1871).
32. C. L., Jr. to his father. 26 May 1828. Kinnordy mss. *L. & L.* I, 185–88.
33. Ms. Notebook 9, p. 68. Kinnordy mss.

appearance. In contrast the houses of Vichy were built of the pure white freshwater limestone and looked much more handsome and cheerful. Lyell noted the distinctive features of both people and customs in Auvergne. There were many black sheep in the fields and frequently also goats. The peasants wore black umbrella hats and blue frocks and, when the ground was muddy, wooden sabots on their feet. The women, he observed, wore gold crosses on the many feast days and black handkerchiefs with a gold fillet behind. The language was distinctive and, Lyell thought, bore a resemblance in intonation to Provençal or even Italian. Goiters were frequent among the people and there were also occasional cretins, as in some parts of Switzerland.[34]

> The waggons drawn by oxen, of a simple structure are picturesque, the population very dense owing to the vines. The sky continually threatens rain, but it falls not.[35]

They maintained a very active pace from the time they left Clermont-Ferrand on 21 May until their return on the twenty-fifth.

> We got under sail by six some mornings & at 5 o'c.[lk] some others & M. certainly keeps it up with more energy than anyone I ever travelled with.[36]

They then spent more than a week at Clermont-Ferrand, making expeditions into the surrounding country to examine various puys not previously visited. The Murchisons and Lyell left Clermont-Ferrand on 2 June to visit the Comte François Dominique Reynaud de Montlosier (1755–1838) at his house near Mont Dore. They found him "an old man of 74 in full possession of faculties of no mean order & of an imagination as lively as a poet's of 25."[37] Lyell remained a day longer than the Murchisons at the Comte's house in order to make a final effort to find the junction between the granite of the Puy chain and the freshwater strata of the Limagne. He succeeded in finding it, he thought, at Dourtol and, from the fact that the freshwater limestones showed signs of alteration by heat at their line of contact with the granite, he concluded that the granite had "made its appearance at the surface at a later period than even the freshwater tertiary beds

34. Ibid., pp. 79–80.
35. Ibid., p. 84.
36. C. L., Jr. to his father. 26 May 1828. Kinnordy mss. *L. & L.* I, 185–88.
37. C. L., Jr. to his father. 6 June 1828. Kinnordy mss. *L. & L.* I, 188.

have, tho' they contain the remains of quadrupeds." This was just the opposite of what Scrope had believed, namely, that the freshwater strata had been laid down in depressions in the pre-existing granite. It also suggested very strongly that the country had been elevated and the freshwater strata uplifted and inclined by the intrusion of granite in a molten condition from below. In that case the Auvergne district would offer a demonstration of Hutton's theory of uplift and of his insistence that granite was often younger than the stratified rocks lying above it. Thus Lyell felt that his discovery "will throw a new light on this remarkable country."[38]

On June 6 Lyell reached Mont Dore where Murchison and his wife had preceded him. Mont Dore lies in a deep valley eroded out of the side of the old volcano whose trachyte core rises above the village as the Puy de Sancy, the highest peak in Auvergne.

> The scenery of Mont Dore [Lyell wrote] is that of an Alpine valley, deep, with tall fir woods, high aiguilles above, half cov.^{d} with snow & cataracts & waterfalls. A watering place with good inns at the bottom of the valley.[39]

At Mont Dore he had hoped to find a letter from Kinnordy "with the news of those small family-history details of home, which are interesting when one is far away" but instead found his father's reproachful letter concerning the Rossetti article. It depressed him for the moment but the real success and interest of the geological journey with Murchison soon restored his cheerfulness.

For the next few weeks they made this place their base for long rides into the surrounding country. Their "plan of operation" was "that of comparison of the structure of different parts of the country." They worked very hard, setting off on horseback often at as early as five, and on one day they rode fifty-five miles. For the most part they thrived on it. "I believe," wrote Lyell to his mother, "that I & my eyes were never in such condition before & I am sure that 6 hours in bed, which is all we allow, & exercise all day long for the body & geology for the mind with plenty of the vin du pays which is good here, is the best thing that can be invented in this world for my health & happiness." Murchison, although hypo-

38. Ibid. The granite platform of Auvergne on the whole was much older than Lyell thought, but had been subject to later igneous intrusion by veins of younger granite.
39. Ibid.

chondriacal and addicted to strong medicines, was equally vigorous. Lyell remained delighted with the Auvergne.

> Mont Dore is partially cov.ᵈ with snow & almost always with
> clouds & the transition in coming up here from the low country
> is violent. Yesterday we rode up from the climate of Italy to that
> of Scotland.
>
> It is the most varied & picturesque country imaginable. There
> are innumerable old ruins for sketches with lakes, cascades &
> different kinds of wood so that we wonder more & more that the
> English have not found it out. The peasantry are very obliging,
> industrious, well-fed & clothed, & to all appearance are the hap-
> piest I ever saw. We have crossed the chain of Puys, the Limagne
> & the valleys leading from Mont Dore, in all directions.[40]

In their study of the country they were attracted as much by the
freshwater strata of Auvergne as by the volcanic phenomena. On
15 June he described their work in a letter to Gideon Mantell:

> We have been here for a whole month, (Murchison & I) work-
> ing hard in a lacustrine formation [so] that I have often thought
> of your neighbourhood & of you & assure you that our respect
> for what Humboldt calls sweet-water productions is greatly en-
> hanced & even the importance of your Hastings series, where
> the joint efforts of fluviatile & marine agencies were combined,
> shrinks into insignificance when compared with what a series of
> purely lacustrine sediments here exhibit. There is our grand
> system of Horsham grits, which cut a fine figure & might with
> their associated oolites bear a comparison with some of the
> first rate members of our oolitic series, & other divisions more
> than a thousand feet thick may represent different parts of the
> secondary series, & their extent, of which I conceive we have as
> yet but an inadequate idea, is such already as to rival many a
> boasted marine formation: but 'there is nothing in them that
> has suffered a sea-change' & I have seen five hundred feet of
> marls composing a line of hills in which the cypris was the only
> fossil & of which the myriads were such, between each lamina,
> that you could only compare them to the mica that divides the
> micaceous shaly sandstone of the Bristol coal field.
>
> Scrope was accused of having exaggerated the extent & impor-
> tance of the indusial limestone but I assure you he much under-

40. C. L., Jr. to his mother. 11 June 1828. Kinnordy mss. *L. & L.* I, 189–91.

rated it. Yet so great have been the disturbances & volcanic action
& waste since the formation of that rock, which you thought
looked so modern, that I assure you I have acquired an immense
idea of its antiquity. . . . I am sure that a much greater number
of quadrupeds might be found in this formation than Cuvier has
got out of the Paris gypsum. For in some quarries the men find
many bones every day but there is not a soul who attends to them
in earnest, & none who visit quarries to encourage the workmen.
All are thrown away.

It will give you some notion of the interest & geological importance of a lacustrine formation when we can have been in
doubt for days whether certain hills belonged to the old red
sandstone or the freshwater, whether certain others were granite or freshwater, i.e. a primary crystalline unstratified rock or a
sedimentary deposit, & that in both these cases we have come at
last to a decided opinion that the strata in question were the
undoubted property of the Lacustrine formation. Indeed I cannot imagine where it is to end & shall not be surprised if this
lake should afford a parallel to a large number of our secondary
formations & the strata in dislocation, elevation above their former level, alteration by trap dykes, verticality in parts, great
inclination in others, induration, thickness, faults etc. will, believe me, compare with almost any part of our series, & you may
therefore attribute our having been left so much in the dark
on these matters or rather having been completely misled, to the
accident of so much interesting volcanic phenomena being in
the neighbourhood & engrossing all attention.[41]

From this letter, and from the paper which Murchison and
Lyell later published on the freshwater formations of Cantal,[42] it
is clear that when Lyell and Murchison first encountered the freshwater formation of Cantal at Neckers and at Champeix they
thought from the appearance and mineralogical characteristics of
the rock strata that they were confronted with a representative of
the new red sandstone of England, a series of red marls and sandstones lying between the coal measures and the lias in England
(p. 213). They were called new red to distinguish them from the
strata of old red sandstone which in England lay immediately be-

41. C. L., Jr. to G. A. M. 15 June 1828. Mantell mss.
42. C. Lyell and R. S. [sic] Murchison, "Sur les dépots lacustres tertiares du Cantal . . ." (1829). Specific page references in the text are to this article.

neath the coal. The new red sandstone is now known to be of Triassic age and the old red, Devonian. To Lyell and Murchison both were very old secondary formations separated from the beginning of the Tertiary period by a long series of formations containing strata many thousands of feet thick.

Other beds of the same formation in Cantal, namely those at Les Chapelles near Issoire and at Cousdes (Fig. 31), resembled in appearance and mineralogical characteristics the stratified rock called the millstone grit which formed part of the coal measures in England. Then at Chambezon near Lempdes they found a sandstone containing many hard kernels of limestone, which exactly resembled the cornstone of the old red sandstone (p. 213). To Murchison these resemblances would be particularly striking because he had spent the preceding summer of 1827 studying secondary strata, including old red sandstone strata, in Sutherland and Ross in the north of Scotland.[43] He and Adam Sedgwick had collected the fossils of the old red sandstone and oolitic strata of Skye and the other western islands of Scotland and had described them in a paper read before the Geological Society a few months earlier.[44] The fossils were marine shells, corals, crinoids, and skeletons of bony fishes, all demonstrating that the strata had been laid down under the sea. The fossils of the strata of Cantal, however, were those of aquatic plants, especially *Chara,* the freshwater Crustacean *Cypris,* and a number of species of freshwater shells including species of *Bulimus, Limnea, Helix, Potamides,* and *Planorbis.* This assemblage of fossils proved conclusively that the strata had been deposited in a clear, calm, freshwater lake, and that the strata corresponded in age to the freshwater formation of Auvergne, to the upper freshwater formation of the Paris basin, and to the lower freshwater formation of Hampshire and the Isle of Wight (p. 206). In his study of the beds of Hordwell Cliff in Hampshire in 1825, Lyell had discovered a new fossil species of the molluscan genus *Ancylus,* which James Sowerby had named *Ancylus elegans* (Fig. 32). Then in the limestone at Veaurs near Aurillac he found this same beautiful fossil shell along with several other species common to the two deposits.

43. R. I. Murchison, "Supplementary remarks on the strata of the Oolitic series . . ." (1829).
44. R. I. Murchison and A. Sedgwick, "On the structure and relations of the deposits contained between the primary rocks and the oolitic series in the north of Scotland" (1828).

For Lyell and Murchison there could be no more powerful demonstration than the discovery of these fossils, that mineralogical characteristics were no guide to the ages of rocks and could not be used to correlate formations in different countries. In the freshwater strata of a single series in Cantal they had found rocks corresponding to the new red sandstone (Triassic), the millstone grit (Carboniferous), and the cornstone of the old red sandstone (Devonian).

> And yet [they wrote] all these varieties of mechanical deposit which, in Great Britain, indicate three great periods in the secondary formations, reveal themselves clearly in Auvergne in tertiary lacustrine formations the upper, marly portions of which show a gradual passage to the inferior sandstone, as we have established. [p. 214, translation mine]

The correlation of strata, therefore, depended on their fossil contents and the future of geology lay with the study of fossils. In a fundamental way this fact would determine the future work of both Murchison and Lyell—for Lyell in his classification of Tertiary formations and for Murchison in his study first of the new red sandstone, then of the old red sandstone, and ultimately of the primitive rocks of the borders of Wales to which he gave the name Silurian.

The very terms old red sandstone, millstone grit, and new red sandstone had been based on the older mineralogical kind of geognosy developed especially by Werner. The terms assumed the existence of universal formations and were based on the concept that at particular periods of the earth's history the same kind of deposit had settled from an ocean, universal or nearly so, over the entire earth's surface. The mineralogical geologists had built their classification of rocks on the belief that rocks with the same mineralogical and lithological characteristics had been deposited at the same time. This belief had misled American geologists in their initial efforts to correlate the formations of North America with those of Europe and it had begun to break down with the study of the fossils of the chalk. In 1821 Alexandre Brongniart showed that there were many strata of sandstone, shale, etc. which contained the same fossils as the chalk, and developed the idea of a Cretaceous formation which was to be identified by its possession of a particular kind of fossil assemblage.[45] Geologists who had been

45. A. Brongniart, "Sur les caractères zoologiques des formations . . ." (1821).

puzzled by the absence of the chalk in North America then found that the Cretaceous formation was represented throughout an extensive area of the eastern seaboard of the United States by beds which had previously been classified simply as alluvial.[46] These discoveries, which were made at nearly the same time that Lyell and Murchison were in the Cantal, represented a similar impact of the study of fossils on the identification and correlation of formations.

The sandstones, marls, and limestones of Cantal exerted an influence on Lyell's thoughts concerning general geological questions. The fossils and detailed structure of the freshwater strata again and again suggested the orderly and undisturbed conditions of a freshwater lake. Yet the geographical extent and great depth of the formations required that if they had been deposited in a lake this must have been a large lake and their deposition must have required an enormous period of time. In his notebook Lyell wrote on 14 June:

Modern Causes—They who ask us to show recent freshw.[r] & marine format.[s] as thick & as elevated as those contain.[g] partly extinct animals, beg the question as to the Uniformity of Nature. For if sedimentary deposits went on as slowly, formerly, as they do now, they must have req.[d] vast periods & no period equally vast can have transpired since the time of History.[47]

His concept of geological time was thus beginning to expand.

When he had an opportunity to study in detail the freshwater strata of the Cantal in the vicinity of Aurillac, Lyell was further struck by their resemblance to modern freshwater deposits. Lyell and Murchison approached Aurillac from the west, across plains covered with heath where the underlying rock of "mica-schist" was barely covered with soil. Presently they observed the surface of the plain strewn with loose broken flints which reminded them of the chalk flints which Lyell had observed scattered over granite hills and plains near Peterhead in Aberdeenshire when he had been on his geological tour with Dr. Buckland in September 1824. When the flints of Banffshire were split open they revealed various fossils characteristic of the chalk, indicating that these flints represented the last remnants of the chalk strata which had formerly covered the granite plains and hills and had later been eroded away. But

46. L. G. Wilson, "The emergence of geology as a science in the United States" (1967).
47. Ms. Notebook 10, p. 89. Kinnordy mss.

when Lyell broke open the flints on the plain of mica schist near Aurillac, he found inside sometimes casts of gyrogonites (i.e. the seed vessels of *Chara*), or the stems of *Chara,* or freshwater shells characteristic of lakes. Instead, therefore, of being the remnants of a former stratum of chalk, a calcareous deposit laid down in deep ocean waters, the Aurillac flints were the remains of a limestone formed in a freshwater lake (p. 184). When Lyell and Murchison arrived at the escarpment formed by the freshwater beds, they found at the bottom of the hill formed by this escarpment "strata of clay and sand resting on mica schist" whereas at the top were strata of white limestone. The road along which they passed reflected "as glaring a light in the sun, as do our roads composed of chalk."[48]

There is in fact nothing more interesting in the appearance of this freshwater formation than its resemblance to the chalk of England, the hills being scattered with similar flints. The limestone on this line of quarries is white and shines in the sun. The upper surface of the limestone is furrowed in the same way [as the chalk] in irregular grooves in which vegetable earth, clay and flints are mixed confusedly, and sometimes the alluvium entering into the fissures in the limestone in the manner of roots is revealed in transverse sections as one often sees in the chalk of Wiltshire, Dorsetshire and elsewhere.[49]

But instead of the marine coral *Alcyonia,* the *Echinus,* and marine shells, all of which are characteristic of the chalk, these strata contained petrified seed vessels of *Chara* and such shells as *Planorbis* characteristic of freshwater lakes. Some of the limestone marl strata near Aurillac showed decisively how slowly and gradually they had been laid down.

In the hill of Barrat, for example, we find an assemblage of calcareous and siliceous marls, in which, for a depth of at least 60 feet, the layers are so thin that thirty are sometimes contained in the thickness of an inch; and when they are separated we see preserved in each the flattened stems of Charae, or other plants, or sometimes myriads of small *paludinae* and other freshwater shells. These minute foliations of the marl resemble precisely some of the recent laminated beds of the Scotch marl lakes, and

48. *Principles* III, pp. 237–38.
49. Ibid., pp. 183–84.

when divided may be compared to the pages of a book, each containing a history of a certain period of the past.[50]

Here for Lyell was the clearest possible analogy between the conditions of past and present!

On 3 July he wrote to his sister Caroline from Le Puy-en-Velay: We have now seen the Cantal district . . . I was there particularly interested with the freshwater or rather lacustrine deposits; as although of an older date than all the volcanoes of that country, and constituting chains of hills, their correspondence when considered foot by foot with the beds which are at our door in the marl loch, is as complete as you can imagine. The same genera of shells & thin sheets of compressed vegetables, & seeds of chara etc. of which we hope to add many new species to the fossils hitherto known.[51]

Lyell found that the fossils in these strata were preserved even when they were overladen with volcanic rocks.

When they reached Le Puy-en-Velay on 3 July they had been for seven weeks engaged in hard geological field work. The weather had been fine throughout and they had spent long hours out of doors. However, the air in the mountains had been pleasantly cool, but at Le Puy it was becoming hot. Lyell told Caroline that if they could continue for six or eight weeks more they would accomplish something.

But I do not think the Murchisons will stand fire. Symptoms of flinching from the heat which makes scarcely any impression on me, begin to betray themselves. Thoughts of a retreat to the Alps, consultations with me whether I think it practicable to proceed farther south in the dog-days have been mooted & I suppose the whole scheme will hardly be persevered in . . . But as far as we have gone I was never with a better man for doing work than M. & as we have 2 weeks before us here that will be a good deal to have secured.[52]

Murchison confessed his own doubts at this point in a letter to Buckland.

We have enjoyed uninterrupted *delicious weather* & have seen

50. Ibid., p. 239.
51. C. L., Jr. to his sister Caroline. 3 July 1828. Kinnordy mss. *L. & L.* I, 191–93.
52. Ibid.

every peak of every high mountain—but we now begin to be scorched, & to call out fire. When my stomach & nerves are a little disorganized I cry *peccavi* & that we must not attempt the Boucher de Rhone & the Subappenines but after all I think we shall be carried on by the Geological ardor—& Lyell is the best whipper-in possible.[53]

At Le Puy-en-Velay they had a letter of introduction from Dr. Buckland to M. Bertrand, a merchant who had written a book on the topography of the Velay district, and they brought him as a gift from Buckland a copy of the latter's *Reliquiae diluvianae*. He not only guided them in examining the geology of the area, but entertained them and introduced them to local society.

The valley in which Le Puy stands and the surrounding countryside gave dramatic evidence of the large scale of recent geological changes there, particularly of the quantity of rock and soil removed by the action of running water. Lyell noted:

The Loire after passing Chamalier takes, opposite [the] old castle of Arlias (at Retournae), a grand sweep, a curve like a river in a plain. . . . When in the gorge the height seems so immense & the width of valley so great that the excavation by modern causes seems immense, but when seen from above it seems more natural.[54]

Lyell and Murchison also went with Bertrand to places where there were layers of river gravel under basalt or interstratified with volcanic breccia at a number of different levels on the hills around Le Puy. Because the beds of river pebbles bore no relation to the present water courses Lyell decided they must have been "derived from some previous state of the valley" and that they seemed "clearly to indicate the progressive excavation of valleys."[55]

After eight days at Le Puy they went on south across the high divide of the Haut Vivarrais:

The descent from the granitic mountains of Velay to Vivarrais (now Ardêche) is exceedingly fine, the outline of the hills very alpine, & the deep valley clothed with rich chestnut trees & vines dressed in the Italian style.

We stayed 3 days at Thueyts, a small town in the Ardêche

53. R. I. Murchison to W. Buckland. 4 July 1828. Murchison mss.
54. Ms. notebook 12, pp. 25–26. Kinnordy mss.
55. Ibid.

where we were able to examine carefully what Scrope in a letter calls "the Pet volcanoes of the Vivarrais" & such they really
are, very far surpassing all the 2 or 300 we had seen in Auvergne,
Cantal & Puy. . . . The craters are so perfect yet the cones covered with such fine zones halfway down of chestnuts, & the lava
currents, eaten into by the rivers, present such splendid colon-
nades of basaltic pillars that it is a country to make everyone
desire to know something, & as the granitic schists in which the
vallies lie are all of one kind there is no danger of the volcanic
matter being confounded by any one with the older rock
through which it has burst or over which it has flowed. The
proofs of their immense antiquity are quite enough to bear out
Scrope though he has terribly overstated some facts while he
overlooked in his haste others as strong as his assertions.

As a counterpoint to the good weather and the geological interest
of the country they found the roads very variable. "For ten miles,"
Lyell continued, "there is a broad road worthy of the magnificence
of the *Grande Nation*—bridges quite splendid, rock blown
through, etc. Then all at once stones and ruts and a narrow lane,
with a frightful precipice, and no parapet." At one of these narrow
spots one of the horses, irritated by flies, kicked off the *voiturier*.
The horses then ran away with Mrs. Murchison and her maid in
the carriage, and they were in terrible danger of going over the
precipice. Fortunately the horses finally stopped at Mayre without
mishap, before Annette, Mrs. Murchison's Swiss maid, who
wished to jump out, could get the door open. This incident is an
indication of some of the trials to which Mrs. Murchison was
exposed during their travels. Her "presence of mind was quite
wonderful," wrote Lyell, "as she is so timid in general." Later
that same day a servant by accident bruised her foot so that she
could walk only with difficulty.

In the same letter, Lyell also told Marianne something of the
costs of traveling in Auvergne.

My share of the Posting is about the same (one 4th of 3 horses)
as the public conveyance would be if there were always any.
Central France is very cheap, a riding horse only 50 sous a day &
at Puy only 40!! at which price 50 may be hired. We could not
comprehend how this can answer & how it can even pay the wear
& tear of the saddles & bridles which are excellent. Murchison
generally bargained for 5 francs a head for bed, dinner, break-

fast & tea for the last two months but henceforth it will be 25 per cent dearer at least. We shall now however be in the land of Post-horses.[56]

Despite his doubts about the heat in the south of France, Murchison decided to go on. From Aubenas in the Ardèche they went down to Montélimart on the banks of the Rhone and then south to Nismes.

Nismes [Lyell wrote] is a glorious remnant of Roman grandeur with an amphitheatre & temple nearly entire. The old aqueduct at the pont du Garde N. of Nimes is as fine as almost anything in Italy.[57]

From Nismes they went to Montpellier where they were on 24 July and which Lyell pronounced "the most luxurious place we have seen." There they learned from the Montpellier naturalist Marcel de Serres of the discovery of a new cave containing the bones of hyenas and other animals at Lunel, a few miles from Nismes, and on 25 July they visited it on their way back to that town. From Nismes they went east to Beaucaire where they crossed the Rhone on a bridge of boats.

Lyell was interested in the ponds or *étangs* of the Rhone delta, bodies of water intermittently connected with the sea. They changed seasonally from freshwater ponds when the Rhone was high to saltwater ponds when the Rhone was low. When the level of the Rhone dropped still further they became isolated from the Mediterranean and then as a result of evaporation became even more salt than the sea. Some freshwater species were not killed by the salt water while others were. Similarly some marine species could survive in the fresh water. The result was an intermixture of fresh- and saltwater species in these ponds exactly like the mixture of fresh- and saltwater fossil species which Lyell had found in Hordwell Cliff on the Hampshire coast. "This suffices to show," Lyell noted, "that in estuary formations deposits of mixed nature may take place, as in Hordwell Cliff, without violent influx & species may have lived where they are."[58]

As they approached Aix-en-Provence, which lay at the bottom of

56. C. L., Jr. to his sister Marianne. 15 July 1828. Kinnordy mss. *L. & L.* I, 193–95 (printed only in part).

57. C. L., Jr. to his sister Caroline. 3 Aug. 1828. Kinnordy mss. *L. & L.* I, 195–96 (published only in part).

58. Ms. notebook 13, p. 12. Kinnordy mss.

a deep valley, the road descended over an escarpment of Tertiary freshwater marls and limestones. Below this escarpment the underlying strata of gypsum extended out in a terrace. The gypsum had been quarried extensively and these quarries were well known for the wealth of fossil fish and plants they contained, but just the year before Marcel de Serres had discovered in it a bed of marl containing many fossil insects. Lyell and Murchison descended about 260 steps to reach the gypsum gallery containing the insect bed. Lyell described it to Caroline:

> It divides into thin laminae as does our Kinnordy insect bed, but is a solid stone. The insects, even the gnats, are beautifully perfect, wings antennae & all . . . There are so many that I am in hopes they will somewhat aid the question as to the climate of these parts when the tertiary strata were formed. The series of strata in which they occur is 400 feet thick, & the fish & shells shew them to be freshwater probably formed in a lake.[59]

South of Aix, on the hills beyond the valley of the river Arc, Lyell and Murchison visited the coal mines of Fuveau, where shafts had been sunk more than 500 feet through strata of this great freshwater formation (Fig. 33). The principal coal seam was nine to twelve inches thick but with additional seams giving a total thickness of about five feet of coal. The coal was "bituminous, highly compact and shining" and was being used for both domestic and industrial purposes.[60] The lower portion of the freshwater formation between Aix and Fuveau was very different both from the freshwater beds on the escarpment to the north of Aix and from any other freshwater formation they had seen in Auvergne or Cantal.

> The great thickness of the regular beds of blue limestone and shale, the quality and appearance of the coal, the large development of the compact grey, brown, and black argillaceous limestones and sandstones, together with the red marls and gypsum, gives to the whole series the aspect of the most ancient of our secondary rocks; and it is only by the occurrence of fluviatile and lacustrine shells, and the seed vessels of charae, that the geologist is undeceived, and recognizes, from the unequivocal

59. C. L., Jr. to his sister Caroline. 3 Aug. 1828.
60. R. I. Murchison and C. Lyell, Jr., "On the tertiary fresh-water formations of Aix, in Provence, including the coal-field of Fuveau" (1829) p. 292.

specific characters of many of these remains the comparatively recent date of the whole group.[61]

Yet the beds of Fuveau formed a continuous series of freshwater strata with those to the north of Aix and the whole series contained the same fossil freshwater shells as the freshwater formations at Aurillac. Therefore, on the one hand, the formation of Aix and Fuveau was geologically recent; on the other hand, it was old enough for the river Arc to have excavated its great valley.

From the gypsum quarry at Aix, Marcel de Serres had already identified more than fifty genera of insects, including flies, moths, and beetles.[62] Lyell gathered a box of fossils to send to Mantell and later, when he was back in London, his entomologist friend Curtis[63] was able to tell him that most of the insects could be classified among living genera of European forms.

In the course of their movements, their letters from England and Scotland failed to keep up with them. This had, Lyell explained, divergent effects on their morale:

> Mrs. M. always gets nervous if she does not hear regularly from her mother & Murchison whenever she does, for after the old lady kept him from travelling 5 years because she should soon die & wished her daughter to be with her, she sent for them Post in the middle of a tour in Scotland & they arrived in time to find her quite well. M. has now made a bolt, as he thinks she will outlive him & he might never get abroad but he is in dread of being summoned back every week, as on the former occasion. Mrs. M. suffers from heat & our motions have been much impeded since we reached the Rhone at Montélimart. But we have done much & never lost a whole day. We get out either on foot or caleche by 4 o'clock A.M. intending to sleep at noon, but when noon comes we are either from home or a cloud or a breeze enables us to work & so it continues till next night. If M. was not unwell about once a week I should be done up, for 5 hours sleep on hard work will not do for me, but make amends on such occasions.[64]

From Aix they reached Marseilles on 3 August and from there traveled along the coast to Toulon. They made geological obser-

61. Ibid., pp. 292–93. Cf. *Principles* III, pp. 276–77.
62. M. de Serres, "Note sur les Arachnides et les Insects fossiles . . ." (1828).
63. John Curtis (1791–1862) F.L.S., author of *British Entomology* (1824–39).
64. C. L., Jr. to his sister Caroline. 3 Aug. 1828.

vations constantly as they went and at Antibes Lyell drew geological sections of the coastal cliffs. On 9 August they were at Nice.

At the beginning of August, while at Marseilles, Lyell still hoped to be in London in September. He had in fact promised his father to spend some weeks at Kinnordy during the autumn. However at Nice they were immobilized, in part by the heat, but principally by Murchison's coming down with an attack of fever—apparently malarial. The weeks of long hours and intense labor with inadequate sleep had at last taken their toll.

Yet the effects of his illness on the expedition were not all bad. Mrs. Murchison, who had been herself feeling ill, "when her mind was thus recalled into exertion in attending him recovered her energy."[65] Moreover, they made use of their enforced leisure to write a paper on the excavation of valleys, "which," Lyell wrote on 20 August, "is at last finished, & after two evenings infliction is intended to reform the Geological Society & afterwards the world on this 'hitherto-not-in-the-least-degree-understood' subject."[66] Their study of river valleys was the one part of their work in the Auvergne which they could write up because their more extensive study of the freshwater strata there and in the Cantal had to await the identification of the shells which they had collected. For this they needed the help of James Sowerby and other expert conchologists in London. They also continued to collect and observe in a quiet fashion:

> We have performed two jaunts with Mrs. Murchison, each at ½ past 4 o'ck. in [the] morning to see certain deposits of fossil shells, with collecting which she has been much pleased & this & the cessation of eternal bustle while the campaign was at its height . . . has restored her health & spirits which had failed sadly.

Lyell also mentioned that:

> We went out in the bay on Sunday with a famous diver who brought up sponges & other creatures that I had never seen alive before. He took down a hammer &, when out of sight, knocked off the stone-perforating shells.[67]

65. C. L., Jr. to his father. 21 Aug. 1828. Kinnordy mss. *L. & L.* I, 199–200 (printed only in part, misdated Aug. 24).

66. C. L., Jr. to his sister Eleanor. 20 Aug. 1828. Kinnordy mss. *L. & L.* I, 197–98.

67. Ibid.

The writing of their paper on the excavation of valleys gave an opportunity to reflect on the great wealth of observations that they had gathered in central France. For Lyell this was particularly important because these few weeks of rest and reflection were to mark the great turning point in his life. He had come out to central France with the idea of gathering new material to fill out his book on geology. He had been seeking "analogies between existing Nature and the effects of causes in remote eras," but he had been more than a little surprised by the abundance and significance of those they had found. In the *massif central* of France they had seen extinct volcanoes of varying ages, exhibiting signs of degradation in proportion to their age, valleys which had been repeatedly filled with lava and repeatedly reexcavated by running water, and sheets of basalt, which must originally have flowed over the floors of valleys and plains, now capping the tops of outlying hills—a dramatic demonstration of the immense bulk of rock and soil that had been removed by running water since the time of the eruption which produced the igneous rocks. They had seen all of this immense accumulation of volcanic products—the record of a long chain of eruptions extending far back through Tertiary times—yet it was the freshwater strata occurring among them which were especially revealing. For these strata had been laid down under tranquil conditions—comparable to those in Kinnordy loch, as determined by the shells and plant remains found in them—and laid down during a very long period of time as measured by their thickness. Yet all the ages during which these sediments had gradually collected in the bottom of large lakes in central France had existed prior to the first volcanic eruption. In fact, Lyell and Murchison thought they had found in France a series of freshwater strata which spanned a period of time equal to that represented by marine and freshwater secondary strata of Great Britain.

The volcanic eruptions and their associated earthquakes had greatly elevated the freshwater strata and had folded, inclined, and broken them. Yet where the freshwater deposits had not been altered by heat in immediate contact with the igneous rocks, they were in their physical characteristics as well as in their fossils exactly like the modern sediments found in the Scottish lakes.

The great antiquity of these freshwater deposits, like the antiquity of those which Mantell had discovered beneath the chalk in the Weald district, and the still greater age of the coal measures, had a special significance in relation to the old idea of a universal ocean, which had been an integral part of the Wernerian scheme. For freshwater deposits could only be laid down in relation to land areas and if, in ancient geological times, large areas of land had existed, the ocean could not have been universal.

When Lyell and Murchison arrived at Nice they called on Giovanni Risso, then about fifty years old and a professor in the lycée at Nice. Risso had gained a European reputation as a naturalist through the publication of his work on the natural history of southern Europe, particularly of the neighborhood of Nice—a great treatise in five volumes.[68] Risso had collected the fossils of the marine Tertiary strata around Nice and had made pioneering studies of the distribution of marine animals at various depths of water in the Mediterranean. He was, therefore, an oceanographer as well as a naturalist and a geologist.

The Tertiary strata around Nice consisted of beds of gravel, or conglomerate, sandstone, and an occasional bed of blue marl all dipping uniformly at an angle of about 25 degrees towards the Mediterranean. They had been elevated to heights of 200 to 600 feet above the sea. Most of the beds of gravel and sand contained very few fossil shells, but Risso had found a bed of marl near the church of St. Madeleine which contained a great many fossil shells, very well preserved. He directed Lyell and Murchison both to this spot and to another called La Trinita. It was probably to these places that Lyell and Murchison went on their two expeditions with Mrs. Murchison at half past four in the morning. From these beds Risso had collected and identified more than two hundred species of shells and ten species of corals of which eighteen per cent were species still living in the Mediterranean. The channel of the Magnan River cut a section through these inclined beds for a distance of about nine miles from the base of Monte Calvo to the Mediterranean. Since its bed was dry after eight months without rain at Nice, Lyell was able to ride up the bed of the river for six or seven miles.

The beds of Tertiary gravel and sand in the vicinity of Nice showed Lyell how thick deposits of gravel might form as a consequence of the long-continued action of rivers. The pebbles in the stratified beds were the same as those brought down from the Alps by the Var and other rivers along the coast when they were in flood during the winter rainy season. Since the Mediterranean was 3,000 feet deep a short distance offshore, the gravel washed out by

68. G. A. Risso (1777–1845), *Histoire naturelle des principes productions de l'Europe méridionale* . . . (1826).

modern rivers was necessarily deposited on a sloping bank. Lyell thought that the beds of Tertiary gravel had similarly been deposited on a sloping offshore bank, a fact which would largely account for their regular dip of 25 degrees without the need to postulate any later disturbance. He saw that these beds of gravel would help to explain much that had been puzzling about the conditions under which strata of conglomerate and sandstone had been formed. Geologists such as Buckland had argued that only catastrophic floods of water could deposit such quantities of gravel as were present in many conglomerate formations. The beds along the Magnan river were thousands of feet thick.

> Yet [Lyell noted] Risso has found many Subappenine shells, also remains of fish & impressions of plants, rhododendron apparently, & 'le redoul' [i.e. sumack], bark & fruit of pine & a large quantity of wild chestnut. So that in the Subappenine sea the trees now adorning [the]Appenines grew.[69]

He also wrote in enthusiasm to his father:

> At this very place which Brongniart & Buckland have been at without seeing, or choosing to see so unwelcome a fact, we have discovered a formation which would furnish an answer to the very difficulty which Sedgwick[70] when at Kinnordy put to me. He said, "you who wish to make out that all is now going on as formerly help me to conceive a sea deep enough & disturbed enough to receive in any length of time such a series of strata of conglomerate & sandstone as you have shewn me in Angus." Now here we have just such a series as that in Forfarshire only very much thicker & in the intervening laminated sands are numerous perfect shells, more than 200 species in Risso's cabinet 18 in a 100 of which are *living* Mediterranean species, whose habits are known. By the grouping of these shells & their state, the sea is found to have been in a perfect state of tranquillity except at those periods when the pebbles were washed down.[71]

Lyell was still in doubt whether gravel, which forms conglomerate, was a normal kind of sediment but he noted that the Magnan when flowing "brings yearly multitudes of pebbles" to the sea.

The total effect of these volcanoes, hills, strata, and gorges had the force of revelation for Lyell. "One must travel over Europe,"

69. Ms. notebook 13, p. 50. Kinnordy mss.
70. Adam Sedgwick (1785–1873), professor of geology at Cambridge University.
71. C. L., Jr. to his father. 21 Aug. 1828.

he wrote to Mantell, "to learn how completely we are in our in-
fancy in the knowledge of the ancient history of the globe & to feel
as I do now what splendid discoveries must be on the Eve of coming to light even within the time which we may hope to see."[72] It
was in this spirit that he talked over his plans with Murchison who
encouraged him to follow geology with his whole heart and suggested he go on to Sicily. In writing to his father, Lyell quoted
Murchison as saying:

> At Milan or Verona in 3 or 4 weeks or thereabouts the opera-
> tions connected with our paper will be over, but Sicily is for
> your views the great end; there are the most modern analogies,
> volcanic, marine, elevatory, subsidings etc. etc. I know the island
> as a soldier & if you make straight for Etna [you] will just time it
> right for work, for the season will be exactly suitable. You will
> not write your book in the most satisfactory & conclusive manner
> unless you go there.

Murchison thought that Lyell ought to go on now both because he
was already half way there and because he was "now charged with
a thousand queries which Sicily will answer & Auvergne has sup-
lied."[73] He urged Lyell onward with a special anguish because he so
much wanted to go himself and could not, because his wife's parents
were so anxious for her return to England. Lyell needed little urging. On 21 August he wrote to his father the letter, from which
the preceding passages have been quoted, to announce and to justify his going on. Towards the end of their tour in Auvergne Lyell
had begun to reflect on the meaning of all that they had seen. He
began to develop his emerging ideas in essays of varying lengths in
his notebooks. He wrote on "the laws which regulate the comparative longevity of species," the "Analogy of Geology and History," the "Nature of Geological Records," and other topics all
relating to the interpretation of the history of the earth.[74] The
influence which Auvergne had had on him is apparent in his essay
on the analogy of geology and history:

Analogy of Geology and History

If we regard Auvergne and the works of man as merely belonging to one generation we perceive much that is unintelligible, that is not for the best and the explanation is that the

72. C. L., Jr. to G. A. M. 22 Aug. 1828. Mantell mss.
73. C. L., Jr. to his father. 21 Aug. 1828.
74. Ms. Notebook 12, pp. 83–95. Kinnordy mss.

present state of things has grown out of one extremely different, and everything has not been made merely with a view to the existing race.

The greater number of the cities are built on lofty and often very inaccessible eminences, and with narrow streets, as La Soire, Les Roches, Buron etc., instead of [in the] rich valleys which would now be chosen. There is an historical reason for this. They were once fortresses, when to dwell in the place exposed the inhabitants to plunder and invasion.

So, if we turn to Nature, we perceive that many a valley, where we might expect a fertile alluvial soil and a river, is now filled with a sterile ridge of uncultivated rock. This could not be expected if all the surface were constructed by Nature with a view to the present order of things. But there is a reason for it. This barren rock is a stream of lava which closed the valley and concealed the river. It results from a former system, for which the world was made as for the present, and on which it must depend, as will future ones on it. . . .

It is easy to imagine the general law by which the present course of Nature is governed, viz., that in each period, the earth's surface and its inhabitants should be influenced by their former existence. . . . The danger of misjudging, and giving way to false theories in regarding the system of nature, is when we view it as solely and expressly adapted for the existing order of things, and when we are ignorant that it is merely a subordinate part of a great series of events intended to embrace many such systems. We err as much as when we judge of a political constitution without considering the pre-existent state of the laws from which it has grown.

If it be asked why, in a succession of events, the preceding are made to influence so much all that follow, we may reply that it appears probable that it is impossible it should be otherwise, for it belongs to the whole constitution of things, and if natural causes operate as they do, from day to day continually, one epoch must be affected by the events of another.[75]

When he left England, Lyell had been mentally prepared to seek for explanations of geological phenomena in terms of modern causes, that is, in terms of processes which could be seen to be going on in the present world. In Auvergne and in the south of

75. Ibid., pp. 84–86.

France he had succeeded beyond his expectations in realizing this goal, but in doing so his thoughts had undergone a subtle change. He now saw that not only might analogies be drawn between present and past conditions on the earth's surface, but that present conditions on the earth's surface could only be understood historically. The idea of the present earth as a creation, manifesting God's design, had begun to break down in his mind. Simultaneously Lyell's imaginative grasp of the immensity of time, represented by the course of the earth's history, had begun to expand. He had not yet realized the full implications of the ideas he was developing, but his mind was in ferment and he was eager to compare active volcanoes with the extinct ones he had already seen and to search for more recently elevated strata in their neighborhood.

CHAPTER 8

Italy and Sicily, the Birth of a Scientific Revolution

LYELL'S ATTENTION was now focused intensely upon Tertiary strata which, from his experience in the Auvergne and Cantal as well as at Aix and Nice, offered so many analogies to modern conditions. The first series of Tertiary strata which were studied in detail were those of the Paris basin. There Cuvier and Brongniart had revealed a series of marine and freshwater formations superimposed on one another. They identified each individual member of the series by certain characteristic fossil remains and thus gave to the study of fossils a special importance. The fact that about the same time William Smith was using fossils to identify the long series of secondary strata from the coal to the chalk in England further emphasized their importance. After the publication of Cuvier and Brongniart's report in 1811, Thomas Webster published his description of the London and Hampshire basins in 1814.[1] In these basins Webster found an alternation of marine and freshwater beds similar to that found in the Paris basin and, although the strata were very different in appearance and lithology, he was able to show from their fossils that they corresponded in age. In the same year Giovanni Battista Brocchi published an account of the Tertiary strata of Italy, his *Conchiologia fossile subapennina*.[2] Brocchi distinguished the secondary strata which form the central mountain chain of the Apennines from the Tertiary strata of the lower hills and plains along the coast of Italy. To these latter strata he gave the name subapennine beds. As the title of his work suggests, he devoted particular attention to the fossil shells of these beds and, in fact, described shells from the subapennine beds of the whole length of Italy. On the one hand he recognized the similarity of these fossil shells to the modern species living in the Mediterranean and the Adriatic and, on the other, their dissimilarity to the species of fossil shells from the Paris basin described by Cuvier and Brongniart and by Lamarck.[3] This dif-

1. T. Webster. "On the Freshwater Formations in the Isle of Wight . . ." (1814).
2. G. Brocchi. *Conchiologia fossile subapennina* . . . (1814). Giovanni Battista Brocchi (1772–1826) was professor of botany at Brescia.
3. J. B. de Lamarck, *Histoire naturelle des animaux sans vertèbres* (1815–22).

ference between the fossil shell species of the subapennine beds and those of the Paris basin did not trouble him because he attributed it to their geographical separation and not to any difference in age.[4] The striking similarity of the fossil shells of the subapennine beds to the living shells of the Mediterranean led Brocchi to expect a similar correspondence between the fossil shells of the Paris basin and the living shells of the north Atlantic. There was, in fact, just enough truth in this expectation and just enough demonstrable correspondence between the fossil species of the Paris basin and living species to be very misleading. It would require a different basis for judging the age of Tertiary strata, and one capable of canceling the effects of geographical and ecological distribution, to allow the accurate determination of the relative ages of Tertiary strata from widely separated places. As it was, Brocchi treated the strata of all the Italian Tertiary beds from the Piedmont to Calabria as a single homogeneous series, comparable in its unity to that of the Paris basin, and of corresponding age.[5]

Brocchi's work was large, detailed, and of considerable genius. By its very excellence it helped to deflect geologists from studying the succession of the Tertiary strata, particularly as manifested in the subapennine beds.

In 1811 James Parkinson had observed in Suffolk, England, certain shell-bearing strata, called by the local term "crag," (meaning gravel) which overlay a Tertiary bed of London clay. In contrast to the fossil shells of the London clay which belonged almost entirely to extinct species, three fourths of those of the crag were identical with species living in the North Sea nearby.[6] Some years later W. D. Conybeare in his *Outlines of the Geology of England and Wales* placed the crag as the youngest in the series of British strata and this fact suggested that it corresponded in age to Brocchi's subapennine beds. In fact, Conybeare wrote, "The description of the Italian formations corresponds very closely with that of the basin of London, but there is often considerable difference in the species of shells they contain."[7]

Desnoyers had shown that a group of marine strata in Tou-

4. Brocchi, *Conchiologia* I, pp. 163–67.

5. Ibid., p. 145.

6. J. Parkinson, "Observations on some of the strata in the neighbourhood of London and on the fossil remains contained in them" (1811).

7. W. D. Conybeare and W. Phillips, *Outlines of the Geology of England and Wales* ... (1822) pp. 7–9.

raine in the Loire valley overlay the uppermost stratum of the Paris basin group. These upper marine strata Desnoyers considered analogous to the English crag.[8] Still another Tertiary deposit had been studied in the southwest of France in the vicinity of Bordeaux and its fossils had been described by Basterot.[9]

All these strata contained some species of shells identical with those living in adjacent seas. In some cases the proportion of such species was considerable, yet the difference between the fossil and living faunas was always sufficiently great that the fossils could still be considered the remains of a "former world" clearly separated from the present world.

This was, therefore, the attitude of mind which Lyell and Murchison brought to the study of Tertiary marine strata when they arrived at Nice in August of 1828. However, all of the observations which they had made on the Tertiary freshwater strata of central France had convinced Lyell of the analogy between ancient and modern conditions of deposition. At Nice they had found conglomerate strata with, in places, interstratified layers of loamy marl, very rich in shells of which eighteen per cent were living Mediterranean species.

From Nice to Genoa they followed the new coast road which for much of the way went along a ledge cut out of the side of the steep slopes or cliffs of the Maritime Alps which there rise abruptly from the sea. "The road," Lyell wrote, "is always in sight of the sea often overhanging it on a precipitous steep of some thousand feet. Hills covered with old olive trees & now & then large orchards of lemon-trees. These here & there exchanged for vines. The palms (Musa) in many gardens of considerable height & great prickly pears hanging over walls. Sea deep up to the rocks which rise boldly out of it: scarcely ever a sail."[10] Wherever a stream or river entered the sea, there was always a low level plain lying between the mouth of the stream and the steep rise of the mountains. Now and then the road descended from the hillside to cross one of these plains which "from above," Lyell wrote, "have the appearance of bays deserted by the sea."[11] Yet these plains were not so low as they looked from above and their strata of gravel, sand, and marl,

8. J. Desnoyers, "Mémoire sur la craie, et sur les terrains tertiaires de Cotentin" (1825) pp. 231–48.

9. B. de Basterot, "Description géologique du bassin tertiaire du sudouest de la France" (1825).

10. C. L., Jr. to his father. 26 Sept. 1828. Kinnordy mss. *L. & L.* I, 202–04.

11. *Principles* III, p. 164.

which contained many marine shells, were sometimes 200 feet or more above the level of the sea. Thus the strata must have been elevated since the time they were first deposited, although the amount of this elevation decreased as they went eastward, being only 100 feet at Genoa as compared to 8–900 feet in the vicinity of Nice. At Genoa two Italian naturalists, Professor Viviani and Dr. Sassi, drew the attention of the English travelers to the line of an old sea beach 100 feet above present sea level. From Genoa Lyell and Murchison turned back on their track as far as Savona where they collected a number of fossils from strata of blue marl. They then turned north to cross the Apennines to Alessandria. On the way they studied the Cadibona coal basin which appeared to be a freshwater deposit. From Alessandria they went to Turin where they had a very important meeting with Signor Franco Bonelli, a distinguished conchologist and director of the museum of zoology at Turin[12] (Map 9).

Bonelli had a very large collection of shells from the subapennine beds of northern Italy and he was able to tell Lyell and Murchison that their collection of fossil shells from the Savona marl corresponded to subapennine species. Bonelli had also observed that the fossil shells from the strata of the hill of Superga near Turin differed significantly from those of the subapennine beds and corresponded more closely to the fossil shells of the strata of Bordeaux in France, described by Basterot. Lyell and Murchison visited this hill, where they found strata of fine sand, marl, and some conglomerate inclined at an angle of seventy degrees.[13] These strata were identical in fossil content to strata they had already encountered in descending the northern slope of the Apennines on the road from Savona to Alessandria. They felt, therefore, that they had already acquired more insight into the strata of the Piedmont than the local geologists and considered publishing a note on their observations. However, Lyell and Murchison felt that the chief value of their field studies would be "to render us quite competent to judge the merit of & to understand the various works both of the ancients & moderns on this country."[14]

From Turin they went to Milan where they arrived 8 Septem-

12. Franco Andrea Bonelli (1784–1830) was in 1811 appointed professor of zoology at the Imperial University, Turin and in 1825 became director of the museum of zoology.

13. *Principles* III, p. 211.

14. C. L., Jr. to his father. 26 Sept. 1828. Kinnordy mss.

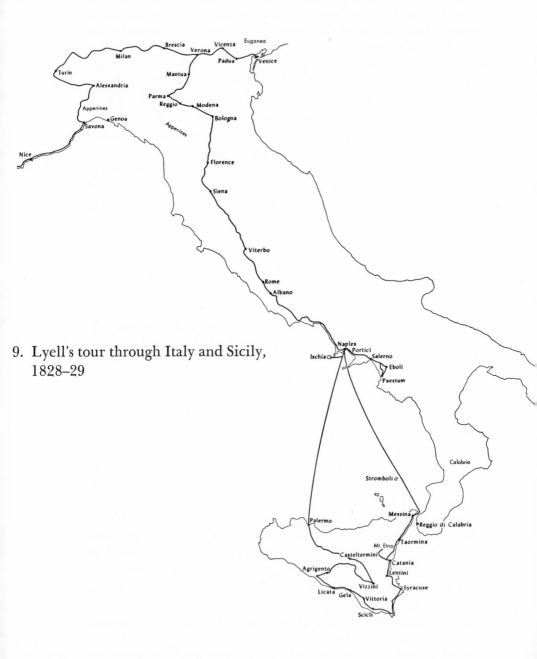

9. Lyell's tour through Italy and Sicily, 1828–29

ber. There Lyell wrote to John Herschel to tell him of his new plan to continue on his own to the south of Italy and Sicily and to ask for information and advice about these areas.

I am prepared with a moderate stock of queries & of difficulties to be answered, I hope, by studying a more modern volcanic district. The effects of earthquakes on the regular strata & the light thrown on the excavation of valleys by lavas are subjects to which I have directed a large share of attention. I should therefore be anxious to examine such parts of the coast of Sicily or Calabria as afforded evidence of elevation or subsidence either by the aid of buildings etc. raised or sunk as at Baiae, Temple of Serapis . . . or by help of modern species of shells lifted up, or sea-beaches. Wherever you observed signs of such effects of earthquakes in Sicily I should be glad to have the localities & where you saw the greatest fissures still open. The disturbance in the freshwater strata of Auvergne & Cantal due to volcanic action is so much greater than I had been led to expect & that of the subappenine beds from Montpellier to Savona containing as they do nearly 20 per cent of decided living species of shells, that I cannot but think that Calabria & Sicily must afford proofs of strata containing still more modern organic remains, raised above the level of the sea.[15]

He asked for a reply at Florence or Naples.

The next few weeks were spent studying the geology of the Euganean hills and the areas around Vicenza where they found the volcanic phenomena were "just Auvergne over again."[16] Lyell spent several days at Padua in preparing for publication their paper on the excavation of valleys, while Murchison and his wife went to see Venice. Because they had received no letters from the time they had left Marseilles, Mrs. Murchison was sure her mother was dead and was exceedingly depressed. Though he had thoroughly enjoyed his months of cooperative field work with Murchison, Lyell was somewhat relieved to see them depart for the Tyrol on 26 September. He set off the same day for Verona on his way to Parma where he had a letter of introduction from Dr. Buckland to Professor Guidotti, professor of chemistry at the University of Parma and formerly professor of natural history there.

15. C. L., Jr. to J. F. W. Herschel. 9 Sept. 1828. Roy. Soc. Lond. mss. *L. & L.* I, 200–02.

16. C. L., Jr .to his father. 26 Sept. 1828. Kinnordy mss. *L. & L.* I, 202–04.

Guidotti gave him a very friendly welcome and they spent three days from early morning till night discussing geology and fossils. "He has the finest collection of fossil shells in Italy," Lyell wrote to Caroline, "& as they chiefly belong to the most modern formation it was of first rate interest to me to get from him a multitude of facts."[17] He gave Lyell a set of the fossil shells from the subapennine beds which belonged to species still living in the Mediterranean.

The most important stratum of the subapennine formation was a marl, greyish-brown to blue in color. Near Parma Lyell found some examples of this marl which were thinly laminated like the freshwater marls of Auvergne and Provence. Signor Guidotti also told him of hills in the vicinity where this marl bed was 2,000 feet thick and yet appeared throughout to have been formed by very slow and gradual accumulation.[18] Lyell was able to compare the species which Guidotti had found in the different subapennine beds with those which Signor Bonelli of Turin considered characteristic of the same beds in his locality and found that the two men agreed remarkably.[19] Guidotti's collection contained more than 1100 extinct species "as perfect as when they lived," and he was adding to it at the rate of fifty new species a year.[20]

When he left Parma Lyell went by diligence to Bologna, where he visited the museum, and from there to Florence. On the road over the Apennines the *vetturino* went so slowly that he was able to get out to walk up the hills and thereby study the geology of the country as he went. At Florence Lyell had an introduction to Signor Targioni who introduced him to Professor Nesti and Baron Bardi. These gentlemen showed him the museum and advised him to visit the freshwater formation in the upper valley of the Arno. When Lyell rode there, he found a deposit "corresponding delightfully with our Angus lakes in all but age & species of animals. Same genera of shells."[21] The larger vertebrate fossils were those of elephant, hippopotamus, rhinoceros, and mastodon.

While he was at Florence Lyell received a letter from Murchison in the Tyrol. Mrs. Murchison had received such satisfactory

17. C. L., Jr. to his sister Caroline. 10 Oct. 1828. Kinnordy mss. *L. & L.* I, 205–07.

18. *Principles* III, pp. 158–59.

19. C. L., Jr. to R. I. M. 10 Oct. 1828. Murchison mss.

20. C. L., Jr. to his sister Caroline. 10 Oct. 1828. Kinnordy mss. *L. & L.* I, 205–07.

21. Ibid.

accounts from her parents that he hoped to be able to carry out the rest of his tour in relaxed fashion. Lyell also received there a letter from Scrope with geological information and practical hints for his trip to Sicily.

From Florence Lyell took the road to Siena, traveling alone in a gig. The weather was fine so he was able to work out the geology of the country as he went along. "I have gone several miles to right and left whenever I fancied," he wrote to Murchison, "& have found the road afford a fine section throughout." At Siena he visited the museum where Sig. Mazzi showed him "a great collection of Subappenine blue marl & yellow sand shells," but gave him none so Lyell made his own collection as he went along.[22]

The road from Siena to Viterbo crossed a volcanic area but this had now lost its novelty for him. However, he felt certain that the volcanoes were more recent than the subapennine strata associated with them and this fact, together with his observations of the depth of freshwater travertines formed in basins among the subapennine hills, suggested to Lyell that the subapennine strata were perhaps older than he had thought.

> I have found in my tour since I saw you so much novelty, although almost entirely amongst more recent strata than we were engaged in in France, that I begin to look on Subapennine as of immense respectability in point of age.[23]

He had traveled by Colle and the valley of the Elsa river:

> ... which was a favourable tour for me [he wrote to Marianne] as bringing down the chain of geological events to a later period than any of equal extent which I had seen, except perhaps in the upper Val d'Arno. But the lacustrine formation of Elsa was new to me not only as containing in it much travertin, just like the Bakie limestone, but because there are hot springs still producing the same rock.

At Viterbo he gave up his gig and went to Rome in a coach in which he conversed the whole day in Latin with a Roman priest and two Scots students for the priesthood. After a week at Rome he arranged to share a post chaise with four Frenchmen to Naples where they arrived in two days' travel. On the way he persuaded the whole party to stop to see Lake Albano, which was the crater

22. C. L., Jr. to R. I. M. 14 Oct. 1828. Murchison mss.
23. Ibid.

of an old volcano and "with which they were fortunately delighted."[24]

When he arrived at Naples on Friday, 24 October, Lyell called on the geographer Colonel Ferdinand Visconti to whom he had an introduction from Captain William Smyth, author of a geographical description of Sicily. Visconti gave him friendly assistance and information. Of the rest of the population Lyell gave a picturesque account to Marianne:

> But the people—nothing you ever heard of them is, I believe, exaggerated. It seems as if one half of an immense population, noisy & cheerful, had nothing to do & the habits, of course, of those to whom Time is of no value are most inconvenient to anyone who wishes to make good use of his. On an expedition the hour spent in bargaining is a nuisance to which even the N. of Italy is a joke. . . . You order a fiacre, 5 porters come & after a dreadful squabble you see your *sac de nuit,* umbrella, *2 hammers* & cloak devided among them. The four who are not paid stop the horse, then follow etc. No sooner off ½ mile & two ragged boys jump up behind, come as cicerones, won't get off— stop the carriage, off again—both jump up. The driver says, "You must have a cicerone sir."—"Well, I will only pay one"— "Noi siama uno signor!"[25]

At Naples Lyell also found that the steamboat which plied to Sicily had been requisitioned by the government so that he would have to wait there twelve days (Map 10). He therefore went immediately to Ischia, a volcanic island lying in the sea a few miles to the northwest of Naples (Fig. 34). He expected to meet there a party of geologists who had just preceded him to the island, but missed them. This circumstance actually gave him more time to study the geology of the island by himself during the next three days. To his great satisfaction he found in the central mountain on Ischia, called Epomeo, all the characteristics of an old volcano which was "a most admirable illustration of Mont Dore with the difference . . . of the substitution of marine for freshwater & the consequent abundance of organic remains."[26] The island was founded on strata which were very rich in shells. On the sides of

24. C. L., Jr. to his sister Marianne. 20 Oct. 1828. *L. & L.* I, 207–10.

25. Ibid. "We are one, Sir."

26. C. L., Jr. to R. I. M. 6 Nov. 1828. Murchison mss. *L. & L.* I, 210–13 (printed with certain errors in copying).

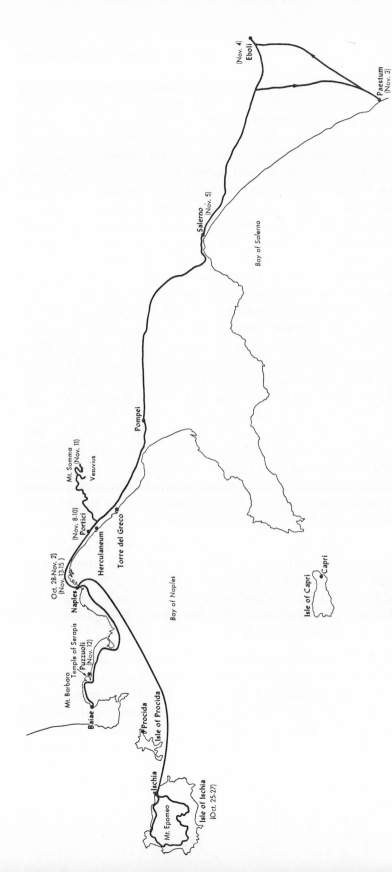

10. Lyell's excursions in the vicinity of Naples, November 1828

Epomeo he found beds of "striped & ribboned altered marl" and strata of clay but did not at first find any shells in them. The resemblance of these clays to the shell-bearing strata below struck him because high on Mont Dore in the Auvergne he had seen marls which resembled the "green cypriferous marls" of the horizontal freshwater strata in the Limagne below. "At last," he wrote to Murchison, "at an enormous height corresponding in Ischia to what the great cascade is in Mt. Dore I found in a mass of this clay, marine shells unaltered & belonging to the same class as those in the lower regions of Ischia."[27] This observation was of supreme importance to Lyell because it confirmed, and firmly fixed in his mind, the idea that uplift on an enormous scale could occur, and had occurred, in association with volcanic activity. In this clay stratum he had found some thirty species of shells most of which, he realized immediately, were recent, that is, similar to species still living in modern seas. On his return to Naples Lyell had his collection of shells from Ischia identified as to species by Signor Costa, a former professor who had been displaced from his chair at the University of Otranto on account of his "constitutionalist" opinions. When he had studied them, Costa was able to tell Lyell that all of his thirty species of Ischian shells were identical with species still found living in the surrounding Mediterranean. This fact told him that not only had the strata of Ischia been uplifted by volcanic activity but they had been uplifted in the period of time since the modern fauna had become established in the Mediterranean. He wrote in triumph to his sister Eleanor:

> . . . so let the box go to the bottom, or the shells be annihilated by Douaniers I will let the world know that the whole Isle of Isk, as the natives call it, has risen from the sea 2600 ft. since the Mediterranean was peopled with the very species of shell-fish which have now the honour of living with or being eaten by us —our common oyster & cockle among the rest.[28]

Costa had been collecting living species of shells from the waters of southern Italy and Sicily and had discovered several species not previously known to be present in the Mediterranean. His work illustrated how essential to the development of paleontology was a knowledge of the natural history of living shells. Lyell noted one species, *Verrus rugosa*, which had first been described by

27. Ibid.
28. C. L., Jr. to his sister Eleanor. 9 Nov. 1828. Kinnordy mss. *L. & L.* I, 213–16.

Linnaeus from the north Atlantic, then by Lamarck from the coast of West Africa, and which Costa had recently found in the sea around Sicily. Similarly he had found in the Mediterranean two other species, *Solen callosum* and *Marginella muscaria Lam.*, previously thought to occur only in distant tropical waters. He had also found one species, *Nerita helicina*, described by Brocchi as fossil, living in the sea near Puzzuoli.[29]

When he had first discovered that Ischia had been uplifted from the sea, Lyell had next looked for signs of elevated beaches or sea cliffs on the island which would give some sign of the successive stages of this uplift. He found them almost immediately in the precipices which formed the north and south sides of the summit ridge of Epomeo. The northern escarpment, 1000 feet high was especially striking.

> The abrupt manner in which the horizontal tuffs are there cut off, in the face of the cliff, is such as the action of the sea working on soft materials might easily have produced, undermining and removing a great portion of the mass. A heap of shingle which lies at the base of a steep declivity on the flanks of Epomeo . . . may once, perhaps, have been a sea-beach, for it certainly could not have been brought to the spot by any existing torrents.[30]

These observations in Ischia, together with others which he was soon to make in Sicily, of the effects of the sea in determining the forms of elevated land, were to influence Lyell's ideas of the origin of land forms almost too deeply. He was in later life to see elevated sea cliffs and the effects of sea erosion where in fact there were none, and where the phenomena were the result of atmospheric erosion, rain, and running water.

During nearly three weeks at Naples Lyell studied the lavas of Vesuvius, still fresh from the great eruption in 1822, and visited Herculaneum and Pompeii. In the museum at Pompeii he studied the objects discovered at these sites. He also studied accounts of the great earthquake of 1783 in Calabria and observed its effects at different places in the countryside. For this purpose, and to study the travertine strata of the plain south of Salerno, he made an expedition on 4 November by gig to Paestum.

On 11 November Lyell made a second expedition to Vesuvius

29. Ms. notebook 18, pp. 23–24. Kinnordy mss.
30. *Principles* III, p. 127.

and on the 12th he seems to have gone by boat to Puzzuoli. In the *Principles* he recorded his observations there:

> If we coast along the shore from Naples to Puzzuoli we find, on approaching the latter place, that the lofty and precipitous cliffs of indurated tuff, resembling that of which Naples is built, retire slightly from the sea, and that a low level tract of fertile land, of a very different aspect, intervenes between the present sea-beach and what was evidently the ancient line of coast.[31]

The new deposit, containing marine shells of species commonly living along the coast, had been raised about twenty feet above the sea. One of the beds contained many "remains of works of art, tiles, squares of mosaic pavement of different colours, and small sculptured ornaments, perfectly uninjured."[32] These artifacts showed that the bed had been formed within historic times and the interesting fact was that this bed occurred below, as well as above, beds containing sea shells. Therefore, since the time when the buildings from which these fragments were derived had stood upon the site, the ground had subsided beneath the sea and had later been reelevated.

Lyell confirmed the fact of subsidence and later elevation in the vicinity by the famous ruins of the temple of Serapis standing by the coast just to the north of Puzzuoli (Fig. 35). Three pillars of the temple, each forty-two feet high, remained standing. For about twelve feet above their pedestals their surface was smooth and unaltered, but above this height was another zone, also of about twelve feet in which the marble of the pillars was deeply bored by a species of marine bivalve *Lithodomus.*

> The perforations are so considerable in depth and size that they manifest a long continued abode of the Lithodomi in the columns; for, as the inhabitant grows older and increases in size, it bores a larger cavity, to correspond with the increasing magnitude of its shell. We must consequently infer a long continued immersion of the pillars in sea-water, at a time when the lower part was covered up and protected by strata of tuff and the rubbish of buildings, the highest part at the same time projecting above the waters, and being consequently weathered, but not materially injured.[33]

31. *Principles* I, p. 449.
32. Ibid., p. 451.
33. Ibid., p. 453–54.

Because the present level of the temple floor was about one foot below the high-water level of the bay of Naples, the site of the temple must have been elevated some twenty-three feet since the time when these pillars stood upright in the sea. Because the temple had certainly not been built in the first place beneath the sea it must have first subsided before being reelevated. There were other evidences of subsidence in the area because in the sea to the northwest of the temple of Serapis, at a short distance from the shore, were the completely submerged ruins of two other temples. Lyell later determined that the elevation of the temple of Serapis had occurred in all probability during the great earthquake of 1538 accompanying the volcanic eruption which produced Monte Nuovo to the northwest of Puzzuoli. He was particularly impressed by the amount of elevation and subsidence which had occurred at Puzzuoli while the rest of Italy remained relatively undisturbed. In his notebook he wrote:

> Everything now indicates partial activity in the agents of change & general rest. Every cause in its individual operation is governed by this principle. There are intervals of inactivity, or if, as in some rivers and cliffs, constant waste, it is perpetually shifting its place.[34]

At Naples Lyell received letters from Charles Daubeny and Dr. Buckland, both of whom had visited Sicily and who, now that they had learned he was planning to go there, wrote with advice and information. Dr. Buckland urged him to take certain articles of food, because the country was so poor and the inns so bad. Accordingly, Lyell bought tea, sugar, cheese, and four bottles of brandy—this last item because Mrs. Buckland said it would keep off malaria. Yet despite the discomforts and hardships of Sicily, which he found his friends had not exaggerated, Lyell enjoyed his visit there.

Lyell's tour through Italy had confirmed magnificently what he had hoped and expected to find. When he had parted from the Murchisons at Padua in September he had expected to find the subapennine strata younger and more recently elevated as he approached Naples where there was the active volcano of Vesuvius and where earthquakes were of common occurrence. He was already convinced that volcanic activity and earthquakes were the agency by which

34. Ms. Notebook 18, p. 146. Kinnordy mss.

rock strata were elevated, and he had hoped to find evidence of recent changes of land level around Naples. This he had found. It
delighted but did not surprise him. However, the geology he was
about to encounter in Sicily would astonish him greatly.

At this point in his travels Lyell considered that the youngest
formation he had encountered embraced the subapennine strata,
which at Nice and in the north of Italy contained about eighteen
per cent of living species of shells. In Ischia and at Pozzuoli he had
found strata containing the same species of shells as occurred in
the Mediterranean, but these he looked upon as having been elevated yesterday, geologically speaking. They represented more or
less contemporary deposits of the Mediterranean sea bottom. Lyell
was not at this point prepared to consider strata in which all of the
fossils belonged to living species, as of great geological age. In
Sicily, in the vicinity of Etna, also an active volcano, he expected
to discover further geological phenomena to extend and confirm
what he had seen in the neighborhood of Naples. In this expectant frame of mind he embarked on 16 November on the boat for
Messina where he landed on the eighteenth. He described his
initial adventures to Dr. Buckland.

> On my arrival at Messina I went to my banker Cailler, a dull,
> fat, vulgar, heavy, stupid John Bull. Told him I wanted cash,
> just landed, etc. "You shall be served sir."—"Where can I find
> Mr. Broadbent the American Consul?"—"Mr. Broadbent! God
> bless your soul, Sir, Mr. B.! don't enquire for him. More than
> two years ago he was building & ventured on the scaffolding
> before the wall was set. It gave way & down he fell with the
> master mason—both killed."—"Sorry to hear it, and may I ask
> where the English Consul lives, for I want a passport for Reg-
> gio."—"The English Consul! Sir—God bless your soul (Of course
> I thought he had fallen off a scaffolding)—Why can't you see
> across the street where the English Arms are?"
>
> I then learnt where Power lived, a gentlemanlike & obliging
> man . . . He got me a trustworthy muleteer for a reasonable
> price & sent a box, by a friend of his to Naples, containing my
> collection of the Tertiary rocks round Messina which are very
> curious.[35]

From Messina Lyell went south along the coast to Taormina

35. C. L., Jr. to W. Buckland. 27 Nov. 1828. [copy] Mss. in Dept. of Geology,
National Museum of Wales, Cardiff.

and thence to Catania on muleback. On his road he skirted the eastern base of Mount Etna (Map 11).

> . . . Etna, which rises near the sea in solitary grandeur to the height of nearly eleven thousand feet, the mass being chiefly composed of volcanic matter ejected above the surface of the water. The base of the cone is almost circular, and eighty-seven English miles in circumference; but if we include the whole district over which its lavas extend, the circuit is probably twice that extent. The cone is divided by Nature into three distinct zones, called the *fertile,* the *woody,* and the *desert* regions. The first of these, comprising the delightful country around the skirts of the mountain, is well cultivated, thickly inhabited, and covered with olives, vines, corn, fruit-trees and aromatic herbs. Higher up, the woody region encircles the mountain—an extensive forest, six or seven miles in width, affording pasturage for numerous flocks. . . . Above the forest is the desert region, a waste of black lava and scoriae; where, on a kind of plain, rises the cone to the height of about eleven hundred feet, from which sulphureous vapours are continually evolved.[36]

As he rode south along the coast, Lyell noted:

> Etna is very grand from this side, much more than any engraving gives idea of. The small cone at top without snow & a stream of white smoke, fleecy as clouds & higher than they are generally. Then a broad flat zone of snow sufficiently irregular in outline to be picturesque, then the woody region & then the line below with yellow autumnal tint.
>
> My guide Rosario says that when sea is high, Etna smokes most.[37]

The cone of Etna was on the whole symmetrical except for the interruption produced by a deep, broad valley, the Val del Bove.

On 24 November Lyell and his guide reached Zaffarana on the upper border of the fertile region on the slopes of Etna. Above Zaffarana he entered the ravine-like valley of St. Giacomo. As he rode up the ravine he saw that the ridge on the north side was formed by modern lavas of Etna whereas the south side exposed a series of beds, "composed of tuffs and lavas descending with a gentle inclination towards the sea." At the upper end of the ravine of

36. *Principles* I, pp. 361–62.
37. Ms. Notebook 19, p. 38. Kinnordy mss.

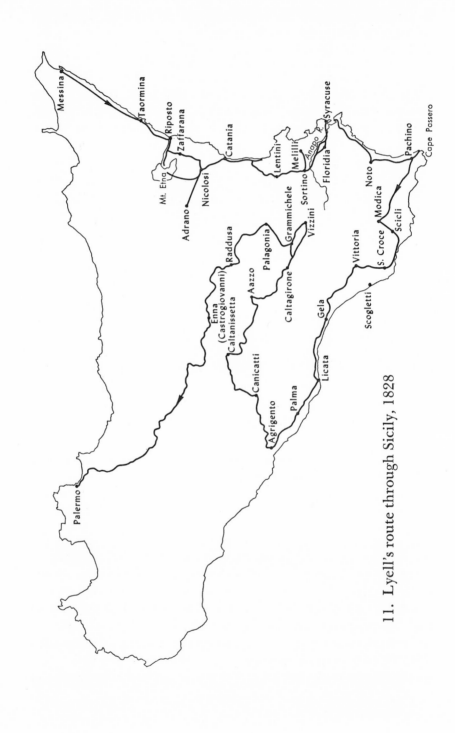

11. Lyell's route through Sicily, 1828

St. Giacomo he rode through a narrow defile, the Portello di Calanna, to enter the broader Val di Calanna whose walls rose much higher on the ascending slopes of Etna.

> Here again we find, on our right, many currents of modern lava, piled one upon the other, and on our left a continuation of our former section, in a perpendicular cliff from four hundred to five hundred feet high. As this lofty wall sweeps in a curve, it has very much the appearance of the escarpment which Somma presents towards Vesuvius and this resemblance is increased by the occurrence of two or three vertical dikes which traverse the gently-inclined volcanic beds.[38]

When Lyell first rode into the Val di Calanna he thought from the resemblance of the cliff on the south side to the escarpment of Somma that he had entered a lateral crater of Etna. However, if that were so the beds exposed in the cliff should be inclined away from the Val di Calanna in all directions. Instead they all sloped with a uniform inclination eastward toward the sea showing that they had all originated as outpourings from the principal cone of Etna.

At the top of the Val di Calanna Lyell rode through another defile, the Rocca di Calanna, to enter a third enormous valley whose vertical walls rose at its upper end close to the very summit of Etna (Fig. 36). The grandeur of the scene struck him forcibly. As recorded in the *Principles:*

> Let the reader picture to himself a large amphitheatre, five miles in diameter, and surrounded on three sides by precipices from two thousand to three thousand feet in height . . . This plain has been deluged by repeated streams of lava, and although it appears almost level when viewed from a distance, it is, in fact, more uneven than the surface of the most tempestuous sea. Besides the minor irregularities of the lava, the valley is in one part interrupted by a ridge of rocks.

The precipices surrounding the Val del Bove differed strikingly from the precipice of the south side of the Val di Calanna in that, in contrast to the few vertical dikes of lava there present, here there were an immense number of vertical dikes on all sides.

The face of the precipices already mentioned is broken in the

38. *Principles* III, p. 85.

most picturesque manner by the vertical walls of lava which traverse them. These masses usually stand out in relief, are exceedingly diversified in form, and often of immense altitude. In the autumn, their black outline may often be seen relieved by clouds of fleecy vapour which settle behind them, and do not disperse until midday. . . .

As soon as the vapours begin to rise, the changes of scene are varied in the highest degree, different rocks being unveiled and hidden by turns, and the summit of Etna often breaking through the clouds for a moment with its dazzling snows, and being then as suddenly withdrawn from the view.

An unusual silence prevails, for there are no torrents dashing from the rocks, nor any movement of running water in this valley, such as may almost invariably be heard in mountainous regions. Every drop of water that falls from the heavens, or flows from the melting ice and snow, is instantly absorbed by the porous lava. . . .

The strips of green herbage and forest-land, which have here and there escaped the burning lavas, serve by contrast, to heighten the desolation of the scene. When I visited the valley, nine years after the eruption of 1819, I saw hundreds of trees, or rather the white skeletons of trees, on the borders of the black lava, the trunks and branches being all leafless, and deprived of their bark by the scorching heat emitted from the melted rock.

The circular form of the Val del Bove and the thousands of vertical dikes in its precipice walls again suggested to Lyell that he had entered an enormous volcanic crater. However, having been mistaken once, he carefully explored the walls of the Val del Bove, especially on the upper side.

If the supposed analogy between Somma and the Val del Bove should hold true [he wrote], the tuffs and lavas at the head of the valley, would dip to the west, those on the north side towards the north, and those on the southern side to the south. But such I did not find to be the inclination of the beds; they all dip towards the sea or nearly east, as was before seen to be the case in the Valley of Calanna.

In some places the walls of the Val del Bove cut through buried volcanic cones which had formerly been lateral cones on the sides of Etna. When this was so the beds of lavas and tuffs dipped in all directions at steep angles of from thirty-five to fifty degrees. By contrast, the beds conforming to the sides of Etna all dipped eastward to the sea at low angles of fifteen to twenty-five degrees.

When Lyell came to consider how the Val del Bove had been formed, he decided that not only was it not a crater, but neither had it been formed by running water because it was deepest on its upper side, whereas a valley formed by a stream should have become deeper as it descended. The only way left for the Val del Bove to have been formed was by subsidence. Perhaps as a consequence of volcanic eruptions, its underlying support had been removed and the floor of the valley had sunk.

The significance of the Val del Bove for Lyell was that it offered a cross section of Etna, cut into the very core of the mountain. In the walls of the Val del Bove Lyell could see how the mountain had been gradually built up from successive layers of lava and tuff. Successive groups of lateral cones had formed on the slopes of Etna, carried on their eruptions, and later been buried as the growing bulk of the mountain overwhelmed them.

> There seems nothing [he continued] in the deep sections of the Val del Bove, to indicate that the lava currents of remote periods were greater in volume than those of modern times; and there are abundant proofs that the countless beds of solid rock and scoriae were accumulated, as now, in succession.[39]

He concluded that Etna must have been formed slowly over an immense period of time. To the very end of his life Lyell would return to Etna and to the Val del Bove to observe one or another aspect of its remarkable phenomena.

On reaching Catania, Lyell made an expedition to the island of Cyclops, in the sea opposite Etna. He recognized it as a detached portion of a lava flow which had intruded between sedimentary strata. On Cyclops this lava was capped with clay and he saw a similar clay visible at a distance on the mainland at the foot of Etna. Some peasants told him that this clay contained shells:

> . . . so I hastened thither & found 700 feet & more up Etna in beds alternating with old lavas, sea shells, fossil, but many I know of modern Mediterranean species. This is just what everyone in England & at Naples & Catania told me I should *not* find, but which I came to Sicily to look for—the same which I

39. Ibid., pp. 87–101.

discovered in Ischia, & which if my geological views be just will be found near all recent volcanoes & wherever earthquakes have prevailed for some thousand years past.

Some of the shells which Lyell obtained from these beds still kept the color which was characteristic of living representatives of the species present in the nearby sea. He was particularly excited by this find because, since they underlay Etna, they would enable him to determine "the zoological date of the oldest part of Etna."[40]

At Catania Lyell met Dr. Giuseppe Gemmellaro to whom he had an introduction from John Herschel. Gemmellaro had published on Etna, and through him Lyell was invited to stay at his brother's house at Nicolosi on the side of Etna. The Gemmellaro brothers made the study of Etna their avocation. "The elder G." Lyell continued in his letter to Marianne, "is a kind of laird and chief magistrate. Cannot talk French or English, so we talk half Latin, half Italian and so always get on with one or other." A few days later, on 1 December, accompanied by a guide, Lyell ascended to the top of the cone of Etna which already had some snow upon it at this season of the year; old Gemellaro started him off "in the middle of a coolish night." Lyell recorded:

Left Nicolosi 3 hours before daybreak, moonlight, falling stars, low mist came & went. Some way above Nicolosi entered old woods oak, beech.[41]

At daybreak they reached the upper border of the woody region where they made a fire for breakfast. Lyell noted that although the oak and chestnut trees around their stopping place were reputed to be two thousand years old, they stood upon currents of modern lava—another indication of the great age of even the youngest parts of Etna. Dr. Martin Rudwick, who has himself ascended Etna, has described what Lyell saw:

As they climbed higher through the forest zone and into the zone of grassland, the main string of volcanic cones was reduced by the sheer scale of the mountain to the appearance of small pimples; and on climbing still higher, the view to the south opened out beyond the plain of Catania to the low hills of the Val di Noto toward Syracuse. Finally, in the desert zone of volcanic ash near the summit crater, the whole of eastern Sicily

40. C. L., Jr. to his sister Marianne. 29 Nov. 1828. Kinnordy mss. *L. & L.* I, 216–20.
41. Ms. notebook 19, p. 127. Kinnordy mss.

and the tip of Calabria were spread out around them like a map, while almost directly below them the broadly conical form of the mountain was gashed by the Val del Bove.[42]

During the climb up the cone Lyell experienced some of the symptoms of mountain sickness which forced him to go slowly. When they reached the lip of the crater, so much vapor was rising from it that he could see nothing clearly within. Lyell recorded in his notebook:

On summit, wind but clear. Large mass of ice round inner lip [of crater] with hot vapour issuing between it & crater. One side of crater broken down, a kind of trench. Inspired much sulphureous vapour, which for hours after my descent I tasted, like having been half suffocated over a brazier.

There are no dikes known in crater of Etna. A small stream of mud was descending crater, but this proceeds not far. Like all water it passes under ground soon. Must not this consolidate lavas?[43]

Since he had a commanding view of the Val del Bove he made a sketch of it, as Dr. Buckland had asked him to do[44] (Fig. 37).

The morning after his ascent Lyell awoke to find Etna capped with a new fall of snow which Rosario, his muleteer, said made it "white like a dove." At Nicolosi sleet was falling so Lyell remained "a willing prisoner" with the Gemmellaros and read their collection of books about Etna.

On 5 December Lyell took leave of the Gemmellaros at Nicolosi and set out on an expedition to Aderno, a day on which his horse broke loose and was nearly drowned when it swam the river Simeto just above a waterfall. On 7 December he reached Catania where he found he had been "elected an honorary member of the Gioenian Society of Catania, the only body which publishes in the

42. M. J. S. Rudwick, "Lyell on Etna and the Antiquity of the Earth" in C. J. Schneer ed., *Toward a History of Geology* (1969), p. 294. Dr. Rudwick believes that Lyell's ascent of Ætna was "the imaginative climax of his whole expedition" and that it "was also the intellectual climax of his journey, but only in retrospect, for its full significance could not be grasped until he could relate it to the geology of the surrounding area." Ibid., p. 295. The latter statement is I think the truer. Lyell's ascent of Etna was certainly an important part of his experience during his tour of Sicily but I know of no evidence of his special excitement as an immediate result of it. Some of his discoveries later in Sicily did astonish and disturb him.

43. Ms. Notebook 19, p. 127.

44. C. L., Jr. to his sister Marianne. 29 Nov.–Dec. 1828. Kinnordy mss. *L. & L.* I, pp. 216–20.

two Sicilies any memoirs on Natural History & Philosophy & theirs are very respectable."[45] The man and boy whom Lyell had commissioned before he went to Nicolosi to collect shells for him from the strata at the foot of Etna "brought a glorious set of shells" and with his work at Catania thus completed Lyell was ready to continue southward. In the predawn darkness on 9 December he crossed the plain of Catania, following the line of sea beach. "Before the sun rose from the sea, all the snow of Etna was glowing with red, like another dawn in the west," he wrote. "I have seen this sight three times, a proof of fine weather and early rising."[46] On the southern edge of the plain of Catania he was confronted with the rising ground of the great plateau of the Val di Noto.

Just after he crossed the river Simeto Lyell rode up on to the low plateau above Primosole where, on looking back at Etna, he saw its enormous bulk resting as it were on a platform outlined by the low clay hills above Catania and at Aderno where he had been a few days earlier. He paused to draw a sketch of Etna (Fig. 38) from this point because it showed clearly how Etna lay above, and was therefore younger than the line of clay strata which outcropped in the hills around its base. These were the same strata from which the man and boy had obtained fossils for him above Catania.

In the valley of San Paolo, a quarter mile west of Primosole, Lyell explored a deep gorge cut through the limestone of the plateau. This limestone resembled somewhat one he had seen near Verona. Slightly yellow in color, it was very thick bedded and without any clear stratification even though it was exposed in vertical precipices one hundred feet high on either side of the gorge. Such fossil shells as he could find in it were broken or were merely the impressions where the shells had been.

From Primosole Lyell rode on to Lentini where the hills above the town formed an escarpment capped with the same hard, compact limestone as at Primosole, with pecten and madrepore fossils in it. The underlying portion of the escarpment consisted of "a ferruginous tuff, partly volcanic, sedimentary."[47] Tuff was an Italian name for a volcanic rock of earthy texture composed of bits of scoriae and loose matter discharged from a volcano. Near the bottom of the escarpment was another stratum of limestone contain-

45. Ibid.

46. C. L., Jr. to his sister Caroline. 11 Dec. 1828. Kinnordy mss. *L. & L.* I, pp. 221–27.

47. Ms. Notebook 20, p. 36. Kinnordy mss.

ing "many turbinated shells, [i.e.] casts—corals, branching." Underneath this limestone again was a bed of peperino, an Italian name for a volcanic rock formed by the cementing together of volcanic sand, cinders, or scoriae.

In one place in the limestone at Lentini Lyell found some "imbedded volcanic pebbles covered with full grown serpulae." This curious fact showed that after the volcanic rock had become rounded into a pebble by the action of waves or running water, a long time had elapsed to allow for the growth of the serpulae before the pebble had become embedded into the limestone. The whole process of the deposition of the sediment containing that pebble had therefore occurred very gradually over a long period of time.[48]

At this point Lyell was uncertain of the age of the limestone at Primosole and Lentini. He wrote in his notebook:

> If limestone above Lentini be very recent, it offers at least *casts* of shells which look like an ancient limestone.[49]

The strata on the sides of the valley above Lentini were not really horizontal as they appeared at first. Instead the strata on the northwest side of the valley dipped northwest while those on the southeast side dipped southeast; the valley had apparently been cut out of the crest of anticline and the strata around Lentini had actually been much curved and upheaved.

Lyell stayed overnight at Lentini where the inn was, by the usual standard of country inns in Sicily, quite comfortable; it actually had glass in the windows and not many panes broken. He was awakened next morning by the firing of guns in front of the churches to announce the Mass. That day, 10 December, he rode on to Melilli where he had an introduction to the priest, a fellow member of the Gioenian Society of Catania. The good father invited Lyell to stay overnight, but Lyell declined. He explained to Caroline:

> There was a lady there whom his valet officiously informed me was a *near* relation of his, who I perceived was against the company of a stranger, which I believe he desired. She is the mother, said Rosario, of those children you saw & I believe none here know who the father is.[50]

48. *Principles* III, p. 73.
49. Ms. Notebook 20, p. 39. Kinnordy mss.
50. C. L., Jr. to his sister Caroline. 11–31 Dec. 1828. Kinnordy mss.

Lyell found a room at another house, but next morning the priest sent his nephew "a youth of 15 with a grand shovel hat & silk gown" to show Lyell a circular valley which he thought was a volcanic crater. Lyell and the youth followed a river cut through limestone which reminded Lyell of the valley of the Wye below Chepstow in Monmouthshire. Then they came out upon the circular valley, Gozzo degli Martiri cut out of the yellowish and white limestone strata in great steps. Although it was certainly not a volcanic crater, the site was very interesting geologically and Lyell sketched it[51] (Fig. 39). In the stream at the bottom of Gozzo degli Martiri Lyell found the limestone changed into "a white rock, like marble" in the vicinity of dikes of a volcanic rock exactly like the trap rock of Scotland.[52]

When he had finished examining Gozzo degli Martiri Lyell crossed the hills to Sortino in the valley of the Anapa river, where he visited the caves of Pentalica. These caves opened in the limestone walls of the river valley. Lyell got a man to dig a hole in the floor of one cave to search for fossil bones as Dr. Buckland had asked him to do, but since the tools were not good, they did not dig very deeply and found nothing.

From Sortino Lyell rode down the Anapa valley. On either side of the valley rose cliffs of horizontal white limestone strata to a height of four hundred to six hundred feet, revealing the great depth of the Noto limestone. The limestone terminated near Floridia in a great escarpment, several hundred feet high. But because, as the river Anapa descended, the beds of horizontal limestone presented in the walls of its valley were lower and older, Lyell estimated the total depth of the formation at more than eight hundred feet.

Lyell's geological observations had occupied him so fully on this day (10 December) that he did not reach Syracuse until after the gates of the city had been closed. He then returned to Floridia where the inn was so bad that he requested a room from the pharmacist who was also the mayor and was comfortably housed. The next day (Thursday 11 December) at Syracuse, Lyell summarized in his notebook the results of his observations since he left Catania:

Nothing can be more evidently identical than the whole Val

51. *Principles* III, p. 110.
52. Ms. Notebook 20, p. 48. Kinnordy mss.

di Noto *calcaire grossier* of Primosoli, Lentini, Melilli, Sortino & Syracuse. In many parts the rock assumes somewhat of a corn-brash character & this, carried to excess no doubt, is the con-glomerate of Floridia, for it is not, as Daubeny calls it, a breccia. The thin laminae & schistose tendency of that of Floridia shew that the interstratified pebble-beds, & probably the loose sand, calcareous near Syracuse, also covered by harder [rocks] are the lower part of series & would be found below the rocks of San Paolo at Primosoli if [the] section went deeper.

In all the localities above mentioned pectens are common wherever there are fossils, & a gigantic one in particular, but all are usually either casts or fragments. The rock sometimes passes into a compact semicrystalline limestone, probably when near volcanic centres. At Primosoli, Lentini & Sortino & Melilli when this happens there is peperino near.

I have seen no wood in the formation; fossils [are] rarer in the decided peperino, where I have seen it, than in the lime-stones.[53]

When Lyell rode over the Noto limestone he seems at first to have taken it for an older formation, perhaps one of Tertiary age, but likely older than the clay on the hills above Catania. In his sketch of the geology of Sicily published in 1825, Charles Daubeny had described a "breccia" or conglomerate, which "replete with shells, not far, if at all, far removed from existing species, seems to fill up the hollows in most of the older rocks of Sicily."[54] Daubeny said that the breccia rested on a calcareous marl, a rock quite dif-ferent in character and lacking fossil shells.[55] Since Lyell seems to have been using Daubeny's "Sketch" as a guide in his tour of Sicily and since initially he had no reason to doubt the accuracy of Daubeny's interpretation of the order of the strata, he probably assumed that the limestone of the Val di Noto was the same forma-tion as the "calcareous marl" described by Daubeny and he prob-ably also assumed that it was, as Daubeny called it, one of "the older rocks of Sicily." Doubts seem to have begun to arise in his mind first when he encountered the conglomerate limestone at the foot of the escarpment at Floridia because this rock, which lay at the bottom of the Val di Noto series of limestones, resembled so

53. Ibid., pp. 66–67.
54. C. Daubeny, "Sketch of the geology of Sicily" (1825) p. 117.
55. Ibid., p. 254.

closely Daubeny's breccia. These doubts tended to increase as a result of his observations at Syracuse.

When Lyell reached Syracuse he visited the public museum where he learned of the recent death of a friar who had possessed a fossil collection. He immediately arranged to buy them. It was not a large collection, but the specimens were good. They represented a larger number of fossils from the quarries around Syracuse than Lyell could hope to collect by himself and more than had ever been described before from these strata.

Next morning Lyell made an even more significant discovery. He described it to Murchison:

> The morning I started from Syracuse, when mules were loaded, I heard that shells were found in a clay or brick earth S. of harbour. I had a longish day before me, but sent round the steeds & took a boat & landed on the finest preserve of shells which I had seen before or have since. I worked with the boatman & got about 30 good species. Now that I know how rare these localities are I regret I did not return & give a whole day.[56]

From the south side of Syracuse harbor Lyell made a sketch of the limestone hills, rising on either side of the Anapa valley (Fig. 40). He was anxious to determine the relationship of these beds of clay to the Val di Noto limestone. In his notebook he recorded of the blue clay:

> The dip is N. Westerly, perhaps 10° & straight in towards the hills of valley of Anapa. Hence, as far as can be inferred these clays are older & w.ᵈ pass under the *calcaire grossier* of Sortino. No argument contra, tho' mere clay, because solid limestone with shells overall.

However he was not perfectly certain and further on he noted:

> In consequence of the numerous small bays it is easy to be deceived in the dip of the beds S. of harbour, but these afford also the means of perceiving that the beds dip N.W. or inland.
>
> The strata may be curved however, as I have not examined many places.

A complicating fact in his mind was that the limestone beds at Melilli had dipped uniformly eastward toward the sea. However, the bed of the Anapa river, in its lower portion as it approached

---

56. C. L., Jr. to R. I. M. 16 Dec. 1828. Murchison mss.

Syracuse, cut through clay strata. The escarpment of Val di Noto limestone which rose above the coastal plain behind Floridia and Syracuse reminded Lyell of the escarpment of the oolite above Cheltenham in Gloucestershire. It was about the same height and similar in form.[57]

From Syracuse Lyell rode to Noto where he stayed overnight in an uncomfortable inn. Next day he found there a remarkable freshwater formation of travertine containing well-preserved fossil reeds and leaves of dicotyledonous plants. From Noto to Pachino the road crossed a calcareous sandstone which at first seemed to contain no fossils, but after much searching Lyell discovered a fragment of an oyster shell which proved that the whole formation was marine. He continued on to Cape Passaro at the extreme southeastern tip of Sicily where he enjoyed the hospitality of "a good simple honest priest" in a house which reminded him of a humble Scottish highland manse.

At Cape Passaro Lyell found layers of volcanic trap interposed between the limestone strata, and the limestone in the vicinity of the trap had been converted to marble. In this limestone were many hippurites, fossils which Lyell had not found elsewhere in Sicily. Since the strata at Cape Passaro dipped to the south, Lyell decided that they must be younger than those beds of calcareous sandstone he had passed over on the road between Noto and Pachino (Fig. 41).

Despite the few days of sleet and rain which had kept him at Nicolosi and a light rain at Syracuse, Lyell had so far enjoyed mostly good weather on his tour. The rainy season in Sicily was coming on, however, and was already unseasonably late in starting. To complete his explorations, Lyell was engaged in a race with the weather. Once the rains began, the streams, which in the dry season could be easily forded, would become impassable and the packed clay of the mule paths would become bottomless mud. When he wished to proceed westward along the coast from Cape Passaro, he found that the streams near the sea were already too swollen to ford, so he had to go inland to Spaccaforno where he slept overnight in the rented cell of a Capuchin monk. From Spaccaforno he went to Scicli standing "in the bottom of one of those remarkable deep circular valleys which abound in this country."[58] The next evening at Santa Croce Lyell had to sleep in a room next

57. Ms. Notebook 20, pp. 72–82. Kinnordy mss.
58. Ibid., pp. 102–03.

the mule stable which he thought was at least a little better than sleeping with the mules themselves. However, when he reached Licata two days later on 16 December, he had enjoyed a week without rain so that his luck with the weather was holding very well.

At Scogletti Lyell found beds of conglomerate sandstone, which he referred to as "pebble beds," overlying and sometimes unconformable with beds of sandstone and calcareous sandstone, which he considered to be the same formation as the calcareous sandstone between Noto and Pachino and the strata at the base of the escarpment at Floridia. These overlying "pebble beds" he thought were:

> . . . no doubt the calc.[areous]—aren[aceous] breccia of Dr. Daubeny. This last contains here echinus, mammillated terebre?, but only saw these in loose fragments from the curious breccia which is interposed between the arenaceous laminated upper stratum & the regular under-formation.[59]

Thus as he rode westward along the southern coast of Sicily Lyell expected to find the breccia "with shells, not far, if at all, removed from existing species,"[60] overlying and younger than the series of limestones and sandstones forming the great Val di Noto formation.

The next day (15 December), at Terranuova, Lyell saw thick beds of sandstone which reminded him strongly of those at Floridia and still more strongly of those south of the Anapa river near Syracuse.[61] In the stones of the buildings there he saw large fossil pectens. On 16 December Lyell reached Licata where he noted:

> There is nothing in the valley of the Fiumo Salso at Licata which could indicate to a traveller, or even to a mineralogist, that this country was of more recent formation than the oldest secondary districts of England and France.—The valleys are worn down to near level of sea, just declivity left for rivers to flow. . .

> The plain of Licata is a large flat of blue clay like some plain of the Weald. It is surrounded by a great amphitheatre of hills of whitish looking clay & white stone from 3[00] to 500 feet high[62] [Fig. 42].

59. Ibid., p. 104.
60. Daubeny, "Geology of Sicily," p. 117.
61. Ms. Notebook 20, p. 110.
62. Ibid., p. 126.

Despite the lateness of the season the weather had remained so consistently fine that at Licata Lyell decided he would attempt to reach Castrogiovanni in the interior. Dr. Daubeny had described a great escarpment overlooking the valley of Enna in which the strata rose to more than 2800 feet above sea level.[63] During these days along the southern coast of Sicily, when Lyell was spending eleven hours each day in the saddle, the sun in the middle of the day was warm enough to bring out a few lizards and a number of butterflies and moths. There were, Lyell observed:

> Many flowers in bloom, a blue iris, daisies, marigold, rosemary & numerous splendid shrubs by the sea-side some of which I remember in the garden at Bartley. The olives are old & picturesque & their light green & the rich green of the caroubiere [*Ceratonia siliqua*] with very rarely a deciduous tree, make it quite unlike winter in appearance.[64]

There is perhaps a trace of homesickness in his reference to Bartley. It was nearly eight months since he had left England.

On the road from Licata to Palma Lyell observed that the strata of hard white claystone visible in the escarpment above Licata dipped toward the west, which meant that as he rode westward he would be crossing higher and younger strata. When he reached Girgenti (Agrigento) Lyell found that the strata overlying the clay were indeed exposed in an inclined position in the hill of Girgenti. But to his considerable astonishment, these overlying strata consisted first of a blue clay with shells and over that, strata of calcareous sandstone which seemed identical with the calcareous sandstone at the base of the escarpment of Floridia and Syracuse. If the strata of Girgenti were identical with those of Floridia and Syracuse, they must underlie the great Val di Noto limestone, with its 800-foot thickness. But Dr. Daubeny had described the hill of Girgenti as composed of "breccia" containing fossil shells "not far, if at all, removed from existing species." Daubeny had considered the "breccia" as the youngest formation in Sicily, but if it were the same formation as at Florida, the Val di Noto limestone was still younger. Yet when Lyell had studied the Val di Noto limestone it had reminded him of a secondary limestone, of the English oolite for instance, or of the calcaire grossier, the Tertiary limestone of the Paris basin which contained fossils almost entirely of extinct species. But if the Val di Noto limestone looked old, it

63. Daubeny, "Geology of Sicily," p. 254.
64. C. L., Jr. to his sister Caroline. 11–30 Dec. 1828.

was not old; instead it was the youngest formation in Sicily. He wrote later in 1833 in the third volume of the *Principles:*

> In the course of my tour I had been frequently led to reflect on the precept of Descartes, "that a philosopher should once in his life doubt every thing he had been taught"; but I still retained so much faith in my early geological creed as to feel the most lively surprise, on visiting Sortino, Pentalica, Syracuse, and other parts of the Val di Noto, at beholding a limestone of enormous thickness filled with recent shells, or sometimes with the mere casts of shells, resting on marl in which shells of Mediterranean species were imbedded in a high state of preservation. All idea of attaching a high antiquity to a regularly stratified limestone, in which the casts and impressions of shells alone were discernible, vanished at once from my mind.[65]

Lyell did not mention when he became aware how recent a formation the Val di Noto limestone was, but whatever his idea of its relative age before he reached Girgenti, it was there that he became convinced that it lay above and was therefore younger than the "breccia" which Dr. Daubeny had considered the youngest formation in Sicily. He probably suspected that the fossil shells from the bed of blue marl at Syracuse belonged to species living in the Mediterranean, but he could not be certain that they did until he had them identified, at least provisionally, by Costa at Naples. Lyell did not yet know enough either of the Mediterranean fauna, or of Tertiary fossil conchology, to identify them himself.

Yet a sense of the full meaning of what he was discovering began to dawn on Lyell as he worked along the south coast of Sicily. This is shown by the drastic change in his plan of route which he made at Licata. He had been traveling and geologizing against time in an effort to complete his tour before the rains came to make the rivers impassable and the country hopelessly boggy. The unexpected continuance of dry sunny weather had caused him to decide to turn back and follow a path eastward to recross the Val di Noto formation. He felt certain in his own mind that the "breccia" was younger than the Val di Noto limestone, but when strata were as much disturbed as those of Sicily, there was always the possibility of mistaking the order of superposition. Moreover, the spell of dry weather which had continued since he was at Syracuse now made

65. *Principles* III, pp. x–xi.

travel through the Val di Noto country practicable in a way which it had not been when Lyell was at Syracuse. He described the purpose of his plan in a letter to Murchison, written from Licata:

> For I shall then get a line of section which no one has yet made, & by passing thro' Caltanisetta, Castrogiovanni etc. to Militello shall be able to persuade others to what I have convinced myself of [namely] that Daubeny's recent breccia is not the uppermost formation & that Gemellaro's new Map of V. di Noto[66] is a much less near approximation to the structure of this Isle than Daubeny's sketch. I have found shells hitherto in all localities of Dr. D's blue clay, but not where the sulphur mines abound.[67]

In a later letter Lyell also told Murchison:

> I got so astounded by the results I was coming to, in my tour from Etna round by *C. Passaro* that I began to doubt them; & not without some struggle with my desire to get out of the inns & horse-paths & other evils I struck back again to Val di Noto right through the centre of the isle.[68]

When he turned inland Lyell followed a winding path first northeast to Cannicatti and Caltanissetta, where he was about 21 December, and then almost due east to Piazza.[69] From Piazza he went southeast to Caltagirone and thence to Vizzini where he was "within a day's ride of Catania again." He described the landscape of the interior of the island to Caroline:

> The centre of the isle is without wood, down with grass & wheat in clay soil—the latter a few inches high. It ought to be 1 1/2 feet & the farmers are alarmed at the extraordinary want of rain, which has been so favourable to me as the clay districts are got hard again & often I have performed a ride of summer's length, & [what would be] usually [a ride of] 2 days in this month.[70]

At Caltanissetta, where at a distance he could see the heights of Castrogiovanni, Lyell found the strata of the blue clay formation

66. This seems to have been a map drawn for Gemmellaro's paper on Sicily. C. Gemmellaro, "Sopra la fisionomia delle montagne di Sicilia" (1828).

67. C. L., Jr. to R. I. M. 16 Dec. 1828 [Licata]. Murchison mss.

68. C. L., Jr. to R. I. M. 12 Jan. 1829 [Naples]. Kinnordy mss. *L. & L.* I, 232–34.

69. Lyell's dates are a little confused during this period because when he reached Palermo he found he was two days out in his reckoning.

70. C. L., Jr. to his sister Caroline. 11–30 Dec. 1828. Kinnordy mss.

greatly "tossed about."[71] In exposures of the clay he collected some twenty species of fossil shells beautifully preserved and retaining their original colors, as in the similar bed of blue clay on the south side of the harbor of Syracuse. He was still uncertain about the position of this blue clay because he wrote a reminder to himself:

Mem. Daubeny

Make out the relations between the blue clay form! & the limestone which succeeds it between Terranuova & Cape Passaro.[72]

At Caltagirone on 22 December Lyell found the blue clay overlain on the tops of the hills by a bed of yellow sand; this order was identical with what he had seen in the subapennine beds of northern Italy. He refers to the blue clay as subapennine in a way which suggests that he was not yet aware of how different the fossil species of this clay were from those of the subapennine beds.

Beyond Caltagirone the sedimentary strata began to be intermixed again with volcanic rocks. Near Grammichele Lyell thought he saw the same succession of blue marls by yellow sandstone as occurred in the subapennine beds of the Italian peninsula, but was puzzled by what he found. In his notes he observed:

On first entrance to [the] volcanic district [there is] not much limestone, but a brown marl with white outer surface under lava, but as in one place limestone rests on marl? it cannot be Subapp. marl?

Or should we consider the marl or clay (in one place blue under lava) as Subapp. with peperino & lavas intermixed, disturbed during deposition & then calcareous matter coming on in upper part more recent than the Subapp. beds.[73]

These notes reveal Lyell not only as yet unaware of the identity of the fossil species in the Sicilian Tertiary strata, but also, despite his experience of the preceding months in Auvergne, Italy, and Sicily, as still tending to follow the older mode of recognition of strata by their appearance, physical characteristics, and order of superposition.

The disturbance of the sedimentary strata by volcanic intru-

71. Ms. Notebook 20, p. 141. Kinnordy mss. Cf. *Principles* III, p. 66.
72. Ibid., p. 170.
73. Ibid., p. 6.

sions was especially clear in the hill of Novera near Vizzini where horizontal limestone strata butted up against inclined strata of tuff separated only by a vertical fissure filled with volcanic sand. The abrupt way in which the limestone strata were cut off showed that the volcanic eruption must have occurred beneath the sea when the limestone strata were still beds of soft sediment.[74]

The strata were often intersected by sheets of igneous rock. In some cases these were intrusives. In others they were extrusives; sheets of lava had flowed out under the sea and later sediments had settled on top of them. Commonly the sedimentary strata were greatly disturbed and altered:

I also observed not far from Vizzini [Lyell wrote later] a very striking illustration of the length of the intervals which occasionally separated the flows of distinct lava currents. A bed of oysters, perfectly identifiable with our common eatable species, no less than *twenty feet in thickness,* is there seen resting on a current of basaltic lava; upon the oyster bed again is superimposed a second mass of lava, together with tuff or peperino.[75]

He also saw a bed of coral in which the corals stood "erect as they grew," indicating tranquil conditions undisturbed by volcanic activity; yet this coral bed, a foot and a half thick, lay in the midst of a series of alternating volcanic and sedimentary layers. Such facts showed that the volcanic activity which had raised and disturbed the Val di Noto had occurred not at one time, but over a very long period of time. Lyell's purpose in his ride through the interior was to obtain a new section of the strata of the Val di Noto with their interspersed volcanic rocks. From his observations, especially those at Caltagirone, he decided that the blue clay formation must be divided into two quite distinct deposits, the upper being the blue marl, so rich in shells at Syracuse; the lower, the white laminated marl which commonly contained beds of gypsum, sand, sulfur, and sometimes rock salt. He found no fossils in these lower beds until near Raddusa, where he found some fish scales and fishbones. At Castrogiovanni the same fossils occurred in these beds even more plentifully, but there Lyell was more impressed by the fact that he had revealed in one immense escarpment—rising to a height of 3800 feet above sea level—all of the

74. Ibid.
75. *Principles* III, p. 73.

strata of the great Val di Noto formation from the white limestone
down through the white laminated marl to a blue clay and gypsum
without shells.[76] Since all members of the series were represented
at Castrogiovanni, their order was revealed decisively. At the
same time they demonstrated the continuity of the strata from east
to west in Sicily because the upper portion of the section was
identical with that at Syracuse.

On 29 December 1828 Lyell reached Palermo, coming from
Castrogiovanni, and just in time. The next day the rains came;
the roads became seas of mud and the streams at once impassable.
The next nine days he spent waiting for the captain of a sailing
packet to make up his mind to depart for Naples. He occupied his
time with social visits, one of them with the American Consul, Mr.
Gardner, who gave him some fossil shells. "I drank tea there,"
wrote Lyell, "and was glad to see again a regular English fireside
and tea-table tho' all American." He also visited Lord Northampton who had a house at Palermo and who, on hearing of Lyell's
travels and explorations, determined to make a collection of Sicilian fossils. During his stay there a young English artist died of
"Fatigue, bad Inns, bad food & cold," a demonstration that the
hardships of Sicily were not to be trifled with. Lyell was shocked
by the poverty and actual starvation—"children exposed in frightful nakedness, positively howling at night in my street & now &
then well dressed persons begging piteously."[77]

On 9 January Lyell sailed from Palermo and, after a few days
at Naples, where he received the first letters to be delivered to him
since going to Sicily, and where in the museum he also identified
his collection of Sicilian shells, he set off for Rome.

When Lyell identified some of his collections of Sicilian shells
at Naples with the help of Costa, he found that they consisted almost entirely of living species. In Lyell's collection of shells from
Castrogiovanni, Costa found fifty-nine species, all living.[78] Lyell
was deeply impressed by the almost complete absence of extinct
shell species because in the subapennine beds about forty per cent
of the fossil shells belonged to extinct species. The difference between the fossils of the Sicilian strata and those of the subapennine
beds was, therefore, very great. To Murchison Lyell described

76. Ibid., p. 64. Cf. Ms. notebook 21, pp. 41, 47. Kinnordy mss.
77. C. L., Jr. to his sister Fanny. 1–10 Jan. 1829. Kinnordy mss. *L. & L.* I, 227–32
(printed only in part), p. 229.
78. Ms. notebook 21, pp. 104–06. Kinnordy mss.

the similarity in appearance between some of the Sicilian marls and those of the hill of Superga near Turin and then added:

> But these are mineralogical identities & go for nothing. What will you say if I tell you that even the blue marl with its capping of yellow sand [at Caltagirone] cannot be Brocchi's Subapp. beds. I am come most unwillingly to this conclusion. But the numerous extinct species which characterize the Subapps. are wanting here & living shells are present too plentifully to admit a doubt that it is more related to our own epoch than that remote one when the Parmegiano & Placentino beds were deposited.[79]

Thus the Tertiary strata of Sicily, which together constituted a formation between two and three thousand feet thick, were entirely distinct from the subapennine beds and more recent than them. Yet these Sicilian strata, which with respect to their fossils seemed so young, had been elevated very slowly and gradually over an immense period of time, with many intervening periods of rest and subsidence. And towering over a platform composed of these strata containing fossils of living species, was the great mass of Etna.

> This volcano is placed as if to give just & grand conceptions of Time to all in Europe. . . . It is a cone of volcanic matter superposed to shelly beds. Subordinate to this cone are 70 to 100 minor volcanoes differing very widely from each other in age. Nothing can be more beautiful than the view from many parts of Etna down into these wooded volcanoes covered with oak & pines & with their craters variously shaped. Monti Rossi is not the most recent of these nor is it by any means the loftiest. It was formed in 1669. . . . Their number is a clear indication of time. . . .
>
> The number of years then which would roll away before all the great mountains in the woody region disappeared would be very great. The times of History would but little diminish their number & several repetitions therefore of that duration of time must be calculated back ere we can strip the flank of Etna of these numerous craters. But in doing so we should but slightly lessen the total bulk of this great mass. . . . The height might

79. C. L., Jr. to R. I. M. 12 Jan. 1829. Murchison mss. *L. & L.* I, 232–34.

have been then nearly the same & the diminution of some 100 to
500 feet of lava might attend the disappearance of the 80 minor
cones, but we should then [make] another multitude, perhaps
equal, of buried cones appear & should then have to calculate
the time required for their successive eruptions. . . .

And here it must be considered how much must be supplied
for waste, for boulders are strewed over country of vast size from
this—great valleys have been excavated & ravines—the ruins of
the oldest craters, since partly filled with the lavas of modern
Etna are on such a scale as to indicate, if repaired, a considerable
magnitude. So that after the removal, by a retrospect of so many
thousand years, [of] the whole of modern Etna with its 80 cones
and all its buried craters, we should see so much results of waste
restored that we cannot pronounce how large the prior volcano
might have been. Matter must rise from the sea again which
the winds & rivers have swept down. Even independent of these
powers, the self-destroying power of a volcano is such that it
often consumes one & the same parts & thus the ultimate results
but feebly indicate the sum of change.[80]

Lyell seems to have written the above essay in his notebook before he reached Naples and probably while he was waiting at
Palermo to sail. When he wrote it he still thought that Etna rested
on subapennine beds. Therefore, the realization that Etna was
built upon a formation more recent than the subapennine increased still further the greatness of the vista of past time which
Sicily had opened to him.

Yet the great age and size of Etna was not the only fact which
had impressed itself on Lyell's mind in Sicily. He had gone to
Sicily convinced that the elevation of sedimentary strata occurred
in association with volcanic activity and earthquakes. The earthquakes occurred, he thought, by the intrusion of molten rock
(lava if it reaches the earth's surface) into strata beneath the earth's
surface. This molten material raised the strata and then cooled to
form a solid platform on which the elevated rocks rested. By repeated earthquakes and intrusions, strata might be elevated into
the highest mountains. Lyell had found in Sicily abundant confirmation of this theory because he found the elevated strata of the
Val di Noto intruded by dikes and interstratified with sheets of
igneous rock. However, Lyell also realized that if his theory were

80. Ms. notebook 21, p. 113–18. Kinnordy mss.

true, a volume of subterranean molten rock equal to the whole bulk of southern Sicily measured from the bottom of the Mediterranean sea to the heights of Castrogiovanni 3,000 feet above sea level, had been intruded successively into the strata. As he wrote later, "The dimensions of the Etnean cone shrink into insignificance, in comparison to the volume of this subterranean lava."[81] He added that although the discovery that Etna was built upon strata containing only species of shells and zoophytes still living in the Mediterranean was staggering, it was a fact easier to accept when seen beside similar enormous changes in the period of living species.

As Lyell pondered the fact that most of Sicily had been formed since the time when the Mediterranean fauna first appeared, he came to yet another startling conclusion. The species of plants and animals on Sicily were almost certainly older than the land itself. They must have migrated there from Africa or Europe after Sicily had begun to appear above the waters of the Mediterranean. Because geological changes destroyed old land areas and created new ones more rapidly than a change of species occurred, species had to be prepared to migrate and to adapt themselves to new circumstances if they were not to become extinct. Lyell began to see species as engaged in a continual battle against extinction and he became interested in their capacity for adaptation.

All of these ideas taken together—the immensity of geological time, the slow and gradual nature of geological change, the tranquil conditions existing throughout the past history of the earth—together constituted a revolution in science. Lyell's vision of the history of the earth had changed utterly. He had gone to Sicily, hopeful and confident; he returned certain and unshakable. He had sought geological analogies to modern processes; he had found such an unexpected wealth of them as staggered his imagination. This scientific revolution had occurred as yet only within his own mind, but he was determined that it would not remain confined there.

Lyell's letters written from various points on his return journey are full of the sense of excitement created by his discoveries in Sicily. He was now certain that the beds of the hill of Superga, the subapennine hills, and Sicily were not parallel and contemporary but represented different and successive epochs. From Naples

81. *Principles* III, p. 107.

he wrote to Murchison, "I am beginning now to be able, when I
see large collections [of fossils], to distinguish between any marked
difference in the proportion of lost species and genera."[82] He was
looking forward to taking up work on his book again. He hoped
to gain not only fame but enough money to cover the extra expenses of his hobby. His travels in Sicily had given him a very clear
idea of what he wanted to express in it:

> It will not pretend to give an abstract of all that is known in
> Geology, but it will endeavour to establish the *principles of
> reasoning* in the science & all my Geology will come in as illus-
> tration of my views of those principles, & as evidences strength-
> ening the system necessarily arising out of the admission of such
> principles which as you know are neither more nor less than that
> *no causes whatever* have from the earliest time to which we can
> look back to the present ever acted but those *now* acting & that
> they never acted with different degrees of energy from that
> which they now exert.[83]

At Rome he heard from his sisters for the first time since Auvergne and was relieved to learn that his father approved of his
Sicilian expedition.[84] Here too he received letters from Scrope
and Murchison with an account of the sensation which had been
created by the reading at the Geological Society by Murchison of
their joint paper on the excavation of valleys. Seventy persons
were present and a hot debate followed.[85] At Rome Lyell also
examined again some of the travertine deposits which now meant
much more to him in the light of his Sicilian experience. Monte
Mario he found to be of the same age as the Sicilian formation
and not subapennine. He saw that the travertine of Tivoli had
been laid down in an ancient small lake. He studied the various
varieties of travertine in the museum at Rome.[86] At Siena he reexamined sections of the subapennine beds and found that the
upper sandstone beds were more closely related to the formations
of Sicily than was the blue marl underlying the sandstone beds in
the subapennine formation; that is, the uppermost part of the
subapennine formation showed a closer relationship to the lower
portions of the Sicilian formation indicating that the Sicilian

82. C. L., Jr. to R. I. M. 12 Jan. 1829. Murchison mss. *L. & L.* I, 232–34.
83. C. L., Jr. to R. I. M. 17 Jan. 1829. Murchison mss. *L. & L.* I, 234–35.
84. C. L., Jr. to R. I. M. 12 Jan. 1829. Murchison mss. *L. & L.* I, 236–37.
85. C. L., Jr. to his sister Marianne. 21 Jan. 1829. Kinnordy mss. *L. & L.* I, 238–39.
Cf. G. P. Scrope to C. L., Jr. 23 Dec. 1828. APS mss.
86. C. L., Jr. to R. I. M. 22 Jan. 1829. Murchison mss. *L. & L.* I, 139–42.

formation represented a more recent geological period than the subapennine. While there he received a present of a set of fossils from Padre Ricca to whom he had been given a letter by Lord Northampton.[87]

If the tertiaries from the N. of Italy to Cape Passaro shall ultimately correspond to my present view of them [he wrote to Murchison], they will I think establish forever the elevation theory, but I am the more afraid of their certainty in proportion as they suit so beautifully the system I anticipated. . . . in the main I am sure I cannot now be shaken & Ischia & Etna form one extremity of the series & perhaps Parma etc. the other. . . . I feel myself feebler in relation to the subject in proportion as I grow less so in comparison to other geologists. We want nothing short of a radical reform in geology & we shall have one soon if honest men will travel and write and travel again.[88]

At Genoa Lyell talked with a young physician, Dr. Sassi, who had just written a memoir on the geology of the Albenga Basin,[89] and at Turin he conversed again with Signor Bonelli, who confirmed most of Costa's identifications. Bonelli was astonished at Lyell's Sicilian results. "I begin to think," he said, "the day *may* come when the retiring of the ocean will be doubted & disputed by many."[90]

Bonelli promised Lyell a list of characteristic shells from the hill of Superga and from the subapennine beds to be sent to him within two months' time and to be published for comparison with Costa's lists of the fossil shell species which Lyell had collected in Ischia, Calabria, and Sicily. When he reached Geneva on 5 February, Lyell called on Augustin Pyrâme de Candolle, professor of botany, to talk over with him the ideas he had developed on the relationship between geological history and the geographical distribution of plant species. Lyell thought that the reason Sicily had very few species of plants peculiar to itself, whereas an island like Corsica had many distinct species found only there, was that Sicily was geologically new, whereas Corsica was geologically old. By now it is clear that Lyell had grasped the idea that, in the course of geological time, species were steadily dying out and steadily being replaced by new species. In a sufficient period of time all spe-

87. C. L., Jr. to his father. 7 Feb. 1829. Kinnordy mss. *L. & L.* I, 244–46.
88. C. L., Jr. to R. I. M. 22 Jan. 1829. Murchison mss. *L. & L.* I, 239–42.
89. A. Sassi, "Essai géologique sur le bassin tertiaire d'Albenga" (1829).
90. C. L., Jr. to R. I. M. 5 Feb. 1829. Murchison mss. *L. & L.* I, 242–44.

cies became extinct to be replaced by new ones; in any fraction of this time a corresponding fraction of the total number of species would have died out and been replaced. In an island, such as Sicily or Corsica, separated by sea from other areas of land, the new species, which arose to replace those that had died out, would be peculiar to that island, because they would have come into being there and would not have had an opportunity to distribute themselves elsewhere. By contrast, when an island like Sicily first rose from the sea, as Lyell now believed it had risen from the sea, it would be a bare surface with no native species of plants of its own. Consequently any plants that it acquired would be those which could colonize it from neighboring areas of land. Hence arose the paradox, which so much struck Lyell, when he contemplated the geological history of Sicily—that the plants growing on the island belonged to species much older than the island itself. Corsica, with its numerous species peculiar to itself, had a flora which, in just this measure, had arisen since the island had been formed. The native Corsican species had arisen on Corsica.

This elegant hypothesis depended completely on the assumption that each species of plant or animal had come into being at one particular place—its "center of creation"—from which it had been distributed in ever-widening circles. If it did not encounter geographical barriers, its total area of distribution would be related directly to its age as a species. In fact, most sites where plants grow are narrowly encompassed by geographical barriers to their distribution, in the form of seas, deserts, and mountain ranges. In addition, factors of climate, elevation, and rainfall determine where plants can grow. In the light of this complex of factors it was not easy to determine whether a particular plant species had arisen at one time, at one center, or simultaneously at several places. However, from his vast knowledge of the modern geographical distribution of plant species, Candolle had built up a reasoned argument to show that the present distribution in many instances was such that a species could have arisen only at one place. It was to discuss the evidence for this argument with Candolle himself that Lyell had come from Italy by way of Geneva instead of by Lyons. They had "a famous botanico-geological discussion" and Candolle gave him a copy of his essay on geographical botany.[91] Lyell considered this:

91. A. P. de Candolle, "Géographie botanique."

. . . the most beautiful generalization of a multitude of facts which I think was ever produced in Natural History. I am now convinced that Geology is destined to throw upon this curious branch of enquiry & to receive from it in return much light & by their material aid we shall soon solve the grand problem whether the various living organic species came into being gradually & singly in insulated spots or centres of creation or in various places at once & all at the same time. The latter cannot, I am already persuaded, be maintained.[92]

On 10 February Lyell left Geneva for Paris where he arrived four days later, traveling night and day except for six hours' rest at Dijon. Since it was midwinter, the diligence went on sleighs over the deep snow of the Jura, and the passengers were required to get out and walk up the hills. Immediately on his arrival he attended one of Constant Prevost's lectures where he met other geologists of Paris. Élie de Beaumont was at this time beginning to expound his ideas on craters of elevation and the elevation of mountain chains, so Lyell was soon involved in intense geological discussion. However, he had his own aims to pursue. He called on Jules Desnoyers, who in 1825 had shown that the Tertiary strata of the lower Loire basin were younger than those of the Paris basin. When he told Desnoyers of the new ideas which had been suggested by his Sicilian tour, in particular that the Tertiary formations were of different ages and could be placed in chronological order according to the proportion of representatives of living species among the fossils found in each, Desnoyers told him that he had come to similar conclusions and in fact had already printed the first part of a memoir, "On the Tertiary Formations more recent than the Paris basin."[93] Desnoyers was glad to have support for his novel conclusions and attached to the portion of his memoir already printed a note on their conversation and the agreement of their views.[94] At the same time he told Lyell that Dr. Gérard Paul Deshayes,[95] the owner of a very large collection of fossil shells, had come to the conclusion that the Tertiary strata might be arranged in a chronological series on the basis of differences in their species of fossil shells. Lyell went directly to see

92. C. L., Jr. to his father. 7 Feb. 1829. Kinnordy mss. *L. & L.* I, 244–46.

93. *Principles* III, p. xiii.

94. J. Desnoyers, "Observations sur un ensemble de dépôts marins . . ." (1829).

95. Gérard Paul Deshayes (1797–1875) was born at Nancy and studied medicine at Strasbourg and Paris.

M. Deshayes, who explained that the Tertiary strata could be
separated into three successive geological periods.

Deshayes had observed in arranging his collection of fossil and
living shells that of some one thousand species of fossil shells which
he had obtained from the Tertiary strata around Bordeaux, about
two hundred corresponded to species described by Brocchi from
the subapennine beds but hardly any occurred in the calcaire
grossier formation of the Paris basin. By contrast, of one hundred
species of shells which he had from the London clay, almost all had
their counterparts in the calcaire grossier. Thus there appeared to
be a distinct correspondence between the formations of the London basin and of the Paris basin and between the Bordeaux formations and the subapennine beds, with a more distant relationship between the Bordeaux formations and those of the Paris
basin.[96] Deshayes had decided that these differences represented
differences in geological age; the Paris and London basins must
belong to an earlier geological period because they contained almost no living species of shells, whereas about a quarter of the
fossil shell species from Bordeaux appeared to be still living.

"Deshayes," Lyell told Mantell, "is acknowledged to be the
Cuvier of tertiary shells, no mean acquirement now that they
amount in his museum, including those living in Mediterranean
& the channel, to above 3,000 species."[97] Since Deshayes' conclusions were based on the study of thousands of fossil species, Lyell
saw that his own collections from Italy and Sicily would be but a
minor addition to the fossil evidence already assembled. Therefore, he asked for Deshayes' help in drawing up a grand catalog
of fossil shells from all the Tertiary strata of Europe to give him a
broad basis for geological inferences. Deshayes offered to name
Lyell's Italian and Sicilian fossils and, in exchange, Lyell offered to
send Deshayes as many English Tertiary fossils as he could obtain.
Deshayes had as yet very few fossil shells from the crag of Norfolk, a
formation known to contain at least some living species as fossils.
Lyell bought a copy of Deshayes' book on the fossil shells of the
Paris basin[98] in order to help him out (Deshayes had lost a considerable amount of money on it), and bought a large number of
his duplicate fossils for Gideon Mantell.[99]

96. Ms. notebook 23, pp. 31–34. Kinnordy mss.
97. C. L., Jr. to G. A. M. 19 Feb. 1829. Mantell mss. *L. & L.* I, 246–48.
98. G. P. Deshayes. *Description des coquilles fossiles des environs de Paris* (1824).
99. C. L., Jr. to G. A. M. 24 Feb. 1829. Mantell mss.

Still another of Lyell's activities in Paris was the purchase of geological books to use as references in writing his own. He found that many important treatises were in German and lamented his ignorance of that language. He attended a soirée at Cuvier's and also called upon him during the day to see about some plaster casts of fossil bones which he had asked Cuvier's workmen to make for Mantell when he had been in Paris nine months earlier, but which were not yet done. Cuvier cut through the difficulties at once on this occasion, and invited Lyell into his own private study or workroom of which Lyell sent Marianne a vivid description.[100]

On 24 February Lyell arrived again at his chambers in the Middle Temple, after an absence of nearly nine months. He found his servant, Hall, who had returned to London from Clermont-Ferrand, in July 1828, very ill in bed without any medical attendance, so immediately summoned Dr. Richard Bright (1781–1858), in whom Hall had great faith. The disease was consumption and Bright held very little hope. Hall, however, was to recover for a long career of further usefulness, but for Lyell it was a depressing homecoming. However, the prospects for his scientific work were too bright for him to be held down very long. His eyes were stronger than he ever remembered them, he told Caroline, and "I am said to be looking in remarkable good health & very handsome barring that I am grown balder. Therefore, I trust is craniology going out that I may follow the example of your friend the gallant Officer & cover my crown with some fine curling locks."[101] He was obviously in top form.

100. C. L., Jr. to his sister Marianne. 21 Feb. 1829. Kinnordy mss. *L. & L.* I, 248–51 (misdated 23 Feb.).
101. C. L., Jr. to his sister Caroline. 26 Feb. 1829. Kinnordy mss. *L. & L.* I, 251–52.

CHAPTER 9

The *Principles of Geology*, 1829–1830

IN THE WEEKS which followed his return to London Lyell was exceedingly busy. He had to unpack his boxes of fossils which had come by sea from Palermo, attend meetings of the Geological Society, the Royal Society, and the Linnean Society, see friends, and catch up on news. His joint paper with Murchison on the excavation of valleys, read at the Geological Society the previous December, had created such a sensation that W. D. Conybeare wrote a reply in the form of a paper on the formation of the valley of the Thames, which was read at the Geological Society at the meetings of 15 May and 5 June 1829.[1]

Lyell and Murchison described in their paper various localities in central France where river valleys had, at an earlier period, been filled by currents of lava. The streams of lava, descending by gravity, tended to follow the water courses, but these the lava sometimes blocked or redirected. In such instances the rivers had often excavated new valleys which cut through both the lava and the underlying gneiss. In the vertical sides of the gorges thus created was commonly recorded a history of the earlier states of the valley, the beds of gravel deposited when it flowed at a level higher than the present, and the layers of lava representing successive volcanic eruptions. In the valley of the Sioule near Pont Gibaud and in the valley of the Ardeche near Thueyts, Lyell and Murchison found that these rivers had cut deep gorges through lavas so recent that they were still covered with loose scoriae, indicating that erosion by rivers was much more powerful than erosion by rain and frost. They were deeply impressed by the quantity of rock and earth which had been carried away by the Sioule. They wrote:

> This enormous quantity of rock and soil has been carried, we say, through this gorge in times comparatively recent; for the products of Côme and Chaluzet are as modern in comparison with the ancient basalts of Auvergne, as are the latter in reference to the lacustrine strata where on they rest.

1. W. D. Conybeare, "On the hydrographical basin of the Thames . . ." (1829).

If the Sioule could do so much within a brief period of geological time, then the total work of the rivers of central France over much longer periods must be far, far greater. The rock and soil washed away bore "witness to the force of causes that have operated, and are still operating, in nature, to an extent far beyond the calculation of many geologists."[2] The whole burden of Lyell and Murchison's paper, therefore, was in support of Hutton and Playfair's theory that, over long periods of time, rivers had such power that they could excavate and form the valleys in which they flowed.

In his reply Conybeare began by contrasting the two schools of thought which had attempted to explain the origin of river valleys. Those who attributed the formation of valleys to the gradual eroding action of the streams which flowed in them he called fluvialists, while those who considered that valleys had been formed by the waters of the ocean which covered the land at the time of the great flood, he called diluvialists. Hence this controversy over the origin of river valleys is often referred to as the fluvialist–diluvialist dispute.

Conybeare's paper presented a carefully reasoned argument to show the difficulty in assuming that the Thames valley had been formed by the gradual action of its river. Most of the tributaries of the Thames rise upon the slopes of the Cotswolds, but three of them rise beyond the Cotswolds and cut through its escarpment. All of these tributaries descend into the plain of Oxford. South of Oxford the river cuts through the Oxford chain of hills and farther on in its progress toward the sea it cuts through the Chiltern hills. If the Thames were dammed at the level of the present ridge of the Oxford hills, it would form a large lake in the plain of Oxford which would drain northward into the valley of the Ouse. Thus, when the Thames first began to cut its way through these hills, it could not have done so unless the country to the north were higher than it is at present. If the valley had been worn by the river it was necessary to assume that the space between the Oxford hills and the Cotswolds had originally been filled so that a uniformly inclined plane, descending to the east, extended between the summits of the two ranges of hills. In this event enough materials to fill the whole intervening valley must have been removed by the river. While Conybeare marshaled a number of supplementary arguments, it was clearly the sheer vastness of the river's

2. C. Lyell and R. I. Murchison, "On the excavation of valleys, as illustrated by the volcanic rocks of central France" (1829) p. 24.

work which he could not accept. Conybeare also noted the distribution of gravel containing pebbles derived from the transition rocks of hills to the north of the valley of the Warwickshire Avon. This gravel appeared distributed over the hill tops in lines extending from the northwest, and its distribution (which is, in fact, the result of glacial action) was such as could not have been produced by the drainage of the present streams.

To account for these phenomena, Conybeare suggested four occasions in the geological past when the land surface might have been sculpted by ocean currents. Of these, only the last, which had spread the superficial gravel containing bones of extinct mammals over many hilltops, represented the biblical flood.

Conybeare's paper, carefully and frankly reasoned though it was, served principally as an overt expression of opposition to the ideas of Lyell and Murchison. Conybeare never published it in full, which perhaps indicates that he had some hesitancy ultimately about the validity of his conclusions. To Mantell, Lyell described the meeting at which it was read:

> A splendid meeting last night. Sedgwick in chair. Conybeare's paper on valley of Thames directed against Messrs. Lyell & Murchison's former paper was read in part. Buckland present to defend the "diluvialists" as Conybeare styles his sect & us he terms "fluvialists." Greenough assisted us by making an ultra speech on the impotence of modern causes. "No river," he said, "within times of history has deepened its channel one foot!" It was great fun for he said—" 'Our opponents say, 'Give us Time & we will work wonders,' So said the wolf in the fable—to the lamb—'why do you disturb the water?'—'I do not; you are further up the stream than I.'—'But your father did'—'he never was here'—Then your grandfather did so I will murder you.' 'Give me *time* & I will murder you,' so say the fluvialists" Roars of laughter in which G. joined against himself. What a choice simile! M. & I fought stoutly & Buckland was very piano. Conybeare's memoir is not strong by any means. He admits 3 deluges before the Noachian! & Buckland adds God knows how many catastrophes besides so we have driven them out of the Mosaic record fairly.[3]

The next meeting, two weeks later, was equally vigorous. On this occasion Adam Sedgwick, now president of the Geological Society,

3. C. L., Jr. to G. A. M. 16 May 1829. Mantell mss. *L. & L.* I, 252–53.

came to the support of Lyell and Murchison, to Lyell's great delight. At this meeting also there was read a paper by Matthew Culley, a land surveyor, in which he described the effects of a flood on a small stream called the College which flowed from the Cheviot hills. As a result of heavy rains this stream had brought down several thousand tons of gravel and sand and had carried away a stone bridge in the course of building.[4] Such a demonstration of the effects of modern causes was particularly relevant to this argument and provoked a further discussion.

This dispute was for Lyell, however, an incidental diversion. Since his return to London at the end of February, his real work had been the revision and extension of his manuscript of the *Principles*. While in Italy he had bought a number of Italian geological works and, as he read these, he found it necessary to modify greatly his account of the historical development of geology. Lyell was almost the only English speaking geologist to read Italian geological works in the early nineteenth century. He had discovered that geology was studied at a high level in Italy and had been since the seventeenth century. It was characteristic of Lyell's approach to geology that he should consider the historical development of its ideas and assumptions necessary to understand the present state of the science. During June he also wrote unwillingly, and in some haste, a review of Andrew Ure's new book on geology for the *Quarterly*.[5] This review was never published because Lyell would not give the time to it which Lockhart thought necessary. He was unwilling to appear as a critic of a work which would be in competition with his own when it was published. At the same time Lyell had little use either for the book or for its author whom he described privately as "an unprincipled hypocrite & libertine of Dublin well known in the annals of crime."[6]

About 20 June Lyell left for Scotland. On his way north he passed through Norfolk in order to study the geology of the crag which was of special interest to him after his study of the recent strata of Sicily. Like the Sicilian strata, the crag contained a large proportion of fossil shells which belonged to species still living in the sea. Because he considered it the most modern formation in England, Lyell wished to show that the crag also lay uppermost in

4. M. Culley, "A few facts and observations as to the power which running water exerts in removing heavy bodies" (1834). Cf. C. L., Jr. to G. A. M. 7 June 1829. Mantell mss. *L. & L.* I, 253.

5. A. Ure, *A new system of geology* . . . (1829).

6. C. L., Jr. to G. A. M. 19 March 1829. Mantell mss.

relation to the other beds. He spent several weeks in late June and
early July at this task, during which he "saw every foot of the
coast from Walton in Essex to Hunstanton." He found the crag
to be a very modern formation, corresponding in age to the recent
limestones of Palermo. There were "*casts* of pecten etc. & corals"
which indicated a warmer sea than the present. In his mind's eye
Lyell reconstructed the ancient geography:

> In other parts there are lignite deposits like [the] Plastic Clay
> but with Crag animals, & elsewhere (always when approaching
> the original border of the basin) there are *littoral* deposits shew-
> ing every gradation from regular strata to an alluvium tumbled
> into a deepish sea near the ancient coast whereby land produc-
> tions got intermixed with broken sea-shells.[7]

These littoral deposits had previously been confused with "diluvium," the kind of loose deposit, actually a product of glacial action, which William Buckland supposed had been left behind by
the flood. While he was on this tour Lyell received from John
Hawkins, the antiquary, a copy of Raspe's Latin essay on the natural history of the earth.[8] Lyell wrote to Hawkins that it served
as "an agreeable travelling companion" and he later discussed its
contents in the *Principles*.[9]

In Yorkshire Lyell first called on John Phillips at York and then
went to Shap to trace the distribution of granite pebbles which
had, like the pebbles studied by Buckland and Conybeare in the
Thames valley, been transported from the north. These pebbles
appeared to have passed through a gap in the hills of the Stain-
moor range. In order to account for the movements of these pebbles, Lyell found it necessary to suppose that England had been
immersed beneath the sea. "That England has undergone subterranean movements since the Shap boulders were on their travels,"
he wrote, "may be proved, I think for they belong to an alluvium
as old as the crag & which alluvium, when it reached the sea, got
intermixed with crag shells & lifted up with them afterwards."[10]

When he reached Kinnordy in July Lyell settled down to work

7. C. L., Jr. to R. I. M. 11 Aug. 1829. Murchison mss.

8. R. E. Raspe, *Specimen historiae naturalis globi terraquei...*(1763). John Sidney Hawkins (1758–1842) of Lower Grove, Brompton, Sussex was an antiquary who
had known Raspé personally when he was younger.

9. C. L., Jr. to J. Hawkins. 25 Jan. 1830. Sussex Co. Rec. Soc. mss. Cf. *Principles*
(1830) I, pp. 51–52.

10. C. L., Jr. to R. I. M. 11 Aug. 1829. Murchison mss.

further on his manuscript of the *Principles*. He had begun to study German and continued this pursuit with his sisters at Kinnordy. He wished urgently to be able to read Hoff's recent work on geological changes which had occurred within historic times.[11] By 11 August he was able to tell Murchison that he had read one third of Hoff. He added:

> Since I was here I have written a new Ed.ⁿ of one 5th of my 2 vols. The Italians with Hooke & Ray had got far in the doctrine of earthquakes, especially Hooke. I trust I shall make my sketch of the progress of Geology popular. Old Fleming is frightened & thinks the age will not stand my anti-Mosaical conclusions & at least that the subject will for a time become unpopular & awkward for the clergy, but I am not afraid. I shall out with the whole, but in as conciliatory a manner as possible.[12]

Lyell was, therefore, hard at work during his holiday at Kinnordy and it was perhaps for this reason that he prolonged his stay there until late in October by which time he had rewritten much of the *Principles*. The comfort of living at home, together with freedom from dinners and meetings of societies, was probably conducive to writing. Except for a brief excursion to the coalfield of Fife, he did little geological field work.

At the beginning of October he heard that W. D. Conybeare had met with a severe accident by falling out of his gig on his head and was now lying unconscious, in danger of his life. Although they were diametrically opposed in their views of geology, Lyell had the deepest respect for Conybeare, who was in fact one of the great founders of English geology. To Murchison he wrote:

> I was shocked at Conybeare's accident—a greater loss to Geology we could not suffer than his non-recovery for he had that candour that would have brought him round to the truth whatever it may prove to be. It quite throws a damper on me in writing for I never wrote a chapter without the inspiriting idea of having him as an antagonist.[13]

Happily, Conybeare was to recover. The incident, however,

11. K. E. A. von Hoff. *Geschichte der durch überlieferung nachgewiesenen natürlichen Veranderungen der Erdoberflache*. Lyell used only the first two volumes published in 1822 and 1824 respectively.
12. C. L., Jr. to R. I. M. 11 Aug. 1829. Murchison mss.
13. C. L., Jr. to R. I. M. 5 Oct. 1829. Murchison mss.

throws a revealing light on the sense of mutual trust which underlay the violent theoretical disputes at the Geological Society.

On 22 October Lyell arrived back in London. At this time he seems to have been close to the completion of the manuscript of his first volume, because he hoped to get his book out in the spring in time to allow him to go to Iceland the following summer. A few days later he wrote to his father:

> I have gone over my first chapters & think I have cut out all that any Bishop could object to so that if I was ever a candidate for a King's college professorship I might send my book to Joshua Watson.[14] But it will be difficult I think to state facts & not endanger the popularity of a subject which the world can well do without. It is, however, going on fast.[15]

On 26 October he sent a portion of the manuscript of his second volume to John Murray to give him a measure of the length of the whole work. Lyell wished to keep the first volume by him because he was continually referring to it. He estimated the length of the two volumes at 1,292 pages of manuscript which would make 646 pages of type set in the size of the *Quarterly Review*.[16] The first two volumes of the *Principles* had therefore already taken shape although Lyell continued to work intensively upon them during the succeeding months. On 12 November he wrote again to Murray to say that he had rewritten half of the first volume and that it was running one-sixth longer than the first copy.[17]

While he was thus hard at work Lyell was cheered by the return of Sedgwick and Murchison from their summer's tour of southern Germany and Austria. To Fleming he wrote:

> Sedgwick and Murchison are just returned, the former full of magnificent views. Throws overboard all the diluvian hypothesis; is vexed he ever lost time about such a complete humbug; says he lost two years by having also started a Wernerian. He says primary rocks are not primary, but, as Hutton supposed, some igneous, some altered secondary. Mica schist in Alps lies

14. Joshua Watson (1771–1855) was a leading layman of the high church party in the Church of England. In 1806 he had revised the Reverend William von Mildert's Boyle lectures and in 1815 the latter's Bampton lectures for publication. Watson was one of the organizers of King's College, London and an arch-representative of conservative theological opinion.

15. C. L., Jr. to his father. 25 Oct. 1829. Kinnordy mss.

16. C. L., Jr. to J. M. 26 Oct. 1829. Murray mss.

17. C. L., Jr. to J. M. 12 Nov. 1829. Murray mss.

over organic remains. *No rock* in the Alps older than *lias.* Much of Buckland's dashing paper on Alps wrong.[18] A formation (marine) found at foot of Alps, thicker than all the English secondaries united.[19]

The conversion of Sedgwick, it must be noted, was away from a residual belief in Wernerian ideas and from belief in Buckland's idea that the former presence of the biblical flood waters was reflected in the surface features of Europe. It was not conversion to the more subtly radical and far-reaching ideas which Lyell was developing in the manuscript of the *Principles.* These Sedgwick would accept only slowly and painfully—perhaps never completely. Yet even his limited conversion was important. Lyell wrote of it to Marianne:

S. [Sedgwick] has become unwillingly convinced that even the least argument for the diluvialists is disproved by the newer formation at the foot of the Alps between Bavaria and Wurtemburg. I am glad of this for he will drag after him in no time all the divines of Cambridge where his *ipse dixit* is even more authoritative than that of our Oxford friends & then the dispute will lose all chance of appearing personal between Murchison, Lyell & Co. & Buckland, as Mrs. B. & some others choose almost to think it. I fear, however, that Conybeare & B. backed by Moses may hold out some time. It is a theoretical error that retards the science & prevents many facts from being observed & systematized.[20]

Lyell was also encouraged in his writing by the fact that general interest in geology and zoology, as reflected in attendance at the meetings of societies, seemed to be increasing.

Toward the end of November he began to suspect that if he were to go to Iceland the following summer, as he planned to do, he would only be able to get out the first of the two volumes of his projected work.[21] About this time, too, he began to be concerned because he had not received from John Murray any definite proposal for publication, although he had discussed the matter with him on 2 November. He wrote to Fleming that "Murray is rather hanging fire about making an offer for my work, as I

18. W. Buckland. "On the structure of the Alps . . ." (1821).
19. C. L., Jr. to J. Fleming. 31 Oct. 1829. *L. & L.* I, 256–57.
20. C. L., Jr. to his sister Marianne. 2 Nov. 1829. Kinnordy mss.
21. C. L., Jr. to L. Horner. 24 Nov. 1829. Kinnordy mss. *L. & L.* I, 257–58.

am trying to keep the copyright. I still hope to get out the 2 vols. & be off with Allen[22] to Iceland in May."[23] He was almost ready to start printing volume one, so on 2 December he wrote again to Murray to ask whether he ought to try to make an arrangement with another publisher.[24] This brought an immediate response. Murray had been under the impression that he was going to Iceland before he began printing. His offer to publish was direct and generous:

> I will print 1500 copies of your work in 2 vols. 8vo to sell for 30/ at my own cost and risque, & give you Four Hundred Guineas for permission to do so, at 6, 9 and 12 months date from the day of publication. I will tell you candidly that this is taking the whole *risque* of a first publication upon myself and securing to you one half the profit. After this Edition shall be sold, the Copyright being entirely your own, we can bargain again for subsequent editions.[25]

John Murray was not a great publisher for nothing. Lyell replied immediately to thank him "for being so explicit as to leave me nothing more to do but to say I shall be happy to accept the offer, & shall be glad to know if I can take part of the M.S. to Clowes's on Monday morning."[26]

Lyell was still rewriting volume one but he expected to be finished with it by the end of December. The second volume, however, was only "in a manner written" but he hoped to rewrite it during the time that the first volume was going through the press.[27] On the Monday he took a portion of his manuscript to the printer. He was anxious that the type should be large and clear.[28]

By late December Lyell finally gave up his plans for a trip to Iceland the following summer, because otherwise he would have had to defer his second volume another year. Murray had urged that he get the first volume out by April, "for Sir you must not wait till the fine weather comes or people will not read."[29] By the end

22. If he went to Iceland he had agreed to take the son of Thomas Allen of Edinburgh with him.

23. C. L., Jr. to J. Fleming. 26 Nov. 1829. Kinnordy mss.

24. C. L., Jr. to J. M. 2 Dec. 1829. Murray mss.

25. J. Murray to C. L., Jr. 3 Dec. 1829. Kinnordy mss.

26. C. L., Jr. to J. M. 4 Dec. 1829. Murray mss.

27. C. L., Jr. to G. A. M. 5 Dec. 1829. Mantell mss.

28. J. Murray to ? Parker. 6 Dec. 1829. Kinnordy mss. The *Principles* is a model of clear typography and is set in Bell 12 point Monotype.

29. C. L., Jr. to his sister Marianne. 23 Dec. 1829. Kinnordy mss.

of the year he could send 100 pages of manuscript to the printer and had "lots of wood-cuts done." Murray began to advertise the book and at the December meeting of the Royal Society various of the fellows asked him "Well, when are you out."[30] He took no Christmas holiday except to spend a weekend with Gideon Mantell at Lewes. They drove to Shoreham to examine the cliffs and on Monday went "to Brighton and walked under the cliffs as far as Rottingdean" in intensely cold weather.[31]

On the first of January 1830 Lyell received his first sheet from the printer. He had now come to realize the magnitude of the task in which he was involved. That very morning Scrope had written to him, "That you will distance the field I have no fear, but this is not all that is to be done, for you *have a science to create*." This, Lyell was ready to admit, was only too true and he added, "what enhances the difficulty not a little, it cannot easily be *created* on sound principles without making war on many prepossessions with which the public will not part easily. To do this honestly & without getting into a scrape requires much dexterity."[32]

The winter of 1830 was severe and, although Lyell was hard at work, he sometimes found his life slightly bleak. There is a trace of loneliness in his letter to his sister Caroline on 23 January:

The snow then & snow again has made the roads or streets quite impossible. I never saw London so detestable. But I am quite well & have not leizure to be annoyed at trifles. I wish two or three of you were living with me here in town. I don't mean as laundresses in the temple exactly but to make tea for me and other important offices as for example to judge, as Mrs. Murchison did of my title page only, . . . how much was to go out as not understandable by a lady.[33]

By the beginning of February Lyell had corrected proof to page eighty of his book.[34] As he went along, the book was changing its plan and form under his hand. "I cannot," he wrote to Mantell, "resist the temptation of throwing in at the beginning of vol. 1 certain essays on the uniformity of the order of Nature, on the ancient climate of the globe & other magnificent subjects which I

30. C. L., Jr. to his sister Eleanor. 30 Dec. 1829. Kinnordy mss.
31. Mantell, *Journal*, p. 73.
32. Scrope quoted by C. L., Jr. in a letter to Mrs. Whitby of Newlands, Hants. C. Lyell, Jr. to Mrs. Whitby. 1 Jan. 1830. Mss. Linnean Soc. London.
33. C. L., Jr. to his sister Caroline. 23 Jan. 1830. Kinnordy mss.
34. C. L., Jr. to J. Fleming. 3 Feb. 1830. *L. & L.* I, 259–60.

had intended for vol. 2. But they will come as well now & thus I have been writing each essay as it went to press."[35] On 15 February he had still only reached page ninety-six. His slowness resulted from the fact he was writing these chapters as he went along and had not yet started to use the manuscript which was already prepared. He was particularly proud of the new theory he had developed to account for changes of climate in the course of geological time. He had, he assured Mantell, "a receipt for growing tree ferns at the pole, or, if it suits me, pines at the equator, walruses under the line & crocodiles in the arctic circle." Such a theory was particularly necessary to him because of the very clear evidence that, for instance, the climate of Britain in the period of the Tilgate forest beds had been subtropical or tropical. In formulating this theory, which forms chapters seven and eight of the *Principles,* Lyell had been to the Admiralty to obtain unpublished data of exploring expeditions from Sir Francis Beaufort (1774–1857) the hydrographer there.[36]

By 26 February Lyell had reached page 128 in proof, of which every word printed since the beginning of the year had been newly written. He hoped soon to "fall upon old stores written at Kinnordy." Although he was worried about meeting his deadline of May he was not discouraged. "I enjoy the work much," he told Eleanor, "as the excitement is great & I can get such assistance as perhaps no place but London can afford."[37] Even on 10 March he announced that he had only reached page 144 and had not yet got through his introductory essays.[38] On 22 March he promised Murray to be finished by the first week in June and on the twenty-seventh he added, "I am getting on so fast that I have no fear of being ready by end of May as I find the M.S. in a good state to the end."[39]

By 23 April, as a result of printing manuscript already prepared, Lyell had leaped ahead to page 256 and was proceeding at the rate of thirty pages a week.[40] He was getting on so well that he considered making a geological expedition via St. Petersburg and Moscow to the Crimea during the summer and proposed to Sir Philip Egerton, who was interested in geology, that they go to-

35. C. L., Jr. to G. A. M. 5 Feb. 1830. Mantell mss.
36. C. L., Jr. to G. A. M. 15 Feb. 1830. Mantell mss.. *L & L.* I, 261–62.
37. C. L., Jr. to his sister Eleanor. 26 Feb. 1830. Kinnordy mss.
38. C. L., Jr. to G. A. M. 10 March 1830. Mantell mss.
39. C. L., Jr. to J. M. 22 March and 27 March 1830. Murray mss.
40. C. L., Jr. to G. A. M. 23 April 1830. Mantell mss. *L. & L.* I, 264–65.

gether.[41] By 5 May he had reached page 300 and on 11 May had passed page 320. On this day he decided his plans for the summer. "After divers schemes, Iceland—Pyrenees—W. Indies—the Crimea, Black Sea etc.," he wrote to Eleanor, "—I have definitely settled positively for the last time for the Pyrenees because I find I shall be just released at the nick of time for them."[42] Captain Cooke, a naval officer, had undertaken to accompany him.

Lyell allowed some of his close friends, most probably William Broderip and Charles Stokes, to read the *Principles* in manuscript and in proof sheets.[43] To Mantell he wrote on 13 May:

> You may form some idea of my book by a friend, one of two who has read 200 pages, asking me "Pray is vol. 2 to contain *facts?* I trust not, for really we have had *enough* of them before." He was no geologist but a good judge of readable philosophy.[44]

On 18 May he had corrected proof to page 336 and on 31 May to page 384. He finished correcting proofs and completed the index of the *Principles* on 22 June just before entering the coach for Southampton to cross to Le Havre on his way to Spain.

As early as the beginning of May, Lockhart, as editor of the *Quarterly Review,* had wished to settle upon a reviewer for the *Principles* so that such a person might read the book in page proof and have his review written to emerge in the July issue of the *Quarterly,* immediately after the publication of the book. He consulted Lyell, who described the interview to Scrope:

> Lockhart when he met me the other day said "Who is to review your book. I am quite anxious to settle it but cannot get on. Buckland has not time, nor Sedgwick, & when I determined on asking Scrope some dissuaded me saying that Conybeare would do it best. Now without pretending to judge as a geologist I do not see why. Another thing I know of old that Conybeare promises but does not perform, in the reviewing line. Have you any objection that I should apply to Scrope?"
>
> "Certainly not, but I told you not to consult me because I might get into as great a scrape as Buckland when he concocted

41. C. L., Jr. to Sir Philip Egerton. 26 April 1830. *L. & L.* I, 265–67.

42. C. L., Jr. to his sister Eleanor. 11 May 1830. Kinnordy mss. *L. & L.* I, 267–68.

43. William John Broderip (1789–1859) barrister and later magistrate was an enthusiastic amateur conchologist. Charles Stokes (1783–1853) was a member of the Stock Exchange and a collector, amateur naturalist, and antiquary.

44. C. L., Jr. to G. A. M. 13 May 1830. Mantell mss.

with Coplestone a review of his own Reliquiae Dil. which is never forgotten against him & not without reason."

"But I don't ask you to club with Scrope, but what is there against his doing it? Has he the knowledge?"

"Not only that, but he is much more likely to agree with me in the main than Conybeare, so that of course I am not unwilling."

"Well I shall offer it to him for as to his style of writing in the only works I have seen, they may say what they please, *but I know no one who writes better.*"

Have you heard from him?[45]

Scrope replied immediately:

Your conversation with Lockhart is very agreeable flattery. He has not applied to me yet on the subject. If he does I shall accept conditionally demurring till I have seen your book. I misdoubt my capacity as your reviewer, more particularly as I presume there will be much discussion on the determination of age *by organic remains* etc. of which I am an incompetent judge. Again I fear I should not be able to hit the exact line in discussing your anti-Mosaical heresies, not being an adept at playing the hypocrite I shall hardly write with the proper *unction* of the Quarterly reviewer, concerning "that profound historical and theological cosmogonist" the worthy Patriarch.[46]

Lockhart did write to Scrope to ask him to review the *Principles* and after he had read a portion of the book in sheets, Scrope agreed to do it. On 11 June he wrote to Lyell full of questions.

I believe I have not yet acknowledged the receipt of any part of your book which I have up to the 304th page. I am delighted with it as you may well suppose. I have neglected geology of late and am not quite *au courant* of the progress made in it latterly on the Continent. I cannot therefore tell exactly by how much you are in advance of the rest of the world. Ferussac and some others I believe, have been fighting away for "existing causes" for a long time past, but with what success I hardly know.

What I admire in you is the assurance with which you speak of doctrine still supported by the Bucklands, Conybeares etc.

45. C. L., Jr. to G. P. Scrope. 6 May 1830. Kinnordy mss. (ms. copy).
46. G. P. Scrope to C. L., Jr. 8 May 1830. APS mss.

as exploded errors, past praying for. You stride on instead at so rapid a pace that there is no time for them to contest the point with you. Your sketch of the History of Geology is admirable and illustrates so usefully the absurdity and mischief of the Theo-geological systems, that to strengthen my argument against them, you must allow me to give an abstract of it in my article. If between us we can succeed in freeing Geology, once and for-ever from the clutches of Moses, we shall have deserved well of the science. I am somewhat afraid though of Lockhart's scissors, having felt that he can use them pretty freely, and in the most treacherous manner too, as the sheets are printing off, so as to leave one no appeal.

You are aware that I think you carry your principle rather too far when you argue for the endless or rather *beginning-less* succession of past changes. I shall be obliged to fight this point a little, particularly as you are rather unjust to those who *look for a beginning,* classing them with the miracle mongers, as if the actual order of Nature could not admit of the creation of new worlds as well as new genera or new continents. You get over the argument from change of climate very triumphantly I own, or certainly with great ingenuity and a brilliant theory, which as I never met with anything like it before I take to be your own. I mean the *summer and winter of your annus magnus.* But I can-not help thinking there is an assailable point or two even in this explanation, and the other main arguments such as the much more generally crystalline texture of the early strata, the occur-rence of gneiss, *mica slate, greywacke* etc. etc. *only* in the ear-liest stratified deposits, etc. you scarcely deign to mention, though how you can get over them I cannot divine.

I am charmed with your *aqueous* power of destruction & reno-vation & wait with impatience for the igneous.[47]

Lyell promptly wrote a long reply to this letter. The most in-teresting portion of it is that in which he discusses his indebted-ness to his predecessors and points out those ideas in the *Principles* which are essentially new. With reference to the effectiveness of existing causes Lyell wrote:

Ferussac has done nothing but believe in the universal ocean up to the chalk period till lately. Prévost has done a little, but is a

47. G. P. Scrope to C. L., Jr. 11 June 1830. APS mss.

diluvialist, a rare thing in France. If any one has done much in that way, I have not been able to procure their books. Von Hoff has assisted me most, and you should compliment him for the German plodding perseverence with which he filled two volumes with facts like tables of statistics; but he helped me not to my scientific views of causes, nor to my arrangement. [1] The division into aqueous and igneous cause is mine, no great matter, and obvious enough. Von Hoff always goes on geographically. For example, he will take as a chapter "changes in the boundaries of sea and land" and under this may come alterations by earthquakes as well as currents etc. Von Hoff took his "waste of sea cliffs" as far as Britain is concerned, from Stevenson—very meagre. I have done mine from actual observation, principally in coast surveys. [2] My division into destroying and reproductive effects of rivers, tides, currents, etc. is, as far as I know, new—[3] my theory of estuaries being formed is contrary to Bakewell and many others, who think England is growing bigger. In regard to Deltas, many facts are from Von Hoff, but the greater part, not. [4] All the theory of the arrangement of strata in Deltas and stratification, etc., is new as far as I know, and the importance of spring deposits. Von Hoff thinks all that is now going on, a mere trifle comparatively, though he has done more than any other to disprove it.[48]

Lyell here lists four ideas, in addition to his new theory for the origin of changes of climate, which were new and original in the *Principles*. They were: (1) the division into aqueous and igneous causes; (2) the division into the destructive and constructive activities of rivers, tides, and currents; (3) the theory of the formation of estuaries; and (4) the theory of the arrangement of strata in deltas and the cause of stratification. They are ideas developed in chapters ten to seventeen of the *Principles,* and had been probably first sketched out in the earlier manuscript drafts of 1827 and the summer of 1829, but were rewritten and greatly developed during the months of February, March, and April 1830.

Lyell could not answer Scrope's objection that the older strata were generally made up of crystalline rocks such as gneiss, mica-slate, greywacke, etc., without describing some recent observations by Sedgwick in the eastern Alps which he was not free to dis-

48. C. L., Jr. to G. P. Scrope. 14 June 1830. *L. & L.* I, 268–71.

cuss. Since the time of Werner the crystalline nature of these rocks had been taken to mean that they had been laid down under conditions drastically different both from the conditions under which the later "mechanical sediments"—sandstone, limestone, shale, etc.—had been deposited and from modern conditions. However, Sedgwick had found "an encrinital limestone alternating with genuine mica schist and the *white stone* of Werner." Therefore the parent materials of mica schist must have been deposited under conditions similar to those of the limestone and within the same period of time. Whatever had been the cause, its crystalline structure was *not* the product of great age. By this time Lyell suspected that the crystalline structure was the result of the alteration of ordinary sediments by heat, but he was not yet ready to affirm such an opinion even to Scrope.

He also had to answer Scrope's criticism that he seemed to assert that the earth had had no beginning. He denied that he necessarily implied this. "All I ask," he wrote, "is, that at any given period of the past don't stop inquiry, when puzzled, by refuge to a 'beginning,' which is all one with 'another state of nature,' as it appears to me." He added:

> It is not the beginning I look for, but proofs of a *progressive* state of existence in the globe, the probability of which is *proved* by the analogy of changes in organic life.

Again and again in his writing he uses the word "analogy" in the sense of Bishop Butler and it seems to have pervaded both his view of the history of the earth and the proper mode of reasoning about it. Lyell also described with what careful diplomacy he had written the *Principles*. "If I have said more than some will like," he told Scrope, "yet I give you my word that full *half* of my history and comments was cut out, and even many facts; because either I or Stokes or Broderip, felt that it was anticipating twenty or thirty years of the march of honest feeling to declare it undisguisedly."[49] His diplomacy in writing was his great strength because it won for the *Principles,* and for geology, a wide, intelligent, and attentive audience. Moreover, he was quite sincere in his respect for the prejudices of his readers which, he thought, arose from deep and honest emotion and saw that politeness to them in writing was but the counterpart of ordinary politeness in human relations.

49. Ibid.

The *Principles* was published in July and it at once caught the attention of the reading public.

THE PRINCIPLES OF GEOLOGY

Although the *Principles* as published was rewritten in one continuous effort from the beginning of November 1829 until June 1830, its structure had already been established by the earlier versions of his manuscript, which Lyell modified in detail and to which he was prepared to add additional chapters, but which he never abandoned. As a result, three portions of the book are clearly distinguishable. The first portion, included in the first four chapters, was the historical sketch of the development of geology. This historical sketch served a polemical purpose for Lyell because he was able to trace the ideas of his diluvial opponents, Buckland and Conybeare, to their roots in such seventeenth-century cosmogonists as Burnet and to apply the powerful weapon of ridicule to historical figures rather than to his contemporaries. Even in the first version of the manuscript, written in 1827, there was a historical introduction, but Lyell rewrote and greatly amplified this during the spring of 1829 after his return to London from Italy. It was then that he incorporated his accounts of eighteenth-century Italian geologists, many of whose works he had brought back with him from Italy.

The second portion of the book, represented by chapters five to nine, was an interpolation between the historical introduction and the main body of the book. These chapters were written during January and February of 1830 and embodied Lyell's conscious effort to "create the science" and to express the consequences of the uniformity of nature in the history of the earth.

The main body of the book, in the original manuscript version, which Lyell rewrote and greatly extended while at Kinnordy during the summer and autumn of 1829 and again revised for the press during the late winter and spring of 1830, began with chapter ten. At the opening of this chapter Lyell repeated his definition of geology as "the science which investigates the former changes that have taken place in the organic, as well as in the inorganic kingdoms of nature."[50] This definition of the aims of geology was one which he had thought out and written, in a number

50. *Principles,* p. 167. Cf., p. 1. Specific page references to this work are given in the text.

of successive versions, in his notebooks during his tour of Italy and Sicily in 1828. He then proceeded to divide the "agents of change" into two great classes, the aqueous and igneous.

> The *aqueous* agents are incessantly labouring to reduce the inequalities of the earth's surface to a level, while the *igneous,* on the other hand are equally active in restoring the unevenness of the external crust. [p. 167]

The effects of aqueous agents he further subdivided into destructive and "reproductive."

In his discussion in chapters ten to twelve Lyell presented a massive array of evidence to show how great the effects of running water could be in excavating river valleys and in transporting silt. He used examples from the valleys of the Po and the Mississippi to demonstrate his case. In succeeding chapters he took up the "reproductive effects" of running water, that is, the deposition of sediments in lakes or seas. He contrasted the formation of deltas in lakes and inland seas with their formation along the borders of the open ocean and showed that in the ocean, tides and currents might prevent or hinder the growth of a delta by sweeping away the sediments as fast as they were brought to the river's mouth. In all smaller rivers he considered tides and currents to be capable of removing sediments faster than the river could bring them down, with the result that, instead of a delta, an estuary would be formed. This effect led him to consider the distribution of sediments over the sea bottom, and he mentioned the Dogger Bank in the North Sea as an example of a shoal formed by deposition of sediments by currents. Since the modern sea bottom is difficult to study, he suggested examining the ancient strata for traces of the effects of tides and currents (p. 311).

In chapter eighteen Lyell began his discussion of igneous agents, which he subdivided into volcanic activity and earthquakes. In five chapters he gave a long and detailed discussion of all the phenomena of volcanic activity, including a history of the eruptions of Vesuvius and a description of Etna. His principal purpose was to show that even the largest volcanoes such as Vesuvius and Etna had been built up gradually by a long series of successive eruptions no one of which was more violent, or on a larger scale, than those which occur today, or which have occurred during the historic period of time. He ridiculed Alexandre Brongniart's assertion that in past geological epochs geological events had occurred on a scale a hundred times greater than any modern ones.[51] After describing the current of lava discharged from Skaptár Jokul in Iceland in 1783 he said:

> Had Skaptár Jokul therefore been a volcano of the olden time, it would have poured forth lavas at a single eruption, a hundred times more voluminous than those which have been witnessed by the present generation. If we multiply the current before described, by a hundred, and first assume that its height and breadth remain the same, it would stretch out to the length of nine thousand miles, or about half as far again as from the pole to the equator. . . . Amongst the ancient strata, no igneous rock of such colossal magnitude has yet been met with, nay it would be most difficult to point out a mass of igneous origin of ancient date referrible to a single eruption, which would rival in volume the matter poured out from Skaptár Jokul in 1783. [pp. 375–76]

But his use of irony was infrequent and restrained. On the whole Lyell depended upon the mere description of modern geological changes to show how considerable they were when taken together. This is particularly true of his enumeration in his final chapters of the effects of the various earthquakes recorded during the hundred and forty years before 1830. When all the changes of land level produced by earthquakes in this relatively short period of time were listed together, the effect was to suggest a land surface which was fluctuating continually.

This account of modern igneous and aqueous geological processes, which occupied seventeen chapters of the *Principles* and formed by far the greater part of the book, fulfilled the promise in the title "to explain the former changes of the earth's surface by reference to causes now in operation." It represented the plan of the book as Lyell originally conceived it in 1827, though greatly enriched by his observations made during his tour of Italy and Sicily in 1828–29. However, it was not exactly the fulfilling of the original plan which made the book so revolutionary. Most of his evidence for the chapters on aqueous and igneous causes was secondary, derived from the travels of Basil Hall, from von Hoff, and from other writers. They represented skillful organization and clear exposition, all pointing toward a common goal, but were

51. A. Brongniart. *Tableau des terrains* . . . (1829) p. 52.

not in any single feature startlingly new. Yet the book as a whole *was revolutionary,* and the long account of aqueous and igneous agents was important because of the broad setting and powerful reinforcement which it gave to ideas that were distinctly new and original.

These original ideas were presented in the four chapters sandwiched between the historical sketch and the rest of the book. Lyell's conscious effort to create the science of geology anew, contained in them, proved more subtly difficult than he had at first expected. In his own thinking he had come to consider the world as regulated by natural laws which were uniform through time. His attitude seems to have been influenced by his reading of Butler's *Analogy* which he quoted first in his review of the Geological Society's *Transactions* in 1826. Bishop Butler was writing to provide arguments for the existence of God and for a future life for man. His basic view was that, since the universe and everything in it was the creation of God, that is, of a single deity, it must be uniform. Moral consequences, Butler thought, could be ascribed to the general course of nature, which was but to say that they could be ascribed "to him who appointed it [i.e. nature] and put things into it: Or to a Course of Operation, from its Uniformity or Constancy, called natural; and which necessarily implies an operating Agent."[52] Since uniformity and constancy were the characteristics of the natural order, we could not infer anything of another world which was not comparable with the one we know. This idea must have had for Lyell an immediate implication because even if the geological past were considered another world separated from the modern one by a gulf of time, still we should not be justified in inferring anything about it except by analogy with modern conditions. Butler, in fact, made the temporal implications of his thought explicit:

> But it is evident, that the Course of things, which comes within our View, is connected with somewhat past, present and future, beyond it. So that we are placed, as one may speak, in the Middle of a Scheme, not a fixt but a progressive one, every Way incomprehensible: incomprehensible, in a manner equally, with respect to what has been, what now is, and what shall be hereafter.[53]

52. J. Butler. *The analogy of religion, natural and revealed, to the constitution and course of nature* (1740) p. 50.
53. Ibid., p. 197.

Lyell quoted this statement in his review of the *Transactions*. He also quoted Butler's statement that "those things, which we call Irregularities, may not be so at all." Lyell was using Butler in this instance to suggest that the difficulties which geology made for religion were perhaps more apparent than real. So little was yet known in geology that its operations could not yet be clear, but as the science progressed it increased "our admiration of the grandeur and variety of nature's operations."[54] In this early expression of his ideas Lyell defended geology against the charge of irreligion and at the same time tried to develop a set of ideas with which to interpret geological phenomena. This was still his problem in writing the *Principles*, but it was further complicated by the fact that by this time even geological phenomena in some respects seemed ambivalent. What is remarkable about Lyell is the way in which he followed a consistent line through a maze of confusing and contradictory evidence. Even when confronted with seemingly insoluble difficulties, he did not abandon his faith in the uniformity of nature.

The one factor which, more than any other, would reduce the jumble of geological evidence to order was time. If strata were to be deposited and upheaved quickly, if valleys were to be excavated overnight, these events would indeed assume the dimensions of catastrophes; but if very long periods of time were allowed, they might be accomplished gradually by the ordinary action of rain, wind, and waves to wear down the land and earthquakes to build it up again. Lyell wrote:

> We know that one earthquake may raise the coast of Chili for a hundred miles to the average height of about five feet. A repetition of two thousand shocks of equal violence might produce a mountain chain one hundred miles long, and ten thousand feet high. Now, should one only of these convulsions happen in a century, it would be consistent with the order of events experienced by the Chilians from the earliest times; but if the whole of them were to occur in the next hundred years, the entire district must be depopulated, scarcely any animals or plants could survive, and the surface would be one confused heap of ruin and desolation. [p. 80]

In postulating the uniformity of physical laws and the uni-

54. [Review of] "Transactions of the Geological Society of London . . . 1824" (1826) pp. 536–40.

formity of the course of nature through past geological ages, Lyell was faced with a genuine dilemma, because in one crucial aspect it was clear that the conditions on the earth's surface had changed. In the British strata from the coal measures up to the chalk, all of the plant and animal remains which had been found had suggested that the climate of Britain had formerly been tropical, or subtropical, and therefore much warmer than the present. These secondary strata had been studied intensively by members of the Geological Society; the marine formations were in many instances rich in corals whereas the freshwater and delta formations contained many large reptiles including crocodiles and turtles. Because of their cold-blooded physiology the larger reptiles are necessarily confined to a warm climate in which the temperature of air and water will allow their bodies to function. The plants in the coal, while clearly different from modern species and genera, still seemed more analogous to modern tropical forms such as tree ferns than to the plants of northern climates. In general the flora and fauna of the coal, of the Stonesfield slate, and of Gideon Mantell's Tilgate forest beds, in each case formed a complex strongly suggestive of tropical or subtropical conditions. Furthermore, these facts were in agreement with the features of adjacent strata which had been laid down under marine conditions and which, by the presence in them of corals and of large shells belonging to tropical genera, suggested more the conditions of modern tropical oceans than those of the cold waters of northern seas.

Lyell was fully aware of the weight of this evidence and accepted the fact that the climate had changed even though his close friend, Dr. John Fleming, had opposed this conclusion in an article published in April 1829, and had denied the evidence on which it was based.[55] The most decisive evidence for Lyell was the fossil shells of the Tertiary strata of Italy and Sicily. These shells belonged to species still living in the Mediterranean, but the fossil representatives were larger than those in the Mediterranean and corresponded in size to shells of these species from the Indian Ocean. Because size of shell in a species was correlated with the warmth of the sea, the large size of the fossils clearly demonstrated the existence of tropical conditions at the time they lived.

If changes of climate had occurred in geological history, and

55. J. Fleming, "On the . . . evidence . . . that the arctic regions formerly enjoyed a milder climate . . ." (1829). Cf. W. D. Conybeare. "Answer to Dr. Fleming's view . . ." (1829).

if Lyell were to maintain his principle of uniformity, he had to account for the climatic changes in terms of geological changes brought about by the kinds of processes now in action. That is, he had to maintain the uniformity of physical laws, of the course of nature, and of geological processes at the same time as he accepted the nonuniformity of climate and environment. Similarly, he had to accept the nonuniformity of the species of plants and animals which made up the flora and fauna in past geological ages. He was able to accept this latter instance of nonuniformity because he felt that the fossil species of the secondary strata were at least analogous to modern species. The large reptiles, for instance, often performed roles fulfilled in modern times by the larger mammals. He thus had at least a tentative awareness of the concept of the ecological niche.

The need to explain the change from a warmer condition of the earth's surface in the past to the cooler modern conditions was the greater because catastrophic theories already offered an explanation. Cosmogonists, from René Descartes onward, had assumed that the earth had first been formed as a hot, molten mass. This idea was strengthened by the fact that the earth's shape was an oblate spheroid, slightly flattened at the poles. It would have assumed this form originally as a fluid sphere rotating about its axis, which later gradually cooled to form a solid crust.

At the beginning of March 1830 Lyell bought and read Sir Humphry Davy's *Consolations in Travel,* then only recently published. It was a small book which had been prepared for the press after Davy's death and contained his final reflections on science. Davy asserted that "it is impossible to defend the proposition, that the present order of things is the ancient and constant order of nature, only modified by existing laws." Since the interior of the earth was in the beginning still a hot molten mass, it radiated enough warmth to maintain a tropical climate over the whole surface of the earth. The first forms of life to appear were those which could bear high temperatures, but as time went on, and the earth cooled further, other forms of life were permitted to appear.

But in this state of things there was no order of events similar to the present;—the crust of the globe was exceedingly slender and the source of fire a small distance from the surface. In consequence of contraction in one part of the mass, cavities were opened, which caused the entrance of water, and immense volcanic explosions took place, raising one part of the surface, depressing another, producing mountains and causing new and extensive depositions from the primitive ocean.

With still further cooling, however, and the thickening of the earth's crust, conditions became more stable until a point was reached when the creation of man occurred, "and since that period there has been little alteration in the physical circumstances of our globe."[56]

In this theory, if it can be so called, Davy presented in epitome the assumptions about the earth's history common to catastrophist geologists in 1830. The history of the earth thus offered is short in time, apocalyptic in its events, and brought about by forces without counterparts in modern geological processes. It was, therefore, scarcely susceptible of scientific investigation and might be seen as a vision, or not at all. Yet it had features which made it difficult to combat. Its description of the beginning of the earth was based upon a plausible scientific argument and, if the earth had begun as a molten mass, its later cooling followed necessarily. It offered a progressive scheme for the earth's history, and discoveries in paleontology seemed to make some sort of progressive scheme essential. Unfortunately, if it were accepted, such a scheme would stop inquiry just where it should begin. It was to prevent the necessity for acceptance of Davy's viewpoint that Lyell developed his theory of climate.

Lyell's theory was entirely in keeping with his general approach to geological problems. He began by considering the factors which determine climatic conditions on different parts of the earth's surface at present. In doing so he necessarily began with the ideas developed in Alexander von Humboldt's essay "On Isothermal Lines," published in 1817.[57] Humboldt had compared the mean annual, and summer and winter temperatures of various places on the earth's surface, and had correlated the climate of a country not only with its latitude but with its altitude, proximity to the sea, and relation to the prevailing winds. Humboldt also contrasted the temperatures of the northern and the southern hemispheres and related the differences to the greater proportion of sea to land in the southern hemisphere. From Humboldt's data Lyell con-

56. H. Davy, *Consolations in travel* . . . (1830), pp. 135–49. Quoted in *Principles,* p. 144.

57. A. von Humboldt, "Des lignes isothermes . . ." (1817). This essay was translated into English. "On isothermal lines . . ." (1820–21).

cluded that whereas areas of sea tended to moderate extremes of temperature in whatever latitude they lay, areas of land might have quite different effects depending upon whether they lay below or above 40 degrees of latitude. In high latitudes near the poles, areas of land tended to chill the climate, especially if they were elevated, because they tended to accumulate quantities of ice and snow. He had in mind the great glaciers which cover Greenland. By contrast, land areas in lower latitudes near the equator tended to have a warming effect upon the climate. The temperature of the land rose above that of the sea, and the heat radiated into the atmosphere caused warm winds.

As a consequence of these effects, Lyell concluded, any geological change that elevated large areas of land in the vicinity of the poles would exert a strong cooling effect on world climate. Conversely, if the area of the ocean were extended in high latitudes, and the land area there were restricted to low islands and archipelagoes, the climate of the world would become distinctly warmer. This was indeed "a receipt for growing tree-ferns at the pole or . . . pines at the equator."[58] Lyell showed that because the present climates of the earth were the complex result of the sun's radiation and of the rotation of the earth—those forces which produce the winds and consequently the ocean currents—acting upon the present physical geography of the earth, any change in that physical geography would inevitably alter the climate. Consequently, in its past geological history, the earth's climate must necessarily have been different from its present climate. This was a new and striking idea. "Here, then," wrote John Herschel, "we have at least a cause on which a philosopher may consent to reason; though whether the changes actually going on are such as to warrant the whole extent of the conclusion . . . may be considered as undecided."[59]

Lyell's next task was to show that the distribution of land and sea in past geological ages, which could be inferred from the nature of the strata, would have tended to produce, according to his theory, the kind of climate in which the fossil plants and animals could have lived and which, therefore, had actually existed (p. 125).

The widespread distribution of the strata of mountain and

58. C. L., Jr. to G. A. M. 15 Feb. 1830. Mantell mss.
59. J. F. W. Herschel, *A preliminary discourse on the study of natural philosophy* (1831) p. 147.

transition limestones in northern Europe, Asia, and North America, said Lyell, indicated that when these strata had been laid down, a broad expanse of deep ocean had extended across the northern hemisphere. The land area appeared to have been restricted to scattered islands. He thought that the fossil flora of the Carboniferous period was analogous to the present insular flora of the oceanic islands of the south Pacific. The presence of extensive oceans in the northern latitudes would have had the effect of maintaining a temperate climate there and of warming the climate of the whole earth.

Lyell traced the changes which had occurred at the end of the Carboniferous period and showed that the coal strata of the west of England had been upheaved by repeated earthquakes while at the same time those of Germany had been at rest. Considerable changes in the geography of the northern hemisphere had occurred.

> Yet the sea still extended over the greater part of the area now occupied by the lands which we inhabit, and was even of considerable depth in many localities where our highest mountain-chains now rise. The vegetation, during a part at least of this new period (from the lias to the chalk inclusive), appears to have approached to that of the larger islands of the equatorial zone. These islands appear to have been drained by rivers of considerable size, which were inhabited by crocodiles and gigantic oviparous reptiles, both herbivorous and carnivorous, belonging for the most part to extinct genera. Of the contemporary inhabitants of the land we have as yet acquired but scanty information, but we know that there were flying reptiles, insects and small insectivorous mammifera, allied to the opossum. [p. 133]

Among other things, the large delta deposit which Mantell had discovered in the Tilgate forest beds, indicated that larger land areas had arisen during this period. The climate, however, still appeared to have been tropical.

Lyell next sketched the changes which had occurred at the end of the secondary and the beginning of the Tertiary period. Much mountain building and volcanic activity had occurred. There was evidence, too, of a considerable cooling of the climate. Lyell showed that it was at this time that the peninsula of Italy and the Alps had begun to be elevated.

Down to the period, therefore, when the rocks, from our lias to the chalk inclusive, were deposited, there was sea where now the principal chain of Europe extends, and that chain attained more than half its present elevation and breadth between the eras when our newer secondary and oldest tertiary rocks originated. [p. 137]

The Pyrenees, he showed, rose at the same time, as did also the chalk area of southeastern England.

These great changes should, according to Lyell's theory of the factors governing climate, have produced a great change of climate; that is just what had occurred:

There is, therefore, confessedly a marked coincidence in point of time between the greatest alteration in climate and the principal revolution in the physical geography of the northern hemisphere. It is very probable that the abruptness of the transition from the organic remains of the secondary to those of the tertiary epoch, may not be wholly ascribable to the present deficiency of our information. We shall doubtless hereafter discover many intermediate gradations . . . ; but it is not impossible that the interval between the chalk and tertiary formations constituted an era in the earth's history, when the passage from one class of organic beings to another was, comparatively speaking, rapid. For if the doctrines explained by us in regard to vicissitudes of temperature are sound, it will follow that changes of equal magnitude in the geographical features of the globe, may at different periods produce very unequal effects on climate, and, so far as the existence of certain animals and plants depends on climate, the duration of species may often be shortened or protracted, according to the rate at which the change in temperature proceeded.[60] [p. 139]

Lyell's sketch of geological history and his demonstration of the way in which geological changes may alter the climate of the earth and thereby determine the extinction of large numbers of species is one of the most remarkable passages in the *Principles*. It demonstrates the discrimination with which he applied the principle of uniformity. It was a uniformity of process, but not of result.

60. Lyell's correlation of change of species with geographical changes is confirmed and extended by N. D. Newell, "Revolutions in the history of life," in C. C. Albritton, Jr., ed. *Uniformity and Simplicity* (1967).

The slow but continual action of the forces which produced erosion, subsidence, and elevation might produce a dramatically different set of conditions upon the earth's surface. Geological changes in a narrow area might alter the climate over a much larger portion of the earth's surface. The combined removal of some areas of land and the elevation of others from beneath the sea destroyed one set of environments for plants and animals, and created another.

Lyell had gone far to demonstrate that the past history of the earth was "one uninterrupted succession of physical events, governed by the laws now in operation" (p. 144), but he had yet to deal with the most difficult question—the origin of the successive assemblages of plant and animal species which had populated the earth during past geological periods. The creation of new sets of species was a kind of event without apparent parallel in the present-day world. Therefore, the repeated emergence of sets of new species during the earth's history appeared to be nonuniform with the present "course of nature." This fact was a source of satisfaction to the defenders of the biblical account of the earth's history, who saw in the tumultuous visions of catastrophic geology the hand of God in the creation of the world. To them the appearance of a new population of plants and animals was proof that God had intervened miraculously to alter the uniform action of physical laws.

In his *Consolations in Travel,* Davy gave as his principal reason for believing that the conditions during former geological ages were widely different from those of the present, the apparently progressive development of animal and plant life.

> . . . in those strata which are deepest and which must, consequently, be supposed to be the earliest deposited, forms, even of vegetable life, are rare; shells and vegetable remains are found in the next order; the bones of fishes and oviparous reptiles exist in the following class; the remains of birds, with those of the same genera mentioned before, in the next order; those of quadrupeds of extinct species in a still more recent class; and it is only in the loose and slightly-consolidated strata of gravel and sand, and which are usually called diluvian formations, that the remains of animals, such as now people the globe are found, with others belonging to extinct species. But, in none of these formations, whether called secondary, tertiary or diluvial, have

the remains of man, or any of his works been discovered. [pp. 144–45]

Lyell quoted this, and other similar passages from Davy, in the *Principles,* because they posed an explicit challenge to his assertion of the uniformity of physical laws in past geological ages. He then arranged his argument as a direct answer to them.

Lyell pointed out that all the inferences which had been drawn as to the greater warmth of the ancient climate were based on the assumption that the relation of ancient plants and animals to their environment was governed by the same physical laws as today.

> If this postulate be denied, and the prevalence of particular families be declared to depend on a certain order of precedence in the introduction of different classes into the earth, and if it be maintained that the standard of organization was raised successively, we must then ascribe the numerical preponderance in the earlier ages of plants of simpler structure, *not to the heat,* but to those different laws which regulate organic life in newly created worlds. . . . Before we can infer an elevated temperature in high latitudes, from the presence of arborescent Ferns, Lycopodiaceae, and other allied families, we must be permitted to assume, that at all times, past and future, a heated and moist atmosphere pervading the northern hemisphere has a tendency to produce in the vegetation a predominance of analogous types of form. [p. 146]

As he developed it further, Lyell's argument was denying the force of that evidence which eventually would have meaning in terms of evolution. Yet the questions which he raised were fundamentally ecological. He pointed out that not only was the fossil record incomplete, but the kinds of fossils which were preserved would reflect the kind of environment which had existed *in the particular area where the strata were formed, at the time they were formed.* Marine strata would not preserve the remains of land animals, and if the land areas of northern Europe during the secondary period had consisted of islands scattered in a broad sea, they would not have offered an environment favorable to land mammals (pp. 148–49). However, the discovery of even one specimen of a mammal in the older strata was fatal to the doctrine of progressive development, wrote Lyell, and such a specimen had been found in the Stonesfield slate (p. 150). Furthermore, a much younger Tertiary formation, the plastic clay, had been found to be entirely lacking in mammalian fossils. Thus, Lyell concluded, there was no real evidence in geology for the doctrine of progressive development. The origin of man, however, he felt was clearly recent.

It is important to note that Lyell specifically disclaimed that his principle of uniformity implied an eternal recurrence of similar events (pp. 156–57). Yet he thought that the introduction of man would produce a lesser change than that which occurred when, for instance, Britain had established a colony in Australia. In other words, the changes brought by the introduction of man were on a scale uniform with the present order of nature. This avoided the real question of how the origin of man had occurred, but it was a reasonable argument to demonstrate that, in whatever manner man had arisen, the natural order of the world in other respects had remained uniform throughout. Furthermore, the fact that certain genera of marine animals had survived from the earliest geological periods until the present indicated that "amidst the great variety of revolutions of which the earth's surface has been the theatre, there has never been a departure from the conditions necessary for the existence of certain unaltered types of organization" (p. 161).

The great consequence of the principle of the uniformity of the "course of Nature" through time was that it gave every feature of the present natural world significance for the interpretation of events in the past. Lyell saw it as a spur to investigation:

> The geologist who yields implicit assent to the truth of these principles, will deem it incumbent on him to examine with minute attention all the changes now in progress on the earth, and will regard every fact collected respecting the causes in diurnal action, as affording him a key to the interpretation of some mystery in the archives of remote ages. Our estimate, indeed, of the value of all geological evidence, and the interest derived from the investigation of the earth's history, must depend entirely on the degree of confidence which we feel in regard to the permanency of the laws of nature. [p. 165]

The publication of the *Principles*, organized as it was around this doctrine, produced a sensation. In the *Quarterly Review* it re-

ceived very favorable treatment at the hands of Scrope.[61] William
Whewell, however, in the *British Critic*, criticized the book more
severely.[62] Whereas Scrope was personally committed to the battle
against Mosaic geology, Whewell was an ordained clergyman and
fellow of Trinity College, Cambridge. His position was basically
opposed to that of Lyell, but he was a man of strong mind who
was prepared to consider fairly ideas to which he was opposed,
confident that he could conquer them on their own terms.

The first thing which Whewell noted about the *Principles* was
that it involved a restatement of the Huttonian theory and had the
same effect of requiring immense periods of time to accomplish
the wearing down of land and the deposition of the sediments
represented by the strata. However, whereas Hutton had believed
that extraordinary convulsions were necessary to uplift the strata,
Lyell argued that the effect of repeated earthquakes and volcanic
action on the same scale as known today would accomplish this.
Whewell was skeptical, but he wrote:

> Though we are not prepared to assent to all the opinions which
> he propounds, it is impossible to think otherwise of his work
> than as a most skillful and masterly attempt to combine into a
> consistent view a large mass of singularly curious observations
> and details, which no one but an accomplished geologist could
> have put together. [p. 186]

Whewell described briefly the multitude of discoveries in paleontology made during the previous quarter century and the effect
which they had had in forming the opinions of geologists. Most
geologists had drawn from the mass of recently described geological phenomena conclusions directly opposite to those of Lyell.

> In the dislocation of provinces, in the elevation of hills from the
> bottom of the sea, in the comminution and dispersion of vast
> tracts of the hardest rock, in the obliteration and renewal of a
> whole creation, they seemed to themselves to see, without the
> possibility of a mistake, the manifestation of powers more ener-
> getic and extensive than those which belong to the common
> course of every-day nature . . . They spoke of a break in the

61. [G. P. Scrope], [Review of] "Principles of Geology . . . by Charles Lyell." (1830).
62. [W. Whewell], [Review of] "Principles of Geology . . . by Charles Lyell . . ."
(1831). Specific page references given in the text.

continuity of nature's operations; of the present state of things as permanent and tranquil, the past having been progressive and violent. [p. 190]

Whewell took particular note of Lyell's observation that the strata of southern Italy and Sicily, though elevated thousands of feet, contained multitudes of fossils belonging to the same species as lived in the Mediterranean. The mere description of such a fact seems to have startled him, somewhat in the same way as it did Lyell when he first came upon it. "The discontinuity," Whewell wrote, "which separated us from former creations is partly removed; and we are led by an intelligible road into those remote periods and states which at first appeared involved in darkness and disorder" (p. 193). Yet Whewell concluded his review with a long declamation against Lyell's theory which he said "must speedily fall back into the abyss of past fantasies and guesses from which he has evoked it in vain." (p. 204)[62]

In his presidential address before the next annual meeting of the Geological Society, Adam Sedgwick mentioned the *Principles* with a mixture of praise and criticism. Like Whewell he was fundamentally opposed to Lyell's central doctrine, but was less perceptive in his analysis. If Lyell's principles were true, Sedgwick said, "the earth's surface ought to present an indefinite succession of similar phenomena."[63] Unfortunately this was only partly true because Lyell had argued that the uniform action of physical laws and geological processes might at different times produce highly dissimilar phenomena. In retrospect Sedgwick's somewhat shallow discussion of the *Principles* looks rather odd beside his extravagant praise for Élie de Beaumont's new theory for the elevation of mountain chains.

But most important, the *Principles* was read; copies sold rapidly and half of them were gone by autumn when Lyell returned to London from his tour to the Pyrenees. Lyell had started a revolution in men's thinking about the history of the earth.

---

63. A. Sedgwick, "Address to the Geological Society . . . 18 February, 1831" (1834) p. 304.

CHAPTER 10

The Second Volume of the *Principles*, 1830–1832

AFTER HIS LONG, concentrated effort of writing the first volume of the *Principles*, Lyell was eager to get out into the field again and explore the geology of a new country. At the suggestion of George Poulett Scrope he decided on Spain, primarily because he wished to visit the district around Olot just south of the Pyrenees. In 1808 the American geologist William Maclure had reported the existence of extinct volcanoes with craters and lava currents in the neighborhood of Olot.[1] According to Maclure, the volcanic district extended from Olot for a distance of fifteen leagues to Massanite in the Pyrenees. If Maclure's report were accurate the volcanic district of Olot was almost as extensive as that of Auvergne. Lyell learned of Olot through the account of Maclure's report given in Charles Daubeny's book on volcanoes.[2] In the various plans for travel in the summer of 1830, which he had considered and rejected for one reason or another, it was clear that Lyell wished to see more of volcanic districts. Volcanoes were of particular interest to him both because they were one of the most dramatic manifestations of modern geological causes and because they seemed to be associated with areas of uplift of stratified rocks. He had decided finally to explore Olot as a result of his happy encounter with Captain S. E. Cooke R.N. who had traveled in Spain and knew the Spanish language.

After their departure from London on 22 June, Lyell and Cooke crossed from Southampton to Le Havre where, being delayed by the tide, Lyell spent a day examining the cliffs of the coast and reading Élie de Beaumont's new theory of the elevation of mountain chains which had just appeared in the *Annales des Sciences Naturelles*.[3]

Louis Élie de Beaumont had been appointed in 1827 professor

1. W. Maclure, "Sur les volcans d'Ollot . . ." (1808).
2. C. Daubeny, *A Description of Active and Extinct Volcanoes* . . . (1826) pp. 247–48.
3. L. Élie de Beaumont, "Recherches sur quelques-unes des révolutions de la surface du globe . . ." (1829).

of geology at the École des Mines, Paris, at the age of twenty-nine. A year younger than Lyell, he had come to England in 1822 to study the methods used in compiling the geological map of England prepared by G. B. Greenough for the Geological Society of London. After his return to France he had begun in collaboration with Ours Dufrénoy, director of the École des Mines, to prepare a geological map of France. His new theory of a series of revolutions in the history of the earth, each of which had resulted in the elevation of certain mountain ranges, was at least in part an attempt to interpret geological information which he had gathered in preparing the geological map of France.

Élie de Beaumont thought he detected lines of parallelism between certain mountain ranges and he thought that when mountain ranges were parallel with each other, they had been elevated at the same time. He had detected three periods of major disturbance, the first occurring at the end of the Jurassic period when in Germany the Erzgebirge, and in France the Jura mountains, were elevated. Then had followed a long interval of tranquillity during which the green sand and chalk strata had been deposited. At the end of the Cretaceous period another violent upheaval elevated part of the Pyrenees, the mountains of Provence, and the Apennine range of Italy. At the end of the Tertiary period still another violent convulsion elevated the western portion of the Alps between Marseilles and Zurich.

Élie de Beaumont's memoir was inspired by the idea that the elevation of separate mountain ranges might somehow be related as a connected series of phenomena, but it was marred by an excess of youthful ambition and sweeping inferences drawn quite uncritically. His basic assumptions were directly opposite to those of Lyell, for he wrote:

> One has attempted in vain to explain, by the action of the slow and continuous causes which we see at work on the surface of the globe, the totality of geological phenomena which are observed in high mountains. One does not in this way arrive at any satisfying result. Everything indicates in fact that the rearrangement of the strata of a whole chain of mountains is an event different from those of which we are daily witnesses.[4]

Lyell, after he had read this passage, wrote to Scrope.

4. Ibid., p. 6 (translation mine).

In my comments on the Huttonian theory, I throw out that there have been in regard to separate countries, *alternate* periods of disturbance and repose, yet earthquakes may have been always uniform, and I show or hint how the interval of time alone, may make the passage appear abrupt, violent, convulsive and revolutionary.

Élie de Beaumont had argued that the elevation of mountain ranges was an abrupt process of little duration, but Lyell thought he had no evidence for this view. He added:

> Whatever may be said of my theories, there are sweeping conclusions in E. de Beaumont, for which I would not be answerable for a good deal. At the same time his work is in many parts, as far as I can judge without being able to test the facts, of great merit. . . . I do not half comprehend what he would be at, yet I have talked much with him on geology in general.[5]

From Le Havre Lyell and Cooke crossed the mouth of the Seine to Honfleur and went by coach through Normandy and Brittany to Bordeaux. Enroute they detoured to see the ancient Celtic monument of Carnac near Quiberon Bay. At Bordeaux they encountered J. F. D'Aubuisson who, now prevented by his work as an engineer from keeping up with the current developments in geology, regretted its transformation "into a zoological science."[6] They were at Toulouse on 9 July, and Lyell was impressed by the calm and order of the elections then being held in France. He was in a holiday mood and already felt much stronger than before he left London.

From Toulouse they went by diligence to Foix on the northern slope of the Pyrenees, and thence to Ax-les-Thermes where Lyell spent two days exploring the local strata and collecting fossils.[7] They crossed the central chain of the Pyrenees by mule. As they went Cooke studied the various species of pine trees, and found several new to him. Occasionally they collected insects. Near Bourg Madame on the Spanish frontier they found freshwater strata; although the Spanish strata were much older, some of them strongly resembled those of the loch of Kinnordy. Lyell was

5. C. L., Jr. to G. P. Scrope. 25 June 1830. *L. & L.* I, 273–75. I have corrected what I believe to be two misreadings of the original holograph in the printed version of this letter, namely, "done" for "alone," and "conclusive" for "convulsive."

6. C. L., Jr. to his sister Marianne. 9 July 1830. Kinnordy mss. *L. & L.* I, 275–77.

7. C. L., Jr. to his sister Caroline. 21 July 1830. Kinnordy mss. *L. & L.* I, 278–80.

studying a Spanish grammar so as to prepare himself for an excursion into Spain. However, except for a short hike through the valley of Puycerda, he found he could not enter Spain at this point so he and Cooke separated. Cooke wandered westward along the Pyrenees to Luchon where Lyell would meet him later; Lyell went to Perpignan and thence by diligence to Barcelona. His excursion into Spain lasted a fortnight (Map 12). At Barcelona he was introduced to the Count d'Espagne, captain-general of Catalonia, who gave him a special passport and letters and offered him a bodyguard, which he declined. "With a mule and a guide on foot . . . ," Lyell wrote, "I got on without one misadventure through a glorious country for a geologist. Saw Monserrat, the salt mines of Cardona, Vich and the volcanic district round Olot and returned across the Pyrenees by Massanet to Ceret."[8] The volcanoes of Olot (Fig. 43) impressed him particularly and he described them to Scrope.

> Like those of the Vivarais, they are all both cones and craters, subsequent to the existence of the actual hills and dales, or in other words no alteration of previously existing levels accompanied or has followed the introduction of the volcanic matter, except such as the matter erupted necessarily occasioned. The cones, at least fourteen of them mostly with craters, stand like Monpezat, and as perfect, the currents flow down where the rivers would be if not displaced. But here, as in the Vivarais, deep sections have been cut through the lava by streams much smaller in general, and at certain points the lava is fairly cut through, and even in two or three cases the subjacent rock.[9]

He also saw there the traces of a great earthquake which had buried buildings at Olot four centuries earlier. Maclure had reported a volcanic eruption at Olot in 1428, but Lyell looked up the man who had provided Maclure with his information on the history of Olot and, after reading the sources, decided that there had been no volcanic eruption there within historic times.

From Olot he rode up the valley of the Tech through a great forest of cork oaks to Cerat. When he reached the French border Lyell found that, while his own passport and that of his guide were in order, the passport for his mule required a signature which was unobtainable. The local magistrate was, in fact, able to sign Ly-

8. C. L., Jr. to his sister Fanny. 8 Aug. 1830. Kinnordy mss. *L. & L.* I, 280–82.
9. C. L., Jr. to G. P. Scrope. 10 Aug. 1830. *L. & L.* I, 283–85.

12. Lyell's tour in Spain and possible routes, July 1830

ell's own passport without being able to sign that for "Monsieur le Mulet." With some difficulty he obtained another mule whose papers were in order! Fortunately he was able to get across the frontier before it was closed as a consequence of the new revolution in France.

From Perpignan Lyell went to Bagnères de Luchon where he met Cooke on 16 August. Here he received a letter from his clerk, Hall, telling him that the *Principles* had been published on 24 July.[10] They then worked westward along the northern slopes of the Pyrenees. Lyell described the great elevation of the stratified rocks on Mont Perdu to his mother:

> In other chains the loftiest & central parts consist of rocks which do not enclose any remains of shells & corals &c. and you must go to the flanks or to the low grounds at their base in order to collect such objects. Here, on the contrary, you find at an elevation of between 9 & 11 thousand feet a profusion of sandstones & limestones in the very middle of the Pyrenees full of plants, shells & zoophytes many in so perfect a state & in such thick beds that you cannot doubt for a moment that you see the bottom of an old sea, now covered by glaciers, or so high that it supports no vegetation.[11]

They slept in a shepherd's hut on the mountain and next day descended again with a fine harvest of fossil shells. On 10 September they were at Bayonne. There Lyell received a letter from Broderip with the news that his book was being enthusiastically received at London by geologists of widely varying shades of opinion.[12] Some of their observations in the Pyrenees had seemed to Lyell to throw new light on the problems of sedimentation. He described them to Scrope:

> On the flanks of the Pyrenees is an extensive formation of vertical, curved and contorted beds of thinly laminated sandstone, sand, clay, slatey marl, slatey limestone, etc., all thinly bedded, as well as thinly laminated. The only organic remains in a thickness of many hundred feet are numerous and beautiful impressions of fuci. The sandstone slabs have almost all the ripplemark, visibly and exactly preserved. The fuci are spread out

10. C. L., Jr. to his father. 17 Aug. 1830. Kinnordy mss. *L. & L.* I, 288–91.
11. C. L., Jr. to his mother. 25 Aug. 1830. Kinnordy mss.
12. C. L., Jr. to his sister Marianne. 10 Sept. 1830. Kinnordy mss. Printed with omissions in *L. & L.* I, 295–96.

conformably to the planes of lamination, bending with the undulations of the ripple mark. The ripple mark is strongest in the
sands, and indicated by layers of mica. A section longitudinal
to the furrows, and ridges, gives a slightly undulatory lamination: transverse, gives a wavy and curved line, and other figures
common in primary and secondary rocks. An inspection
whether of the surface or of the transverse section of the laminae
of a ripple-marked slab, shows at once that such a disposition of
laminae is the effect not of the action of running water upon matter deposited, but on matter depositing. The general notion, I believe, has been that the furrows have been scooped out; it is not
so, the ridges are made by addition, not the grooves by subtrac-
tion. Hence a difficulty may be got over.—How could 600 feet and
more of ripple-marked beds be formed in succession? How could
the ripple influence the bottom at such a depth? Answer, It arranged the sediment in that way near the surface, which fell
through an undisturbed medium hundreds of feet in that form,
and fell in that order on the bottom.

This ingenious answer is not accepted today. Such a thickness of
uniformly laminated beds can be formed by the gradual subsidence
of the sea bottom at almost exactly the same rate as new sediments are deposited, or by turbidity currents at considerable depths
in the sea. It does illustrate that early geologists, such as Lyell,
were frequently faced with geological phenomena in all their com-
plexity, and that the greater their skill in interpretation, the more
bewildering might be the problems with which they were presented. Yet this theory suggested by Lyell, he himself considered
no more than a hypothesis to be tested. He went on in the same
letter:

Qy. If sand and mud be spread through a river, going at such a
rate as to hold it in suspension, and a wind blows against it and
raises a ripple does not this cause lines of retardation which
cause matter to fall from the upper part in long coils. Try experiments. . . . I threw sand and small pieces of dead leaves wa-
terlogged into a creek, the sands of which were ripple-washed,
the depth of water being about six inches. The fresh matter was
washed to and fro, sometimes all in suspension, sometimes
thrown down irregularly, but every now and then all the vegetable matter arranged itself along the axis of the ridges, and
waved backwards and forwards, as if growing in lines upon the

top of the ridges. After a whole hour of this movement there was no tendency of the newly-injected matter either to increase the ripple-mark, or to diminish it by settling in the hollows. It is evident that the preservation of the ripple mark is consistent with considerable agitation of the bottom.[13]

This incident illustrates forcibly how, once the idea of uniformity had firmly implanted itself in his mind, Lyell was repeatedly led from his observation of puzzling phenomena in the strata to the study of how sediments were actually transported and deposited in streams and rivers today. William Whewell was very perceptive when he coined the term "geological dynamics" for the studies described by Lyell in the *Principles*. The essence of what Lyell was saying was that the surface of the earth was not static, but dynamic and undergoing continual processes of change. He concluded his letter by urging Scrope to carry out experiments on sedimentation in a trough of water. "After a due series of failures, blunders, wrong guesses, etc.," he wrote, "we will establish a firm theory."[14]

At Bayonne Lyell spent three or four rainy days examining the cliffs along the sea, accompanied by a somewhat reluctant Captain Cooke. Afterwards he started north to Bordeaux while Cooke left on an expedition into Spain. On 27 September Lyell arrived at Paris.

Lyell found that the July revolution in France had exerted profound effects upon the scientific world of Paris. Constant Prévost, who had received proof sheets of the *Principles* in advance of publication in order to prepare a French translation, had made little progress with it. Instead he had "been waiting on the King with an address from the Geological Society of Paris, since which he has been dining with his majesty as a *scavan* in the uniform of of a bold dragoon of the National Guards."[15] The writing and publishing of scientific work seemed to be at a standstill. Lyell found Deshayes living from hand to mouth by writing for encyclopedias. Deshayes was an unworldly scholar who had given up the practice of medicine because he was unable to collect a sufficient proportion of his fees from patients to make a living. At the same time, he had become the best conchologist in Europe and had spent

13. C. L., Jr. to G. P. Scrope. 11 Sept. 1830. *L. & L.* I, 296–99.
14. Ibid. Scrope ultimately published a paper on ripple marks. See G. P. Scrope, "On the rippled markings . . ." [1831].
15. C. L., Jr. to J. M. 30 Sept. 1830. Murray mss.

every cent he could obtain to buy books on natural history. As a result of his difficulties Deshayes had not got very far during the previous year and a half in identifying Lyell's Sicilian and Italian shells. Lyell then did something both enterprising and munificent. He offered to assist Deshayes financially to the extent of paying him three months' salary, approximately £100. In order to do this he had to engage in a bit of mild chicanery by telling Deshayes that it was actually Murray who would be paying him. Lyell then wrote to Murray to explain his action.

> Although I expend this on my *own account* (& it will cost me 3 months pay of his valuable time) I have been obliged to make use of your name & to represent to him, that you had at my request agreed that he should receive so much from you for zoological assistance given to me etc. He would not have become a stipendiary of *mine,* but has of course no objection to become a joint workman with me, for the public.[16]

During the first month, while Lyell was in Paris, Deshayes was to give him instruction in the identification of shells. Then he was to spend the next two months drawing together the results of his study of the fossil shells of the various Tertiary strata.[17]

When Lyell and Deshayes began to study the latter's collection of Tertiary shells, together with Tertiary shells from other collections at Paris, with special reference to the strata from which they came, they soon found confirmation of the fact that the Tertiary strata in different places were not contemporaneous but belonged to successive periods. They arranged the lists of species in tables. Lyell described their work to Scrope on 8 October:

> The results are already wonderful as confirming the successive formations of different basins and the gradual approximation of the present order of things, and will settle, I hope for ever, the question whether species come in all at a batch, or are always going out and coming in. A multitude of other surprising conclusions arise, and the harmony of the whole with the phenomena of earthquakes and volcanos, of geological superposition, of the position of land-quadrupeds (fossil), of contents of freshwater lake formations etc. is very beautiful.[18]

16. Ibid.
17. C. L., Jr. to his sister Marianne. 2 Oct. 1830. Kinnordy mss. *L. & L.* I, 301–03.
18. C. L., Jr. to G. P. Scrope. 8 Oct. 1830. *L. & L.* I, 304–06.

To his sister Marianne, Lyell described how he was spending his time with Deshayes:

In order to make myself fully master of the details from which my great tables of shells are to be drawn up I have gone through a great part of Deshayes's collection systematically, following Lamarck. I had no idea that shells so studied could be so interesting or that the arrangement was so philosophical, being founded on the *animals* which inhabit the shells. With an immense collection before you of recent and fossil shells (35,000 individuals & 8500 species) all well arranged in their natural groups & with a clever conchologist at your elbow you may in a short time make yourself master of more than I ever expected to know.[19]

He decided to make a collection himself and found that he had a fair start with his Italian and Sicilian shells and some 800 shells of fossil species which he was able to buy from Deshayes. From the collection of fossils which Lyell brought from Mont Perdu in the Pyrenees, Deshayes was able to determine that these mountains consisted of strata of the same age as the chalk.

On 9 November Lyell returned to London from Paris. He went directly from the coach to a meeting of the Geographical Society where Basil Hall complimented him on the *Principles* with the remark, "Well, I will tell you fairly, I did not think you could have written such a book." Arrived at his rooms he read for the first time, and with great pleasure, Scrope's review of his book in the *Quarterly*. Murray had described this article as "at once masterly and popular" and had paid Scrope £100 for it as proof of his sincerity.[20]

At this time Lyell expected to begin work immediately on his second volume and to have it out in five or six months. Murray thought it was important for the second volume to appear while interest in the first volume was still strong. Lyell was much pleased by the favorable reception which his book had enjoyed in London. When the second volume was out and a second edition printed and sold he hoped to earn as much as £1000 from it. "Should I realize my expectation of 2d Ed.," he wrote to Marianne, "I shall have earned rather more than what would make on an average of £100 a year ever since I left Oxford, which is as much as that

19. C. L., Jr. to his sister Marianne. 19 Oct. 1830. Kinnordy mss. *L. & L.* I, 308–09. Published only in part.
20. C. L., Jr. to G. P. Scrope. 9 Nov. 1830. *L. & L.* I, 309–11.

miserable work of the Royal Society of secretary would have yielded."[21]

In this buoyant mood Lyell once again shifted his quarters from Crown Office Row to new rooms in 2 Raymond Buildings, Gray's Inn. They were larger and his clerk Hall would now live in the kitchen "with his wife who is to serve instead of Thomas." The rooms also had the advantage of being on the same staircase as those of William Broderip "whose library & great collection of recent shells worth some £1000 will enable me to dispense with laying out money some of which would have been necessary otherwise. I shall also be very near Stokes." Already Lyell was finding that he must conserve his time. He refused a number of invitations to dine out and resolved to attend a club dinner only once a week. He felt that since he could now see the possibility of ultimately earning his living by writing on geology, he would work hard at it.[22]

Lyell's most serious distraction at this time was the contested election for the presidency of the Royal Society in which John Herschel and the Duke of Sussex were rival candidates. The scientific activities and reputation of the Royal Society had been declining for a number of years especially under the previous president, Davies Gilbert. Lyell joined with a group of other fellows of the Royal Society, who were seriously interested in science, to place Herschel's name in nomination and to promote his candidacy. Dr. Fitton, Robert Brown, the botanist, and Lyell were particularly active in working for Herschel. Lyell wrote to Mantell to ask his support for Herschel and to urge him to come to London for the election.[23] Unfortunately, because he was severely ill, Mantell could not come.[24] Despite this energetic campaign Herschel lost the election to the Duke of Sussex by seven votes. Contrary to expectation, however, the Duke of Sussex was to give responsible and magnanimous leadership to the Royal Society.

In mid-December Lyell decided to go home to Scotland for a five-week Christmas holiday. It was well over a year since he had last seen his parents and sisters and he admitted to feeling "somewhat homesick & fancy that I shall work with better heart after my return."[25] Before he left London he sent to the *Philosophical*

21. C. L., Jr. to his sister Marianne. 14 Nov. 1830. Kinnordy mss. *L. & L.* I, 312–14.
22. Ibid.
23. C. L., Jr. to G. A. M. 20 Nov. 1830. Mantell mss.
24. Mantell, *Journal,* p. 88.
25. C. L., Jr. to G. A. M. 14 Dec. 1830. Mantell mss.

Magazine a reply to a charge of minor plagiarism in the citation of classical authors made by W. D. Conybeare in his review of the *Principles*. This reply was sufficiently decisive and devastating.[26] Since Conybeare not only respected, but liked Lyell and considered him a friend, he would not have made the original charge except for the evident haste and excitement with which he reacted to the *Principles*. This was the sole occasion on which Lyell broke his rule not to reply to attacks and criticisms.

While he was at Kinnordy on holiday Lyell received the issue of the *British Critic* for January 1831. In it he read William Whewell's review of the *Principles*, a long and masterly essay, which deeply impressed him. He was particularly struck by Whewell's facility in the coining of new terms, such as "geological dynamics" to describe the subject of Lyell's investigations. Lyell, therefore, wrote Whewell both to thank him for the review and to ask his advice concerning the naming of the various Tertiary formations. This latter portion of his letter is of considerable interest:

> . . . let me communicate the present state of my coinage, for you have fairly announced that something must come from somebody's mint. I have taken your hint & have Meiosynchronous instead of Palaeosynchronous. I now stand thus

$$
A - \text{Tertiary formations}
\begin{cases}
\text{I Proeliminal?} & \begin{cases} \text{a. Asynchronous} \\ \text{b. Eosynchronous} \end{cases} \\
\begin{array}{l}\text{II Liminal? or} \\ \text{Penultimate}\end{array} & \begin{cases} \text{a. Meiosynchronous} \\ \text{b. Pleiosynchronous} \end{cases}
\end{cases}
$$

B – Contemporary formations

> The only terms and divisions on which I feel quite decided are first to separate Tertiary & Contemporary. The latter are to take in all since Adam & all that shall be until his posterity die out, whether roasted by the summer heat or frozen out by the winter of the *annus magnus*. In short all strata which shall contain "anthropites" imbedded in them. Next I am quite sure that the three groups Eosyn-, Meio- & Pleiosyn- are natural, at least at present & practically useful. Pleio- are Sicily, Sienna, English Crag etc.—πλειον or a decided majority of contemporary or living species of shells—95 per cent in some, 65 perhaps in oldest. Meio- takes in Superga near Turin, Bourdeaux basin, Loire & Tou-

---

26. "Reply to a Note in the Rev. Mr. Conybeare's Paper . . ." (1831).

raine, Vienna basin etc., a minority of living species yet 30 per
cent sometimes. It is the mastodontic era. Eo-ηως-is the dawn or
first appearance of a few existing species—Paris basin or Paleo-
therian era—one per cent 12 in 1200 species. A few more will
come by & by, for it is in tropics they have turned up identical
both fresh & salt water. Asyn- & now this might take in Gosan &
other older tertiaries if established. Perhaps the term will be
equivocal, even applicable to all secondary formations also. But
what I am much in want of are two good terms to group the subdivisions of I and II. Penultimate might do but then antepenultimate would be too long. Could liminal & preliminal be used.
The distance at present between the Eo- & Meio- is immense.
Perhaps architecture or fortification would give terms. One set
might be the outer or approach gate formations, the others the
door or entrance hall etc. Besides avoiding the jingle of too
much "synchronian," one may often affirm that a stratum is
"liminal or penultimate" & yet not be able to say whether pleio-
or meio-. I confess I have a leaning to your penultimate if I could
get something in the place of antepenultimate.[27]

Whewell replied promptly to this somewhat flattering appeal in a
letter of 31 January. With respect to nomenclature he wrote:

> The termination *synchronous* seems to me to be long, harsh
> and inappropriate. For the fact to be described is not that the
> species are contemporary *with us,* the wretched materials for
> future *anthropites:* but that they are identical with *recent* species
> wh. we take for our type of comparison. I would therefore use a
> term expressing either *identical* or *recent:* perhaps better the
> last. Then your terms would
>   1. aneous, 2. eoneous, 3. meioneous 4. pleioneous. Do you like
> this?—They are shorter than yours. The misfortune is that the
> termination neous would rather look like a mere termination as
> in erro*neous* than a derivation from νεος. I had once thought of
> ταυτο.
>   1. atautic, 2. eotautic, 3. meiotautic 4. pleiotautic better in
> form, but neither so short nor so significant. Either I think is
> preferable to pleiosynchronous. The words meioneous & pleion-
> eous, (or whatever terms you take) might be spelt mioneous,
> plioneous etc. and would be so according to the Latin & Old
> English spelling in which the Greek ει became i; but this has

27. C. L., Jr. to W. Whewell. 21 Jan. 1831. Whewell mss.

often been violated lately. I like your introduction of ηως, though it is somewhat poetical;

After some further more or less desultory suggestions and mention of general news Whewell added in a postscript:

> It has occurred to me that καινος is a better word than νεος and I propose for your 4 names 1. *acene* 2. *eocene* 3. *miocene* 4. *pliocene*. The term cene is right as in epicene—αι becoming e as well as οι. For eocene you might say speniocene but I like your eo better. Is not this shortest & best?[28]

Lyell agreed it was. "I cannot say," he wrote, "how thankful I am for your *Postscript* in which you presented me with καινος. It is curious that νεος was thought of in Paris & abandoned by me & Deshayes on the same ground." He thought that for the time being he would avoid using the term "acene" to describe "a group older than Eocene yet apparently by position & genera of shells tertiary." To his letter Lyell also added a postscript:

> Wanted—a term for the much abused word "diluvium" & a definition of what is really meant by said diluvium as the confusion of ideas on the subject is great. I propose to adopt Bigsby's term Protalluvion & my definition will be transported matter which has been spread by aqueous causes (no matter what) on land, which land at the time had emerged from seas or lakes. In short not a true subaqueous deposit, the said transported matter being no longer referrible to the existing *levels* of the water drainage of the country.[29]

"Diluvium" consisted of glacial deposits of various kinds and were at the time an insoluble puzzle to geologists as belief in the former occurrence of a universal flood receded.

Lyell returned from Scotland by coach in mid-February. The weather was mild but during the journey he had to turn out twice to walk half a mile because the horses could not pull the coach through the mud. On his arrival at London he went that evening to a meeting of the Geological Society to catch up on the news.[30]

28. W. Whewell to C. L., Jr. 31 Jan. 1831. APS mss.

29. C. L., Jr. to W. W. 17 Feb. 1831. Whewell mss.

30. C. L., Jr. to his mother. 18 Feb. 1831. Kinnordy mss. A letter to Dr. Fleming (*L. & L.* I, 315–16) dated 2 Raymond Buildings, Gray's Inn, February 7, 1831, which would suggest that he had returned to London early in February, is misdated and must be 1832. It refers to his lectures and his forthcoming marriage. In February 1831 he was not yet engaged.

At the beginning of March Lyell launched upon a new venture by seeking the professorship of geology at King's College. He was probably led to do this by the favorable review of the *Principles* which Whewell had given him in the *British Critic.* The full title of this journal, *The British Critic, Quarterly Theological Review and Ecclesiastical Record,* will suggest both its theological pre-occupations and the nature of its readership. "Many of my old friends (Lay-Bp. Watson[31] & Co.) regard me once more as one of them," he wrote to Whewell, "because I have been treated with such respect in the 'theological'; for by falling into the society of Lawyers, Geologists & other sinners I had for the last ten years been nearly estranged from them."[32] Basking thus in the warmth of orthodoxy he was led to think that if he sought the geological chair at King's College he would be unopposed. Perhaps he wanted the post because it would give him a small but nonetheless significant income and, possibly more important, would give him an established and respectable position in the eyes of his family and of the world. At any rate he went after it. To Mantell he wrote in mid-March:

> About 8 days ago I asked Sedgwick to sound Bp. of London on the propriety of adding a geological chair to King's College & me as a Professor & as he & others bit immediately & our least of all great men, our Oxford Copleston, Bp. of Llandaff alone expressed scruples I was obliged to canvass through my friend the Archbp. of Canterbury & several leading big-wigs who all declared in the most handsome and liberal manner that they were disposed to allow the utmost latitude to a geologist provided he came by his theories as straightforward deductions from facts & not warped expressly to upset scripture. Such were nearly their words—an interview with Copleston did not quite assure me that he would not oppose, but I have already set so many orthodox reverend & one venerable & one Episcopal friend, to work upon him that he seems disposed to stand neutral & we ask no more.

He went on to explain his reasons for seeking the position:

> "A local habitation & a name" will be desirable to me & perhaps a good set of lectures under such auspices may afford me a profit-

31. Joshua Watson (1771–1855), prominent Anglican layman.
32. C. L., Jr. to W. W. 20 Feb. 1831. Whewell mss.

able & pleasurable way of giving vent to some of the unreadable stores of geological information amassed in my travels. Scrope says "if all your views are thus taken at once into the bosom of the church instead of having to fight their way for half a century it will astonish me more than the passing of two reform bills."

In a second portion of this letter, dated March 17 and evidently written several days after the first portion, Lyell added:

I have been within the last week talked of & invited to be Professor at King's College of Geology—an appointment in the hands entirely of Bp. of London, Archbp. of Canterbury, Bp. of Llandaff & two strictly orthodox Doctors Doyly & Lonsdale. Llandaff alone demurred, but as Conybeare sent him (volunteered) a declaration most warm & cordial in favour of me as safe & orthodox he must give in or be in a minority of one.[33]

Edward Copleston, Bishop of Llandaff and Dean of St. Paul's, was a high churchman opposed to both tractarianism and dissent.[34] He had been provost of Oriel College when Lyell was a student at Oxford. He was intensely conservative and opposed to all extremes or rather to all doctrines which might disturb the settled and comfortable order of Church of England thought. On 18 March he made his reservations to Lyell's candidacy explicit in a letter to J. G. Lockhart:

My own scruples are limited to two points. I should not like to weaken the belief in a positive act of creation, particularly of the creation of man—about the period usually assigned to it. Nor again the belief in a universal deluge since that event. If Mr. Lyell assures me that his philosophical views have no such effect my objections are at an end & I know his pretensions on every other count are of the highest order.[35]

Lockhart showed this letter to Lyell, as the bishop must have intended him to do, and on 28 March Lyell wrote the bishop.

33. C. L., Jr. to G. A. M. 16 March 1831. Mantell mss. (This letter printed in part *L. & L.* I, 316–17.)

34. Edward Copleston (1776–1849) was a tutor at Oxford 1797–1810, 1814–26 provost of Oriel. In 1826 he was appointed dean of Chester and in 1827 bishop of Llandaff and dean of St. Paul's.

35. Copy of a letter from E. Copleston to J. G. Lockhart. 18 March 1831. Kinnordy mss.

In regard to the first point I may observe that I combat in several chapters of my second volume the leading hypothesis which has been started to dispense with the direct intervention of the First Cause in the creation of species, & I certainly am not acquainted with any physical evidence by which a geologist could shake the opinion generally entertained of the creation of man within the period generally assigned.

2dly. In regard to the second point *I certainly do consider* that there are numerous well ascertained phenomena (especially those relating to the existence of hundreds of uninjured volcanic cones of different & high antiquity made up of loose sand & scoriae on several parts of our continents) which do militate strongly against the doctrine that a deluge has passed over *the whole earth* within the last 4000 years. The facts already described by eminent foreign and English geologists relative to this subject & the inferences drawn from them have been confirmed by me in several districts which I have laboriously investigated in France, Italy & Sicily. These I hope to advert to in my second volume.

But I am acquainted with no physical evidence tending in any degree to invalidate the opinion that the whole inhabited earth πασŋ ἡ γŋ οικομενŋ may not have been deluged within the last 3 or 4,000 years.[36]

One could wish that Lyell had not written this letter. He compromised himself more than he intended to and perhaps more than he realized while he was writing it. To allow the bishop to make any stipulations whatever concerning his scientific views was to become party to the same kind of dishonesty in which the bishop himself indulged. For whereas his colleagues were content that Lyell's geological views should be naturally inferrable from the evidence and not inspired by antagonism to the church, the Bishop of Llandaff desired further that they should be confined within limits prescribed by theology. This could not be done without drawing a distinction between the opinions which one would privately hold and those which one would publicly state— the latter then assuming the nature of lies. Furthermore, in his effort to satisfy the bishop, Lyell is not quite candid. His studies of Tertiary shells had already convinced him that species became extinct one by one in the course of time and that new species

36. Copy of a letter from C. L., Jr. to E. Copleston. 28 March 1831. Kinnordy mss.

were introduced one by one. The extinction of old species and the introduction of new species, therefore, had the appearance of being a regular and natural phenomenon. Even though Lyell did not accept Lamarck's theory of transmutation of species, he could hardly believe that the introduction of new species required the repeated intervention of the First Cause. If so the First Cause would become so much an integral part of the natural order as to blur the very distinction which he wished to maintain. Similarly, at this time Lyell probably did not believe in the reality of the biblical flood as a geological phenomenon. He had seen how poorly founded was most of the evidence adduced in support of it. Thus his distinction between the whole earth and the whole inhabited earth has very much the appearance of a quibble. If it was not intended to deceive it was at least intended to allow others to deceive themselves.

But if Lyell's letter were not as wholeheartedly frank as it might have been, it was still an uncomfortably honest one so far as the Bishop of Llandaff was concerned. He wrote the following reply:

Deanery, St. Paul's
March 30, 1831
Dear Sir,

I have to thank you for the candid statement of your opinion in reference to the two points which I said appeared to me of essential importance to the cause of Revealed Religion—points which I should be unwilling to surrender, except compelled by absolute demonstration.

On the first of these you have removed all hesitation from my mind.

On the second I still pause for though I am the last man to contend for the maintenance of a belief contrary to the truth, yet until the contradiction is established I certainly feel it to be rash, & in my particular situation unjustifiable, to encourage doctrines which militate against the language of Scripture as understood & interpreted by the Church. Truth will ultimately prevail—and I by no means wish to check free enquiry. If the result should be unfavourable to the doctrines of the Church, it will then be time enough to review our declarations, and to accommodate them to the advanced state of science without sacrificing (as I feel assured we never shall be driven to sacrifice) the cause of Christianity.

In the meantime I should seem to be acting a treacherous part if I hastened on the change, a change which I know would be embarrassing and distressing, & which perhaps would put in jeopardy the faith of many.

You have already intimated that the denial of a universal deluge might be reconcileable with the belief of the destruction of the human race by that catastrophe which is all that seems to concern the truths of religion.

If I were satisfied that the doctrine would not be proposed in a form offensive to religious minds and would be objectionable only in the way of inference—and *that inference* not necessarily injurious but capable of being reconciled with revelation I would not resist the appointment of a person who held it. For I need hardly assure you that upon every other account I am sensible of the great advantage King's College would derive from the accession of so distinguished a person as yourself to the institution.

And I am persuaded also that you would not wish to fill the situation, after the explanation I have now given of my feelings, if you thought it likely that the effect of your physical dissertations would be unfriendly to Christianity.

Having said this much I will only add that my voice will be for your appointment whenever the election takes place.

> I remain Dear Sir
> with great respect
> Your most obed.^t Serv't
> E. Llandaff.[37]

This is a document of most tortuous hypocrisy. If it had any purpose it was intended to confine Lyell's lectures still more closely within the bounds of orthodoxy. Christianity so construed was evidently not compatible with freedom of inquiry or of thought. The faith of the people can only be sustained by the careful suppression of awkward truths. In fact, the bishop does not sound very confident of the doctrines for which he stood. This letter made Lyell furiously angry. To Marianne he wrote:

In his answer he thanked me for my candid statement & taking it as if for granted that I sh^d make out my position he expressed his fright in a manner that was really quite extraordinary & requests me in pretty plain terms to have the charity to spare

37. E. Copleston, Bishop of Llandaff to C. L., Jr. 30 March 1831. Kinnordy mss.

"the Church the necessity of altering its declaration about the universality of the flood,"[38] that he concedes that the drowning of all men ought to satisfy all reasonable folk. He says he shall vote for me,—but he hopes I shall understand in accepting the Professorship that I am not to put the *inferences* from my facts but let others draw them!! What a capital assessor of the Holy Office would he have made. Broderip after perusing this most singular episcopal production said—"My old Tutor, just what he always was—a *riggler* from beginning to the end of the letter—& what a compliment to you Mr. Carl, to be entreated by the right rev[d] suppliant not to pull down the whole concern upon them & about their ears!—& then to be termed a *distinguished person!*—suppliant did I say no—he writes as if in the agonies of dereliction; why a malicious follower of Tom Payne w.[d] give your executors a £100 for this letter."

I shan't answer it. If he were alone to give away the chair I would not take it from him, but though he assumes as if he were, he cannot, I believe, stop it if he would.

Lyell still looked forward to obtaining the chair although some of his friends assured him it would be more trouble than it was worth. "It places a man who wishes to devote himself steadily to a branch of science," he told Marianne, "in a much more agreeable, influential & respectable situation; and it is not like taking orders, a step without a retreat."[39]

During this feverish episode Lyell was somewhat distracted from the writing of his second volume. Even before his preoccupation with the King's College chair he had complained that he found it difficult to evoke the same energy and spirit with which he had written the first volume. Now in early April he felt that he was at last writing again with his old fire.[40] Later in April, although he was making steady progress, he felt himself stale and wrote to Mantell to suggest a geological excursion somewhere in the country. On Saturday 21 April Mantell got up at three in the morning to meet him at Horsham, and they went together to Stammerham quarry on foot.[41] There they spent the afternoon and returned to dinner at the inn at Horsham after which they went on to Lewes where Lyell spent the weekend with Mantell.

38. These quotation marks are not justified by any passage in Copleston's letter.
39. C. L., Jr. to his sister Marianne. 7 April 1831. Kinnordy mss.
40. Ibid.
41. Mantell, *Journal,* p. 95.

After this break from writing and correcting for the press, Lyell remained hard at work in London until near the end of May. On the twenty-sixth, however, he went down to Cambridge by coach, with Dr. Buckland, W. D. Conybeare, and Charles Daubeny from Oxford. They were invited for a whole week of celebrations to return a visit which Sedgwick, Whewell, and other Cantabrigians had recently made to Oxford. "We were lionized with a vengeance," Lyell wrote to Mantell, "—lectures, experiments (optics, polarization) feasting, geologizing & evening party going & nocturnal smoking & cigars."[42] Lyell had during the preceding months been in touch with J. S. Henslow concerning botanical questions which had come up during the writing of the second volume. During this visit he saw Henslow a good deal and it is certainly possible and even very likely that he then met a young undergraduate friend of Henslow named Charles Darwin. If so, the encounter was casual. Probably the renowned author of the *Principles* was too distant and awful a figure for Darwin to approach easily.

Both Conybeare and Lyell received *ad eundem,* that is to say, honorary M.A. degrees at Cambridge and then returned together to London in a chaise. Conybeare was in very much a holiday mood and wished to be introduced to various persons at London, among them Mrs. Somerville; Lyell accordingly invited Mrs. Somerville and her daughters to come to breakfast to meet him.[43] June proved a busy month. Mr. Lyell and Tom came down from Scotland to spend a few days with Lyell. Conybeare, who was staying with friends at Dulwich, dropped in frequently and spent one morning in Lyell's rooms writing a piece of fun about *Anoplotherium palaeotorium,* or "weaponless old Tory," an extinct species peculiar to the Irish bogs. Its organs of progression were "very imperfectly developed" but its claws were "singularly calculated for grasping, tenacity and climbing" and it had been rendered extinct by "a sudden increase of light in the system."[44] Since Conybeare was himself something of an Oxford Tory, there was a certain amount of self-parody in this humorous sketch.

The month of June 1831, busy as it was for Lyell with the visits of Conybeare and of his father and brother from Scotland, and work on his second volume, was distracting for him in yet another way. He fell in love. On one of the occasions when he had attended

42. C. L., Jr. to G. A. M. 22 June 1831. Mantell mss. *L. & L.* I, 318–19.
43. C. L., Jr. to Mrs. Mary Somerville. 3 June 1831. Somerville mss.
44. C. L., Jr. to G. A. M. 22 June 1831. Mantell mss.

a party at Mrs. Somerville's house he had again met Mary Horner
(Figs. 44, 45), the eldest daughter of Leonard Horner. She was
then twenty-three years old and must have been at the height of
her remarkable beauty. Horner was at this time warden of the new
London University and the family lived in London. Lyell's ac-
quaintanceship with Horner in the Geological Society and through
mutual friends at Edinburgh had caused him to call at their house
in Bedford Place. One day in the early spring of 1829 he had gone
with his brother Tom to ask Horner for a recommendation to a
Spanish master and there for the first time he saw Mary. He later
recalled the occasion to her:

> . . . you were sitting in the drawing room, working at a large,
> beautifully coloured purple dress which fell from your lap upon
> the floor. That was soon after you had left Edinburgh, when you
> were very blooming & had no plague about the University etc.[45]

They became acquainted in a shy, distant way. Lyell later re-
proached himself for not having made advances more promptly.
Apparently when he finally did so Miss Horner, who was not lacking in pride and independence, received them rather frostily.
Then for a long time Lyell thought he should never overcome her
apparent dislike for him. Things might have continued to drag on
in this unsatisfactory manner, but in the spring of 1831 Leonard
Horner resigned as warden of the London University as a result of
prolonged disputes with certain of the professors. The worry and
dissension had undermined his health, so he resolved to take his
family to Bonn, on the Rhine, to live there for a time. Mrs. Horner was to leave London in June with four of her daughters, including Mary. It was during these few weeks before their departure
that Charles Lyell and Mary Horner, faced with their forthcoming
separation, realized that they were attached to each other. Lyell
made a sudden decision. On 25 June he told Marianne that he
hoped to be at Kinnordy in three weeks time.[46] On the first of July
he was still busy with his book, but a few days later he set out for
Germany to make a geological tour of the Eiffel district. Before
launching on this tour, however, he visited Mrs. Horner and her
daughters at Godesberg near Bonn. On 12 July Lyell made his
proposal to Mary Horner and was accepted. Nothing could be
considered settled, however, until her father had been consulted

45. C. L., Jr. to Mary. 22 Dec. 1831.
46. C. L., Jr. to his sister Marianne. 25 June 1831. Kinnordy mss.

and his consent obtained. Leonard Horner was then at Edinburgh. Mary and Charles both wrote to him immediately. Horner was surprised to hear that Mr. Lyell was at Godesberg because he had come on the steamer from London "with his father, who told me that he was in Hampshire."[47] Since they would have to wait at least two weeks to receive Horner's reply, Lyell spent a number of days going on walks with Mary and sometimes with her sisters and then made his six days tour of the Eiffel. On 27 July he was back at Godesberg and two days later they received the long-awaited letter containing Horner's consent to their engagement. Lyell then wrote an account of his fiancée and her family to Marianne:

> I am sure you would like them all here exceedingly. I say nothing of my sweetheart because if you do not think her already the most perfect of beings I shall accuse you of high treason. Her name is Mary Elizabeth. She has learnt all your names ages etc. & regrets she never has become acquainted with any but my father for a day or two & with Tom.[48]

To his mother Lyell described his visit:

> I have been idle, gloriously idle the last week—absent—at times —lost my hammer on our excursion, offered a Thaler's reward for it—3 s.—recovered it by a wonder—knocked down Mrs. Horner's barometer for the bath & broke it, but mean to get a new one Sat.^{y}—went on an exped.^{n} with them & lost my note-book with all the geology of the Eiffel in it—advertized it at a village school & on Sunday at 3 neighbouring churches—reward 2 Thalers & advert.^{t} daily 1 s.—recovered it—picked up in a wood! As a set off Mary lost a beautiful broach in a walk but not owing to her absent fits I presume: Frances lost a ring. M. Plainzler the obliging & liberal keeper of the Hotel at Godesberg used to say as we returned from excursions "Encore une perti, Monsieur?"[49]

On 2 August Lyell said goodbye to Mrs. Horner and her daughters and went by steamer down the Rhine to Cologne and thence to Rotterdam and London. On the voyage he read the two volumes of Macculloch's *Geology*.[50] He also began to keep a journal of his

47. K. M. Lyell, *Memoir of Leonard Horner* . . . (1890) vol. I, p. 251.
48. C. L., Jr. to his sister Marianne. 27–29 July 1831. Kinnordy mss.
49. C. L., Jr. to his mother. 2 August 1831. Kinnordy mss.
50. Ibid. Cf. J. Macculloch, *A system of geology* . . . (1831).

activities which he was to send in regular installments to Mary Horner during the forthcoming year of their engagement.

Despite bad inns and very sour black bread which upset his digestion, Lyell had also accomplished a successful geological tour during his six days in the Eiffel district. This district, which he described to Marianne as "a wild mountainous tract on the left bank of the Rhine . . . only reclaimed from feudal vassalage by the French revolution," lay a few miles to the south of Bonn.[51] It was a country of wooded hills and numerous ruined castles. The rocks often reminded him of the slates and shales of Forfarshire in Scotland.

Lyell's purpose in visiting the Eiffel district was to see yet another district of extinct volcanoes, one which Leopold von Buch had used to develop his theory of the origin of dolomite by volcanic action.[52] Daubeny had also visited and described the district.[53] A striking feature was a number of conical hills with craters at their tops. These craters usually contained lovely little lakes, nearly circular in form. However, Lyell found that although the hills bore the conical shape and the crater of a volcano, the walls of the crater were made up not of lava and scoriae, but of sedimentary strata of sandstone and shale. Yet, on one side of the lake of Gemunden Maar he found a considerable quantity of volcanic rock and some scoriae, and saw the whole surface of the soil sparkling with volcanic sand.[54] He concluded that the hills had been produced by gaseous explosions of volcanic origin, which had forced the strata upward, but these explosions had not been followed by any significant outpouring of lava and scoriae such as would have given rise to the normal type of volcanic cone.

On 7 August Lyell was back in London where, on his arrival, he sent another chapter of the second volume of the *Principles* to the printer. On the steamer and while waiting at Rotterdam he had been writing and revising industriously. At his rooms he found Broderip who congratulated him on his engagement saying "I am heartily glad of it, tho' I feel more a batchelor than ever having no one but good old Stokes to look to when we lose you." Lyell also found that Leonard Horner was due to arrive in London so immediately invited him, as his future father-in-law, to breakfast.

51. C. L., Jr. to his sister Marianne. 27 July 1831. Kinnordy mss.
52. L. von Buch, "Ueber das vorkommen des dolomite . . ." (1824).
53. Daubeny, *Volcanoes*, pp. 45–65.
54. *Principles* III, p. 196.

There were so many letters, congratulations, and questions to think of that he could not settle to work, so went to the Athenaeum "to get a genteel elegantly served dinner for 2.6^d with all the newspapers etc." There he met various friends who asked him for news of his tour and of the current troubles in Holland. Then, he went on to Mary:

> . . . returned home, tried to compoze my thoughts—could not—determined to sit down & write a letter to you, was trying to settle whether it should be on a folio sheet or what else, when in came Brown the Botanist—said he would stay & drink tea—always good company in a tête-à-tête on all subjects. After an hour's coze in stepped Stokes to ask if I had yet been heard of. Some enquiries about the Eiffel but more about the Dutch fighting war.[55]

At John Murray's Lyell found that the first volume of the *Principles* was within a week of being sold out and that Murray wanted to reprint it. This fact led him to believe that there was more to be earned in both reputation and money by preparing a second edition of his book than by lecturing at King's College. For this reason he decided to reduce his course to nine lectures and to give them within the space of one month so as to save as much of his time as possible.[56]

During August Lyell worked hard at his second volume. He felt rested. "My holidays," he told Mary, "have made me as one refreshed from sleep."[57] He printed and corrected some fifty pages of text, much of which he had also written during this time. He was also printing and correcting forty-five pages of tables of Tertiary fossil shells compiled by Deshayes at Paris, and getting plates done, as well as reading and visiting. His drawing of Olot which was to form the frontispiece of volume two was recognized with delight by Fortunato Prandi when he saw it lying on Lyell's table. "Ah! that is Olot indeed," he exclaimed. "Well I fought there for thirteen days, five were we encamped on that hill by the church; & so the hollow was the crater & the cone a volcano. How odd, I never dreamt of that!"[58] It is a pleasant tribute to the accuracy of Lyell's draftsmanship.

55. C. L., Jr. to Mary. 8 Aug. 1831. Kinnordy mss.
56. Ibid.
57. C. L., Jr. to Mary. 15 Aug. 1831. Kinnordy mss.
58. C. L., Jr. to Mary. 26 Aug. 1831. Kinnordy mss.

On the first of September he left by steamer for Edinburgh for his long awaited holiday at Kinnordy. At Edinburgh on 4 September he went to dine at the house of Mr. Macbean, the Horner's family solicitor. Next morning he was invited by Macbean to breakfast with Henry Cockburn, solicitor general of Scotland, one of the founders of the *Edinburgh Review,* and a close personal friend of the Horners. Macbean had been showing Lyell the boundaries of a new borough as altered by the Reform Bill when Cockburn arrived. "Cockburn gave me a moderately good reception," Lyell wrote Mary, "a bow & if I remember right a shake of the hand. We all began to move to the breakfast room when the Solicitor exclaimed (the first sentence I heard from him) 'Is it Mr. *Lyell?* Lord I thought it was some *damned* surveyor come about your map.' Then he shook my hand in right good earnest."[59] Cockburn invited Lyell to visit Bonaly, his country house on the slope of the Pentland hills, the following day. When Lyell went Cockburn first showed him the house and grounds of which he was passionately fond and then they went for a country walk. Cockburn was full of anecdotes of the great Scotsmen he had known, including John Playfair, the mathematician and geologist. In the intervals of visiting in Edinburgh Lyell was still writing his second volume. On 7 September he went by coach to Glamis where his sisters Marianne and Caroline met him with a carriage. An hour later they were at Kinnordy. He found the place "in great beauty the more so after the unusually sunny summer."[60] The morning after his arrival his servant Hall also arrived from London with an additional twenty pages of printed proof for the second volume. Immediately Lyell set to work "in the 'India Paper Room' a most cheerful drawing room" at Kinnordy.[61] It had for him the advantage that it was little used and he was in no one's way. The wallpaper was covered with birds and other ornaments and Lyell said it had not faded since it had been made for the room in 1796.

Yet despite his eagerness to work in the India Paper Room he could not entirely avoid the activities of country life, in which he took great delight. With Marianne he went collecting mushrooms on the hills, he went to church, called on his neighbors, and went riding with his sisters. "Our stud is in pretty good order," he

59. C. L., Jr. to Mary. 1 Sept. 1831. Kinnordy mss. *L. & L.* I, 330–32.
60. C. L., Jr. to Mary. 8 Sept. 1831. (No. 1) Kinnordy mss.
61. C. L., Jr. to Mary. 8–14 Sept. 1831. Kinnordy mss. *L. & L.* I, 337.

wrote to Mary. "My dun is a capital beast & Meggie & Donald the ladies horses are as quiet as is compatible with a sufficient degree of life and spirit."[62] He promised Mary to have a colt, Wellington, trained for her so that they could ride about the county together. But by dint of rising early and working steadily, so that social activities were no more than a series of pleasant breaks from his labor, he maintained his progress on volume two. He was also distracted by the turbulent state of politics.

In November 1830 the Duke of Wellington had resigned as prime minister and a new government unanimously committed to the reform of parliament had been formed by the Whig peer, Lord Grey. Fifty years of Tory government in Great Britain had come to an end at a time when the country appeared almost on the brink of revolution. The revolution at Paris in July 1830 had been followed by uprisings in the Swiss cantons, at Hamburg and in Hesse, Saxony, and Brunswick. In September Brussels and other Belgian cities revolted against the Netherlands. During the autumn of 1830 agricultural laborers in the southern counties of England rioted, demanding higher wages and breaking the threshing machines which threatened to destroy their livelihood. In London and in the provincial cities there were active groups of radicals who demanded the reform of parliament and who were but the foci of deep political feeling which extended throughout the country.

The new Whig government had acted vigorously to suppress the agricultural laborers' revolt, while at the same time the laborers' wages were increased. Yet as 1831 began, radical newspapers and revolutionary talk flourished. The Whigs did not possess a majority in Parliament and the actions they had taken against the agricultural laborers had made them unpopular with the working classes. The general discontent had come to center on a demand that Parliament be made more truly representative. This demand had brought the Whig government to power despite its weakness in the present Parliament, and the introduction of a reform bill, which was the government's only reason for existence, was also its only hope for survival.

On 1 March 1830 Lord John Russell described the government's proposals. They would require the elimination of 168 boroughs which currently sent representatives to Parliament, more than a

62. Ibid.

quarter of the whole, and the creation of 98 new seats to give representation to such large towns as Manchester and Birmingham and in general to distribute parliamentary representation throughout the country according to population. This measure would destroy the pocket boroughs, those with but a handful of voters, usually under the exclusive control of a single great landowner. At the same time the government proposed to extend the franchise to every landowner who paid an annual rent of at least £10.

Although the Whig proposals for reform were received with horrified astonishment and disbelief by the Tory members of Parliament, they met with widespread enthusiasm throughout the country. The support generated for the measure was sufficient that, despite the government's lack of a majority, the reform bill passed its second reading on 22 March 1831 by a vote of 302 to 301. In further debate, however, the government was defeated on a motion to amend the reform bill and Lord Grey advised the King to dissolve Parliament. After some hesitation, William IV did so on 22 March and the country proceeded to a general election in April. In this election the Whigs won a majority of 140, and in the new Parliament the reform bill again passed its second reading, this time by a majority of 367 to 231.

The debate on the bill began on 24 June and continued through the summer of 1831. When it concluded on 21 September the bill was finally passed by the House of Commons and sent to the House of Lords. The question then was what would the House of Lords do? Naturally an aristocratic body, it might be expected to oppose reform, but the peers were about equally balanced between Whigs and Tories and in the background was always the possibility that the King might create additional Whig peers to force the passage of a reform measure. In estimating the likelihood of the creation of new peers, both the government and the Lords took into account their respective estimates of opinion in the country. In several by-elections held through the summer the Tories had won seats by considerable majorities, a fact which suggested that some of the support for reform, so clearly evident in the general election in April, had since ebbed away. When, therefore, a parliamentary by-election was to be held in Forfarshire in September 1831, both Whigs and Tories attached importance to it as a tangible sign of the state of public opinion.

The Tory candidate was Mr. Donald Ogilvy, a brother of Lord Airlie, whose estate of Cortachie lay next that of Mr. Lyell, and the Whig was Mr. Halliburton, a brother of Lord Aboyne. Mr. Lyell, as a large landowner, adhered to Tory principles and opposed reform. Lyell, however, was a liberal. He explained to Mary the dilemma in which the election placed him.

> Mr. Donald Ogilvy breakfasted with us & afterwards canvassed our votes. My father promised his. I told him I felt very much the being so placed but I could not vote for him & should therefore stay away as I was unwilling to vote against his family with which we have been so long & intimately acquainted, & against my father & as a man I scarcely knew opposed him. At the same time I was no tory, as he knew & as this was a party question entirely I could not support him. He explained to me the moderation of his views which were very much mine but he admitted that such was not really the moderation of all his following. He is so gentlemanlike a man & so natural a character as compared to Halliburton that I wish with all my heart I could vote for him.[63]

Since there were only eighty or ninety qualified voters in the whole county of Forfarshire, every vote was important.

By 21 September Lyell had completed three more chapters of manuscript which he sent to London with his sisters Marianne and Caroline, who were on their way to Hampshire to attend their cousin Fanny Heathcote's wedding. "I am fairly arrived at the last division of my book," he wrote to Mary on the twenty-second, "7 or 8 chapters more, a hard pull yet ere I shall reach the port."

However, he was occasionally distracted. On 27 September he wrote in his journal to Mary:

> I have overcome today the fit I had of disinclination to work, not a feeling of idleness either for then I might have enjoyed leisure. But the election & the thought of the harm it will do Tom was one thing, & other matters, small affairs in themselves, & an unpleasant feeling of doubt how I sh^d treat the subject [in a way] which can allow [it] to [be] crammed into the remaining 140 pages of vol. 2. All these things gave me a distaste for the job. . . . When a chapter is only to be recast or corrected or a revize made or such kinds of work it can be done in whatever humour one is in. But the first draught of a subject, when all

63. Ibid.

your invention is at work, requires the mind to be quite free from any other subject at least anything that frets or annoys.[64]

On the whole, however, he kept working. Dr. Fleming came from Fife for a visit of several days and they talked over the prospects for Lyell's new professorship at King's College. Dr. Fleming thought the experience of teaching would be very beneficial for Lyell. He could develop his technique of exposition with the opportunity to learn whether his audience was able to grasp his ideas. It would also give him a chance to rehearse as it were new theories before he published them.

On 2 October Lyell wrote out a sketch of his fourth chapter. The weather was wet for several days so he was able to work steadily without being tempted to go walking or riding. He wrote at least twice a week to Mary Horner and his letters were usually in the form of journals with long entries describing the events of each day. While he was at Kinnordy he also wrote out for her an account of his early life, as he remembered it, and sent it in successive installments interspersed among his letters. These reminiscences form a charming, if fragmentary, autobiography and throw much light upon Lyell's personality.

On 3 October the by-election was held at Forfar and Col. Donald Ogilvy was chosen by a very narrow margin. Mr. Lyell's vote had consequently been crucial and the Earl of Airlie and his brother were correspondingly grateful. Undoubtedly the defeated Whig candidate Halliburton was annoyed in equal proportion. Since there was a Whig government in office, his resentment would effectually prevent the promotion of Tom Lyell from lieutenant to commander. The plight of poor Tom who, after remaining far too many years a midshipman, had now spent an unpleasantly long time in the rank of lieutenant, was to trouble Lyell much during the ensuing months. He later told Mary:

My brother found not only a letter from Lord Panmure awaiting him at Portsmouth, but leave of absence from the Admiralty to go & vote for Halliburton whose cause the gov't took up keenly. Tom says that if he had had it in time he is sure he might have gone to Admiralty & pocketted his commission at once & that now he is ruined & the name of Lyell in the black books of the Whigs for ever & that he is indifferent to what be-

64. C. Lyell, Jr. to Mary. 26 Sept. 1831. Kinnordy mss.

comes of him etc. I cannot tell you how much I have given up at times & how much I have hurt at times my pride in asking favours first to get Tom afloat, then to bring things within an ace of his getting promoted & now this election has not only destroyed all but perhaps shut the door for ever. He has sacrificed to a certain extent his health & constitution in a vile service & has been abandoned as have the rest of our family from the peculiar & extraordinary indifference of my father to act except in this case when it was against his interest.[65]

The incident throws a revealing light on the degree to which political factors then determined promotion in the British navy.

However there were powerful political forces other than the gentry present even in the Scottish countryside. When Colonel Ogilvy proposed to hold a county ball at Forfar, the people of Forfar let it be known that if the reform bill then before the House of Lords were thrown out they would smash to pieces the carriages of the Tories assembled for the ball. Ogilvy accordingly cancelled plans for the ball.[66] A few days later, on returning in the family carriage from a sale of ladies' work at Dundee, Lyell's sisters encountered further signs of popular feeling.

As they came back through our village of Kerry [Kirriemuir] at night, a mob of about 40 reformers *hissed*. They put down the windows lest stones should be thrown, but this it seems was not intended. They think that as they had four horses it was taken for Lord Airlie's carriage, but perhaps it was in honour of my father's Toryism.[67]

Occasionally the social life of Angus became oppressive. The custom of prolonged dinners accompanied by heavy drinking still lingered on in the county—a remnant of eighteenth-century habits which had died out in the rest of Scotland. Lyell describes one such occasion.

It was just an Angus set-to of the old regime & I thank my stars I was out of it. They arrived at 1/2 past 6 o'ck & waited dinner 1 hour. Gentlemen rejoined the ladies at 1/2 past 12 o'k!! They in the meantime had had tea & a regular supper laid out in the drawing room. After an hour with the ladies . . . only one

65. C. L., Jr. to Mary. 12 Nov. 1831. Kinnordy mss.
66. C. L., Jr. to Mary. 30 Sept.–3 Oct. 1831. Kinnordy mss. *L. & L.* I, 344.
67. C. L., Jr. to Mary. 15–17 Oct. 1831. Kinnordy mss. *L. & L.* I, 345–46.

[gentleman] quite tipsy, they returned to the dining room to supper at 1/2 past one o'k! The ladies did not go to *this* supper.[68]

Yet aside from such occasional outbursts of archaic exuberance, country social life was friendly and temperate. Lyell enjoyed particularly the mere being at home with his parents and sisters after the loneliness of his bachelor life in London.

On 21 October he sent his clerk Hall off to London by a sailing smack from Dundee. At this point Lyell found that he had sketched out all the chapters for his second volume except one, but his sketches were still so rough that he did not know how much more work he had to do.[69] A week later he himself left Kinnordy to go by coach to Edinburgh where he called again on Macbean, the lawyer, and on Mrs. Leckie, a widowed aunt of Mary Horner. Of this visit he wrote Mary, "I felt a kind of sympathy for her living so alone as I have done the greater part of my life & often wished I had some relation or connexion within reach."[70] The following day he boarded the steamboat for London.

Once back in London Lyell was caught up in the intense scientific life of the capital. Even before he had unpacked he went off to dine with the Linnean club and to hear "a learned botanical paper by Rob.ᵗ Brown on the fructification of the Orchideae" at a meeting of the Linnean society.[71] With meetings of the Linnean, Geological, Geographical, and Royal societies, the more casual social life of the Athenaeum club, Sunday morning breakfasts with his bachelor friends Stokes and Broderip, dinners with Dr. and Mrs. Somerville in Chelsea or the Horner's friends, the Mallets, in Hampstead, he had no lack of engagements to fill his time. On the contrary it was a constant struggle for him to keep free his hours of work. He frequently complained that people did not respect his time as they would if he were engaged in a profession, as he had been when a barrister. It was his aim to establish science, and in particular geology, as a profession to which a man might be expected to devote his time as to any other profession. He also hoped that when such professional status was achieved for science, men might be able to make their living at it. At a meeting of the Geological Society he had to face some of the controversy

68. C. L., Jr. to Mary. 11 Oct. 1831. Kinnordy mss.
69. C. L., Jr. to Mary. 9 Oct. 1831. Kinnordy mss.
70. C. L., Jr. to Mary. 25 Oct.–1 Nov. 1831. Kinnordy mss.
71. C. L., Jr. to Mary. 3 Nov. 1831. Kinnordy mss. *L. & L.* I, 349.

which the publication of his first volume had provoked. It was, however, not as bad as he expected.

> Fitton declared to the meeting his conviction that my theory of earthquakes w.^d ultimately prevail. Greenough made one of his ultra-sceptical speeches saying that once he only doubted what "stratification" meant but now he was quite at a loss to conceive the meaning of the term "sea" in Geology & he thought no one could explain what "the sea" meant. Fitton gave him some hard hits for thus fighting shadows & "assisting the cause of darkness" by doubting elementary truths. B. Hall with more humour said as a sailor that he felt alarmed at hearing the existence of a great mass of waters (for he w.^d no longer give offense by talking of "the sea") called in question.[72]

In London the struggle over reform continued to shake the nation to its very foundations. On 8 October the House of Lords had defeated the reform bill on its second reading. The excitement which followed was such that Great Britain seemed on the verge of revolution. On 30 October there were riots at Bristol in which the jails were broken open, the Bishop's palace was burned, and twelve persons were killed. There were many public meetings and an outpouring of radical newspapers. Yet through all these events Lyell stuck firmly to his work. He explained to Mary:

> As for public affairs, I have long left off troubling myself about them, as knowing that one engaged in scientific pursuits has as little to do with them, in point of influencing their career, as with the government of the hurricanes or earthly motion; and if one becomes annoyed, there is an end of steady work. Even Whewell is frightened about the Reform Bill.[73]

Shortly after Lyell's arrival at London, his clerk, Hall, arrived with the manuscript which had been prepared at Kinnordy. The smack in which Hall had sailed from Dundee had encountered terrible storms and head winds which had kept them ten days at sea. A day or two later Lyell went to see Parker who was in charge of printing for John Murray to see about enlarging his second volume to allow him to answer "De Beaumont, Sedgwick, Conybeare & Co."[74] At this time he still envisioned the *Principles*

72. Ibid.
73. C. L., Jr. to Mary. 17 Nov. 1831. Kinnordy mss. *L. & L.* I, 352–53.
74. C. L., Jr. to Mary. 5 Nov. 1831. Kinnordy mss.

as a two-volume work and he hoped to get the second volume out in January. It would include what he had already written and printed and, in addition, an account of his Italian and Sicilian observations, as well as Deshayes' tables of Tertiary fossil shell species which extended to some fifty pages in themselves. With the manuscript written at Kinnordy, sent to press immediately after Hall arrived in London, Lyell now had some 300 pages printed. Because he was anxious that a review should appear in the *Quarterly* immediately after the book was published, he consulted Lockhart and then wrote to William Whewell to ask him to undertake the review. Although it was a little unusual for an author to arrange for the review of his own work, Lyell's main reason for approaching Whewell was the excellent critical review of the first volume which Whewell had done for the *British Critic*. "I am, moreover, interested for my own sake in the job's not falling into the hands of some journeyman performer," he told Whewell, "whose clumsy puff (to please the publisher) will be much less creditable to me than the overhauling which I am prepared to expect from you."[75] If Whewell would do it he would send him the 300 pages already printed in sheets. After some hesitation because of a previous article which he had done for the *Quarterly*, which had never been used, Whewell agreed to do it. Lockhart had agreed either to publish Whewell's review of the second volume of the *Principles* or to return the manuscript within twenty-four hours so that Whewell might publish it elsewhere.[76] The sheets then went off to Whewell, and Lyell promised to send more as they became ready. A fortnight later Whewell wrote that he was so pleased with these 300 pages that he had already begun to write the review for the *Quarterly*.[77] Two days later, after thinking over the delay which there would be in getting out these 300 pages already written if he waited until he had completed his work as he envisioned it, Lyell decided to launch them as his second volume.[78]

This thought was taken up late on Sat[y] at 8 o'[k] P.M. That night I saw Parker & after many plans suggested about getting the tables out etc. & the abandonment of this plan & of certain

75. C. L., Jr. to W. W. 10 Nov. 1831. Whewell mss.
76. J. G. Lockhart to C. L., Jr. 13 Nov. 1831; C. L., Jr. to W. W. 14 Nov. 1831. Whewell mss.
77. C. L., Jr. to Mary. 2 Dec. 1831. Kinnordy mss.
78. C. L., Jr. to W. W. 4 Dec. 1831. Whewell mss.

illustr[s] & deciding on others, we resolved that it was possible—
a consultation with Brod. that night—hardly slept—off to Murray next morning—not up—sent down to ask me to return to
break[f't]. Went to Athenaeum instead—then to John—all settled!
To be out before Xmas![79]

Actually they did not bring out the book until early in January
1832, but even that was within little more than a month. Lyell
had planned to dedicate his second volume to Roderick Murchison
because he had originally intended it to include the discussion of
the Tertiary strata based in part on their joint tour to the Auvergne and northern Italy. This had been "the best & longest
geological tour which I ever made" he told Mary, and was "the
tour which made me what I am in theoretical geology—or completed my views on that."[80] He had already told Murchison that
he was to receive this dedication, but now that the second volume
had nothing directly to do with Tertiary geology, but was solely
concerned with the natural history of species, he decided instead
to dedicate it to William John Broderip and to dedicate the
third volume to Murchison. As a keen amateur naturalist and
geologist Broderip had given him much helpful criticism in the
writing of both his volumes. When Lyell told Broderip of his intention, "He was more overjoyed than I have seen him many a
day & the day after he declared that if a legacy of £5,000 had
been left him it w[d] have given him less pleasure."[81]

THE PRINCIPLES OF GEOLOGY, II

The second volume of the *Principles* is one of Lyell's finest
pieces of writing. He was concerned to give a comprehensive picture of the animal and plant worlds as they exist today under the
present conditions of geography and climate. He showed that the
life of plants and animals depends completely upon climate, but
that geography, not climate, has been the factor which has determined the distribution of animal and plant species over the earth's
surface. A species can only be distributed within an area of geographically continuous means of dispersion.

It was Lyell's primary purpose to trace the "changes of the organic world now in progress"[82] (p. 1). He wished to study the vicis-

79. C. L., Jr. to Mary. 6 Dec. 1831. Kinnordy mss.
80. C. L., Jr. to Mary. 2 Dec. 1831. Kinnordy mss.
81. C. L., Jr. to Mary. 6 Dec. 1831. Kinnordy mss.
82. *Principles* II. Page references to this work are given in the text.

situdes to which species are subject at present, in order to determine whether these modern changes may be sufficient to explain the extinction of so many species and their replacement as revealed by the paleontological record. The question immediately before him was whether the modern species were in fact descended from the extinct fossil species. This question had been raised by Lamarck in his *Philosophie zoologique* which Lyell had read first in 1827. It had been renewed by Étienne Geoffroy St. Hilaire who, in 1828, had argued strongly that the modern assemblages of plants and animals were in fact descended from the successive fossil assemblages of plants and animals which were in turn related to one another by descent.[83]

Lamarck had argued that species had no real existence in nature but were in fact the artificial creations of the classifying naturalist. After reviewing Lamarck's arguments which stressed the blurred boundary separating species from varieties and the tendency for the characteristics of species to vary under different conditions of geography and climate, or in the case of plants, under cultivation, Lyell summarized the contrary evidence which tended to show that species are real and stable entities. He first tried to show, with a variety of examples, that "belief in the reality of species is not inconsistent with the idea of a considerable degree of variability in the specific character" (p. 36). For instance, using an argument developed by Frederick Cuvier, Lyell showed that domesticated animals were able to be domesticated because they already possessed in the wild state instincts which were suitable for domestication. They were social animals accustomed to live in groups or herds under a leader, so they found it easy to give to man in a domesticated state that obedience which they had given to the leader of their flock in a wild state. Thus an apparently large change in their way of life had required only a minor change in their instincts.

A further fact which indicated that species were real and distinct entities was that in most cases hybrid crosses between species were impossible, and that when they did occur the offspring were usually sterile. The degree to which inter-specific crosses in plants were prevented was indicated by the fact that, although bees conveyed pollen from one kind of flower to another indiscriminately, very few hybrid crosses occurred (p. 54). The same reasoning ap-

83. É. Geoffroy St. Hilaire, "Mémoire . . ." (1828).

plied with even greater force, Lyell pointed out, to wind-pollinated species of plants. If the rarity of hybridization indicated that species were distinct entities it also suggested that new species could not often arise from hybrids. This was particularly true of animal species with complex instinct patterns.

> So also we find that amongst a most numerous class of spiders there are nearly as many different modes of spinning their webs as there are species. When we recollect how complicated are the relations of these instincts with co-existing species, both of the animal and vegetable kingdoms, it is scarcely possible to imagine that a bastard race could spring from the union of two of these species, and retain just so much of the qualities of each parent-stock as to preserve its ground in spite of the dangers which surround it. [p. 58]

Lyell realized that the exactness of a species' adaptation to a particular mode of obtaining food and to a particular set of circumstances, including other species, imposed on it a certain rigidity. If a species became altered in its features in random fashion it would no longer be adequately adapted to its particular way of life.

Lyell was severely critical of the theory of progressive development, which was already a generalization based on the paleontological record, as well as "of the fancied evolution of one species out of another" (p. 60).[84] Yet he presented all of the evidence known to him which had been adduced to support these theories. This included the fact that the mammalian brain in the course of its embryological development "assumes, in succession, the various forms which belong to fishes, reptiles, and birds, before it acquires those additions and modifications which are peculiar to the mammiferous tribe" (p. 63). Lyell, however, thought that such facts as these demonstrated "the unity of plan that runs through the organization of the whole series of vertebrated animals" but did not necessarily support the theory of transmutation of species (p. 64).

Lyell turned next to the geographical distribution of species. This he saw as a question of central importance. If species were fixed and real entities existing through a determinate time span, their present distribution must reflect both their history and the geological history of the areas they occupy. The study of the geo-

84. This seems to be the first, or at least a very early use of the word "evolution" to signify the development of new species from preexisting ones.

graphical distribution of plants and animals had really only become possible as a result of the growth of collections from all over the world during the eighteenth century. Candolle said that Linnaeus was the first writer not only to give the localities from which plants came, but to describe the particular nature of the habitats in which they grew.[85] As botanists followed his example a fund of information accumulated which allowed the serious discussion of the geographical distribution of plants.

Lyell based his treatment of plant geography very largely on Candolle's essay and on the discussion of the geographical distribution of species in Prichard's *Researches into the Physical History of Man*.[86] Both Candolle and Prichard had argued that species were real and stable entities. Candolle believed that, although botanists had sometimes multiplied the number of species unnecessarily by relying on differences in the leaves and stems which commonly are variable, the reproductive parts in such cases were stable. Prichard, whose primary purpose was to demonstrate that the different races of mankind were all of one species, also discussed the geographical distribution of plants and animals. Linnaeus had suggested that all of the species of plants and animals at present distributed over the earth's surface had all spread from one point represented by those few mountains which stood above the waters when the earth was still enveloped by the primeval ocean. Since these mountains had been situated in a warm part of the earth, they would have on their peaks and slopes and in their valleys every conceivable type of climate and could consequently supply species suitable for every portion of the earth's surface. The opposite point of view, put forward by Rudolphi,[87] was that all plant species had arisen in the places where they now grow and that they had in effect been called into being by the particular conditions of climate, soil, and moisture under which they grew. Thus the same species could originate simultaneously at different points on the earth's surface where the conditions were identical. Rudolphi was influenced by such facts as that many of the plants which grew on the Alps grew also on the mountains of Norway

85. A. P. de Candolle. "Géographie botanique" (1820) p. 359.

86. J. C. Prichard (1786–1848), *Researches into the Physical History of Man* (1813). Lyell used the second edition entitled *Researches into the physical history of mankind* (1826).

87. Karl Asmund Rudolphi (1771–1832). A native of Sweden, Rudolphi was professor of anatomy and physiology at the university of Berlin from 1810 until his death. He wrote extensively on natural history, anatomy, and physiology.

but at no intervening point. To all appearances, similar conditions at these two widely separated places had been responsible for the origin of the same set of species. This theory was in agreement with the doctrines of Lamarck according to which living organisms could mold themselves to the requirements of the environment so that identical environments should produce identical kinds of organisms. There was still a third point of view, originally advocated by Willdenow,[88] that each species had arisen at a "center of creation" from which it had spread to its present area of distribution over the earth's surface. Instead of the single center of creation suggested by Linnaeus, Willdenow thought there were many centers each located on the primitive mountains which were the first to be left dry as the waters of the primeval ocean receded. Thus one might recognize different botanical regions each defined by the mountain range from which it had originated.

Each of these theories was put forward essentially as a speculation, but as knowledge of plant geography grew, particularly with the first voyage of Captain Cook, which revealed the rich and distinctive botany of New Zealand and Australia for the first time, more definite patterns of the geographical distribution of plants began to emerge. Descriptions of the plant collections made on Cook's voyage by Joseph Banks and Daniel Solander[89] were never published, but their specimens were used by Robert Brown when he wrote on the flora of New Holland in 1810. Brown pointed out that there were three great geographical divisions of the plant world—those of the Old World, including Europe, Asia and Africa; the New World, including North and South America; and Australia.[90] The differences between the floras of Europe and of the Americas were pointed out strikingly in 1807 by Alexander von Humboldt in his *Essai sur la Géographie des Plantes,* included as part of the great work in which he described the results of his travels in Central and South America with Aimé Bonpland during the years 1799–1804.[91] In his essay on geographical botany for

88. Karl Ludwig Willdenow (1765–1812) was born at Berlin and studied medicine at the university of Halle. In 1798 he became professor of natural history and superintendent of the botanic garden in the newly founded university of Berlin. Willdenow observed peculiarities in the world distribution of plants such as the similarity between the plants of eastern Asia and North America and between those of the Cape of Good Hope and Australia which led him to develop the view that the geographical distribution of plants is the product of their history.

89. Sir Joseph Banks (1743–1820); Daniel Charles Solander (1736–82).

90. R. Brown, *Prodromus florae* . . . (1810).

91. A. von Humboldt, *Essai sur la géographie des plantes* . . . (1807).

the *Dictionnaire des sciences naturelles* in 1820, Candolle summarized the works of these writers and the results of these travelers, as well as others.

The most outstanding fact that emerged in Candolle's essay was the great difference between the plant species of Europe and America or Africa and equinoctial America even when the climate, soil, and altitude were very similar. "A certain degree of analogy, indeed, of aspect, and even of structure, might very possibly be discoverable between the plants of the two localities in question," Candolle wrote, "but the *species* would in general be different."[92]

The difference moreover, between groups of species living under similar conditions on different continents was greatest where the continents were separated by a wide ocean, such as that between Africa and South America. The northern parts of North America, northern Asia, and northern Europe, which were connected by closely adjoining land areas across the Bering Straits, shared many species in common and showed great similarity between others. Islands lying in the ocean distant from continents had only a small number of plant species, but these were usually distinct and peculiar to the islands. Those which were not peculiar to the island were usually species belonging to the nearest area of mainland. On the basis of significant differences in species, Candolle had been able to establish twenty-seven well defined botanical regions on the earth's surface. The existence of so many distinct groups of species, often adapted in their form and structure in similar ways to similar sets of conditions, suggested strongly that these species had arisen separately and probably in the regions where they now lived. Some species were distributed erratically in places far from their apparent place of origin, but these could usually be accounted for by the agency of man or the possession of some unusually effective means of distribution. The mosses and fungi, for instance, which are extraordinarily cosmopolitan, reproduce by minute spores which can be carried by the wind for any distance and are consequently distributed almost universally through the atmosphere.

In his treatment of the geographical distribution of animal species, Lyell followed Prichard's treatment. Prichard had developed the view that each species had originated on the earth's sur-

---

92. Candolle, "Essai," p. 402 as translated and quoted in *Principles* II, p. 68.

face at a single place from which its members had spread themselves over a greater or lesser area. Each species, he thought, had arisen from a single stock and very likely, as Linnaeus had suggested, in a single pair.[93] The evidence, which Prichard summarized and Lyell recapitulated, began with Buffon who had noted that, although the same conditions of temperature and climate might have been expected to produce the same animals in different parts of the world, this was not the case. The animals of South America differed greatly from those of Africa and India. Buffon realized that certain groups of distinct species were limited to certain regions, separated from the rest of the world by natural barriers such as oceans, deserts, or mountains.

Lyell then took up the question of how animals might distribute themselves and gave examples of many different kinds of animal migrations. Yet the possibilities for the migration of land animals across areas of sea were limited and a wide ocean could impose an almost insuperable barrier. Where conditions were similar in widely separated places the same phenomenon occurred with animals as with plants—the species were similarly adapted, but quite distinct.

> So in regard to snakes; we find the boa of America, represented by the python, a different though nearly allied genus in India. America is the country of the rattle-snake, Africa of the cerastes, and Asia of the hooded snake or cobra di capello. [p. 103]

Lyell also discussed the geographical distribution of fishes, molluscs, including marine, freshwater and land forms, zoophytes, insects, and man.

After he had thus summarized the available factual information relating to the geographical distribution of species, Lyell proceeded to consider what it meant. In so doing he moved distinctly beyond the simple concept of Prichard that each species had arisen at a geographical center from which it had been distributed, because he saw the problem in the longer perspective of geological time. It was necessary to account, therefore, not only for the present distribution, but also for the fact, demonstrated by the portions of the fossil record already studied, that

> . . . there have been many entire changes in the species of plants and animals inhabiting the land. . . . Each species may have had

93. Prichard, *Researches into the physical history of mankind,* pp. 31–47.

its origin in a single pair, or individual, where an individual
was sufficient, and species may have been created in succession
at such times and in such places as to enable them to multiply
and endure for an appointed period, and occupy an appointed
space on the globe. [p. 124]

In stating this hypothesis Lyell did not attempt to say how species
may have been "created"—his views on this question at this time
are an enigma. He did say that each species had been "created" in
a nice relation to the environment in which it found itself, with
respect to space, time, and the existence of other species. It was
also an essential feature of Lyell's hypothesis that the "creation"
of new species occurred more or less uniformly throughout the
earth and that such inequalities in the number of peculiar indige-
nous species as might exist were the result of unequal barriers to
distribution. For instance, the fact that an island like St. Helena
in the South Atlantic had an unusually large proportion of species
peculiar to itself did not mean to Lyell that the "creative power"
had there been exerted with unusual force. It meant simply that
as new species had arisen on St. Helena they had no opportunity
to distribute themselves over a wider area because of the surrounding oceanic barrier.

Lyell next had to deal with the difficulty "that the distribution
of species approaches too nearly to what might have been expected,
if animals and plants had been introduced into the globe when
its physical geography had already assumed the features which it
now wears" (p. 127). His study of Tertiary shells had shown him
that many species were in fact far older than the present distribution of land and sea. If species in general were equally old they
ought to be more uniformly distributed, and botanical and zoological provinces more blended together. However, after species
had been introduced to the earth's surface their stay there was
limited. Sooner or later they became extinct. Lyell took up the
factors which might produce their extinction. His approach is
ecological.

Every naturalist is familiar with the fact, that although in a
particular country, such as Great Britain, there may be more
than three thousand species of plants, ten thousand insects, and
a great variety in each of the other classes, yet there will not be
more than a hundred, perhaps not half that number, inhabit-
ing any given locality. There may be no want of space in the

supposed tract; it may be a large mountain, or an extensive moor, or a great river-plain, containing room enough for individuals of every species in our island; yet the spot will be occupied by a few to the exclusion of many, and these few are enabled, throughout long periods, to maintain their ground successfully against every intruder. [p. 130]

In addition to emphasizing the relationship of each species to the physical conditions of its environment, Lyell stressed the dynamic nature of the interactions among species. Forest herbs depended for their living space on the trees under which they grew; insects controlled the growth of the populations of plants on which they fed; the insects in turn were controlled by their own parasites. The remarkable feature of insects, however, was their ability to increase their numbers very rapidly. "A scanty number of minute individuals," wrote Lyell, "only to be detected by careful research, are ready in a few days, weeks or months, to give birth to myriads which may repress any degree of monopoly in another species, or remove nuisances, such as dead carcasses, which might taint the air" (p. 134).

An increase in the numbers of an insect species also influenced those animals which fed on it but to a lesser degree. Since most insectivorous animals feed on more than one species, and sometimes on other animals as well, the great abundance of one kind of insect would simply lead them "to subsist more exclusively upon the species thus in excess, and the balance may thus be restored" (p. 138–39). With multitudes of examples Lyell delineated the dynamic balance which exists among various species in nature and the intricate network of interactions by which it is maintained. As a result,

... the possibility of the existence of a certain species in a given locality, or of its thriving more or less therein, is determined not merely by temperature, humidity, soil, elevation and other circumstances of the like kind, but also by the existence or nonexistence, the abundance or scarcity, of a particular assemblage of other plants and animals in the same region. [p. 141]

But the assemblage of other plants and animals was continually fluctuating and might be subject to radical change, as when a new species migrated in from another district. The activities of man had especially drastic effects, for man not only destroyed forests

Fig. 35. The Temple of Serapis (frontispiece to the *Principles*, 1830).

Fig. 36. The Val del Bove (frontispiece to vol. II of the *Principles*, 1832).

Fig. 37. Lyell's sketch of the view from the summit of Etna into the Val del Bove (*Principles*, vol. III, p. 93).

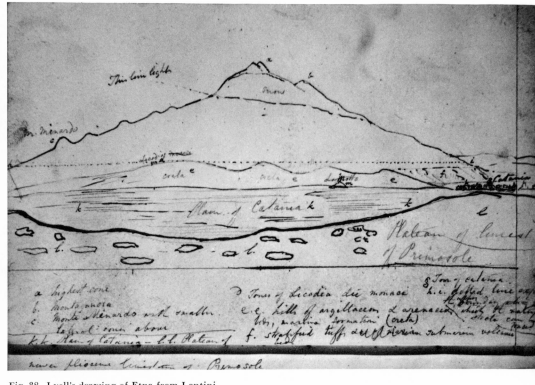

Fig. 38. Lyell's drawing of Etna from Lentini.

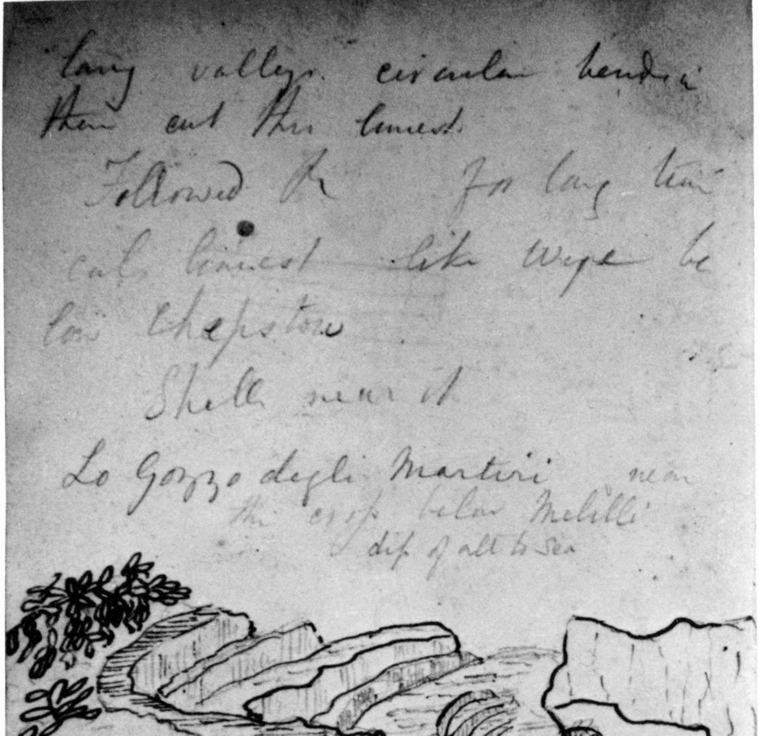

"long valley. circular bends in them out this limest.

Followed R   for long thro
calc limest like Wye below Chepstow

Shells near it

Lo Gozzo degli Martiri near
the crop below Melilli
dip of all to sea

This supposed crater consists of strata of the yellowish & white lime st of Noto compact & honeycomd in part shelly. Some of the lava shela in a poporine conglon containing fragm of volc black

Fig. 39. Lyell's drawing of Gozzo degli martiri.

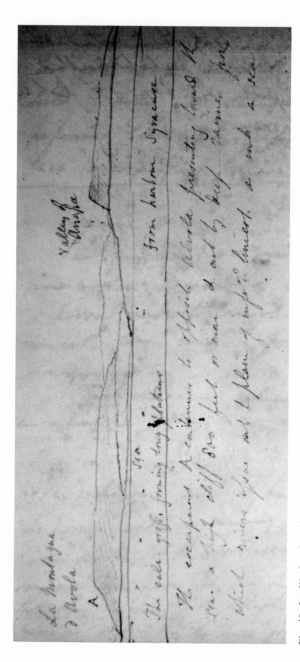

Fig. 40. Lyell's drawing of the Val di Noto escarpment from the south side of the harbor of Syracuse.

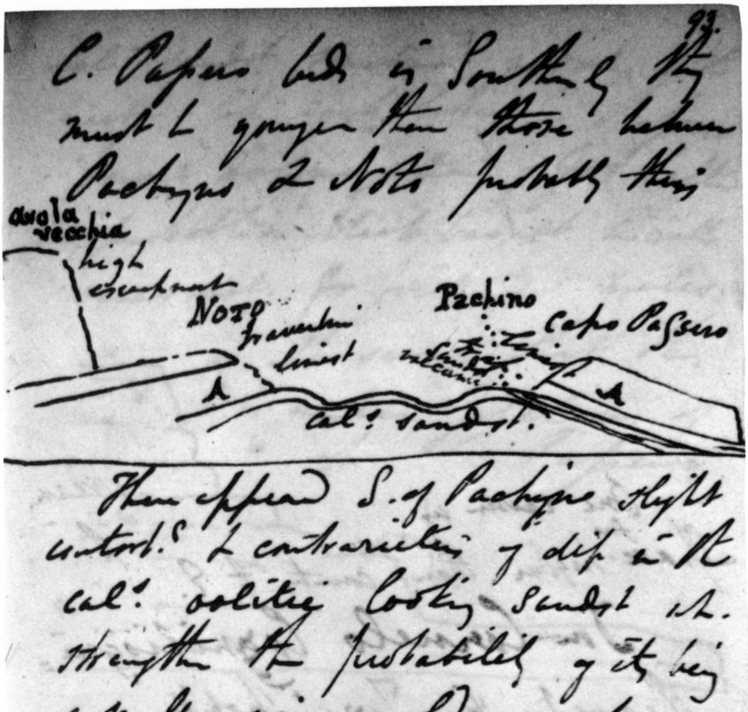

Fig. 41. Lyell's drawing of the strata at Cape Passaro.

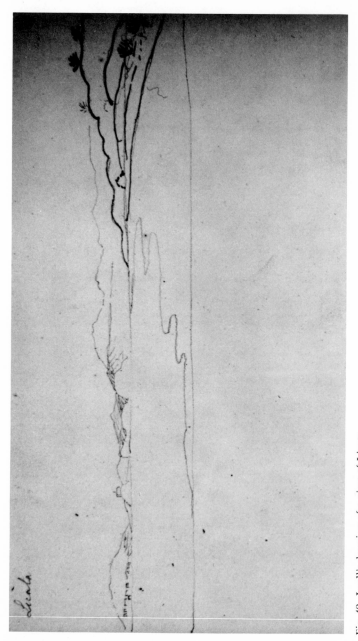

Fig. 42. Lyell's drawing of a view of Licata.

Fig. 43. The volcanoes of Olot (frontispiece to vol. III of the *Principles*).

Fig. 44. Mary Elizabeth Horner in 1831 (aged 22). By an unknown artist. Courtesy of Lord Lyell of Kinnordy.

Fig. 45. Charles Lyell in 1836. Drawing by J. M. Wright. Courtesy of the National Portrait Gallery, London.

Fig. 46. John Murray II (1778–1843). By Henry William Pickersgill, R.A. Courtesy of Mr. John Murray.

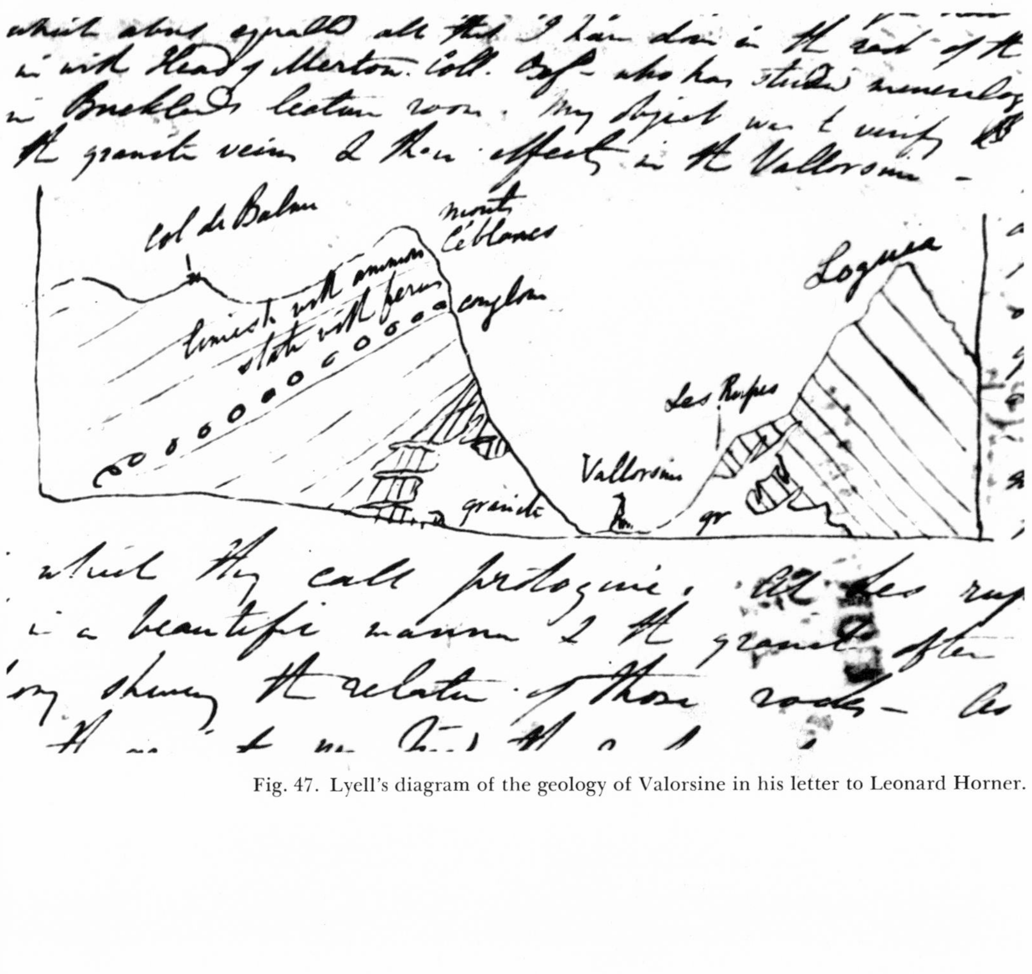

Fig. 47. Lyell's diagram of the geology of Valorsine in his letter to Leonard Horner.

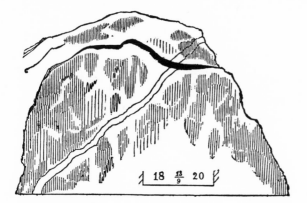

Fig. 48. The sea level mark at Gräsö near Oregrund, Sweden.

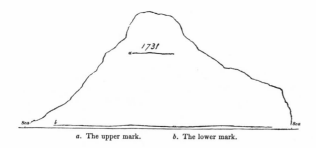

a. The upper mark.   *b.* The lower mark.

Fig. 49. The sea level mark made in 1731 in the harbor of Löfgrund, Sweden.

Mark at Koon Island, near Marstrand.

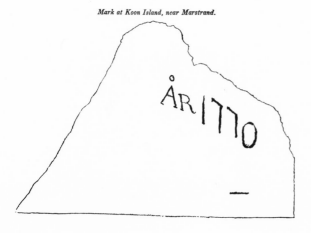

Fig. 50. The sea level mark made in 1820 at Koon Island near Marstrand, Sweden.

Fig. 51. Emma Darwin in 1839, aged 31, and Charles Darwin in 1837, aged 28. Both portraits by George Richmond. Courtesy of the Royal College of Surgeons of England.

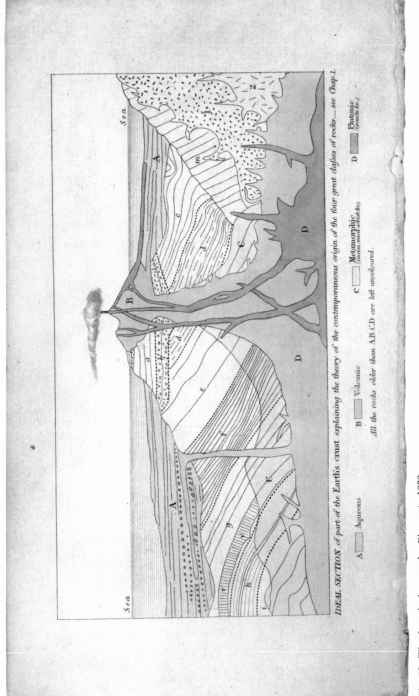

IDEAL SECTION of part of the Earth's crust explaining the theory of the contemporaneous origin of the four great classes of rocks.— see Chap. L.

A ▢ Aqueous   B ▣ Volcanic   C ▢ Metamorphic *(gneiss, mica-schist &c.)*   D ▦ Plutonic *(granite &c.)*

All the rocks older than A.B.C.D are left uncoloured.

Fig. 52. The frontispiece to the *Elements*, 1838.

and drained marshes, but he transported species across oceans to new continents where they sometimes multiplied so much as to drive out some of the native species.

Every species which has spread itself from a small point over a wide area, [wrote Lyell] must, in like manner, have marked its progress by the diminution, or the entire extirpation, of some other, and must maintain its ground by a successful struggle against the encroachments of other plants and animals. [p. 156]

Because such migrations occurred regularly, numerous species must, just as regularly, have been driven to extinction.

The mind is prepared by the contemplation of such future revolutions to look for the signs of others, of an analogous nature, in the monuments of the past. Instead of being astonished at the proofs there manifested of endless mutations in the animate world, they will appear to one who has thought profoundly on the fluctuations now in progress, to afford evidence in favour of the uniformity of the system, unless, indeed, we are precluded from speaking of *uniformity* when we characterize a principle of endless variation. [p. 157]

The ability of species to spread and migrate was important in an even more fundamental way. Geological changes were steadily destroying old environments and creating new ones. If species could not colonize those new environments they should soon be rendered extinct by the destruction of their old habitats. In some instances quite local geological changes could affect the populations of plants and animals over vast areas. The sinking of the isthmus of Panama would connect the Caribbean flora and fauna with those of the Pacific Ocean, with great and unforeseeable effects on each other. An elevatory movement at the straits of Gibraltar, cutting off the Mediterranean from the Atlantic Ocean, would result in a decrease in its level and an increase in its salinity with drastic consequences for its flora and fauna as well as secondary effects upon the climate of surrounding regions. By these and other examples Lyell showed that "amidst the vicissitudes of the earth's surface, species cannot be immortal, but must perish one after the other, like the individuals which compose them" (p. 169).

In his first volume Lyell had discussed the general cooling or warming of the whole earth's surface which might be produced by large-scale changes in the distribution of land and sea. Now he pointed out that in a period when the earth's surface was becoming warmer there would be a tendency for plant and animal species to migrate from the equator toward the poles. Since they had spread from a common center in the region of the equator, the flora and fauna of the northern and southern hemispheres would tend to be similar. By contrast, when the earth's surface was in a cooling phase, plant and animal species would tend to move from the poles toward the equator. The species of the northern and southern hemispheres having for a long time been widely separated would tend to be quite distinct in character. Since in the modern period the species of these two hemispheres were, in fact, quite different, Lyell suggested that this was one more piece of evidence that the earth's climate had undergone a general cooling "during the epochs which immediately preceded our own" (p. 171).

Each change of climate would bring about some migration of species. If it were a cooling change, arctic species would invade the temperate zone and species on the mountains would descend into the lowlands. These migrations revealed a fatal flaw in Lamarck's theory of the transmutation of species. Lamarck had argued that when conditions changed a species simply changed itself to adapt to them. Lamarck had written:

> Suppose, for example, that the seeds of a grass or any other plant that grows normally in a damp meadow, are somehow conveyed first to the slope of a neighbouring hill where the ground although higher is still rich enough to allow the plant to maintain its existence. Suppose that then, after living there and reproducing itself many times, it reaches little by little the dry and almost barren ground of a mountain side. If the plant succeeds in living there and perpetuating itself for a number of generations, it will have become so altered that botanists who come across it will erect it into a separate species.[94]

Lyell pointed out that the conditions required for the survival of a plant included more than a suitable soil. A species in constant competition with others would have neither the time nor the opportunity to adapt. The same objection applied to other kinds of change, wrote Lyell:

> However slowly a lake may be converted into a marsh, or a marsh into a meadow, it is evident that before the lacustrine

94. J. B. Lamarck, *Zoological philosophy* ... (1914) p. 39.

plants can acquire the power of living in marshes, or the marsh plants of living in a less humid soil, other species, already existing in the region, and fitted for these several stations, will intrude and keep possession of the ground. [p. 174]

Finally Lyell was faced with the question of how new species might arise to repair the gradual extinction of so many old species. He had no ready answer. Since the number of species is very large and the rate of extinction and replacement slow, the chances of our actually witnessing the birth of a new species, he thought, were comparatively small. Because historical records of the introduction of new species were as yet lacking, he wished to turn to geological records which contained "remains of living species" (p. 183). These records, he wrote, would enable us

... to infer whether species have been called into existence in succession or all at one period; whether singly or by groups simultaneously; whether the antiquity of man be as high as that of any of the inferior beings ... or whether the human species is one of the most recent of the whole. [p. 183]

There is a sense of anticlimax to this passage. The reader has been led to see species as a totality of real entities, jostling one another for living space on the earth's surface. He has been shown that the continued life of a species of plant or animal depends not only on the continuance of a certain set of physical conditions but also on the maintenance of a delicate balance in its interactions with numerous neighboring species; that the conditions necessary for any one species cannot be maintained for long in the course of geological time; and that, as a result, species are continually becoming extinct. But, as to the source of new species to replace those extinguished or the question of the first origin of this extinct species, which must have had a beginning, as surely as it now has an end—with these questions the reader is left entirely in suspense. One reader who was to be left with the question of the origin of species hanging unanswered in his mind was Charles Darwin, who in 1832 was wandering across the Pampas of South America.

CHAPTER 11

Marriage and Professorship, 1832–1833

WHEN HE DECIDED to bring out his second volume of the *Principles* at the beginning of December 1831, Lyell had already written the first chapters of what was to be volume three. By 13 December he was at work on chapter six, but, he told Mary, "the excitement of vol. 2 being over I c^d not work with spirit."[1] There were numerous distractions. London was living under the double threat of an impending cholera epidemic and a reform bill. Of the two, the cholera was the less disturbing. Lyell thought it was just one more among the many diseases which added uncertainty to life. The epidemic, long awaited as the disease progressed from place to place on the continent, was slow to reach London. With the delay, the alarm lessened. Lyell described the prevailing feeling to Mary:

> At Athenaeum tonight Maule the barrister said to me "Very true, people were frightened at first & so was I, but now I find they think as little about the cholera as they do of damnation, *or any other contingency.*"[2]

At Christmas time Lyell went down to Hampshire to spend the holiday with his aunts, Mrs. Heathcote and Miss Mary Lyell and his sisters, Marianne and Caroline, at Jermyns, a country house near Romsey. Tom arrived off his ship at Portsmouth in time for Christmas dinner and they had "a very merry cheerful evening."[3]

Lyell had at this time already decided to give up his professorship at King's College. The great success of his first volume seems to have been the factor which led him to this decision. "If in England," he wrote to Mary, "a man really wants to have the satisfaction of influencing public opinion in his favourite science & getting fame at the same time, the way is certainly to give Murray a readable book rather than K.C. a popular course of lectures."[4]

1. C. L., Jr. to Mary Horner. 13–16 Dec. 1831. Kinnordy mss.
2. C. L., Jr. to Mary. 6 Jan. 1832. Kinnordy mss.
3. C. L., Jr. to Mary. 24–26 Dec. 1831. Kinnordy mss. (*L & L.* I, 359).
4. Ibid.

This was not a simple decision. He had originally sought the professorship in order that he might have a position to hold him in London and keep him at geology in case his income should be reduced to the point where he was compelled to supplement it. Now his books seemed to offer him the additional income—more necessary to his sense of security than to his actual wants. Early in January, however, his faith in the income to be derived from writing received a jolt when he had a disagreement with Murray over the amount he was to receive for his second volume (Fig. 46).

Lyell had felt that he was at a disadvantage when negotiating with Murray. He thought that Murray tended to be evasive and unreliable in coming to any verbal agreement. There was in fact a touch of snobbery in his attitude because he thought that Murray was not a gentleman. Murray may have had some of the push and some of the uncertainty of a successful businessman. His extravagance and occasional ostentation were those of a man unsure of his social position and he could be both sensitive and erratic. After they had discussed the matter of the second volume on the morning of 31 December, Lyell sent a note to Murray to say that "it would be more satisfactory & prevent the possibility of mistake if before public.ⁿ you w.ᵈ state what you conceive your arrangement with me now to be."[5] Murray then apparently requested Lyell to call to see him, but Lyell said he could not because he had to attend a meeting of the council of the Geological Society.[6] Finally on 7 January Murray sent a brief note to say that he was going to give 150 guineas for the first edition of volume two "being in the same proportion as the 200 guineas for the 1st edition of the first volume."[7] This note made Lyell furious because he thought that, since the price of the second volume was 12 shillings as compared with 15 shillings for volume one, and since he had received 200 guineas for volume one, he should get 160 guineas for volume two. He was particularly incensed because he thought that Murray had already driven a hard bargain for volume one and had told him that the profits for volume two would be considerably larger than those for volume one. He forthwith wrote to Murray to say that the latter had "miscalculated the sum which would be due" to him.[8] He received no reply. When he had heard nothing after a

5. C. L., Jr. to J. M. 31 Dec. 1831. Murray mss.
6. C. L., Jr. to J. M. 3 Jan. 1832. Murray mss.
7. J. M. to C. L., Jr. 7 Jan. 1832. Kinnordy mss.
8. C. L., Jr. to J. M. 7 Jan. 1832. Murray mss.

week's time Lyell sent a very peremptory note requesting Murray to call at his rooms. To this imperious summons Murray replied in hot anger. His original offer, he said, had been based on an equal division of the profits. The 200 guineas which he had paid for the first volume had taken far more than half the profits; the profits for the second volume he calculated at 288 guineas of which 150 guineas was more than half.[9] Lyell replied that in his original offer Murray had mentioned nothing about an equal division of profits but had simply offered a flat sum for permission to publish, and that when they had arranged for the publication of the second volume "you acceded to my proposal that it should be paid for in the same proportion as the first."[10] Two days later Murray wrote to say "There appears to have been a misunderstanding on *both* sides." He explained that while his original offer had been a flat sum, he had added that it was intended to secure to Lyell "one half of the profits." He added:

> The expences of the 1st vol. were larger than I had calculated, the illustrations alone you will recollect exceeded considerably what you had led me to expect, the sale produced less, & my estimated profit was very much reduced, but with this of course you have no concern, as the agreement between us had been ratified.[11]

He concluded by saying that "I am perfectly willing to give up my point & to settle for the book upon your own terms" and enclosed notes accordingly. He also said that he regretted "the unpleasant correspondence which has passed between us." This was a handsome letter and Lyell replied to it in kind, with a full explanation of the sources of his own misunderstanding. He was genuinely mollified for he ended by saying:

> I assure you I have regretted the occurrence of this misunderstanding not as a difficulty in the way of an ordinary transaction of business, but as having happened with one whom I have for many years regarded as my friend.[12]

Lyell often complained privately of Murray—of his procrastination, his evasiveness, his drinking, his extravagance. Yet Murray

9. J. M. to C. L., Jr. 13 Jan. 1832. Kinnordy mss.
10. C. L., Jr. to J. M. 14 Jan. 1832. Murray mss.
11. J. M. to C. L., Jr. 16 Jan. 1832. Kinnordy mss.
12. C. L., Jr. to J. M. 17 Jan. 1832. Murray mss.

was a publishing genius with a genuine feeling for literature. Despite his faults he seems to have been able to attract and hold the friendship of authors. During the coming months he was reported to be in financial difficulties and it was said his notes might not be honored by the banks. Lyell was approached by another publisher with an offer for his third volume. He turned it down flatly.

In February his hopes of earning an income from his books seemed again threatened when Henry de la Beche told him that he intended to bring out a small book on geology.[13] Only a year older than Lyell, de la Beche was a young man, who in 1817 had become a member of the Geological Society and had thereafter devoted most of his time to geology and mineralogy. His income was derived from a family estate in Jamaica, but in 1831 the depressed state of trade and the effects of a slave uprising had practically deprived him of income. "He declines all parties," Lyell wrote, "has given up the secretaryship & is determined to try & profit by cheap books on geology."[14] Lyell thought there was some danger that these cheap books would be largely cribbed from the *Principles* and possibly from the lectures which he was to give at King's College. De la Beche had in fact told Lyell that he intended to found his short work on the *Principles,* though this may have been intended as a compliment. At any rate Lyell was sufficiently alarmed. He told Mary:

> To ease my mind I resolved to go to Murray & consult him, proposing to reprint 2^d Ed^n without much labour of correction & to get out said compendium soon after; but John said "Don't be in a hurry with a new scheme, we must not quarrel with a good thing when we've got it. Your book is popular. Vol. 2 is going with great rapidity on the reputation of vol. 1. The popular character of vol. 2 has not yet begun to tell. Now instead of new schemes let us improve the work."
>
> I sh.^{d} of course like that best for my reputation but then the expence of 3 vols. is so great in these days of cheap books that I necessarily limit the circulation & my fame thereby as well as profit & give De la Beche & such compilers an advantage & they can fatten on my hard labour.
>
> "He must take care how he *pirates* too much. Besides your

13. Sir Henry Thomas de la Beche (1796–1855). Biographical information is taken from D.N.B.
14. C. L., Jr. to Mary. 14 Feb. 1832. Kinnordy mss.

book is really so popular that I have resolved to get it out in a cheaper form & will print an Edition of *3000* if not 3500 immediately that vol. 3 is out, so work away & get it out"—

Certainly this is good news & encouragement but still how can it be cheap.—"Why this size oct°" and the plates etc. "I must fold them & as to the expence of them recollect that when that cost is spread over 9,000 vols. or 10,500 vols. it is trifling. Mr. De la Beche has not yet got rid of 500 vols. & we don't know when he will get rid of his 2^d Ed^n & as to his new work he may not succeed. *There are very few authors, or have ever been, who c^d write profound science & make a book readable* [italics mine, L.G.W.]—& depend on it, if you try to abridge & condense more & still be *popular* you may fail."

With this satisfactory interview I came away in good spirits for it is no small triumph in times when scarce any books will sell & no publishers are willing to undertake works to find Murray ready after selling 4500 vols. of 1st Ed^n to print 9000 more for 2.^{d} E^{dn}. 13,500 vols. with one's name thereunto appended is some notoriety—at least 10 times as much nearly as any English geologist has yet got.[15]

This evidence of the solidity of what he had already achieved greatly cheered Lyell. He had been working hard for many months, his long engagement to Mary Horner imposed strains of its own, he had struggled fruitlessly to help his brother Tom who was caught in an unhappy and thankless service—in the background there was the common anxiety about cholera and the reform bill. Frequently England seemed to be on the verge of revolution and the final outcome of the political upheaval which was taking place in 1831 and 1832 was not yet clear. To those who depended for their income on land, as did Lyell, it seemed entirely possible that reform might end in their losing their land. Faced with occasional unruly mobs and angry meetings, men like Mr. Lyell of Kinnordy retreated into an obstinate and violent Toryism. Although he did not share his father's opinions, Lyell himself did share some of the fears on which they were based. Moreover he was sufficiently aware of the realities of the world to know that the stubbornly reactionary attitudes of men like his father increased the political danger instead of lessening it. However, after his interview with Murray nothing could discourage

15. C. L., Jr. to Mary. 17 Feb. 1832. Kinnordy mss.

him. "Don't believe all that croaking correspondents tell you of Old England going to the devil," he wrote to Mary, "for I believe with Mr. Doorman that things look well. He says he never knew the prospects of the country so bright!"[16]

At this point, on 17 February 1832, Lyell had completed the first draft of twenty chapters for his third volume, which he had begun to write as soon as he had arrived back in London at the beginning of the previous November. He had become quite worried that he would not be able to finish this final volume before he gave his lectures and went to Bonn to be married. In an effort to push the book forward he pared his last three chapters on the ground that they were not essential to the central purpose of the book. He was now ready to begin revising and rewriting his draft in order to be able to send the revised chapters to the printer. Before beginning this phase of his work he went away, immediately after the anniversary dinner of the Geological Society on 17 February, to spend a long weekend with his aunts and sisters at Jermyns in Hampshire. There he went for long walks with Marianne and Caroline and recouped his energies while talking over with them his plans for the future.

Just at this time he was also distracted by the fact that his fiancée's father, Leonard Horner, had come to London from Edinburgh where he had been seeking the post of treasurer of the Bank of Scotland. Since he had resigned as warden of the London University, Horner had had no position and he was anxious to obtain one in order to give his family both greater income and greater security. All of Horner's friends rallied to his support in this cause, especially Henry Cockburn. Lyell canvassed testimonials for Horner from several London bankers including Alexander Baring.[17] In the end Horner decided not to pursue the appointment because the governors of the bank, who were Tories, laid down conditions which made it impossible for him to accept it.

On his return from Jermyns Lyell began to rewrite his manuscript for the third volume. He quickly realized that he was not going to be able to finish it before he was to go to Bonn to be married in the summer. This disturbed him considerably but finally he became reconciled to the fact, so that, as he told Mary, "I was able to go quietly and steadily on without worrying myself at the

16. Ibid.
17. Alexander Baring (1774–1848) banker and member of Parliament who in 1835 was created first Baron Ashburton.

slowness of my progress." He then described the further course of his work:

> . . . after having been nearly a week in writing & rewriting the first 2 chapters I at last resolved on Feb. 29 to begin with an attempt to cut each chapter as short as I c.ᵈ & try how far I c.ᵈ get in March. *Then* write my introductory lecture deriving it as much as possible from the preliminary chapters—then trust to providence & the remaining chapters for the other lecture—& go on, printing the first chapter & writing the others all April & till we meet. The first day Febʸ 29 I did half the first ch. & found that I got on at the rate of a chapter in two days, but then the first 2 of the old set became 4 which rather frightened me, but since that none of the others have *bred*. It is now 13 days since I began & tomorrow morning I begin my recast of the 8th chapter. Every word of the others has been rewritten either by myself or Hall, 9 tenths by the latter from dictation.[18]

After he had got through the eighth chapter he returned on 15 March again to the beginning to see if he could prepare his early chapters to go to the printer. The first chapter he said he found "very difficult & have rather recoiled from it."[19] It was in a sense his first reply to the critics of the first volume of the *Principles*. Although he had sworn not to take any notice of reviews or attacks he was not prevented from countering the arguments of his attackers in his own works. The first chapter of the third volume is therefore a summary and vindication of the approach to geology which he had developed in the whole work. In the preceding volumes he had discussed "the actual operation of the causes of change which affect the earth's surface and its inhabitants" (p. 1).[20] Now he was about to interpret the past history of the earth by analogy with these modern causes of change. Earlier geologists, Lyell argued, had been chiefly misled by their "entire unconsciousness . . . of the extent of their own ignorance respecting the operations of the existing agents of change" (p. 2). They had decided that geological phenomena could *not* be explained by "observation of the actual oeconomy of nature." Having made this decision they next tried to imagine an earlier and different order of nature which would account for the phenomena. They occupied

18. C. L., Jr. to Mary. 13 March 1832. Kinnordy mss.
19. C. L., Jr. to Mary. 16 March 1832. Kinnordy mss.
20. *Principles* III. Specific page references are given in the text.

themselves, Lyell said, "in guessing at what *might be,* rather than in inquiring *what is.*" Proceeding in this fashion, Lyell pointed out, theories were often given credit in proportion as they were the more fantastic in their contrast to the causes "now developed in our terrestrial system during a period, as it has been termed of *repose*" (p. 2). He went on:

> Never was there a dogma more calculated to foster indolence and to blunt the keen edge of curiosity, than this assumption of the discordance between the former and the existing causes of change. It produced a state of mind unfavourable in the highest conceivable degree to the candid reception of the evidence of those minute, but incessant mutations, which every part of the earth's surface is undergoing, and by which the condition of its living inhabitants is continually made to vary. [pp. 2–3]

The effect of these attitudes, Lyell said, was to envelop geology in an aura of mystery which was even considered one of its charms. Here, perhaps, we see a reflection of the romantic movement in its attitude toward science. Lyell was more mundane. He advocated "an earnest and patient endeavour to reconcile the former indications of change with the evidence of gradual mutations now in progress; restricting us in the first instance to known causes, and then speculating on those which may be in activity in regions inaccessible to us" (p. 3).

In 1829 and 1830 Élie de Beaumont had published his startling theory to account for the elevation of mountain ranges.[21] Saussure, who had first studied the structure of the Alps, had, after dismissing his own early conjectures, concluded that he must suspend judgment as to the origin of these mountains until many more facts were gathered.[22] In later years various other writers gave further descriptions of the structure of this great range of mountains but Élie de Beaumont offered the first really comprehensive causative theory for their origin. He began with the fact which had been demonstrated by Bischof and Ste.-Claire Deville that when a fused rock solidified it contracted in volume. Beaumont argued that the earth had once been a molten mass which had cooled to form first a crust upon the surface. With further cooling there would be a radial contraction of the earth as a whole, as a

---

21. Élie de Beaumont, "Recherches sur quelques-unes des Révolutions . . ." (1829–30).

22. H. B. de Saussure. *Voyages dans les Alpes . . .* (1779–96) vol. III, p. vii.

consequence of which the crust solidified at an earlier stage would become folded and wrinkled. With still more cooling and contraction the crust would be subjected to great pressure and would break along one or more lines. Along each line one side might sink down while the other would rise up to form a project-ing edge which would constitute a mountain range. The side that had sunk down would continue to be subject to lateral pressure which would throw it into a series of undulating folds parallel to the line of break. These undulations would produce a series of ridges and valleys which would decrease in height as they receded from the line of fracture. Meanwhile the interior fluid mass of the earth which was under great pressure might be forced up through the fissure. In this way, said Beaumont, the granite masses found at the heart of the Alps and along the axes of other mountain ranges were formed.[23] Élie de Beaumont's theory brought together a broad range of facts about the structure of the Alps and in several respects it represented at least a plausible preliminary hypothesis for the formation of mountains. However, Élie de Beaumont not only set forth his ideas with an irritating air of finality, but he stated as emphatically as possible that the forces which had raised his mountains were vast and catastrophic, entirely unlike any mod-ern earth process. The strength of Élie de Beaumont's theory was that he drew attention to the world-wide extent of the earth movements which had occurred at the close of the Cretaceous period and the beginning of the Tertiary epoch.[24] He greatly exaggerated the degree to which different mountain chains were parallel with one another and used this supposed parallelism to argue that they had all been elevated at one time.[25]

Élie de Beaumont also reviewed the evidence provided by the presence on the Jura of erratic granite boulders which had origi-nated in the high Alps and which had attracted the attention of geologists ever since Saussure had first pointed them out.[26] For him they were evidence of the latest "révolution" which had over-taken the earth in the form of a deluge. In a manner reminiscent of the Rev. William Buckland he went on to describe a number of diluvial deposits.

23. I am indebted for this abstract of Beaumont's theory to F. D. Adams, *The birth and development of the geological sciences* (1938) pp. 393–94.

24. Élie de Beaumont, "Révolutions" (1829) pp. 325–26.

25. Ibid., pp. 414–16.

26. Élie de Beaumont, "Revolutions" (1830) pp. 60–61.

Élie de Beaumont's theory was a vigorous and imaginative restatement of catastrophic doctrine supported by an engaging array of geological evidence, some of it new, and the arrangement of the whole characterized by a striking originality. He even attempted to reconcile his views with the emerging uniformitarian doctrines which he mentions as represented by Constant Prévost and Charles Lyell:

> Everything tends to lead us more and more to separate the facts offered for our observation by the sedimentary strata into two distinct classes: one comprising the facts relating to the tranquil and progressive manner in which the accumulation of each of the sedimentary strata has occurred and the other including those facts connected with those sudden interruptions which have established lines of demarcation between different consecutive deposits. After having subtracted, so to speak, the rôle of the violent and transitory phenomena, one would perceive more easily the analogy which those phenomena, which have occurred repeatedly on the surface of the globe during the different periods of tranquillity which have ensued there, appear to have presented to phenomena of the present time.

He was in no doubt of the reality of the intervening periods of catastrophe, some of which at least had resulted in the elevation of mountain ranges. His study, he felt, had shown that

> . . . each mountain range, suitably delimited, presents, in spite of the diversity of the rocks which can enter into its composition, a unique entity which has assumed its actual relief in one time and, so to speak, at a single stroke.
>
> On the other hand my results depart also, and perhaps still further from the supposition of an almost unlimited number of partial elevations occurring at times scattered irregularly throughout the whole duration of geological periods.[27]

Lyell had read the first installment of Élie de Beaumont's theory at Le Havre in June 1830 and views so directly opposite to his own would have come to his attention quickly in any case, but it had been placed squarely in front of him in challenging fashion by Adam Sedgwick in his presidential address to the Geological Society in 1831. Sedgwick outlined Élie de Beaumont's ideas in al-

27. Ibid., pp. 224–26 (my translation).

most eulogistic fashion and said "they seem to be based on an immoveable mass of evidence." He added:

> That the system of M. Élie de Beaumont is directly opposed
> to a fundamental principle, vindicated by Mr. Lyell, cannot
> admit of doubt. And I have decided to the best of my judgement, in favour of the former author, because his conclusions
> are not based upon any *a priori* reasoning, but on the evidence
> of facts; and also because, in part, they are in accordance with
> my own observations.[28]

Thus, simultaneously with the publication of the *Principles,*
there had been a recrudescence of catastrophism, and this revival
of the old doctrine had received the highest scientific approval in
the form of support and commendation by the president of the
Geological Society. In attempting to counteract catastrophism
Lyell was at a fundamental disadvantage because the basic appeal
of catastrophic doctrine was not rational but emotional. It seemed
to offer a new prop to the crumbling foundations of religious cosmogony. It was not that Sedgwick would admit that there was anything whatever wrong with the foundations of religion, but the
very speed with which he accepted Élie de Beaumont's sweeping
theories is suggestive of an underlying anxiety. In judging the
two doctrines there was no critical piece of evidence to which one
could point to decide which was true. Both carried a vast array of
geological evidence in their train. Lyell could show that particular
pieces of evidence which Élie de Beaumont had used were not
sound, or that they could be interpreted in another way. This,
however, was only to whittle at the edges of the theory and would
do little to dislodge the central faith which sustained the whole. He
could only provide an alternative faith which, he said, experience
had shown to be more productive of new discoveries and new
truths in geology. He was keenly aware that the issue was one of
opposing faiths.

In March 1832, when he was struggling with the revision of
chapter 1 of the third volume, Lyell received a letter from Scrope,
who commented on the review of volume two of the *Principles* in
the *Quarterly Review.* In this review, written by Whewell, the
terms uniformitarian and catastrophist had first been used to describe the two opposing views of geology. Scrope wrote:

28. A. Sedgwick, "Address to the Geological Society . . . 18 February 1831" (1834)
p. 311.

As to the dispute he speaks of, which I know has now and then raged pretty warmly between you as a *Uniformitarian* & the *Catastrophists* I do not see any but an imaginary line of separation between you. It is only a dispute about degree, a plus or minus affair; a little concession on either side will unite you in perfect cordiality.[29]

Lyell did not think that the difference between himself and his opponents was merely one of degree. A day or two later he wrote to Whewell and, after quoting the above comment, added:

On this point I cannot budge an inch for reasons to be developed in v. 3. It is of course a question of probability to some extent in the present state of our knowledge, but I consider it a most important question of principle, whether we incline to the probabilities as seen in the last 3000 yrs or possibilities which I hold to be uncalled for by any overwhelming evidence & absolutely inconsistent with some which I shall adduce, at least if deluges must follow paroxysmal eruptions.[30]

Two days later he wrote to Mary Horner that he was still, to his own surprise, struggling with his first chapter. "But in it," he wrote, "I am grappling not with the ordinary arm of flesh but with principalities and powers, with Sedgwick, Whewell & others for my rules of philosophizing as contradistinguished from theirs & I must put on all my armour."[31] He labored at this chapter for over a week, but finally on 30 March was able to tell Mary, "Last night at $\frac{1}{4}$ past 9 $^{o'k}$ I accomplished the great work of sending off by 2nd Post that interminable 1st chapter, which after all will scarcely extend into a seventh page."[32]

Although it had cost him so much time, Lyell's treatment of the issue dividing him from the catastrophists is characteristically brief. He noted that the issue applied particularly to the unanswered questions of geology:

. . . why mineral masses are associated together in certain groups; why they are arranged in a certain order which is never inverted; why there are many breaks in the continuity of the series; why different organic remains are found in distinct sets

29. G. P. Scrope to C. L., Jr. 20 March 1832. APS mss.

30. C. L., Jr. to W. W. 24 March 1832. Whewell mss.

31. C. L., Jr. to Mary. 26 March 1832. Kinnordy mss. *L. & L.* I, 376.

32. C. L., Jr. to Mary. 30 March 1832. Kinnordy mss.

of strata; why there is often an abrupt passage from an assemblage of species contained in one formation to that in another immediately superimposed. [p. 6]

Without mentioning Élie de Beaumont's name Lyell listed some of the causes which the former had postulated to answer these questions: "sudden and violent revolutions of the globe," "the instantaneous elevation of mountain chains," "paroxysms of volcanic energy," and the like.[33] They all manifested a desire, Lyell said, "to cut, rather than patiently to untie, the Gordian knot." He contrasted his own approach:

> In our attempt to unravel these difficult questions, we shall adopt a different course, restricting ourselves to the known or possible operations of existing causes; feeling assured that we have not yet exhausted the resources which the study of the present course of nature may provide, and therefore that we are not authorized in the infancy of our science, to recur to extraordinary agents. [p. 6]

With his first chapter out of the way Lyell went ahead more quickly with the others. By 7 April he had sent the third chapter to the printer. On Sunday the ninth, because he felt the need of some break from his work, he and Hall went by coach to the Zoological Society farm at Kingston Hill. They looked at the kangaroos, quaggas, emus and other strange animals, after which they walked through Combe Wood, a place famous for the occurrence of rare insects. From Combe Wood they walked through Richmond Park to Richmond and on to Putney Bridge, a distance of sixteen and a half miles. From Putney Bridge they took a boat to Chelsea where Lyell dined with the Somervilles. "The day's walk & air has really done wonders for me," he told Mary, "—so much so that I begin to think that if once a week I c^d have such a complete day's holiday & hard exercise I c^d work on the whole year with energy."[34]

He needed energy. The succeeding chapters of his third volume were each costing him much labor and thought. They might well have. In them Lyell presents his classification of the Tertiary strata in chronological order together with the new terminology

33. These quotations by Lyell are from Élie de Beaumont, "Researches on some of the revolutions . . ." (1831) e.g. pp. 243, 262.
34. C. L., Jr. to Mary. 10 April 1832. Kinnordy mss.

he had developed for them. Here the terms Eocene, Miocene and older and newer Pliocene enter the scientific literature for the first time. For each Tertiary epoch thus designated he gave three type formations: one marine, one freshwater, and one volcanic. Lyell's classification of the Tertiary and recent formations added not a chapter but a whole volume to historical geology. Furthermore, it was a volume which bridged the long gap between the geological past and the present.

As the time approached for his lectures to begin, the question arose whether ladies would be allowed to come to hear them. Many of Lyell's friends wished to bring their wives and, in some cases, their daughters, but the interest extended even farther than that. Many ladies had applied to Archdeacon Cambridge for admission, but he had refused them after having first consulted Lyell. Lyell himself thought it would be "unacademical" to allow ladies in the class room.[35] The existence of the demand was a tribute to the success of the *Principles*. The book had aroused great curiosity to hear the author. He told Mary, "I c^d have a class of 600 or 700 if I admitted ladies."[36]

On Tuesday 1 May Lyell gave his first lecture. There were few ladies and, he told Mary, "a pelting pitiless rain & Easter vac.^{n} thinned the numbers to some 80 perhaps."[37] However, the lecture was a success:

All think I got over my lecture famously & I got some subscribers by it in the room. . . . The excitement of a successful lecture is anything but that calm, studious philosophizing tone of mind wh. is best calculated to elicit truth & lead to speculative views resulting from an extensive induction from facts. . . . Fitton has gone about saying "Lyell's lecture is the best ever given on Geology for 200 yrs. in Europe." I believe I may say without vanity that it was consid^d a most successful effort at extemporizing a lecture. I kept the attention of all fixed, *by not reading*, & you c^d have heard a pin drop when I paused.

Fitton's Irish extravagance was at times comforting. The success of the introductory lecture renewed the demand to admit ladies. The subject came up at a meeting of the Geological Society the next day.

35. C. L., Jr. to C. Babbage. 3 May 1832. Babbage mss.
36. C. L., Jr. to Mary. 1 May 1832. Kinnordy mss.
37. Ibid.

Wed.ʸ Grand disputes at Geological Society about the propriety
of admitting ladies to my lectures. Babbage most anxious to
bring his mother & daughter & Lady Guildford,—Harris to bring
Lady Mary Kerr & so on. I begged them all not to do so & they
promised but at last Murchison said "My wife, however, must
come. I promised to bring her & she wᵈ be much disappointed.
I will not bring her till the doors are closed." Then they all
declared they wᵈ too & so bring the affair to a crisis one way or
other.

So the ladies came. The officers of King's College were even persuaded to give their hesitant approval to what they found it difficult to prevent. The second lecture was also a success and this time
was delivered before a crowd of nearly three hundred. Lyell had
decided to deliver a vindication of his geological theories. He continued to Mary:

> I worked hard upon the subject of the connection of Geology &
> Natural Theology & pointed out that the system which does
> not find traces of a beginning, like the physical astronomer
> whose finest telescope only discovers myriads of other worlds, is
> the most sublime & as there is no termination to the view, as
> regards space, of the acts of creation & manifestations of divine
> power, so also in regard to Time etc., concluding with a truly
> noble & eloquent passage from the Bp. of London's inaugural dis-
> course at K.C., in which he says that Truth must always add to
> our admiration of the works of the creator that one need never
> fear the result of free enquiry etc. etc.

His friends came in strength on this occasion as did the professors
of King's College, many of them in their academic gowns.
Throughout his audience listened in silence, but at the end they
applauded. His servant Hall acted as his "scene-shifter" and
prompter.

> I indulged so much in one or 2 parts that if Hall had not pulled
> out his watch to show me I was going too slow I shᵈ have had
> no time for my peroration. When I saw this I rattled over some
> parts at a great pace, telling them time pressed & they say it had
> an excellent *improvisatore* effect. Then in the middle of a high
> flight towards the end, when venturing to speculate on the rela-
> tive power shown in the creation of an animal endowed with
> instinct & of a globe of inert matter etc., I lost a page. This they

saw. There was no help for it. I was obliged to take my chance, put down the M.S. & extemporize. When I got thro' tho' I found I left out one or two strong points in the M.S.[38]

One of Lyell's principal purposes in this lecture was to remove from his uniformitarian doctrine the taint of being, or tending toward, atheism. He argued, as he had done before, that to say that geology offered no records of the beginning of the earth was not to say that such an event had not occurred. The same applied to the origin of man. He also said that the reason he did not point out connections between geology and natural theology was not that this could not be done, but because the science was as yet too immature. "Proof relied on may face & turn against the cause. Theory, in a new science, ought not to be taught as an allegory."[39] In effect he was arguing for the independence of science from theology. Henry Crabb Robinson, who attended this lecture, commented: "I understood scarcely anything,—but I liked what I did understand." He said that Lyell had distinguished between the inorganic world, for which no beginning could be discerned, and the organic world of which there were "proofs of a beginning." Robinson added:

He decorously and boldly maintained the propriety of pursuing the study without any reference to the Scriptures; and dexterously obviated the objection to the doctrine of the eternity of the world being hostile to the idea of a God, by remarking that the idea of a world which carries in itself the seeds of its own destruction is not that of an all-wise and powerful Being. And geology suggests as little the idea of an end as of a beginning to the world.[40]

Lyell continued to lecture on Tuesdays and Thursdays for the next five weeks giving a total of twelve lectures in all. His lectures were usually based on particular chapters of his third volume. His audience held up well. Most of them were interested members of the general public; only a few were actually students at King's College. His friends and his scientific opponents came. They were frequently the same persons. Ladies came and sometimes went home to read or reread the *Principles*. Lyell had enjoyed extem-

38. C. L., Jr. to Mary. 3 May 1832. Kinnordy mss.
39. C. L., Jr. to his mother. 5 May 1832. Kinnordy mss.
40. H. C. Robinson, *Diary, reminiscences and correspondence* (1869) vol. III, p. 8.

porizing toward the end of his second lecture so much that he read
his lectures no more. They were probably the better for it. After
his lecture on Friday 11 May he wrote to Mary:

> . . . my three old friends Lords Northampton, Selkirk, & Cole
> were present, the two latter having *just* subscribed to *the* course.
> The number now is above 60 but I don't know exactly., Col.
> Clive, Lady Bute & 2 or 3 other good names. It is a singularly
> *aristocratical class.* Only 2 students of K.C. . . . I begin to flatter
> myself that I am (as Lubbock said last night when he came down
> from R.S. chair) doing an immense deal of good to science by
> these lectures which at all events are talked of over London, but
> politics are of course the chief & absorbing subject.[41]

The debate upon the reform bill was now at a decisive stage in
Parliament. There was real fear of revolution if it should fail to
pass the House of Lords; there was widespread unease among the
Tory gentry about the political changes which its enactment
would bring.

On 7 May the prime minister Lord Grey was defeated in the
House of Lords when he opposed a motion to amend the reform
bill and on the eighth he asked the King to create enough peers
to give the government a majority in the House of Lords. The
King refused and Lord Grey offered his resignation, a resignation
which necessarily carried with it the resignations of the whole
cabinet. It was accepted and King William then asked in succession Lord Lyndhurst, Sir Robert Peel, and Sir Charles Manners
Sutton, but each refused. Finally he again turned to the Duke of
Wellington who agreed to attempt to form a new administration.
But the King, the Duke, and the Tory party had misjudged the temper of public opinion in England. The National Union organized
a widespread strike. Work ceased and church bells were rung
nightly. There were public meetings, and petitions bearing thousands of signatures poured in from the provincial cities. The
House of Commons was urged to refuse to pass the budget until
the reform bill had been passed. On Saturday 11 May the National
Union organized an attack on the financial strength of the Bank of
England by urging people to withdraw their deposits and demand
gold. By noon on Monday 14 May it was clear that this maneuver
could succeed. On 15 May, the day that Lyell gave his fifth lecture,
the Duke of Wellington told the king that he could not form a gov-

41. C. L., Jr. to Mary. 11 May 1832. Kinnordy mss.

ernment and the King was forced to recall Lord Grey.[42] Political excitement was at fever pitch. It was, therefore, a tribute both to the stability of English society and to Lyell's reputation that in the midst of this political tumult he could attract an audience to hear lectures on theoretical aspects of geology.

One who took the greatest interest in his lectures was Charles Babbage, who had argued strongly for the admission of ladies. He not only came himself but brought troops of his friends. He also offered to provide Lyell with data on the Temple of Serapis which, he said, "you must give to us,—theories,—shells and all."[43] But perhaps most gratifying to Lyell was to have his fellow members of the Geological Society, often his most vigorous opponents, come to hear him. At the next lecture on 15 May the university of Cambridge was represented in the person of Adam Sedgwick. "Sedgwick being there," Lyell wrote to Mary, "I took a shot at him, which amused Fitton & Co. & made him come up laughing after lecture & shake me by the hand."[44] The lectures seemed to grow in interest and popularity. On Friday 18 May Lyell approached a triumph:

> Dr. Buckland, De la Beche, Col. Salmon,[45] Joshua Watson, Mr. Hobbhouse, Sotheby, Hallam, Babbage, Green (the best lecturer in London), Lord Kerry, B. Hall, Dr. Babington, a great body of professors, in all upwards of 100 attended today. Many came round & declared I was "inspired" today, the best lecture of all etc. Otter said "I admire your courage. You lectured with more spirit, when Buckland came, on the points where you differ, so also when Sedgwick appeared & you rise with the occasion instead of being cowed."[46]

42. I am indebted for the information cited in this and earlier references to the struggle for reform to the account in É. Halévy *A History of the English People in the Nineteenth Century* (1927), vol. III, *The Triumph of Reform (1830–41)*.

43. C. B. to C. L., Jr. 13 May 1832. Babbage mss.

44. C. L., Jr. to Mary. 15 May 1832. Kinnordy mss.

45. I have not been able to identify Col. Salmon further; Joshua Watson (1771–1855), philanthropist and churchman; John Cam Hobhouse, Baron Broughton (1786–1869); William Sotheby (1771–1842), auctioneer and antiquary; Henry Hallam (1777–1859), historian; Joseph Henry Green (1791–1863), surgeon and lecturer, professor in the King's College medical school; Henry Thomas Petty-Fitzmaurice (1816–66). Lord Kerry, became 4th Marquis of Lansdowne on his father's death in 1863; William Babington (1756–1833) or his son Benjamin Guy Babington (1794–1866), both physicians; William Otter (1768–1840), first principal of King's College, 1831–36.

46. C. L., Jr. to Mary. 19 May 1832. Kinnordy mss.

This was high praise and we may forgive Lyell for telling Mary of it. His accounts of his lectures are all from his letters to her and are more full, unguarded, and intimate than he would have written to anyone else. His class of paying subscribers, which had begun with a dozen, had now risen to nearly seventy. The rest were guests of Lyell or friends of friends. On this occasion Dr. Buckland, who during the lecture had heard his theories torn to tatters, "generously came up," Lyell wrote, "& rewarded me with a scientific view done by an artist under his direction of Val del Bove, for my 3ᵈ vol."[47] Lyell, however, was not able to use the drawing in his third volume.

A week later, on 25 May, his two sisters Marianne and Caroline, who were in London, came to hear him lecture. On this day Lyell told Mary:

> I pronounced an éloge on Cuvier[48] today & a digression on the comparative state of advancement of Nat. History in France & England, quoted Herschel & Babbage on the decline of science etc. The episode was I fear rather too long in proportion to the geological part of the lecture, but I am rather glad to have unburdened myself.

Afterwards Marianne and Caroline came with Mrs. Mallet to see Lyell's rooms "which were much admired" and then went to the Mallet's house at Hampstead.[49]

Lyell's next lecture on May 29 went off well with an audience of more than a hundred consisting now principally of men, the number of ladies having thinned. On Friday 5 June, the occasion was a grand one and the next day he described it with satisfaction to Mary Horner:

> Yesterday's lecture attended by D. of Somerset,[50] Lord Henley, Bp. Llandaff, Archdⁿ Wrangham, W. Vernon Harcourt, Sir D.

47. C. L., Jr. to C. B. 18 May 1832. Babbage mss.
48. Georges Cuvier had died at Paris on 13 May 1832.
49. C. L. Jr. to Mary. 25 May 1832. Kinnordy mss.
50. Edward Adolphus Seymour, 11th Duke of Somerset (1775–1855); Robert Henley Eden, second Baron Henley (1789–1841); Edward Copleston (1776–1849), Bishop of Llandaff; Francis Wrangham (1769–1842), Archdeacon of Cleveland; William Vernon Harcourt (1789–1871); Sir David Brewster (1781–1868); Thomas Robert Malthus (1766–1834); Sir Robert Harry Inglis (1786–1855); Edward Law, second Baron Ellenborough (1790–1871); we have not been able to identify Guildford; Sir John Hamilton Macgill Dalrymple (1771–1853), became eighth Earl of Stair in 1841; we have not been able to identify Wishaw, who was a Whig, a friend

Brewster & Lady B., Malthus & his family, Sir R. Inglis, Lady Bute, Ellenboro, Guildford, Dalrymple, Wishaw (who congratulated me & paid me prodigious compliments), Ld Kerry & many others, 130 or more. I was on Etna & I proved to Copleston's satisfaction the volcano to be 70,000 years old & that no *deluge* had passed over it—an hour & 1/4—lots of illustrations. They declared it was my best of all. Murchison & wife there & party. W. Whitman said "You w^d have double your class if you w^d begin another course tomorrow." They say today that since Sir H. Davy's course at R.I. so fine an assembly as yesterday was never collected at a lecture in town. Daubeny was there & a great body of the Profs.[51]

In this lecture Lyell presented the substance of the eighth chapter of his third volume in which he demonstrated the great age of Etna and the fact that, as was shown by the section through it in the Val del Bove, it had been built up very gradually by successive outpourings of lava. Yet none of these ancient lava flows were of greater extent than those which had occurred in modern times. He compared the growth of the volcano to the growth of a tree, and compared the layers of lava to the annual rings in a tree trunk. Lyell conjectured that the eighty lateral cones of Etna might have been formed in the last 12,000 years, but if they were removed the mountain would only be slightly smaller.

Etna might lose, perhaps, several miles in diameter at its base, and some hundreds of feet in elevation, but it would still be the loftiest of Sicilian mountains, studded with other cones, which would be recalled as it were into existence by the removal of the rocks under which they are now buried. [p. 100]

At the same time the lateral cones showed that Etna had not, during the last 12,000 years, been subject to a devastating flood "for none of these heaps of loose sand and scoriae could have resisted for a moment the denuding action of a violent flood" (p. 101).

On Tuesday 12 June, with his final lecture, the course was over. "Stokes told me that at last he had no criticism & that he c.^{d} give

of Lyell and of Henry Brougham; Henry Thomas Petty-Fitzmaurice (1816–66), Lord Kerry, became 4th Marquis of Lansdowne on his father's death in 1863; we have not been able to identify W. Whitman; Charles Giles Bridle Daubeny, M.D. (1795–1867), professor of chemistry at Oxford.
51. C. L., Jr. to Mary. 8 June 1832. Kinnordy mss.

me no more hints, so now," he told Mary, "you see I have arrived at an unimproveable climax."[52] Lyell "rec'd from some of the class, whom I never saw, most enthusiastic letters expressive of their admiration & gratitude. This is worth much."[53] Though Lyell had enjoyed his lectures and realized that they had given him "an actor-like sort of celebrity" he regretted the time they had cost him. He received £86 from the subscribers' fees and made a donation of ten guineas from this to the building fund of King's College.

Early in May when he decided that he could not finish his third volume before he left for Bonn, his first volume had already been out of print several months and the second was selling rapidly. Consequently Lyell thought it would be wise to reprint these volumes in a number sufficient to keep them in print until after his third volume had emerged and he was able to prepare a second edition of the whole work. He wrote to Murray to this effect on 12 May and said that he would attempt only to correct "positive errors" in volumes one and two.[54] Thus during the last weeks of May and the beginning of June he was revising and correcting the first two volumes in addition to preparing and delivering his lectures. As a result, his responsibility for the lectures reduced the amount of time which he could devote to the revision of the reprinted edition and he felt that the latter suffered. His satisfaction at the success of his lectures was thus tempered by the knowledge that the reprint of his first two volumes would be less improved than it would have been without the lectures. Lyell, therefore, decided at the end of May that he would not lecture the following year and sent his decision to Principal Otter.[55] A day or two later, perhaps feeling a little guilty at leaving King's College in the lurch, he asked Dr. Fitton to give the lectures for him as his friend. Fitton at first agreed and Lyell was very pleased "as he enters so fully into the spirit of the 'modern cause' system."[56] When they discussed the matter further, however, and Fitton learned that Lyell intended to be in town during the time of the lectures he demurred, thinking it would be awkward to say in

52. C. L., Jr. to Mary. 12 June 1832. Kinnordy mss.
53. C. L., Jr. to G. A. M. 14 June 1832. Mantell mss.
54. C. L., Jr. to J. M. 12 May 1832. Murray mss.
55. C. L., Jr. to Mary. 1 June 1832. Kinnordy mss.
56. C. L., Jr. to C. B. 3 June 1832. Babbage mss. *L. & L.* I, 387–88.

effect that he was giving the lectures for Lyell simply because Lyell did not have time to give them himself.[57]

One of Lyell's preoccupations during June was to make sure that he had complied with all the legal formalities necessary for his impending marriage at Bonn. There was a question whether the banns should be published in England. None of the lawyers whom Lyell consulted thought this necessary, but the German authorities asked for an attested declaration by two barristers and a magistrate and by the home and foreign secretaries of state that publication of the banns was not required in England for a marriage in Germany.[58]

During his bachelor years Lyell had received from his father an annual allowance of £400 but as part of the marriage settlement Mr. Lyell increased this allowance to £500 per year. Lyell had saved the money he had earned by writing articles for the *Quarterly Review* and what he had received from the *Principles* and thus had several hundred pounds invested in the funds, that is, in British government securities. In addition Mary Horner received from her father under the marriage settlement £4,000 which would yield another £120 per year of income. Thus the young couple would have a secure income of about £650 per year on which to start their married life, entirely apart from what Lyell hoped to continue to earn by writing. At the end of May Mr. Lyell unexpectedly and generously sent Lyell another £200, the final installment of his bachelor's allowance. Lyell wrote to Mary:

> The rents have been well paid this last year which makes me the more glad of this generous donation though I doubt not it w.ᵈ have been made whether or no.[59]

On 14 June Lyell left London. He was saying farewell to his bachelor life—to Sunday morning breakfasts with Stokes, Broderip, and other friends, to evening talks over tea with Robert Brown, to impromptu dinners in his rooms or those of his friends, to which he might contribute the wine, if not the food. In his rooms in the Temple and in Gray's Inn he had written the *Principles* and had become a well known scientist and author. But he

57. C. L., Jr. to Mary. 5 June 1832. Kinnordy mss.

58. C. L., Jr. to Mary. 12 June 1832. Kinnordy mss. Cf. C. L., Jr. to G. A. M. 14 June 1832. Mantell mss. *L. & L.* I, 388.

59. C. L., Jr. to Mary. 29 May 1832. Kinnordy mss.

had often been lonely. He was keenly aware of the desolateness, the ultimate purposelessness of the solitary life and he deeply enjoyed the companionship of a family group. He was ready to marry.

On crossing from Dover to Calais the morning of the fifteenth, he found that he had to wait until ten o'clock that night for a coach and he therefore used the day to go

> ... on a geological expedition to the great sand dunes because I had observed when last at Calais that they were covered by wavy ridges or "the ripple mark" like the sea sands. I was lucky enough to be there when a high wind was blowing—the sea had left a large tract of wet sand on the retiring of the tide & clouds of drift sand were swept along by the wind from the dunes over the beach.—I saw the ripple mark formed;—effaced it & saw it re-formed & finally traced the whole process of formation. I conclude that the mode in which *water* causes the sand to be rippled is precisely similar & as sandstones of all ages are so marked & the cause has been great matter of dispute I was exceedingly gratified by this opportunity of catching nature at work.[60]

On 18 June he arrived at Bonn where he found Mary "looking pale & so much thinner than when I left her." The year of separation, the anxiety about her father's efforts to become treasurer of the Bank of Scotland, and the complicated legal arrangements for their marriage had not been easy to endure. Now that they were reunited, however, Mary and indeed the whole family became much more cheerful. This was as well because when Lyell took the documents, which he had so carefully collected in London, to the burgomaster he found that they would all have to be translated into German by "a sworn translator" and that none could be found nearer than Cologne, thirty miles away. Lyell, therefore, had to go to Cologne to have them translated. Even with the greatest goodwill, he must have been nearly exasperated with his future father-in-law because all of these difficulties could have been avoided if Mr. Horner had brought Mary either to London or to Edinburgh to be married. Lyell was also worried about the possible future need to prove the legal validity of his marriage in Britain in order to protect the claims of his heirs. Even after he had settled these difficulties there was a further delay. "Mary fancies

---

60. C. L., Jr. to his father. 22 June 1832. Kinnordy mss.

waiting till July 12, a week later than I had expected, because it is
the day I made her an offer. So I suppose it will be so."[61] He was
probably pleased at her wish despite the additional delay. The
day was fixed for the twelfth. Yet the time passed pleasantly. There
were parties and expeditions. "Mary and I," he wrote to his sister
Maria, "were allowed to walk for 3 hours or so in our old haunts
at Godesberg which is looking most delightful now & the scenery, both the home views & the distant, are scarcely equalled by
those of any single spot I know." He and Horner went on a day's
geological trip. There were preparations to make. On July 5 he
wrote:

> This morning at breakfast when I saw 2 huge boxes preparing
> for Mary's things for Dundee I exclaimed that *one* ought to go
> direct to London, on which she said that so much of the whole
> w^d be wanted at Kinnordy that it was not worth while to make
> 2 affairs of it. On this I remarked that if so she w^d always have
> such huge packages when visiting Kinnordy! A scene followed
> all the girls protesting it was necessary & my pointing out how
> Mrs. Murchison managed etc. Mary got warm enough for once,
> & after all they have found that they can't fill the boxes.[62]

Finally on the morning of 12 July they were married. The first
ceremony was a civil marriage before the Burgomaster of Bonn.

> Never was anything more presbyterian-like than that ceremony.
> The old boy was not a cut above the baillie of a small Scotch
> town & his clerks might have been Kirriemuirian clerks to a
> writer. These 3 worthies sat before a large ink-stained table on
> which was a large inkstand & numerous goose quills. . . . The
> Burgomeister read in German some articles of the law (code
> Nap.). I had to answer *"ja"* without knowing precisely to what
> except when he asked me if I wished to marry Fraulein H. &
> then documents were given me to sign—Ceremony lasted a $\frac{1}{4}$
> of an hour when we returned Mr. & Mrs. H., M. & I in the
> first carriage. . . . The church looked filled most genteelly.
> When we arrived at the altar I was requested to go into the pri-
> vate room of the Minister, Prof. Sack & give him the note from
> the Burgomeister of his having married us, a license. As I be-
> gan to get a leetle nervous at the Stadt-house, I heard Horner's

61. Ibid.
62. C. L., Jr. to his sister Maria. 5 July 1832. Kinnordy mss.

admonition to take care of the said permit with some apprehension lest I sh^d lose it in the next 10 minutes. When I was asked if I had it by someone in the church I felt for it with fear & trembling, but my pocket not having been picked, I gave it as required & Sack told me he must wait 5 minutes & I must return into the church. He, I suppose, was to read the permit in the interim. . . . Sack performed the service excellently in *English*— much like English service; the lady was asked if she "w^d obey & be subject in all reasonable things etc." which Frances says is better than in Engl^d because the lady is to decide *what* is reasonable. All at once I recollected that he must soon come to the putting on of the rings. As I did not like risking Mary's on my little finger (the only one I got it on to) I had taken the precaution of putting it with my seals & watch key on to my watch ring the day before. I thought immediately of Caroline's letter about the ring, & having to "ferret it out" etc. & wished her far eno' for her prognostification. Then I turned slightly round to see if I was supported by my 2 bridesmen who ought to have stood on the 3^d step behind me but the lazy loons (Mr. R. Barton & Mr. F. Windischmann) were not there, nor the bridesmaids behind Mary, so I c^d get no help. Then thinks I to myself, I have my back to them all, no one can see; Sack is raising up his eyes to heaven & the roof & Mary has hers on the ground why sh.^{d} I not coolly get my pen-knife out & get the one ring off the other ring. So I fumbled "in that common receptacle" that you talked of, got my pen-knife, opened it, & without looking down contrived to get the ring of the watch chain open. Then the Minister had arrived at the donning of the said badges & in my endeavour to slip off the ring the other closed again. I proceeded with the knife to open it when Sack exclaimed in a whisper "one is enough" & putting my hand to Mary who was ready with hers pronounced the prayer ex tempore & very good & the blessing. There was an awkwardish half minute's pause so I suppose the folk thought the rings fitted bad.[63]

Their wedding trip took them up the Rhine to Mainz and thence to Heidelberg (Map 13). At Frankfort Lyell spent a day with von Meyer, the geologist.[64] At Heidelberg they met the nat-

63. C. L., Jr. to his sister Caroline. 14 July 1832. Kinnordy mss.
64. Christian Friedrich Herrmann von Meyer (1801–69).

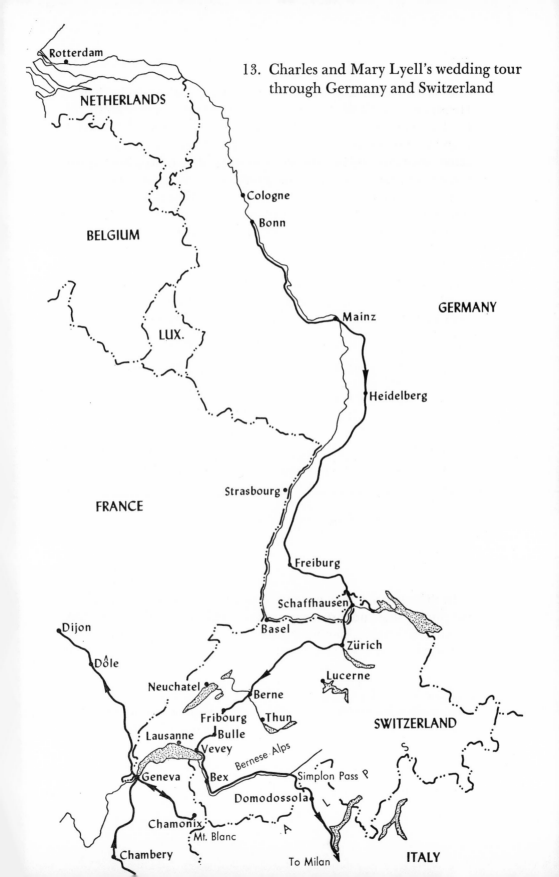

13. Charles and Mary Lyell's wedding tour through Germany and Switzerland

uralists Leonhard and Bronn[65] and examined their collections.[66] He also went on a field trip with Leonhard to examine the superficial deposit, peculiar to the Rhine valley, called loess. Lyell found that the loess contained many of both land shells and freshwater shells as fossils. He thought that this unstratified earth must have been deposited by a great flood occasioned by the sudden release of the waters of a great lake like the lake of Constance.[67] Lyell had frequently observed the geological effects of large scale floods and loess was a unique deposit, puzzling to account for.

They went on to Strasbourg and thence to Freiburg. In the intervals of their tour, whenever he had an empty afternoon or evening, Lyell continued to write his third volume; but for the most part they were traveling and sightseeing. Lyell described part of their journey:

> From Freiburg we have passed through what the Germans call the "Höllethal" or valley of hell, a defile in granitic mountains, but which is too beautifully covered with fir wood to deserve the name. We were obliged to have first 3 & then 4 horses put on in climbing to the higher regions of the Schwartzwald & are sleeping tonight in a village as high as the summit of Catlaw, but in a country which is very well clothed with wood & grass & corn. Mary is quite well & is now writing to her mama. When we are tired of talking about the scenery we form plans for future household economy & travelling schemes & talk of Bonn & she of her visit at Kinnordy which I think she contemplates with as much or more pleasure than any part of the tour itself.[68]

In their journey they were passing through a beautiful and varied countryside and a succession of old and interesting cities. The weather was fine. They were newly married and very happy. Of course, they had a few troubles. Lyell wrote:

65. Carl Cäsar von Leonhard (1779–1862) had been appointed professor of mineralogy and geognosy at Heidelberg in 1818; Heinrich Georg Bronn (1800–62) had been appointed professor of zoology and technology at Heidelberg in 1828 and in 1830 had become one of the editors of the *Jahrbuch für Mineralogie, Geognosie und Palaeontologie*.

66. Mary Lyell to Eleanor Lyell. 18 July 1832. Kinnordy mss.

67. *Principles* III, pp. 151–54. Cf. "Observations on the loamy deposit called 'loess' of the basin of the Rhine" (1834).

68. C. L., Jr. to his mother. 22 July 1832. Kinnordy mss.

I believe I stated that at Strasburg all the wheels of our *new* carriage required mending, 38 francs, & other symptoms of its being a gingerbread sort of a toy, altho' in the meantime a comfortable concern, had led me to apprehend greater mischief by this time. But no new damage yet, save and except that the doors fly open now & then of themselves & then won't shut again because the wheels get between them & the coach. By dint of slamming the s^d doors some of the paint has been worn off, with other improvements, not worth enumerating, but which of course will not enhance the price much when I sell it.[69]

At Schaffhausen they visited the falls which Lyell had seen during his first tour abroad in 1818. They visited the quarries at Oeningen and then went on to Zurich.[70] From Zurich they went to Berne where Lyell hoped to meet the Swiss geologist Bernhard Studer. In 1825 Studer had published a large monograph on the Molasse, a formation of soft green sandstone which extended across northern Switzerland at the base of the Alps.[71] In 1827 he had also published a description of the northern ranges of the Alps, particularly of the mountains in the vicinity of Bern, in which he showed that the stratified conglomerates and limestones of the Alps in places passed without any distinguishable boundary into vari-colored slaty rocks known as schists and sometimes into gneiss.[72] Studer said that the slaty or schistose rocks were known as the flysch in the Swiss countryside and he then gave that name to the whole formation. In some places the schists contained fossils and in other localities gneiss and micaceous schists, containing no fossils, lay above strata of obvious sedimentary origin containing well-preserved fossils. In a second paper Studer described in greater detail the fossil-bearing strata of the Stockhorn range and the coal-bearing strata of the Simmenthal, in the canton of Bern.[73] He had collected a number of fossils from this formation and sent them to Brongniart at Paris to be identified. When Brongniart studied the fossils he found that whereas a number of the fossils could not be identified precisely, there was no doubt that they belonged to the late Jurassic or early Cretaceous period, that is, the beds were high in the series of secondary for-

69. C. L., Jr. and M. E. L. to his sister Frances. 28 July 1832. Kinnordy mss.
70. C. L., Jr. to his mother. 22 July 1832. Kinnordy mss.
71. B. Studer, *Beyträge zu einer Monographie der Molasse.* . . . (1825).
72. B. Studer, "Remarques géognostiques . . . Alpes" (1827).
73. B. Studer, "Notice géognostique . . . Berne" (1827).

mations.[74] In his first paper of 1827 Studer had observed that on the basis of their mineralogical characteristics the Alps had been considered a transition formation, that is, they were thought to date from before the beginning of the secondary period.

> But [he wrote] grave doubts arise against this [view] when one consults the fossils, doubts which, if they be confirmed, would result in leading to quite different ideas of the antiquity of this formation.[75]

This remark suggests the profound effect which the detailed studies of fossils was having on all determinations of the age of formations. But the significant merit of Studer's work was that he demonstrated that the gneiss, schists, and conglomerates of the flysch constituted a single formation and that the gneiss and schists were not necessarily very old rocks, but simply strata which had been altered by heat and pressure.

When they reached Bern Lyell found that Studer was away in the mountains at Gurnigel. On further inquiry, however, he located Studer's brother, a pharmacist, who urged Lyell to make a side journey next day to Gurnigel.[76] At Gurnigel, a small watering place on a mountain side, they finally found Studer who was:

> . . . a good honest, intelligent Swiss, not quite read up to Sat^y night, but not so far behind as to be ignorant of a certain work which made him receive me well & express himself gratified with my visit. He took me to 2 ravines where I saw a considerable section of the flanks of the Alps, very like the Pyrenees.

Studer encouraged them to take the Fribourg road to Vevey instead of the one by Moret in order to see a geological section near Chatel St. Denis. They were told it would take them about two hours, but, Mary wrote:

> . . . we did not return till twice that time had elapsed, while we were making our way along the bed of the river (the Vévayre), jumping from stone to stone in a most beautiful ravine and afterwards scrambling up a very steep bank. The worst was that Charles had not nearly time enough to see all he wished, but he still saw a great deal that was interesting to him. On getting up a height we had the first view of the blue lake of Geneva.[77]

74. A. Brongniart, "Notes sur les coquilles fossiles . . ." (1827).
75. Studer, "Remarques géognostiques . . . Alpes" (1827), p. 9.
76. M. E. L. to her sister Katherine. 30 July 1832. Kinnordy mss.
77. C. L., Jr. and M. E. L. to his sister Frances. 28 July 1832. Kinnordy mss.

Lyell later commented of this excursion that "Mary saw at least how a geologist becomes acquainted with the anatomy of a country."[78]

From Vevey they went over the Simplon pass following the route of 1818, to Domo d'Ossola. The road was very quiet. "War, cholera & other fears seem to have put an end to travelling." At Bex Lyell stopped to see Jean de Charpentier (1786–1855), "now superintendent of the salt mines there," who was known to Lyell as "the geologist of the Pyrenees" because of a work which he had published on these mountains in 1823.[79] Charpentier, however, was to become famous for his studies of glaciers begun shortly after he became superintendent of the salt mines at Bex. He startled Lyell with some of the new ideas he was developing:

> You remember [he told Lyell] that I, among others, was once for a *grand debâcle* which transported all the travelled blocks etc. to great distances, those of the Alps to the Jura among others,—but in regard to the latter I have been much struck with the force of numerous objections. There is so much *order* in their distribution, [they are] not scattered at random, but at certain heights in Alps and Jura & in certain lines. Now many observers, & I among others, have found that the rocks along the levels where the great blocks lie are worn smooth, just as the manner in which glaciers, descending with blocks upon them, wear the rocks. *Above* the lines of these rolled blocks the rocks are never so worn. If, therefore, it were only granted that the Alps were once *higher* than they now are the rolled & angular huge blocks may have travelled on ancient glaciers.

Lyell commented on this hypothesis, ". . . you see they are beginning as usual, *in the last resort,* to seek a natural explanation."[80]

On 7 August they were at Milan and after a few days there, during which they visited museums and art galleries and did sightseeing, they returned to Switzerland via Turin and the Mont Cenis pass. When they reached Geneva on 15 August Lyell sought out the Genevan naturalist and geologist Louis Albert Necker de Saussure (1786–1861). Bernhard Studer's interpretation of the mica schists and gneiss of the flysch as sedimentary strata altered by heat and pressure had been influenced by Necker's observa-

78. C. L., Jr. to his father. 5 August 1832. Kinnordy mss.
79. Ibid.
80. Quoted by Lyell in M. E. L. and C. L., Jr. to her father. 5 Aug. 1832. Kinnordy mss.

tions on the valley of Valorsine where he had described granite veins extending into what appeared to have been formerly fossil-bearing sedimentary beds, but which were now beds of schist, resembling ancient primary rocks.[81] Accordingly Lyell was anxious to visit Valorsine and wished to get advice and directions from Necker.[82]

Mary Lyell was acquainted with younger members of the family of Professor Pierre Prevost,[83] then an old man of eighty-one, and the Prevosts entertained them very hospitably at Geneva.

On 20 August the Lyells went to Chamonix so that Lyell might visit Valorsine. That evening in the inn at Chamonix he met Edmund Head, a fellow of Merton College, Oxford.[84] Head had attended Buckland's geological lectures at Oxford and had studied mineralogy at the Freiburg school of mines where Werner had taught until his death in 1819. He had also traveled with Charles Babbage to Italy where he made the notes on the Temple of Serapis which Lyell had used in preparing one of his lectures at King's College in May. Head agreed to accompany Lyell to Valorsine and they set off next morning, 21 August at five o'clock. Lyell described their expedition to Leonard Horner:

My object was to verify Necker's observations on the granite veins & their effects in the Valorsine. Masses of granite are seen at the bottom sending out veins into gneiss, chlorite & talcose schist & those talcose members of the gneiss which they call protogine. At Les Rupes the veins ramify in a beautiful manner & the granite often turns into porphyry showing the relation of those rocks. As you [pass] up from the granite you find the rocks get more and more [word removed by tear in paper] till at last you get a conglomerate, with decided strata of well characterized mica schist alternating, the conglomerate containing primary pebbles, but none at all of *granite*. Above this is a regular black roofing slate, bluish black with impressions of ferns, turned into anthracite & often talc!! Above again limestone with ammonites, said to be lias limestone, not much altered. I believe the whole series, gneiss & all, to be altered secondary

81. L. A. Necker, "Sur les filons . . . de Valorsine" (1826). Cf. B. Studer, "Remarques géognostiques . . . Alpes" (1827) p. 33.

82. M. E. L. to her mother. 21 Aug. 1832. Kinnordy mss.

83. Pierre Prevost (1751–1839) professor of philosophy and physics in the university of Geneva.

84. Later Sir Edmund Walker Head (1805–68). He was a fellow of Merton College 1830–37 and was later governor-general of Canada 1854–61.

sandstone & conglomerate, of age perhaps of lias. So much for *primary* rocks [Fig. 47].

Lyell and Head were away more than sixteen hours the day they went to Valorsine but Lyell felt that what he had accomplished that day "about equalled all that I have done in the rest of the tour."[85] On his return to Geneva he talked over the phenomena of Valorsine again with Necker. It was from his observations at Valorsine together with other similar observations that Lyell created the concept of the class of metamorphic rocks, that is, of rock strata, originally sedimentary, which have been altered by heat so as to have an entirely different and often crystalline form. The realization that many non fossil-bearing crystalline rocks to be found in mountains were metamorphic removed finally the very foundations of the Wernerian theory. The mineralogical characteristics of rocks and the absence of fossils in them could no longer be taken to imply their great age.

At Geneva Lyell sold their carriage and they went by diligence to Dijon where they spent a few days "at a beautiful country house of Major Power's," who was married to an aunt of Mary.[86] They then proceeded to Paris where Lyell saw Constant Prevost, Gerard Deshayes, and other French naturalists. Deshayes identified the loess fossils for him. At Paris Lyell also met for the first time Louis Agassiz (1807–73), the Swiss zoologist and palaeontologist, of whose work on fossil fishes he had heard at Heidelberg from Hermann von Meyer. Agassiz had arrived at Paris from Neuchâtel in December 1831 ostensibly to study the cholera epidemic which was raging there, but actually to study the collections of fossil fishes in the museum of natural history. In February 1832, Cuvier, impressed with his knowledge and ability, had turned over to Agassiz the materials which he had already collected on fossil fishes.[87] Cuvier's death in May had altered the state of affairs at Paris, but Agassiz was determined to return to Neuchâtel and continue his studies of fossil fish. He was young and very ambitious. Lyell wrote of him to Mantell:

Agassiz, being naturally desirous of the advertizement which my 3.^{d} vol. w^d give to his intended labours on fossil fish which are now far advanced, & being moreover a young man, about 25 only, of great liberality in communicating information, has

85. C. L., Jr. to L. Horner. 25 Aug. 1832. Kinnordy mss.
86. Ibid.
87. E. Lurie, *Louis Agassiz* (1960) pp. 54–57.

offered to answer any queries I may send him while I write vol.
3 or rather print the remainder of it.

Lyell was not one to miss such an opportunity to gain valuable
information and he sent Mantell a list of the questions he had put
to Agassiz at Paris and Agassiz's answers. The most important
question dealt with the great change which had occurred in fossil
life at the end of the secondary period, (Mezozoic) and the beginning of the Tertiary (Cenozoic). Agassiz had already examined
some five hundred species of fossil fishes all but one of which he
considered to be extinct. Lyell asked, "Are any secondary species
identical with tertiary? and Agassiz replied, "Not one. All the
secondary *genera* are *extinct* without exception. Many of the tertiary genera are living ones." This confirmed for fishes what Lyell
already knew from his study of fossil shells; namely that there had
been a great change in species and genera which seemed to coin-
cide with the great changes in the distribution of land and sea
which accompanied the uplift of the Alps, the Pyrenees, and the
Apennines. Lyell added, "He said that the so-called diodon teeth
of chalk are not so but one of the great family *Squalus*, that the so-
called balistes is '*le rayon d'un squale*' & other things new to me."[88]

On 10 September the Lyells were back in London. They came
from Canterbury by stagecoach and arrived at the Bell and Crown,
Holborn.

We left our luggage there [Mary wrote] and walked up to Raymond Buildings [in Gray's Inn] where we were glad to find the
chambers ready to receive us. Hall says he never knew Charles
look so well in his life. He was rather vexed with his wife for
being confined the day before we arrived but her mother is with
her and she assisted us. She has begged me to see her daughter
so I am going to visit her in the sunk story today. We seem
quite established here. Charles is now dictating to Hall, and we
seem quite in comfort although I do not admire the magnificence of the furniture as much as Charles expected. Mr. Broderip paid us a short visit the first evening, and Mr. Murchison,
who is in town for a day, called last night, and Mr. James Hall at
breakfast this morning. So with all our efforts we cannot remain
incog[nito].[89]

88. C. L., Jr. to G. A. M. 10 Sept. 1832. Mantell mss.
89. M. E. L. to her mother. 10 Sept. 1832. Kinnordy mss.

Lyell found on his return that the second edition of volume one of the *Principles* was printed and to be published within a few days. This second edition was enlarged 80 pages by "opening the type," that is, increasing the spaces between the lines so as to make it more easily read and uniform with the second volume.

While they were in London they also engaged in househunting and after some search chose No. 16 Hart Street, a street now changed, but which then led out of Bloomsbury Square, a small square with tall handsome trees very close to the British Museum. The house, Lyell wrote, was:

> ... on the opposite side to the church & about half way between it & square, rent 89£, taxes included 129£. £300 lately laid out on it by the Proprietor, new paper etc., so we can get into it without almost any expense.[90]

He described it to Murchison as "in a nice airy situation, rather a larger house than was absolutely necessary" and "as near to Somerset House & Athenaeum . . . as health & gentility of situation & my purse would permit."[91] The house was probably a smaller brick town house of three or four stories. Its size is suggested by that of the drawing room which Lyell noted was 19 feet by 16 feet and the dining room 17 feet 3 inches by 12 feet 7 inches.[92] He planned to bring the furniture he had had in his rooms at Raymond Buildings and to use some of Leonard Horner's furniture which was stored in a warehouse in London. His clerk George Hall was to serve as major-domo and Mrs. Hall as cook. He hoped to bring in addition a boy from Scotland to help, since much of Hall's time was taken up in writing from dictation for Lyell, correcting proof, preparing the index of the *Principles,* and other such tasks.

On 15 September the Lyells left for Scotland. They took a steamboat from London to Dundee where they landed on the morning of the eighteenth. It was Mary's first visit to Kinnordy and first introduction to Lyell's family. She described the last part of their journey to her father:

> I had been quite well the whole night though it was rather rough, but we were much delighted to get breakfast in a comfortable parlour in the inn at Dundee. We found there a letter

90. C. L., Jr. to L. Horner. 18 Sept. 1832. Kinnordy mss.
91. C. L., Jr. to R. I. M. 29 Sept. 1832. Murchison mss.
92. Notebook 47, p. 62. Kinnordy mss.

from Mr. Lyell begging us to come on in a chaise directly and
to avoid Glammis where the cholera has broken out. We did so
immediately after breakfast and at Forfar found the carriage. I
felt a little nervous as we approached and when we reached the
first gate at Kinnordy there were a number of labourers who
began cheering and they took the horses out of the carriage and
drew it up to the door. There we found waiting Mr. & Mrs. Lyell, our seven sisters and Aunt Mary. I directly guessed Fanny,
Marianne & Eleanor; the others were all told me . . . last night
there was a flag put up on the tower, the people having bor-
rowed one of the Kirriemuir reform flags for the purpose much
to Mr. Lyell's amusement.[93]

A few days later Charles and Mary were remarried privately at
Kinnordy by Dr. Easton, the minister of Kirriemuir. Lyell was
evidently still concerned about the legal validity of his marriage at
Bonn. Only Mr. Lyell and George Hall were present as witnesses.
Mary described it:

The whole ceremony was this. Dr. E., "I presume, Sir, this is
your married wife?" C., "Yes." Dr. E., "I presume, Ma'am, this
is your married husband?" M., "Yes." Dr. E., "Whom God hath
joined, let no man put asunder." He then shook hands with us
both. So now I think we are fairly married. He is to give Charles
a document to keep for his own satisfaction.[94]

Lyell had brought proof sheets of the second edition with him
from London so he spent the mornings at work correcting proof
with his clerk Hall, who had accompanied them. Mary unpacked
her wedding presents sent from Bonn and went riding on a gentle
pony with the Lyell sisters. They spent part of each day out of
doors, the weather being good and the country beautiful.

In mid-November they returned to London and were immediately busy with furnishing their new house. As soon as they were
settled at 16 Hart Street Lyell again began work on his long-de-
layed third volume which would complete the *Principles*. The second edition of volume two was now going through the press, but
its printing was completed early in December. On 27 December
Lyell wrote to John Murray that he was now ready to go to press
with the remainder of his third volume, of which 112 pages had

93. M. E. L. to her father. 18 Sept. 1832. Kinnordy mss.
94. M. E. L. to her sister Katherine. [21] Sept. 1832. Kinnordy mss.

already been printed during the preceding spring.[95] On the last
day of the year he received from Murray a check and note for a
total of £210 which was his payment for the second edition of
the first two volumes.[96]

On Christmas day the Lyells went to church in the morning and
in the afternoon to Hampstead to have dinner with the Mallets.

> We arrived there about three [Mary wrote to her mother] &
> while Mr. Mallet & the boys went to church, Mrs. Mallet,
> Charles & I took a walk on the Heath. It was a beautiful, mild,
> clear day very unlike the time of year. Nobody dined there ex-
> cept Herman Merivale[97] . . . we had our usual agreeable quiet
> day.

At 16 Hart Street they had a party for Hall and his mother, wife,
and three children in the kitchen where they had "roast beef & suet
pudding with raisins & cake with currants." Charles and Mary
spent their happiest evenings alone when Mary read one of Harriet Martineau's tales aloud "while the coffee is dropping through
& again after tea." They had frequent invitations to dinners and
parties and Lyell always had the meetings and affairs of scientific
societies to demand his attention. He worked unremittingly and
Mary may sometimes have been a little lonely. She mentioned to
her mother:

> I generally write an hour or two for Charles on Sundays as Hall
> has a holiday, and after finishing a beautiful & useful tale of
> Miss Martineau's we arranged a little some of the shells in his
> cabinet. It is in the drawing room which I like so much as it
> makes us more together.[98]

On 8 January 1833 they gave their first dinner party with Stokes,
Broderip, and Charles Babbage as their guests.

The winter months of 1833 were largely taken up with seeing
volume three through the press. On 8 March Lyell wrote to Murray that he was sending the twenty-fourth chapter to the printer

95. C. L., Jr. to J. M. 27 Dec. 1832. Murray mss.
96. J. M. to C. L., Jr. 31 Dec. 1832. Kinnordy mss.
97. Herman Merivale (1806–74) succeeded Sir James Stephen as permanent
undersecretary of state at the Colonial Office and in 1859 became permanent undersecretary of state for India. Formerly a student at Oriel College, Oxford, in 1832
Merivale was called to the bar at the Inner Temple and had just begun practice on
the western circuit, so he and Lyell had much in common.
98. M. E. L. to her mother. 26 Dec. 1832. Kinnordy mss.

and that the twenty-sixth would be the last. Since he was in sight of the end he asked Murray to state his terms for publication of the volume.[99] Within three days Murray replied with an offer of £370 for the right to publish the first edition of the third volume.[100] The generosity of this offer suggests that Murray's faith in the continued sale of the *Principles* remained strong. At the beginning of January Lyell had also received an invitation from the Royal Institution to give a course of six or eight public lectures, which would be open to ladies, after Easter.[101] He accepted and also decided to give another course of lectures at King's College, since he could find no one else to assume this responsibility. "Every hour," he wrote Mantell, "is occupied with my last difficult chapter & 2 courses of lectures, to be begun both of them next month."[102]

At the end of April 1833, despite the interruptions brought about by an epidemic of influenza which brought down Lyell himself, the third volume of the *Principles* was published. Its publication brought to an end Lyell's long work of writing and correcting for the press on which he had now been engaged for four years. It also left him free during May to devote his attention to his lectures. He had a large audience of some 250 ladies and gentlemen at the Royal Institution, but because ladies were excluded from all but his introductory lecture at King's College his class there was reduced to fifteen.[103] This small number determined him to give no further course. The following October he resigned his professorship.[104]

THE PRINCIPLES OF GEOLOGY, III

The third and final volume of the *Principles of Geology* was in a sense the first which dealt with geology proper, or what would have been recognized as geology before Lyell began writing. In it Lyell surveyed the whole series of geological formations beginning with the most recent and proceeding back through the succession of Tertiary formations, which had been revealed in part by the work of Desnoyers, but which Lyell himself now developed far

99. C. L., Jr. to J. M. 8 March 1833. Murray mss.
100. J. M. to C. L., Jr. 11 March 1833. Kinnordy mss.
101. C. L., Jr. to C. Babbage. 5 Jan. 1833. Babbage mss. *L. & L.* I, 395.
102. C. L., Jr. to G. A. M. 11 March 1833. Mantell mss.
103. C. L., Jr. to J. Fleming. 1 May 1833. *L. & L.* I, 396–97.
104. F. J. C. Hearnshaw, *The centenary history of King's College London* (1929) pp. 108–09.

more fully and completely. He showed how each of the newer and older Pliocene, Miocene and Eocene formations might be identified by their characteristic proportion of living to extinct species of fossil shells. Much of the geology of Tertiary formations which Lyell gave in this volume represented the results of his long tour through France and Italy in 1828. Because after his introductory chapters his discussion began with the youngest formations, the newer Pliocene of Sicily, he presented the results of this great tour in an order almost exactly the reverse of that in which he had made his observations. Thus he passed from the newer Pliocene of Sicily to the older Pliocene of the subapennine formations and the freshwater deposits near Siena and in Tuscany, to the Miocene of the valley of the Bormida and the hill of Superga near Turin, ending his discussion of Tertiary strata finally with the Eocene freshwater and volcanic formations of Auvergne which he correlated in age with the Eocene marine formations of Aix-en-Provence and of the Paris, Hampshire, and London basins.

The fact that the Tertiary strata in various places were not all contemporary had begun to be suspected well before Lyell began to write the *Principles* and was demonstrated definitely for the strata of the Paris and Loire basins by Desnoyers in 1829.[105] But Lyell here set forth for the first time the whole grand succession of Tertiary strata, gave a method for determining their relative ages, a precise and pithy terminology with which to discuss them, and marine, freshwater, and volcanic representatives of each with which to make specific comparisons. He indicated not only the geological age, but something of the geographical extent of each formation. The third volume of the *Principles* introduced a whole new series of epochs to geology. It provided a bridge to connect the very ancient secondary strata to the present and at the same time offered a language and a technique to equip the student for further study. Before 1833 there was no such thing as Tertiary geology; after that year it was a well-defined and rapidly developing field of study.

In this third volume Lyell also gave in very summary form a discussion of the series of secondary strata. He was less interested in the details of their succession than in the principles to be used in correlating them, and in the problems raised by the transition from the end of the secondary to the beginning of the Tertiary

105. J. Desnoyers, "Observations sur un ensemble de dépôts marins . . ." (1829).

period. Deshayes' study of fossil shells had shown that there was no species of shell common to the chalk, the youngest of the secondary formations, and the Eocene, the oldest of the Tertiary. Furthermore, Agassiz's study of fossil fishes had shown not only that no species but that *no genera* of fishes bridged this gap.

At the same time, the elevation of the chalk, which had occurred at the end of the secondary period, raised many questions about the origin of land forms. If the chalk had originally extended in a continuous sheet from the South Downs to the North Downs over the anticlinal ridge, which is the Weald, in southeast England, then the amount of rock and soil which must have been removed by "denudation" was so immense as to stagger the imagination. It was too great, Lyell thought, to be accounted for by the action of rain and running water. Therefore, he suggested that much of this chalk had been washed away by the action of waves operating against a line of sea coast. He looked back to a time when, he imagined, the Weald was a great inlet of the sea bounded north and south by chalk cliffs now represented by the North and South Downs. In this interpretation he was mistaken, but one reason he doubted that the chalk had been removed by ordinary subaerial erosion was that there was little trace of chalk debris in the alluvium of the Weald (pp. 285–98).

In his twenty-fourth chapter Lyell discussed the relative ages of various mountain chains. He summarized the chief points in Élie de Beaumont's theory of the elevation of mountain chains and noted that most of Beaumont's propositions were "directly opposed to that theory which we have endeavoured to deduce" (p. 339). He concluded that Élie de Beaumont's theory for the cause of elevation was "mysterious in the extreme, and not founded upon any induction from facts" (p. 339). For an explanation of the same phenomena in terms of the gradual action of existing causes, Lyell referred to his earlier volumes. He also mentioned that he had dealt with the abrupt transitions from one set of strata to another in the third and fourth chapters of his present volume.

Lyell then took up the particular case of the elevation of the Pyrenees, which Élie de Beaumont had asserted had arisen suddenly (*à un seul jet*) between the formation of the chalk and the Tertiary strata. Élie de Beaumont's interpretation was based on the fact that the chalk formations were found in vertical, bent, and tilted beds along the sides of the Pyrenees, while at the base of the range these beds were overlain by horizontal Tertiary strata.

Élie de Beaumont, therefore, argued that the elevation of the Pyrenees "has been produced in a space of time comprised between the periods of deposition of the two consecutive rocks, and during which no regular series of beds was formed; in a word, that it was sudden and of short duration."[106] Lyell's criticism of this argument was that in fact a long interval of time had intervened between the deposition of the two sets of beds. He was prepared to waive any objection based on the fact that the series of chalk strata was deposited over a long period of time and that the chalk strata of the Pyrenees were by no means the uppermost of the series, and did not represent the end of the chalk epoch. He could afford to leave this point aside because the horizontal Tertiary strata at the foot of the Pyrenees were in fact of Miocene age; the long period of the Eocene, at the very least, had been interposed between the elevation of the tilted and vertical strata along the sides of the Pyrenees and the deposition of the horizontal strata at their base (p. 343). The fact that this difficulty had been quite unknown to Élie de Beaumont is a measure of the magnitude of Lyell's achievement in revealing the succession of Tertiary formations.

Élie de Beaumont's assertion that mountain chains elevated at the same time are parallel—the most extravagant and fanciful part of his theory—was the easiest for Lyell to refute. He had merely to cite the criticisms which had already been made independently by W. D. Conybeare and Aimé Boué (pp. 348–49). Élie de Beaumont's theory was left in tatters.

In his final chapter Lyell reviewed many instances of the alteration of sedimentary strata where they had been invaded by dikes of granite or of trap rock. He discussed also the puzzling rocks called gneiss and mica-schist which had a crystalline structure similar to that of granite and a stratified arrangement like that of sedimentary rocks. In some instances there was a transition from gneiss to granite. Lyell thought all of these facts could only be accounted for satisfactorily by the "Huttonian hypothesis" according to which "the materials of gneiss were originally deposited from water in the usual form of aqueous strata, but these strata were subsequently altered by their proximity to granite, and to other plutonic masses in a state of fusion, until they assumed a granitiform texture" (p. 367).

106. L. Élie de Beaumont, "Researches on some of the Revolutions . . ." (1831) p. 243. Quoted in *Principles* III, p. 342.

Lyell then coined a new term "hypogene" to describe both granite and such altered strata, meaning to indicate that they had both been formed in the depths of the earth under great pressure. To the altered strata, such as gneiss and mica-schist, he gave the name "metamorphic" rocks to suggest their changed state (p. 375). The introduction of these new terms transformed the whole conception of these rocks which had previously been called "primary" rocks, a name intended to indicate that they represented the oldest of the strata. Actually, Lyell showed, gneiss and mica-schist could be of any age, and many of those formations which had previously been called primary were actually secondary or even Tertiary. This conclusion, similar in general to that of Hutton and Playfair, had the same consequence, namely, that one could no longer assume that the so-called primary strata really represented the first stages in the earth's history. On the contrary, the earth's history as represented in the succession of sedimentary strata stretched backward indefinitely. There was, as Hutton had said, "no vestige of a beginning."[107] Lyell concluded by affirming that just as the ultimate boundaries of the universe were as yet undiscovered by astronomers and were in fact undiscoverable, so "in *time* also, the confines of the universe lie beyond the reach of mortal ken" (p. 384).

At the end of his third volume Lyell added two tables, one "showing the relations of the alluvial, aqueous, volcanic, and hypogene formations of different ages" (p. 386), and a second giving the order of superposition of the European strata. He also gave in an appendix the tables of Tertiary fossil shells which had been compiled by Deshayes and a dicussion of the results to be deduced from them. These tables, Lyell explained, were not intended to list the characteristic shells of each formation but rather "the shells *common* to two or more periods, or common to some tertiary period and to the *recent* epoch" (p. 395). They were thus ideally suited to bring out the continuity of life throughout the Tertiary period, and into modern times, and to show that species had become extinct *gradually* and had been replaced *gradually* by new species. At the end of the tables Lyell gave a discussion of the conclusions to be drawn from them. In a second appendix Lyell listed the fossil shell species which he himself had collected from the Tertiary formations of Sicily, Ischia, and

107. J. Hutton, "Theory of the Earth . . ." (1785) p. 304.

Italy. He also added a glossary of technical terms used in the *Principles*. This was intended to make "the work much more accessible to general readers" (appendices, p. 61). His friends had suggested that it would be useful and he had enlisted their help, particularly that of Mrs. Somerville's daughters, Mary and Martha, in compiling lists of words which needed explaining to the uninitiated. The definitions in this glossary are very simple and clear. Today they are historically valuable because they convey the precise meaning of various terms as they were used in Lyell's day.

The three volumes of the *Principles* now stood together, a massisive and complete work. During much of the remainder of his life Lyell would be revising, enlarging, and reorganizing this book in successive editions, but now, for the first time in four years, he was free of the labor of writing it, and could look about him for a little while to see what he should do next.

CHAPTER 12

The Mature Geologist, 1833–1836

IN JUNE 1833, his lectures finished, Lyell set out for the continent. "We left Hart St. in a hackney coach," Mary wrote, "with Hall & the luggage in another about ten o'clock, got on board the steamer at the Tower stairs—a beautiful evening. Charles & I stood on deck until I became sleepy."[1] It was in a sense a new adventure for them. They intended to make such trips annually, incorporating in them both visits to geological museums and collections and geological field trips. It was part of a plan of life for the next several years which was to combine writing during the winter months with geological field work during the summer.

They stopped for a day at Beauvais, on the road to Paris, to see M. Graves, secretary of the prefecture there, a gentleman who had sent Lyell a large number of fossil shells. During this brief stopover Lyell went with Graves to examine the geology of the valley of Bray, "that pretty little counterpart of our Weald valley."[2] Graves had collected many fossils from the beds underlying the chalk in the valley of Bray and many of these corresponded in age to the fossils which Mantell had collected from the Tilgate forest bed in Sussex.[3] When they went on to Paris they had the coupé of the diligence to themselves. The day was much cooler and, Mary wrote, "Charles walked up the hills & gathered wild roses."[4]

At Paris Lyell went immediately to see Constant Prevost and then he and Mary together spent several days taking lessons in fossil conchology from Deshayes. Both Deshayes and Prevost complimented Lyell on the third volume of the *Principles* which they had received shortly before. The Somervilles were also at Paris and the Lyells visited them. Lyell also met many of the Parisian scientists. "He & Élie de Beaumont are bosom friends," Mary wrote, "although the other party expected they would not be on

1. M. E. L. to Frances and Eleanor Lyell. 13 June 1833. Kinnordy mss.
2. C. L., Jr. to R. I. M. 20 June 1833. Murchison mss.
3. C. L., Jr. to G. A. M. 25 July 1833. Mantell mss.
4. M. E. L. to Frances and Eleanor Lyell. 13 June 1833. Kinnordy mss.

speaking terms. É. de Beaumont has even determined to accompany us to Epernay that he may act as Charles's guide."[5]

Mary must often have been lonely during their stay at Paris for she usually remained at their hotel while Lyell went to see various scientific men. She went shopping and called on Mrs. Somerville, but also spent many hours reading. She found that she was, in one sense, freer than in London, for she found that French ladies were accustomed to go about on their own without an escort, and could do so without fear of being insulted. However, she preferred when possible to go with Lyell and they went one morning together to the quarries of Montmartre where Cuvier had obtained so many remarkable fossils.

Lyell himself had an opportunity while at Paris to estimate the strength of the French opposition to his ideas. He found that Élie de Beaumont, although giving ground on particular points where he had been proved wrong, still stubbornly upheld his own catastrophic ideas. Lyell described the situation to Murchison:

> The object of de B. is to shift the question. The original Elevation craters having failed they want to back out by confounding with that theory all the elevations that have taken place, linear or others. He, de B., is celebrated here for never admitting candidly that he was ever wrong in anything. He makes concessions, but always declaring that they do not affect the results & conclusions which he had given out.

Lyell had gone to call on his antagonist:

> I went to *École des Mines*—was received with great, I had almost said, studied courtesy & De B., besides useful hints, offered to accompany me on my tour to Epernay. I at once accepted & he then wrote to invite Alex. Brongniart, B. Geslin & others to join. All this was like a man of sense, but as a strong party at the G. S. here look on De B. as an ambitious diplomatic character, & as they say he is very sore against me, they only make a joke of it & when after [a] meeting at G. S. he wondered that my work had not been translated & said to Deshayes that altho' he differed from me, it ought to be, they could not suppress a smile.[6]

Their trip to Epernay was on their way to Bonn, so at Epernay

5. M. E. L. to Marianne Lyell. 17 June 1833. Kinnordy mss.
6. C. L., Jr. to R. I. M. 20 June 1833. Murchison mss.

the Lyells said farewell to the French geologists and proceeded on alone. At Bonn they met many old friends and remained there until 25 July when they set off for a geological tour of the country around Mainz.[7] Along the left bank of the Rhine, between Mainz and Mannheim, Lyell found a tract of Tertiary strata which he identified as being of Miocene age. In some places it seemed to be a freshwater formation, in others a marine formation. He decided these sediments had been laid down "in a gulf or sea, which, like the Baltic, was brackish in some parts and almost fresh in others."[8]

At Heidelberg Lyell attended one of von Leonhard's classes in mineralogy which he described to his father:

> When he [von Leonhard] has given a general history of a partic-
> ular mineral he describes a certain number of specimens to 4
> or 5 of the more advanced of his class who have already fol-
> lowed one or two courses. He then passes to one end of the room
> & a small group close round him, each seeing the specimen well.
> He goes on "*Epidote,* this pale green is epidote, the white is
> quartz etc." The others go round the room with their specimens
> at [the] same time so that the whole class is for some time broken
> up into a number of private lecture pupils, till the exhibition or
> "demonstration" is over, when the whole are again intent on the
> general views of the Professor who holds forth in a pleasant,
> easy, extempore strain. The most curious part of the demonstra-
> tion was, & which made me even for the moment doubt whether
> it would do in England, that as the Prof[r] & monitors went
> round each repeating again & again in a low, grave deep tone
> the same or nearly the same set of words & then giving to a pupil
> a specimen from a small tray, it appeared exactly like several
> clergymen communicating the sacrament. I am sure every Eng-
> lishman would have been struck with the resemblance.

During his German tour Lyell wished to see fossil collections wherever possible. From Heidelberg they went to Heilbronn and then to Stuttgart where Lyell had a hasty look at the collections of two geologists, Hahl and Jaeger.[9] At Goppingen they saw a magnificent collection of fossils belonging to a physician, Dr. Hartmann.

At Bayreuth they met Count Munster who possessed one of the

7. C. L., Jr. to G. A. M. 25 July 1833. Mantell mss.
8. *Principles,* 3rd ed., vol. IV, p. 80.
9. C. L., Jr. to his father. 8 Aug. 1833. Kinnordy mss. *L. & L.* I, 400–01.

finest collections of fossils in Germany. Thence the Lyells returned via Frankfurt to Bonn and after a short stay there, returned to England through Belgium stopping only at Liège to see the bones collected from caves by Dr. Schmerling.[10] On 16 September they were back in London.

Lyell immediately began to arrange with Murray for the new third edition of the *Principles,* which would be the first complete edition of the work. They made the format for the *Principles* smaller and cheaper and increased the number of volumes from three to four. The reduction in size meant that a number of the plates, which had occupied a full page in the first and second editions, had to be folded in the new edition. They increased the amount of leading between the lines of type so that the text would be easier to read.[11] The price for the four volume set was to be reduced to 24 shillings, "which," Murray said, "will be a very cheap book."[12]

During the next few months Lyell revised the *Principles* for the new edition, making many corrections and incorporating much new material. In December 1833 he became particularly interested in the question of whether the land of Sweden was actually rising or not. A century earlier the Swedish natural philosopher, Celsius, had noted that the fishermen and sailors along the shore of the Gulf of Bothnia believed that the land was very slowly rising in that area and could give as evidence such facts as that rocks, formerly submerged, now stood above the water, and channels formerly navigable had become too shallow to allow boats to pass through. Marks which Celsius had placed in certain rocks at sea level, stood, after a number of years, several inches above the water level.

Lyell was not inclined to believe that the land could have risen in Sweden, because there had been no earthquakes there or any other disturbances. However, if it were true, it was an exceedingly important instance of a modern change and he determined to explore it.[13]

At the same time he was trying to educate himself in sciences such as chemistry which he thought fundamental to the further

10. C. L., Jr. to G. A. M. 16 Sept. 1833. Mantell mss. *L. & L.* I, 401–03.
11. C. L., Jr. to J. M. 29 Sept. 1833. Murray mss.
12. J. M. to C. L., Jr. 3 Oct. 1833. Kinnordy mss.
13. C. L., Jr. to C. B. 22 Dec. 1833. Babbage mss. Cf. *Principles,* 3rd ed., vol. I, pp. 329–40.

development of geology.[14] In January 1834 Lyell became particularly concerned with the question of the temperature of the interior of the earth. He was inclined to doubt that it was actually a
molten mass at an extreme pressure and thought that the very
presence of a cool, solid crust placed limits on the possible temperatures of the interior. Feeling uncertain of his ground, he wrote
to Charles Babbage to inquire about the physics and chemistry
involved.[15] Lyell had learned from John F. Daniell (1790–1845),
professor of chemistry at King's College, that the melting point of
iron was about 4,000 degrees Fahrenheit and that so long as any
solid iron remained in a mass of molten iron the temperature of
the mixture could not be raised above that point, any more than
the temperature of an ice–water mixture could be raised above
thirty-two degrees Fahrenheit. Daniell thought that because this
was true, it was not possible to assume that the temperature of the
interior of the earth was far above 4,000 degrees: otherwise, the
internal heat would quickly melt the crust of the globe. This was
a point of fundamental significance, because the French mining
engineer and geologist, Pierre L. A. Cordier (1777–1862), had argued from the increase of temperature as one descended in mines,
an increase which he estimated at one degree Fahrenheit for every
forty-five feet of depth, that at a depth of about twenty-four miles
one would reach a temperature at the melting point of iron. If
one accepted Cordier's conclusions, then it was necessary to believe
that the great bulk of the interior of the earth was a hot molten
mass upon which rested a comparatively thin crust. Cordier assumed that the temperature of the earth would continue to rise as
one proceeded towards its center where, accordingly, he thought
the temperature was probably about 450,000° F.[16]

Lyell's objections to Cordier's hypothesis about the temperature
of the earth's interior were only in part objections to the hypothesis itself. More fundamentally he objected to the theory of the
earth's history with which it was connected. Leibniz had developed
a theory of the earth's history on the assumption that the earth began as a very hot, incandescent, molten spheroid, which had gradually cooled to form a solid crust upon the surface, and which was
continuing to cool as time passed. According to this theory, the

14. C. L., Jr. to his father. 24 Dec. 1833. Kinnordy mss.
15. C. L., Jr. to C. B. 16 Jan. and 18 Jan. 1834. Babbage mss.
16. L. Cordier, "Essai sur la température de l'intérieur de la terre" (1827).
I have kept to Lyell's figures in Fahrenheit degrees for the sake of simplicity.

warmer climates, which had existed in high latitudes during the geological past, had been maintained by the larger amount of heat then radiating from the interior of the earth. Such an assumption removed the necessity to explain, in terms of the factors which govern the distribution of climates throughout the world today, the changes of climate which had occurred during the course of geological time. It also placed severe limits to the age which could be assigned to the earth. In these two respects then, first, that it introduced a continuously varying and nonuniform factor into the earth's history and, second, that it suggested that the earth's history was relatively short, sharply defined, and progressive, this theory was incompatible with Lyell's general approach to geology. Insofar as he could, Lyell wished to assume that conditions in the interior of the earth, as well as on its surface, had been stable and self-maintaining over a long period of time.

Therefore, with this wish in mind, Lyell introduced into the third edition of the *Principles* a chapter, essentially new, dealing with the causes of earthquakes and volcanoes.[17] He thought that the two kinds of phenomena must be connected because they usually occurred within the same geographical regions. The presence of active volcanoes, Lyell considered, meant that "there must exist, at some unknown depth below, enormous masses of matter intensely heated, and, in many instances, in a constant state of fusion" (p. 274).

The first question was the source of this heat. Many writers had assumed that the present spheroidal shape of the earth required that in its original state it had been fluid throughout, but Lyell showed that the distribution of materials at the surface of the earth through the ordinary course of geological processes would produce the spheroidal form even if the earth had originally been solid. If, however, the interior of the earth were a hot fluid mass its temperature at the center could not be much higher than that in the upper regions of the fluid because convection currents rising from below would steadily tend to distribute the heat from the center outward. The temperature of the fluid interior would therefore be maintained more or less uniform from its center to its periphery.

If the interior temperature of the earth were 450,000° F., as Cordier calculated it was, the crust of the earth would then,

17. *Principles,* 3rd ed., vol. II, pp. 273–95.

Lyell showed, very quickly be melted (p. 282). Therefore, there could be no such vast reservoir of internal heat as Cordier contemplated, and volcanic action was in any case intermittent rather than continuous. Lyell pointed out too that tides should exist in the supposed fluid internal nucleus, and if the jets of lava thrown out in volcanic eruptions arose from this nucleus, they should be correlated very distinctly with the tidal movements of the oceans. In fact there was no apparent relationship between volcanic eruptions and the tides.

Once he had rejected the hypothesis of the central heat of the earth as the source of volcanic action, Lyell turned to chemical changes to provide an alternative source of heat. The chemistry available to him then seems rudimentary now. To his credit Lyell realized that it was both rudimentary and inadequate, but it was also suggestive. He mentioned the reactions between moist iron filings and sulfur and the explosive decomposition of nitrogen iodide as examples of reactions which emitted a large amount of heat. He mentioned the presence of electrical currents within the earth. The unequal exposure of the earth's surface to the sun's rays would tend to create thermoelectric currents within the earth. Faraday had shown that the daily rotation of the earth within its own magnetic field might set up other currents. These electric currents in turn would generate heat. Sir Humphry Davy had suggested that the interior of the earth might contain a reservoir of unoxidized metals such as sodium and potassium which, as they gradually came into contact with water, would become oxidized with a large emission of heat. There really was no evidence for the existence of such a store of unoxidized metals. Yet Daniell had suggested to Lyell that it might be possible for the oxides of metals to be reduced by hydrogen within the earth and thus a quantity of the free metal might be accumulated.

None of these suggestions as to chemical processes was worth much, but in looking for a continuous and steady source of heat within the earth Lyell was on the right track. He was even right in assuming that it must be the result of some kind of cyclical process. He was writing at this time necessarily in ignorance of the principle of the conservation of energy so he did not yet know the formidable theoretical obstacles there would be to the suggestion of a steady and self-sustaining source of heat within the earth. All he knew at this time was that the geological evidence pointed to its existence.

For the third edition Lyell also rewrote his chapter on the causes of earthquakes. One of the most pronounced phenomena of earthquakes, he noted, was an undulatory movement of the earth. In the eighteenth century the Reverend John Michell had suggested that these wave-like movements might be produced by the expansive force of vapors formed within the earth.[18] The difficulty in this theory was that earthquake waves, though violent, were on a small scale and corresponded more to short sharp vibrations of the earth's surface such as might be produced by a sudden jar. However, beyond this point Lyell was not able to penetrate into the mechanics of earthquakes—a subject which is one of the principal concerns of modern geophysics.

The writing of these two essentially new chapters on the causes of volcanoes and earthquakes (to form chapters nine and ten of the second volume, third edition) occupied Lyell until late in February 1834. When they were printed he went forward much more rapidly with the remainder of the work.

At the annual meeting of the Geological Society on 21 February 1834 Lyell gave an account of the controversy over the level of the Baltic and the rise of the land in Sweden and announced that on account of its importance he had decided to go to Sweden to study the question for himself. He was perhaps provoked to this step by G. B. Greenough, who in his address as president of the society, delivered at this meeting, referred to the rise of the land in Sweden. He raised the question "whether there may not be going on, in the calmest seasons and in the stillest countries, a *chronic and almost imperceptible impulsion of land upwards.*"[19] His point evidently was intended to be that if there existed such a gradual and universal elevation of the land, the particular elevations which Lyell had described as associated with volcanoes and earthquakes were not necessarily caused by these phenomena. He even hinted that they might have no real existence. His speech contained many attacks on the *Principles,* most of them even less effective than his reference to the rise of land in Sweden. Yet he ended with compliments for Lyell. Greenough's skepticism was far-fetched but it needled Lyell nonetheless. He found it particularly galling that such an incoherent series of theoretical criticisms should acquire great weight simply by their being uttered from the presidential

18. J. Michell, *Conjectures concerning . . . Earthquakes . . .* (1760).

19. G. B. Greenough, "Address . . . [to] the Geological Society 21 February 1834." (1838) pp. 58–59.

chair of the Geological Society. On 15 March Lyell expressed his
irritation to Murchison.

> I return Boué's letter with thanks and Phillip's[20] from whom I
> had also heard. I quite agree more especially from what I heard
> at the Brit. Mus. yesterday from some of their folk who were at
> G. S. on Wed^y that the false impression made on the novices
> by the opposition of G. is most injurious & that we cannot too
> often impress upon them, more especially when the P. is not in
> the chair, that the denyer & doubter of *all* elevation is in a
> minority of *one,* absolutely of *one* if we enumerate all our work-
> ing & thinking geologists. You are perfectly right in thinking
> that the audience, such is the weight of G's name as author of
> the map, are perfectly bewildered & think that nothing is
> agreed upon.[21]

In March Lyell was also busy "with the *printing* of vol. 3 & the
recasting of vol. 4" for the new edition.[22] In volume three he had
made relatively few changes, but two of them were important. He
rewrote the section of the fifth chapter of Book IV (which began
in the third volume), dealing with the classification of Tertiary
formations, to include information derived from Deshayes's tables
of Tertiary shells; the tables themselves were then omitted from
this and all subsequent editions.[23] He also announced that he had
changed his opinion concerning the origin of the loess formation
of the Rhine. Lyell had previously thought that this seemingly
unstratified deposit had been "thrown down suddenly from the
muddy waters of a transient flood." During his visit to Germany
the previous summer, however, he had found in deep gravel pits
outside the Mannheim gate of Heidelberg loess interstratified with
gravel. "Here," he wrote, "more than one bed containing land and
fresh-water shells rests upon and is covered by, a stratum of gravel,
showing the effects of successive accumulation."[24] Although the
loess remained in many respects a puzzling deposit to Lyell, he
no longer found it necessary to postulate a single extraordinary
flood to account for its origin. It is now thought to be a glacial out-
wash deposit which had its origin from the ancient glaciers of the
Alps.

20. Ami Boué (1794–1881); John Phillips (1800–74).
21. C. L., Jr. to R. I. M. 15 March 1834. Murchison mss.
22. C. L., Jr. to J. M. 18 March 1834. Murray mss.
23. *Principles*, 3rd ed., vol. III, pp. 301–14.
24. Ibid., p. 410.

In the fourth volume Lyell also revised and enlarged his discussion of the elevation and denudation of the Weald district in
southeast England. He showed that the whole area had been elevated *gradually* and that, during the same period in which it had
been elevated, the chalk strata, which had originally extended
completely over this area, had been gradually removed. Lyell
thought that the removal must have been by the action of waves
at the time when the chalk first rose above the level of the sea,
and that the escarpment of the downs, therefore, represented an
ancient line of sea cliffs similar to those which now form the coast-
line of Dorsetshire. Lyell was very familiar with the destructive
action of waves beating against a seacoast, but he tended to under-
estimate the effects of rain and running water in denuding and
sculpturing the face of the land. The problem in England was
particularly difficult because of the presence of dry valleys in the
chalk hills. When a valley contained no stream, it was difficult to
assign its origin to the excavating power of a stream. These and
other land forms in England were puzzling to a critical geologist
because they had in fact received their principal present outlines
towards the end of the glacial period when the rainfall in Britain
was much greater than it is today. This difficulty prevented Lyell
from fully appreciating the scale of the action of rain and running
water in shaping the land.

Other changes which Lyell introduced into the third edition
were an extended discussion of the secondary formations, a revision and condensation of his criticism of Élie de Beaumont's theory for the elevation of mountain chains, and a further development of his concept of the metamorphism of stratified rocks. He
had completed the printing and correcting of the fourth volume
on 10 May and had only the preface remaining.[25] Eleven days
later, the book completed, he set off alone for Sweden while Mary
went to Edinburgh to stay with the Cockburns.

On the steamer from London to Hamburg Lyell sat on deck
writing to Mary—her cap on his balding head and tied under his
chin to protect him from the wind. He must have been the picture
of a resolute, but slightly eccentric traveler. He wrote:

> I have been 10 hours without a word with my love, but think-
> ing of her more than half the time & comforting myself that she
> is less alone than I am. A great part of the sacrifice we make in

25. C. L., Jr. to J. M. 10 May 1834. Murray mss.

this absence has already been made, for the anticipation of it
made the last season in town less bright & cheerful, tho' a happy
one & very usefully spent.

The second day out was stormy and everyone aboard was seasick,
but the third day he wrote to Mary in a mood of complacent
reverie:

> All yesterday when not too ill to think I lay musing over our
> London campaign of 1833–4 with great pleasure. While making
> at least as much progress as I c^d have done as a bachelor student
> we have been "taking our place" in Society & securing it, which
> will be useful by & by to our friends as to ourselves. Our opin-
> ions on that head have as compleat a unity of thought as is pos-
> sible. When we give a few more dinners we shall see more of our
> best friends still with the same interruption as to time.[26]

On Saturday 24 May the steamer reached Hamburg. After settling at his hotel Lyell made an expedition in a drosky down the
Elbe to examine the cliffs which he had sketched while coming up
in the steamer in the morning. On his way back to Hamburg in
the evening he stopped at Altoona to call on Professor Schumacher, the Danish astronomer royal. By means of this and other
excursions he learned something of the geology of Holstein. From
Hamburg he went by carriage over a wretchedly rough road to
Lubeck. On the way he stopped overnight at Segeberg where "an
extraordinary mountain of gypsum etc. bursts up through the
loose sand." Professor Schumacher had given him a letter of introduction to Geheimrath von Rosen, who in turn arranged for
him to examine the gypsum quarries. From Lubeck he took a
small steamboat down the river. He wrote to Mary:

> The river sometimes opened into a kind of estuary, then con-
> tracted—very picturesque. A fleet of 30 fishing boats was met all
> together in full sail, going to the Baltic. We nearly ran against
> a large brig the Union of Dundee & when the sailors gave ours a
> blessing it was returned in good English by a *Scotch* engineer.

At Travemunde at the mouth of the river he transferred to a larger
steamer to go to Copenhagen (Map 14). At every point he made
observations which had a bearing on some geological question.

26. C. L., Jr. to his wife. 21 May 1834. Kinnordy mss. Published in part in
L. & L. I, 407–11.

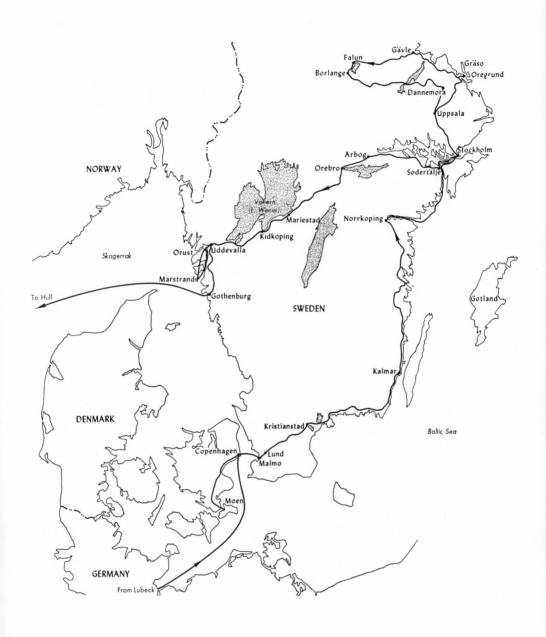

14. Lyell's tour in Denmark and Sweden, 1834

When my luggage was safe we had still 3/4 of an hour & I was ambitious of picking up a shell or two on the borders of the Baltic. I landed as we were alongside the pier in our new boat. It was low water. The shore was covered with *Turbo littoreous, Mytilus edulis, Cardium edule, Mactra, Tellina* & quantities of a minute *Paludina*. I suppose *P. ulva*. The association of the *P.* with the marine shells delighted me as analogous to Mayence basin which was no doubt brackish too.[27]

It had become characteristic of his thought that from piecing together various observations of the natural history of the present lakes and seas he could reconstruct in imagination the environments of the past represented in the strata. His study of freshwater lakes in Scotland had, for instance, enabled him to see the meaning of the freshwater marls of Auvergne and now the Baltic was his key for the interpretation of the beds of the Mayence basin.

At Copenhagen Lyell immediately went to call upon Johann Georg Forchhammer (1794–1865), professor of geology at the University of Copenhagen, whose paper on the geology of Denmark he had read earlier.[28] Lyell was anxious to make an expedition to the islands of Moën and Seeland of which Forchhammer had written a geological description. Lyell and Forchhammer traveled by post chaise from Copenhagen to Stevns Klint on the east coast of Seeland and crossed by ferry to Moën. This island, mainly composed of chalk, also possessed strata of the same age as those at Maestricht in Holland. Lyell was delighted to be able to find the junction between the upper chalk and the Maestricht formation. In his paper of 1828 Forchhammer had described the white chalk of Seeland as overlain by younger strata of coralline limestone. The chalk cliffs in Moën he considered to represent strata which in turn lay above the coral-bearing limestone of Seeland. He had also considered certain strata of blue clay, sand, and gravel, outcropping in the cliffs of Moën, to alternate with the white chalk. Lyell now found that, on the basis of its fossils, the white chalk of Denmark was identical with the upper chalk (chalk with flints) of France and England. Above this chalk the coralline limestone already described by Forchhammer was especially well represented in the quarries of Faxoe, and Lyell found that the intermingling of chalk and Tertiary fossils which it contained was very similar

27. C. L., Jr. to his wife. 28 May 1834. Kinnordy mss. *L. & L.* I, 409.
28. G. Forchhammer, "On the chalk formation of Denmark" (1828).

to that of the Maestricht beds. In Moën, instead of being nearly horizontal as in Seeland, the chalk strata had been violently disturbed and commonly were curved and nearly vertical.

The range of lofty cliffs in Moën is divided into separate masses by ravines, which often intersect them from top to bottom, but are in great part filled up with tertiary clay and sand, masses of which appear to have subsided bodily into large fissures and chasms of the fractured chalk. In consequence of these disturbances the chalk has been made to alternate on a great scale with interposed and unconformable strata of clay and sand. These alternations cannot be explained by supposing the detritus of the superincumbent strata to have been washed in by running water into clefts; but masses of the tertiary beds seem rather to have been engulfed.[29]

The strata of clay and sand, therefore, did not alternate with the chalk as Forchhammer had thought. Lyell was somewhat embarrassed to come to conclusions so opposite to those of his host and guide, but he was able to convince Forchhammer of the truth of his interpretation. His earlier experience with the disturbed chalk strata in the Isle of Wight had undoubtedly prepared Lyell to understand these similar but more complicated phenomena. His skill in the analysis of disturbed strata, however, belies those who said, later in his life, that he was "not . . . a great field observer."[30]

In later explaining this extraordinary geological phenomenon to Prince Christian of Denmark, Lyell said that "had I not studied both the Isle of Wight and Norfolk coast, I should have perhaps fallen into what I called Forchhammer's mistake." The expedition was in every other respect enjoyable:

The scenery was often beautiful—firths & bays running into the green isles, a low undulating country running in Moen into hills 500 ft. high, where the chalk is covered by splendid beech trees, cliffs near 400 ft. high covered with wood at summit & with a fine shingle beach of flint at their base. My companion

29. "On the Cretaceous and Tertiary strata of the Danish Islands of Seeland and Moën" (1838).

30. A. Sedgwick to D. Livingstone. 16 March 1865, in J. W. Clark and T. M. Hughes, *The Life and Letters of the Reverend Adam Sedgwick* (1890) vol. II, p. 412. Sedgwick made this rather acidulous estimate of Lyell in the course of expressing his violent disagreement with Darwin's theory of evolution by natural selection. It ought not to have been taken as Sedgwick's serious estimate of Lyell's work or at least not, in the circumstances, as a competent estimate.

[was] well informed on many branches in which I wanted instruction & anxious to learn of me—& who has taught me much of the geology of regions I have just been seeing & am to see.[31]

On their return to Copenhagen at the end of the third day of this expedition Lyell found waiting for him an invitation from Prince Christian to examine his Highness's collection of fossils the next day. Forchhammer also invited him to a soirée for the next evening to meet the physicist Hans Christian Oersted (1777–1851) and two Danish travelers, Pingel and Olafsen. The opportunity to look over the Royal collection of shells proved very valuable to Lyell, because he was able to see many fossil forms collected from the quarries at Faxoe. This formation represented, he told Mary, "an ancient coral reef, where the genera Cypraea, Oliva, Mitra, Voluta, Conus etc. had already in the chalk era, begun to flourish as now in the tropics." Prince Christian later entertained Lyell to dinner at his country house and talked with him afterwards about scientific matters. "He asked me," wrote Lyell, "to explain Faraday's last discoveries in electricity, of which he heard I was the first narrator to Oersted. He entered into it with pleasure."[32]

In 1831 Faraday had discovered the phenomenon of the magnetic induction of electric currents. He had followed this discovery with the famous series of researches in which he explored the various properties of magnetically-induced electric currents. In 1833 he had studied the phenomena of electrolysis and in January 1834 he had presented his new terms, coined with Whewell's help, *anode, cathode, anion, cation, electrolyte,* and *electrolysis* used to describe the process. In his eighth series of researches, sent to the Royal Society of London on 7 April 1834, Faraday applied his new knowledge of electrolysis and electrochemistry to the behavior of voltaic cells and batteries of cells.

Lyell thoroughly enjoyed his role of an English scientific celebrity at the court of Denmark, but he was anxious to continue on his tour. On 4 June he crossed over to Malmö in Sweden. He wrote to Mary:

I got successfully to a humble inn at Malmö & walked on foot along the shore to the limeworks at Linnhaven & back in a peasant car filled with dry sea-weed. On the sea-side I remarked the extremely small size of the *Cardium edule* & *Mytilus edulis*

31. C. L. Jr. to his wife. 1–5 June 1834. Kinnordy mss. *L. & L.* I, 411–16.
32. Ibid.

which I have since learnt is characteristic of all the truly oceanic species which contrive to live (both fish & mollusca) in the brackish waters of the Baltic. They miss their proper dose of brine, & the farther from the sound the smaller do they become.

When Lyell went at Malmö to buy a carriage for traveling through Sweden his inability in the Swedish language proved an obstacle. "My courage misgave me," he wrote to Mary, "when in stepped a gentlemanlike sort of young man, talking good English & introducing himself as Mr. John Robert Johnson of Malmö, a Swede those mother was English, [&] offered his services as interpreter." Lyell accepted Johnson's help in the purchase of the carriage and then asked him if he would be willing to go to Stockholm as companion and interpreter. Johnson was glad to go, and quickly arranged his affairs. In the meantime Lyell went to Lund where he spent a couple of days with the Swedish geologist Sven Nilsson (1787–1883). He wrote to Mary:

He showed me his fossils, gave me a valuable collection of duplicates & discussed numerous subjects the first day of June 6th when I dined with him. Next day, June 7th, we made an excursion together thro' a country of greywacke with orthoceratite limestone & schist, containing a curious zoophyte called graptolite in great abundance & a few shells. These rocks are seen by the banks of a small brook in a place called Fogelsang (pronounced song) or "song of birds." where I heard the nightingale & cuckoo.

While Lyell was visiting with Nilsson at Lund, Johnson returned to Malmö to pay for the carriage, which had been taken to Lund on trial, and to complete his preparations for departure. On the eighth Lyell returned and they started to drive north through the Swedish countryside. At Nobblo Lyell wrote:

The country to-day from Lund by Hurfra Korby and Wren to this place is like England & scarcely what I had expected. The fir trees have been rarer, I think, than even in South of England & oak & beech & a variety of other "hard wood" of handsome size have been spread over a country much like the New Forest, with the same glades opening here & there but greener & much less heathy in Scania & with this difference that the country here, tho' hardly more hilly than Hants is strewn over with innumerable blocks of granite & other crystalline rocks so as sometimes to resemble the Forest of Fontainebleau.

The roads were good, the weather fine and the people friendly. Even the repairs which the carriage needed from time to time were very cheap. Lyell studied the geology of the country as they went.

> After Christianstadt I made an excursion quite out of the way to visit the lake of Iförsjon in the middle of which is the isle of Ifö (pronounced Ivon) where beneath the sand & boulder formation, under which in general the country is buried, appear in steep cliffs a calcareous green sand of the chalk era with numerous belemnites, some oysters & a few cranias. Of the belemnites, a species, which I believe is only Swedish, was so plentiful that I filled some small boxes full.[33]

The face of the country became now as different as was its geology:

> The appearance of Bläking differs from Scania inasmuch as here, instead of a country strewed over with sand & huge boulders of granite, one has the granite itself often quite bare & smooth, a few trees growing in the clefts, but often fine woods of oak. Huge detached masses of granite sometimes appear among the trees, no high mountains here near the coast, but the bays & sea & promontories & the excellent road winding among the knolls of wooded rock form a pleasing picture.

The first place on the east coast of Sweden which Lyell examined for changes of level was at Calmar and there, from the position of the old castle on the shore, it seemed doubtful that there had been any appreciable rise of the land during the 500 years that it had stood there. After Calmar they turned inland and proceeded north. Lyell described their expedition to Mary:

> If you had a magic glass not to see treasures but *me* you would generally see . . . (I am sorry I cannot sketch) but first come two steeds, small but active, long-tailed & with rope harness, then Johnson driving on the box, with the bread-box by his side, then a peasant put in because of the bread-box & feeling very uncomfortable, because like our friend at Milan, not in his right place, & laughed at by the other peasants, expecially the young women, then by his side "Herr Professor", reading & getting on with some books on geology which he requires to study & think over.[34]

33. C. L., Jr. to his wife. 5–8 June 1834. Kinnordy mss. *L. & L.* I, 416–20.
34. C. L., Jr. to his wife. 10–14 June 1834. Kinnordy mss. *L. & L.* I, 420–24.

To expedite their progress Lyell finally engaged a *forebud,* a man who would ride ahead to the post houses to arrange for fresh horses. Since the horses usually had to be caught in the fields and brought in to be fed, watered, and harnessed, the *forebud* was able to save them much waiting at post houses while this was done. There was so little traveling in Sweden that the only reason post-horses were available was that the peasants had to provide them as part of their feudal duties. Thus although travelers like Lyell paid for their horses, they were really enjoying feudal privileges in being able to travel at all. Even early in the nineteenth century Sweden was noteworthy for its order and social tranquillity. Lyell remarked:

> When I consider how thinly the population is scattered over this vast country & that rich natives & foreigners are passing along the high-roads & that the woods contain no robbers I am lost in wonder. But then every peasant has something; there are scarce any paupers. The cross roads are as good as the high roads, where I have been as yet, except in Scania where they are baddish at least in the South. The peasants drive along in their light cars with loads of deal planks, at the rate of 6 or 7 miles an hour & often kept up with us. They are a well grown race.[35]

At Norkoping Lyell put himself, Johnson, and the carriage aboard a wood-burning steamboat to go along the coast and through the Sodertelje canal and Lake Maeler to Stockholm where they arrived on 17 June. Lyell found waiting for him a letter from Mary, the first he had received since leaving London. She gave him a low estimate of their household expenses, a fact which cheered him because the cost of travel in Sweden was running higher than he had expected. Their income was small enough that Lyell was trying to be economical as he traveled.

At Stockholm Lyell called on the famous chemist, Jöns Jakob Berzelius (1779–1848), who was secretary of the Royal Swedish Academy of Science. Lyell had already learned from Professor Nilsson at Lund that fossil marine shells, belonging to modern species living in the Baltic, had been found near Stockholm.[36] He asked Berzelius about these shells. "Berzelius went at once to the point," Lyell wrote Mary, "& having told me much that he knew

35. C. L., Jr. to his wife. 15–21 June 1834. Kinnordy mss. *L. & L.* I, 425–26.
36. "The Bakerian Lecture. On the proofs of a gradual rising of the land in certain parts of Sweden" (1835) p. 5.

about changes of level, offered to drive me next morning to some interesting spots in his drosky." Accordingly, Lyell returned the next day. He described the occasion to Mary:

On morning of 18th I spent 5 whole hours with Berzelius tête-à-tête. After all kinds of hints, which I noted down for my tour, he drove me to see some alluvial phenomena near the observatory, & in the beautiful royal parks a few miles N. of this city, of Haga & Ulricsdal in both of which are fine lakes & woods & country palaces. Then to Solna where marine recent shells are found some 30 ft. above sea. I profited greatly by my previous acquaintance with littoral shells of Baltic for, by knowing what to look for, I picked up much in short time. . . . While I made drawings & collected specimens B. gathered grass for his well fed & handsome dun pony which he is great friends with & can leave him quite alone. "As he only gets hay," said B. "all the year in the stable, every mouthful of this is sweetness to him."[37]

The spot where they were at Solna was at the foot of one of the eskers, or long ridges of sand and gravel, which Lyell had noted were characteristic of the Swedish countryside. He took them to be ancient lines of beach, but actually they were glacial in origin and represented the beds of ancient rivers which traversed the glaciers. In a gravel pit which had been opened at the base of the esker Lyell found an abundance of shells of *Cardium edule, Tellina baltica, Mytilus edulis,* and others as well. The *Cardium* and *Mytilus* were of dwarf size just as they were found in the neighboring Gulf of Bothnia. The whole assemblage of shells was typical of the living shell populations of the Baltic yet this gravel bed now lay thirty feet above the level of that sea. This was evidence for elevation of a kind which Lyell could not gainsay, because it was of exactly the same kind as had demonstrated elevation to him in Italy and Sicily. Yet it was evidence that Sweden *had been elevated* during the past, not that it was now rising.

The year before Lyell's visit, J. F. W. Johnston had published an article in the *Edinburgh Philosophical Journal* on the phenomenon of the rise of land in Sweden during the present time.[38] Therefore, two days later Lyell went with Lieutenant Colonel Lundstedt, who acted as interpreter for him, to see all the places

37. C. L., Jr. to his wife. 15–21 June 1834.
38. J. F. W. Johnston, "On a gradual elevation of the land in Scandinavia" (1833).

cited in Johnston's article as indicating that the land was rising. Lyell was unimpressed by these proofs, but at the same time he wrote Mary, "Do not draw any inferences from this or other examples of what my general results may prove, for of them I know nothing yet myself."[39]

A day or two later Lyell returned to Sodertelje to examine the canal which had been cut there in 1819 across a narrow barrier of sand, gravel, and clay which separated Lake Maeler from a long narrow arm of the Baltic. The canal lay at the bottom of a valley whose sides were formed of gneiss rock but whose floor was composed of much more recent deposits. Marine shells had been found at various heights in the loam, sand, and gravel of these recent deposits. The shells were of the same species as those at Solna and indicated the same thing, that there had been an elevation of the land, but they indicated also that this elevation had occurred on a much greater scale than the shells at Solna would have suggested. Lyell found the same characteristic assemblage of shells at a height of one hundred feet above sea level. When the upper channel for the canal was cut several buried ships were found, some of them very old because they were held together by wooden pegs. However, an anchor and some iron nails were also dug up. In digging the lower channel the workmen made a still more remarkable discovery; under some sixty-four feet of stratified sand, gravel, and clay they found the unmistakable remains of a small wooden house including a hearth. This house, when built and inhabited, must have stood upon dry land; changes of level must have occurred since in two directions. First the land had sunk and had remained under water until the house was covered over by about sixty feet of stratified sand and gravel; then it had risen again to a level close to the modern sea level.

Lyell was very much excited by this evidence. He wrote to Mary:

The Sodertelje expedition told more than any one I have made in Sweden, & if papers were read at Geol. Committee of Edinburgh meeting I sh^d probably read a short one. Shells of the Baltic nearly 100 ft. high. All that I got at Lubeck save *Mya arenaria* & perhaps that is not a Bothnian gulf species. But what think you of ships in the same formation—nay a house. It is as true as the Temple of Serapis. I do not mean that I discovered all this, but I shall be the first to give a geological account of

39. C. L., Jr. to his wife. 15–21 June 1834.

it . . . I told Berzelius of what I thought of Sodertelje & he was not staggered at my requiring an enormous subsidence & re-elevation. Had Nordewall or Capt. Cronstrand only known that neither a *Cardium* nor a *Tellina* will live in a lake, it wd. have saved them a world of trouble.[40]

After his return to Stockholm Lyell set off north, traveling again by carriage with Johnson on the box. Their first stop was at Upsala where Professor Wahlenberg[41] greeted him very courteously and took him through Linnaeus's garden "where the hedges of fir stand, clipped, as he planted them." At Upsala Lyell found marine shells of Baltic species on top of a hill 100 feet high. He told Mary:

You remember that in the half hour between the 2 steamboats at Lubeck, or rather Travemunde, I collected shells by the quay. Not one fossil have I found, newer than the chalk in Sweden that was not in the number of those found living in this half hour.[42]

While at Upsala Lyell went one day with Professor Wahlenberg to see a meadow where marine plants, including *Glaux maritima* and *Triglochina maritimus,* still grew and where the soil was salt although the sea was now no nearer than Stockholm. In addition to this fact and his finding of marine shells, he had an opportunity to talk with Colonel Bruncrona, who had been chief of the Swedish pilotage for many years. In 1820, as part of a coastal survey for the government of Sweden, Colonel Bruncrona had placed engraved marks to indicate the sea level in that year on a number of rocks along the coast of the Gulf of Bothnia. He gave Lyell the different locations of these marks so that Lyell could check them for any change of sea level in the fourteen years since they had been made. "Nothing could have told more than my stay of 3 days at Upsala," he told Mary, "& it has gone far to satisfy me that I have by *instinct* hit on the best thing wh. cd. have been accomplished in 2 months."

From Upsala Lyell traveled on north to examine Bruncrona's marks at Oregrund and Gefle on the Gulf of Bothnia. Bruncrona had given him an introduction to Lieutenant Olof Flumen of the pilotage who had cut the mark at Gräsö, off Oregrund in 1820

40. C. L., Jr. to his wife. 23 June 1834. Kinnordy mss. *L. & L.* I, 430.
41. Goran [George] Wahlenberg (1780–1851), professor of botany at Upsala.
42. C. L., Jr. to his wife. 26 June–1 July 1834. Kinnordy mss. *L. & L.* I, 431.

(Fig. 48). Flumen immediately arranged to take him to see it. Lyell wrote that they

> Went in a boat about 3½ hours pull with 4 rowers. The plan of the mark & the mode of marking well chosen. I had with me the pilot who made the mark 14 years ago. It seems true, as Galileo said in a different sense, "that the earth moves."[43]

The mark, which they examined, was in the vertical face of a cliff of gneiss, which descended perpendicularly into the water. It had been cut on 13 September 1820 "exactly at the level of the sea on a calm day." On 1 July 1834, when Lyell examined it, the line was five inches and a half above the surface of the water although a northwest wind was maintaining the water level an inch or two higher than it would be on a calm day.[44]

After one day at Oregrund Lyell continued through fir woods on the road to Gefle. There he wished to visit two marks, one cut in 1731 on the island of Löfgrund several miles off the coast, the other cut in 1820 in Esjko sound, six miles to the north of Löfgrund (Fig. 49). The chief pilot at Gefle conducted him and a retired sea-captain of that place, who was supposed to know English, also volunteered to go along. He wrote to Mary:

> The first day it was very cold with the wind against us & slow work. I learnt much about the action of ice in these seas from the sailors & pilot & we landed at Löfgrund & drank milk in some summer fishing huts where we found a nice peasant family. I measured the stone at Löfgrund where there was one mark made in 1731 several feet above the sea . . . We next landed on the island of Esjko Klubb (Aysko-clubb or asho). Could not hear news there of a mark which the pilot thought there was. Then I measured the line cut in St. Olof's stone in Esjko sound & it being late determᵈ to sleep there.

The pilot told Lyell that because the wind was blowing from the east-southeast the water stood four or five inches above its mean level. "As this was the third time I had been told that the sea was several inches above its standard height," Lyell wrote, "I determined to pass the night at Edsko in hopes that the wind might fall."[45] He continued his account to Mary:

43. Ibid.
44. "The Bakerian Lecture . . ." (1835) p. 17.
45. Ibid., pp. 21–22.

The accommodation was scanty enough, but we had taken provisions with us. I slept well for 4 hours & then waking & seeing the sea quite calm I got up & woke the Pilot & told him that as he said the evening before that my observation was incomplete from the state of the wind & sea, perhaps we now had a good opportunity of rectifying it. He was a sprightly good-humoured young man & very intelligent. He immediately jumped up & declared that the sea was in so favourable a state, just at its mean level & quite calm that no time sh^d be lost. With great dispatch all the things & his men were ready & the old Capt., who was never so happy as when sitting in the boat, was down among the first. As for Johnson, who sleeps hard as he says, he was bundled out of bed wondering that "having ordered coffee I sh.^{d} go without it." Away we rowed down the sound & revisited the huge stone & I found the sea as the pilot had predicted several inches lower.[46]

The result of this observation was that he found the water standing 3.58 inches lower than it had in 1820. While he was on this cruise Lyell also saw blocks of granite five or six feet in diameter on the shore of one of the islands. They were bare of lichens, which indicated that they had not been long where they now lay, and the fishermen said they thought these large rocks had been carried there by the ice which, Lyell was told, sometimes packed in the Gulf of Bothnia to a depth of eighteen feet. This observation confirmed his suspicion that the erratic boulders scattered over Sweden had been transported by ice at a time when the country lay under water.

From Gefle they went into the interior of Sweden to Fahlun, where Lyell visited a copper mine in one of his early attempts to learn the geological circumstances of ore deposits. He had also visited the great iron mine at Danemora and he was to visit a silver mine at Sala. The country around Fahlun, Lyell noted, was "a land of goats."[47] He was impressed by the falls of Skjerplinge and the people and cottages of Dalecarlia. On 7 July they arrived back in Stockholm. During his brief stay there he went with Colonel Hallstrom to see at Bränkyrka a shell bed which had not been examined by any geologist. He explained to Mary the purpose of this trip:

46. C. L., Jr. to his wife. 2–7 July 1834. Kinnordy mss. *L. & L.* I, 434–35.
47. Ibid.

Hisinger said "As you have seen Södertelje, and other places what do you expect to find more?" I answered "Either I shall find the fresh-water species which now inhabit the Baltic, mixed with the marine, or I shall begin to think that that sea of old was more salt than now." Accordingly, I found for the first time at B. all the marine shells before met with & in addition the *Neritina* and *Lymnea* I had been wanting.

Before Lyell left Stockholm he again visited Berzelius. Their meeting was friendly.

When I called on Berzelius yesterday he had Jameson's Journal in his hand & showed me my Art. on the Loess, Boué on Beaumont & me, & the end of Greenough's speech at least will do me no harm at all but the contrary.[48] I have enough of you said B. in this number, laughing. One day when I turned the wrong way (as of old at other places) & was going *into* the entrance of the Royal *Acad.* instead of *out* of his apartments he said good humouredly "Ah you will probably come there some day in another way"

Berzelius had evidently described the purpose of Lyell's visit to Sweden to the King because when Colonel Blom had been discussing the new modes of rapid travel by railway and steamboat with the King, the King had remarked, "There is an English gentleman here inquiring at what rate the sea is being turned into land." Colonel Blom said that he knew Mr. Lyell and the King said, "You may learn then from him how soon England will be joined to Sweden, and when we may think of a railroad communication."[49]

On 11 July Lyell left Stockholm to travel in his carriage across Sweden in a southwesterly direction. He went by Sodertelje, Arboga, Orebro, and along the southeast side of Lake Wener to Mariestadt. He reported that they were "getting on famously without a *forebud,* thro' a fine sunny country which smells very sweet, & where the rye & wheat have already a yellow autumnal

48. The three articles mentioned appeared together in the number of the *Edinburgh New Philosophical Journal* (Jameson's Journal) for April 1834, vol. 17. They were: Charles Lyell, "Observations on the loamy deposit called 'loess' of the basin of the Rhine," pp. 111–22; A. Boué, "On the theory of the elevation of mountain chains as advocated by M. Élie de Beaumont," pp. 123–50; G. B. Greenough, "Remarks on the theory of the elevation of mountains," pp. 205–27. This last article was a reprinting of a portion of Greenough's anniversary speech as president of the Geological Society of London.

49. C. L., Jr. to his wife. 10–27 July 1834. Kinnordy mss. *L. & L.* I, 438–42.

colour." Near Lidkoping he geologized Kinnekulli, a mountain or high hill which rises some eight hundred feet above Lake Wener. It was "composed at summit of volc.ᶜ rock or greenstone & below of perfectly horizontal shale & limestone in wh. are trilobites, orthocerae etc."[50]

After crossing over the Gotha Elf river, which drains Lake Wener, he went north to Uddevalla, a town at the foot of a deep bay on the west coast of Sweden. He wished to determine whether the signs of a rising of the land were as clear on this side facing the Skagerrak as on the Gulf of Bothnia. There he spent four days searching for marine shells as signs of elevation, not only in the country around Uddevalla, but also on the islands of Orust and Gullholmen lying out from Uddevalla. At Kured, two miles north of Uddevalla, Lyell found a shell deposit laid open to a depth of forty feet in a quarry. It consisted almost entirely of both broken and whole shells in thin layers. At one spot where the vertical surface of a ledge of gneiss had been laid bare by the quarrymen there were on the gneiss "the circular supports of many large Balani" and fossil barnacles hung suspended in horizontal clefts in the gneiss. This vertical face of gneiss therefore represented an old sea cliff, a fact which was confirmed further by the presence of small fossil zoophytes clinging either to the gneiss or to the Balani. The shelly formations of Uddevalla, therefore, were in fact stratified formations of sand, clay, and gravel, and in several places almost entirely of shells, which had filled up at some former period the deep bays and fiords of a sea like that now bounding this coast.[51]

The species of shells in this deposit were nearly all, or, Lyell thought, perhaps all, identical with species living in the North Sea. They presented an assemblage of species quite different from those which Lyell had collected in the Baltic and had found as fossils on the eastern side of Sweden. It was completely marine with no admixture of freshwater forms. The shells of *Mytilus edulis* were four or five times larger than those of that species found in the Baltic. In order to visit the island of Gullholmen where Celsius, a century earlier, had thought the sea was sinking, Lyell crossed over the larger island of Orust. There, too, he found elevated shell beds and other deposits.

50. Ibid.
51. "Bakerian Lecture . . ." p. 24.

The features of the scenery in the interior of Orust are precisely such as we might suppose the present coast to exhibit if it should be lifted up with its small island, rocks, and friths and if the intervening level flats, where sand, mud, and shells are known to be now accumulating, should be laid dry.[52]

From the seaward side of Orust Lyell crossed over to the island of Gullholmen, where he first examined an iron ring, placed in a rock in the harbour, to which ships had formerly been moored. He ascertained that this mooring ring now stood seven feet five inches above sea level, but he had no exact measure of its former height although the inhabitants all told him that it used to stand lower. In order to be able to make a better determination in future Lyell hired a smith to make a new mark, "on the face of a vertical cliff on the south side of the harbour about a hundred yards from the posthouse."[53]

From Gullholmen he went to the island of Marstrand about twenty miles to the south. There he observed a mark which had been cut on the vertical face of an isolated rock in 1770 to indicate the lowest level of the sea at that time (Fig. 50). This line Lyell found some ten inches above the water which, however, he was told, then stood about fourteen inches above its lowest level. Consequently in 1834 the mark stood really two feet above the lowest sea level, which suggested that the land had risen two feet in sixty-four years.

After completing his observations on Marstrand, Lyell returned to the mainland and went south to Gothenburg, where he arrived on 20 July. The next day he sailed in a steam-packet, carrying Swedish iron, for Hull in Yorkshire; they landed so late in the evening of the twenty-fourth that Lyell only got through the customs "by great exertions & a bribe."[54] The next day he set out by coach to rejoin Mary at Kinnordy.

During their ensuing holiday at Kinnordy Lyell wrote up the results of his tour of Sweden. The one question troubling him was that John Murray had not yet published the new third edition of the *Principles* which had been printed and ready since June. Murray's reason for delay was that he still had on hand, unsold, several hundred copies of the third volume of the first edition.

52. Ibid., p. 25.
53. Ibid., p. 27.
54. C. L., Jr. to his wife. 10–27 July 1834. Kinnordy mss.

The obstacle to selling these copies was that the public would not buy them unless they could also buy the first two volumes which were already sold out. Both Lyell and Murray had over-estimated the number of copies of the third volume which they should print. However, as a result of his Swedish tour, Lyell had already changed some of the views which he had expressed in the third edition; he now felt that the work was in danger of becoming obsolete even before it was published and that if its publication were delayed it would become seriously out of date. While still in Sweden Lyell had asked Leonard Horner to see Murray to urge him to publish immediately. Murray, resenting this interference with his end of the enterprise, wrote to Lyell at Kinnordy to protest that it was "the very worst season for publishing such a work."[55] He also complained that on past editions Lyell had reduced his profits by increasing the expenses of the different volumes with extra woodcuts and plates after they had made their agreement for publication. This latter complaint sounds slightly petulant, but Lyell was certainly going beyond his rights as an author in asking to determine the date of publication. Yet he was willing to pay for his whims. On receiving Murray's letter he wrote immediately to say that he was willing to bear half the loss arising from the unsold copies of volume three if Murray would issue the new edition immediately.[56] Murray, however, declined to bring out the new edition unless Lyell would bear the whole loss which Murray equated to the wholesale price of the unsold copies.[57] This involved some financial sleight of hand because in seeking to justify the printing of the larger number of copies of the third volume he said it had cost very little more to print them, the chief cost being in the original setting up. Thus he wished to charge Lyell the full price of copies which had cost only a small amount extra to print. To this extraordinary proposition Lyell made a very firm and crisp reply. He would pay Murray £150, which was slightly more than half the theoretical loss on the unsold copies, at the time of publication if Murray would publish before mid-October. But "If you resolve on waiting till next year," he wrote, "I beg you will not trouble yourself to write again on this affair."[58] Lyell was angry and Murray realized he had

55. J. M. to C. L., Jr. 2 Aug. 1834. Kinnordy mss.
56. C. L., Jr. to J. M. 6 Aug. 1834. Murray mss.
57. J. M. to C. L., Jr. 19 Aug. 1834. Kinnordy mss.
58. C. L., Jr. to J. M. 21 Aug. 1834. Murray mss.

gone far enough. "Although I do not agree in the equity of your decision," he wrote, "yet as I have never had any quarrel about money, I acted upon it immediately."[59] Satisfied to have obtained publication at last, Lyell wrote to say that he had already written part of a new and "purely elementary work to be called 'Conversations on Geology.' "[60] The title, adapted from Mrs. Marcet's *Conversations on Chemistry,* indicated Lyell's intention that the book should serve the same kind of popular purpose. It developed slowly and would ultimately emerge as a more serious work for students, the *Elements of Geology.*

On 8 September 1834 the British Association opened its annual meeting at Edinburgh. Lyell attended and gave a preliminary report of his observations on Sweden.[61] A few days after the meeting ended, on 13 September, the Lyells returned to London.

Once settled again at 16 Hart Street Lyell continued to write his new elementary book on geology. London seemed very pleasant. The interior of the house had been painted during the summer and the rooms were much brightened. Sophy Andrews, the cook, had a row of flowers in the front basement area which people passing in the street stopped to admire. Lyell and Mary bought her an amaryllis and a heath at Covent Garden to add to her collection.[62] They also went shopping for a carpet and additional furniture. When Lyell called at Murray's on 23 September he found that 900 copies of the third edition of the *Principles* had been sold already so he felt greatly encouraged.[63] He sought to extend his own education in geology. He had again met Louis Agassiz at the British Association meeting, and Agassiz had aroused his interest in fossil fishes. He also attended Daniell's lectures on chemistry at King's College.[64]

Late in October Louis Agassiz arrived in town and on 29 October he and Lyell went together with Dr. Buckland to Brighton to see Mantell's collection. Robert Bakewell, the geologist, and Michael Faraday, who was on holiday from the Royal Institution, were also at Brighton and came to Mantell's house for the evening.

59. J. M. to C. L., Jr. 28 Aug. 1834. Kinnordy mss.

60. C. L., Jr. to J. M. 31 Aug. 1834. Murray mss.

61. "On the change of level of the land and sea in Scandinavia" (1835). Cf. "Proceedings of the British Association at Edinburgh in September 1834." *Edinb. New Phil. J.* 17 (1834): 369–451, pp. 393–94.

62. M. E. L. to her sister Katherine. 10 Oct. 1834. Kinnordy mss.

63. M. E. L. to her mother. 23 Sept. 1834. Kinnordy mss.

64. C. L., Jr. to G. A. M. 1 Oct. 1834. Mantell mss.

Lyell also had a personal reason to visit Brighton because his mother and his sisters, Caroline and Elizabeth, were staying there in lodgings. His mother was in poor health and Elizabeth, for whose sake principally they had come south, was suffering from consumption. They had come down from Scotland both to obtain a change of climate and to consult Mantell and other physicians.

On 27 November Lyell delivered before the Royal Society the first half of his Bakerian lecture on the evidence for the gradual rise of the land in Sweden. A few days later he learned that the Royal Society had awarded him its royal medal for geology, the award being made specifically "for his work on the Principles of Geology." Lyell immediately conveyed this cheering news to John Murray.[65] After the award had been announced he wrote to Mantell to thank him for the warmth of his congratulations and added:

> I can enter fully into your opinion of the importance of the medal as supporting me & my bold views against the power, of which a certain party are fully willing to take advantage. The R.S. is most thoroughly above all that humbug & if there had been a little more cry against me on theological grounds I should only have been the more sure of it.[66]

On 18 December the reading of his paper on Sweden before the Royal Society was completed.

At Christmas time Mantell wrote to tell Lyell that his mother and sisters, who had moved from Brighton to a house at Hastings, were ill. In those days no illness could be taken lightly, so Lyell set off with Mary for Hastings where they found that "all five of them, the 3 ladies & their 2 Scotch maids had had . . . a sort of English cholera."[67] Elizabeth, the chronic invalid, proved the most resistant to their common affliction and was acting as a nurse. His mother was better by the time they arrived but it was still a sick household. They remained at Hastings three days. Lyell was chiefly occupied with writing but walked one day along the cliffs in search of fossils. Scarcely had they returned to London when a letter from Caroline followed them with the alarming news of a renewal of his mother's illness. Lyell then wrote to Mantell to ask him to visit his mother professionally and give whatever medical advice was needed.[68] His brother Henry who

65. C. L., Jr. to J. M. 1 Dec. 1834. Murray mss.
66. C. L., Jr. to G. A. M. 10 Dec. 1834. Mantell mss.
67. C. L., Jr. to G. A. M. 3 Jan. 1835. Mantell mss.
68. C. L., Jr. to G. A. M. 5 Jan. 1835. Mantell mss.

was home from India and staying with them in London also went to Hastings to give what help he could.

In January 1835 Lyell began to make plans for a fourth edition of the *Principles*. The third edition had apparently been selling well and much better than Murray had expected. On 28 January he asked Murray for "a scheme of the new Ed^n with the proposed number of copies, price, terms etc." He left it entirely to Murray to decide the number of copies but urged the advantage of frequent revisions in "so moving & progressing a science."[69] To Mantell he described his methods of work:

> I am obliged to be very careful of myself, having never been strong like you nor capable of much mental exertion at a time. My only chance is by never missing a day if possible to make out a tolerable good aggregate amount of work in the year.[70]

At the anniversary dinner of the Geological Society on 20 February 1835, Lyell was the incoming president. He asked Murchison's advice about the order of toasts and urged Babbage to attend to support him.[71] He need not have been apprehensive. The dinner was a great success. Lyell spoke at some length on the scientific work of Mantell to whom the Society had just awarded the Wollaston medal and whom, he thought, the scientific community of London tended to neglect. He ended by proposing his health.

During the winter of 1835 Lyell revised the *Principles* for the fourth edition, which he wished to see through the press before he left for the continent in June. He wished to include additional woodcuts and plates and urged Murray to increase the price of the work a shilling to allow £30 for new illustrations but Murray refused. The price of the fourth edition remained twenty-four shillings.

Early in April Lyell completed the first volume of the new edition. By mid-May he was beginning to print the third volume. The changes and additions were considerable and he found that the questions raised by geological problems led him ever further into such related subjects as chemistry and natural history. He wrote to ask Dr. Fleming about the proportion of extinct species among the corals of the crag and added:

> I am getting on in Natural History & it would be easy to be

69. C. L., Jr. to J. M. 28 Jan. 1835. Murray mss.
70. C. L., Jr. to G. A. M. 31 Jan. 1835. Mantell mss.
71. C. L., Jr. to R. I. M. Feb. 1835. Murchison mss. Also C. L., Jr. to C. B. 18 Feb. 1835. Babbage mss.

somebody amongst our geologists for *"dans le règne des aveugles les borgnes sont rois."* but the departments of our science are so multifarious that one becomes almost unavoidably a smatterer in everything.[72]

At the same time the office of president of the Geological Society made regular demands on his time. His father had joined the other members of the family at Hastings and then all had come up to London on their way back to Scotland. The house at 16 Hart Street was thus full of Lyells; Mary's sister Frances was also staying with them. They were particularly anxious about Elizabeth. Lyell described her illness as "an obstinate complaint in the trachea."[73] They would not yet admit to themselves what they must have known already, that her lungs were infected and that she had consumption. A few days later they could no longer escape the truth. Mr. Lyell wrote to Mantell to thank him for his kindness to Mrs. Lyell, sending him a copy of his edition of the lyrical poems of Dante, and added:

My report of Elizabeth will not make you happy though she is rosy & full and cheerful and the expectoration & little cough in the same state as when you saw her, but the pulse has never been so good since the 5th, when three or four bright drops of blood appeared with the expectoration. Both Dr. Gordon and Dr. Chambers detected by means of the stethoscope a spot in the right side of the lungs where the mischief lies. . . . The actual state of our poor girl is carefully concealed from her & we appear as little anxious as possible, from perceiving that her spirits are very easily depressed since the alarm on the 5th.

At the end of the letter he admitted "I confess (between you & me) I despair, for how very small a number of those who are attacked with that insidious disease at the age of twenty ever escape."[74]

At the beginning of June Lyell began to print the fourth and final volume of the *Principles.* His chief addition to this volume was a further development of his concept of the class of metamorphic rocks. Adam Sedgwick had recently read to the Geological Society a paper in which he distinguished among cleavage

72. C. L., Jr. to J. Fleming. 27 May 1835. Kinnordy mss. [copy].
73. Ibid.
74. C. Lyell to G. A. M. 28 May 1835. Mantell mss.

planes, joints, and stratification in the structure of the slate rocks of Cumberland and Wales.[75] Sedgwick demonstrated that these slates were stratified rocks which had been subjected to much bending and distortion. Lyell was delighted with his facts, which demonstrated that slate rocks were metamorphosed strata. He wrote to Sedgwick to tell him that he was going to cite his paper in the *Principles*. He went on:

> You will see by this that my "Principles" is undergoing one of its metamorphoses. It is no slight matter to keep up such a work to Saturday night.
>
> Indeed I sometimes think I am in danger of becoming per-petual editor to myself, rather than of starting anything new, except it be that my own work becomes new, & unlike its former self.[76]

By the beginning of July the printing and correcting of the fourth volume was completed. Fortunately, just about this time, the last copies of the third edition were sold, so the difficulty which had delayed publication the year before did not exist. Murray agreed to pay him £255 for publishing this edition, which was less than he expected, but still tolerably satisfactory.[77]

On 7 July Lyell set off for Paris with Mary. They went by coach to Dover, where they crossed by steamer to Calais. A rough crossing made them very ill.

> Nevertheless after a good early dinner we took courage & having reached Calais between 10 & 11 o'ck. in morning, made an ex-cursion to the West in a carriage & then walked home over the sands on foot, collecting shells & I geologizing in my "modern-cause" way as to what was going on upon the beach.

At Paris they first went to Deshayes to have him check Lyell's identifications of the Swedish and Baltic shells and then called on various Parisian scientists. Lyell went alone to a meeting of the Institut de France, which he described:

> When I arrived the room was crowded & all the chairs, appro-priated to strangers, full, so I was obliged to wait a quarter of an hour till one was vacated. While in the ante-room Brongniart,

75. A. Sedgwick, "Remarks on the Structure of large Mineral Masses . . ." (1835).
76. C. L., Jr. to A. Sedgwick. 4 June 1835. [copy] Kinnordy mss.
77. J. M. to C. L., Jr. 6 July 1835. Kinnordy mss.

Père came out, looking, it seemed to me, as well as ever & we had a talk together. Soon after I was in, M. Arago, seeing me, came up & greeted me, shaking hands & asking for *Madame* & my *beau-père* & telling me that von Buch[78] was present, & asking if I knew him. On learning that I did not & wd. be glad to know him, he politely went to where he was sitting in one of the front seats & brought him through the crowd to where I was & then opening the door, took us out of the room, introduced us & telling us we might discuss matters at our leisure, went in again to recover his seat as *Secrétaire Perpetuel*. . . . Von Buch began by complimenting me on my paper on Sweden of which he spoke very handsomely & I discussed some of his last papers . . . When the Institute broke up Élie de Beaumont came up & shook hands with me & M. Milne-Edwards,[79] a French naturalist who is editing Lamarck with Deshayes, a young man of English extraction. . . . Von Buch & É. de Beaumont accompanied me home to this hotel telling me some of the things they were going to write against me in a forthcoming paper on Etna & Vesuvius in support of a darling theory of theirs. The most amusing thing was that in the middle of the Rue Richelieu, just where the cabs & omnibuses were thickest, we happened to come upon that grand subject of speculation, the transportation of erratic blocks, upon which von Buch reddening and elevating his voice exclaimed that my notion in my last Swedish paper of conveying them by ice was most extraordinary—such a mean & contemptible cause to effect so grand & mighty a result. "*Sur ce point là Monsieur je vous ferai la guerre jusqu'à la mort.*" While this was vehemently vociferated, we were scattered & nearly run over by a carriage. As soon as we had rallied, I asked him, if he would not employ ice, what cause could he propose? He then talked much & greatly of *une cause générale, un grand phénomène*, which sent all the blocks simultaneously over the North of Europe & the Alps. To this, as to all his opinions, de Beaumont voiced an obsequious assent. I told him I had proved that some of the largest blocks have travelled since the Baltic was a brackish water sea & therefore that the "*grand phénomène*" must have occurred, as it were, yesterday, to which they made no objection.

78. Alexandre Brongniart, 1770–1847; Dominique-François Arago, 1786–1853; Leopold von Buch, 1774–1853.
79. Henri Milne-Edwards (1800–85) was born in Belgium of English parents.

By this time we had lost our way & passed the Hotel, but soon found our way back to it, where I introduced the Baron to Mary, & he told her that he knew her father before she was born, which we did not know. I then shewed him some of my Forfarshire rocks which I had brought here & he gave his opinion upon their mineralogical & geological characters, with confidence & clearness. I like much what I have seen of him, though I believe him to be far too tenacious of any doctrine he has ever taken up & that he has been spoiled by the deference paid to his authority in Germany which has arisen only partly from his talents & great opportunities of observation, but in great part from his station & influence with his Government as a Patron of Science.[80]

For her part Mary Lyell described Von Buch as "a short healthy looking man, polite but impetuous in his manner."[81]

Lyell also attended a meeting of the Geological Society of Paris, where he met still more of the French geologists, and the elder Brongniart invited him and Mary to dine at Sèvres with von Buch and Élie de Beaumont.

They saw the great porcelain manufactory, with a collection of samples of its wares since its founding in 1740, and went for a walk in an adjoining garden where they admired the view of Paris and St. Cloud over the Seine, the water on tap pumped by steam engines, a menagerie with white peacocks, deer, and Balearic cranes walking about in freedom, and beautiful shrubs. Lyell and von Buch, again deep in conversation, lost themselves among the shrubbery.

Lyell had brought to Paris a collection of crag fossil shells given him by Edward Charlesworth in order that Deshayes might determine the proportion of living to extinct species among them. Lyell had previously brought Deshayes crag shells of which the latter thought more than half were still living species. In Charlesworth's collection he thought the proportion of living species even slightly higher. This proportion suggested that the crag was probably a Pliocene formation.

Toward the end of their stay, Berzelius arrived at Paris and also stayed at the Hotel de Bruxelles. Near the end of July the Lyells left Paris for Switzerland, which they entered at Delle (Map 15).

80. C. L., Jr. to his mother. 11 July 1835. Kinnordy mss.
81. M. E. L. Ms. Journal July–Sept. 1835. Kinnordy mss.

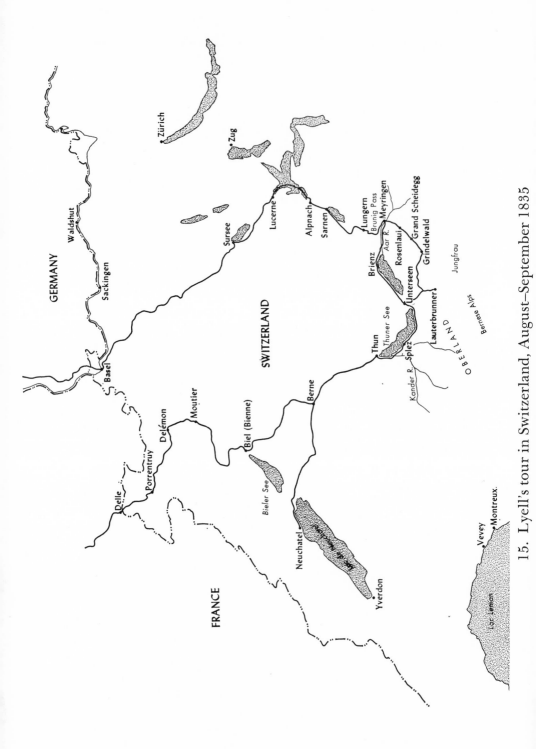

15. Lyell's tour in Switzerland, August–September 1835

At Porrentrui they stopped for two days while Lyell went into the Jura with Professor Thurmann. Thurmann had already published one volume on the geology of the Jura and was about to bring out another.[82]

From Porrentrui they traveled through the Jura by Montiers and Pierre Pertuis to Bienne, thence to Berne where Mary's aunts had a country house and where Lyell renewed his acquaintance with Studer. Then, while Mary remained with her aunts, he went to Neuchâtel by diligence to see Auguste de Montmollin (1808–98) and Louis Coulon, two young geologists. Mary described Lyell's expedition:

> On his arrival late in the evening [at Neuchâtel] he found that M. de Montmollin . . . to whom he had written & sent a letter of recommendation was not at home & said to be 10 miles off at his country seat. Fortunately M. Thurmann had mentioned to Charles that there was a M. Coulon also who studied fossils; he also was absent, but his father offered to drive Charles early next morning to where his son was at a country seat near the lake of Bienne & at the same time he made Charles a present of a beautiful map of the canton of Neuchâtel & a work on its statistics. He also shewed him an M.S. of the geology of the Jura written by von Buch when staying with him 26 years ago [i.e. in 1809] but never published. It contained some good matter & sections. Half an hour after Charles was in bed, M. de Montmollin, who had driven in from the country as soon as the letter had been forwarded to him, came to his door & while Charles was in chemise, a new plan of the day's campaign was agreed upon. It turned out a most profitable day, for M. de M. was just publishing a memoir on some newly discovered phenomena of the district[83] &, after showing his collection at Neuchâtel, he drove Charles in a carriage to many places in the interior of the Jura where the rocks were to be seen.

On his return to Berne Lyell bought a five-hundred foot coil of rope and measured it out in order to use it to determine the depth of the lake of Thun. Mary described the measurement:

> We reached Thun by nine o'clock & set off very soon in a nice covered boat with two rowers to the mouth of the Kander,

82. Jules Thurmann (1804–55), professor of mathematics and natural science at the College of Porrentrui. *Essai sur les soulèvements jurassiques* (1832–36).
83. A. de Montmollin, "Mémoire sur le terrain crétacé de Jura" (1835).

which was turned into the lake of Thun about a hundred years
ago & has already formed a very large delta. We landed & Charles
examined the country for some time & I took a sketch & then
we returned to the boat & measured the depth of the lake at 10
or 12 different points.[84]

Lyell made these measurements in order to get some idea of the
steepness of the slope on which sediments were laid down in the
rapidly growing delta. This very new delta in the lake of Thun
might almost have been created for his purpose. From Thun they
went in a small one horse calêche to Unterseen where Lyell spent
two weeks studying the geology of the Bernese Oberland. He had
really intended to go on to study the geology of the northeastern
Alps around Glarus, known for its fossil bearing slates, and merely
to spend a few days in the vicinity of Thun. However, as he told
Lord Cole, he changed his plan:

> I found when I attempted to understand the geology of the
> neighborhood of the lake of Thun, even with Studer's newly
> published book and map and sections, as he calls them, in my
> hand, that I could not at all comprehend it, nor make out what
> he meant by his numerous formations. I therefore determined
> to make myself master if possible of the geology of this part of
> Switzerland, on which much more has now been written than
> on any other part of the Alps, before I made an attack upon
> less known districts. This I have in some measure accom-
> plished.[85]

He visited every hill and valley on both sides of the lake of Thun
until he was thoroughly acquainted with the locality. He was trying to determine the order of the strata "between the central
granitic axis of the Alps & the great Tertiary valley of Switzerland."[86] They also spent a few days at Lauterbrunner, where Lyell
"went up a considerable height on the Jungfrau to the Roththal
accompanied by a chamois hunter & slept above the perpetual
snow."[87]

When they were ready to leave Unterseen on 1 September, they
sent their baggage by the diligence to Meyringen via Brienz,

84. M. E. L. to her sister-in-law Sophia. 13 Aug. 1835. Kinnordy mss.
85. C. L., Jr. to Lord Cole. 6 Sept. 1835. *L. & L.* I, 453–55.
86. C. L., Jr. to G. A. M. 14 Oct. 1835. Mantell mss., *L. & L.* I, 455–57.
87. M. E. L. to A. Sedgwick. 24 Oct. 1835. [copy] Kinnordy mss.

while they themselves followed a higher route across the mountains. They took their caleche as far as Grindelwald, but also carried a sidesaddle with them so that Mary might ride horseback on the path beyond Grindelwald. At Grindelwald they visited the lower glacier where a man stood ready to fire a small cannon for visitors to hear the echoes. Mary wrote:

> I have no great fancy for cannons, but Charles like to hear them so we had it fired, & it was repeated all round which had a very grand effect. From the glacier we walked up to the inn through meadows covered with purple crocuses, Parnassia & many other flowers.

Next morning they set out early, Mary riding sidesaddle on the caleche horse and Lyell on foot to cross the Scheideck to Rosenlaui, where they stopped for luncheon, and thence to Meyringen:

> We passed through some beautiful fir woods; in descending, curious pendant lichens were hanging from the branches. The flowers were quite like a garden. A sort of purple gentian growing in tufts was very abundant & blue monkshood as tall & of a brighter colour than the garden one. A great many cows & pigs were grazing; the animals are so accustomed here during the long winter to live in the cottages with the inhabitants that they quite expect notice. The kids constantly come up & lick our hands & we can scarcely prevent them following us & the cows & even pigs come up to have their heads patted. . . . We were the first to leave Grindelwald & the last to arrive at Meyringen, Charles finding so much to interest him on the road. Though Rosenlaui is more than two thirds of the way, the last third is by far the worst as great part of the way is like going down stairs on broken, smooth, slipping steps so that it was necessary to walk great part of the way. We came to a boy playing the Alphorn which was about six feet long, but they are sometimes much longer. He played a few notes & then stopped & the echo repeated them all, only rather more softly. It was really very sweet.[88]

At Meyringen Lyell climbed the Urbach Thal where he collected many fossils. On the Jungfrau, at an altitude of nine thousand feet, he found gneiss alternating with a limestone which contained

88. M. E. L. to her mother. 4 Sept. 1835. Kinnordy mss.

ammonites and other fossils. The presence of the ammonites suggested that the limestone was equivalent in age to the lias or somewhat younger, while the alternating layers of gneiss were still another example to show that gneiss had originated as a stratified rock, later metamorphosed by heat.[89]

From Meyringen the Lyells continued their ride on 7 September across the Brunig mountain to Lungern, where they again resorted to a carriage and drove to Sarnen where they spent the night. On the eighth they drove to Alpnach where they took a boat along the lake of Lucerne to Winkel.

> It was rather cloudy [Mary wrote] but the near views were very charming. As Winkel is a large village we expected to have found some sort of a conveyance, but there was nothing to be had but a barrow, into which our luggage was put & we walked to Lucerne about three miles.[90]

That afternoon they took the diligence to Basel which they reached early in the morning. At Basel Lyell again examined the loess and found in it two vertebrae of a fish, the first fossil fish discovered in that formation. They left Basel by diligence, made a side journey to revisit the Kaiserstuhl for Lyell to examine the loess there, and then rejoined the Rhine at Carlsruhe.

On 15 September they continued down the Rhine by steamboat to Bonn to attend the meeting of the German Association for the Advancement of Science. Leonard Horner, Dr. Buckland, and others were there from England. Louis Élie de Beaumont and Leopold von Buch had come from Paris. Lyell enjoyed the meeting. He and Constant Prevost debated fiercely with Élie de Beaumont and von Buch the reality of von Buch's theory of "craters of elevation." Mary reported that Lyell:

> ... has had a famous fight with v. Buch & de Beaumont. It seems to have entertained everybody extremely & to have been the most entertaining day they have had. It seems as if Charles & M. Prevost had quite the best of the fight.[91]

Lyell thought, however, that the benefits of such a meeting, like those derived from the meetings of the British Association, were

89. C. L., Jr. to G. A. M. 14 Oct. 1835. Mantell mss. *L. & L.* I, 455–57.
90. M. E. L. to her sister-in-law Frances. 19 Sept. 1835. Kinnordy mss.
91. M. E. L. to her sister Frances. 21 Sept. 1835. Kinnordy mss.

obtained at no small cost of the time and energy of "good and true workers in science." But Mary enjoyed the opportunity to see old friends at Bonn, and she and Lyell went one day to visit their old haunts at Godesberg.

On their return to 16 Hart Street on the first of October, they found their house in good order. Agassiz was in London and they saw him several times. Mary Lyell mentioned that on 8 October "M. Agassiz dined alone with us & in the evening he & Charles were working about fossil fish together."[92] Lyell was deeply impressed by Agassiz's knowledge of natural history and his enthusiasm for communicating it, but Agassiz's geological ideas were wildly catastrophic. Lyell told Sedgwick:

> I was obliged to compromise half our time day after day most unprofitably in arguing with him. This I did the more zealously from his telling me that he was going to give some lectures on geology at Neuchâtel. He does not flinch at trifles, for finding that the whole cretaceous system from the bottom up to the Maestricht beds had the same fish (so he declares), he deposits the whole during one commotion of the sea.[93]

On Saturday afternoon 10 October, after calling on relatives:

> We proceeded to the Zool.[1] gardens where we saw a most interesting animal, a young orang outang, only arrived yesterday morning. He is the kind that comes nearest to Man & has all the ways of a child & likes to be nursed & petted. He was in the keeper's private apartments, which are kept very warm, & quite at liberty, took hold of our hands & extremely inquisitive in examining everything. He was dres't in a woollen knit shirt like that the little German children wear. He is certainly ugly, but does not seem so mischievous as monkeys generally & so like a black child that one would not be surprised at hearing him speak. They have got three camels also.[94]

Lyell was busy with various kinds of scientific work. On 25 October his youngest sister Elizabeth died at Kinnordy, six days after her twenty-first birthday. Since the previous spring they had not expected her to survive the winter. "I am relieved for my mother's sake that the end was hastened," Lyell told Murchison, "as she has

92. M. E. L. to her sister Katherine. 10 Oct. 1835. Kinnordy mss.
93. C. L., Jr. to A. Sedgwick. 25 Oct. 1835. *L. & L.* I, 457–59.
94. M. E. L. to her sister Katherine. 10 Oct. 1835. Kinnordy mss.

been dreadfully pulled down by watching her child die by inches."[95]

The autumn passed quietly in the house at 16 Hart Street. Mary's sister, Frances Horner, came for a long visit. Lyell began to prepare his president's speech for the anniversary meeting of the Geological Society. By Christmas he reckoned he had spent thirty-five days on the speech; it ultimately cost him fifty days of working time. In November Dr. Heinrich Beck (1796–1863) curator of Prince Christian's shell collection at Copenhagen, came to London for several weeks and spent many days naming the fossil shells in Lyell's collection and comparing them with Edward Charlesworth's collection of crag shells also in London.

Beck knew especially well the living shell species of the North Sea and Arctic waters; therefore he was in a good position to decide whether the fossil shells of the crag were identical with living species. Deshayes had thought the proportion of living species among crag shells was more than half and had considered only sixty-six to be extinct species and the rest to be identical with living forms. Beck thought that almost all of the crag shells were distinct from living species. The difference of opinion arose from the way in which the two naturalists defined a species. For instance, Deshayes considered that the different varieties of *Lucina divaricata* brought from various countries all belonged to one species, whereas Beck considered them to be six or eight distinct species. Since Edward Charlesworth thought that the crag should be separated into two formations of different ages,[96] an opinion which Lyell was not yet ready to accept, the identity of the crag shells interested him intensely.

Lyell wanted to give the Wollaston medal to Deshayes for his contributions to fossil conchology, but there were objections from other members of the council of the Geological Society when he brought the matter forward, and he felt himself too closely linked with Deshayes to insist. In the end they awarded the Wollaston medal to Louis Agassiz for his work on fossil fish, but gave Deshayes £25 from the Wollaston fund for his work on fossil shells. Lyell thought that part of the opposition to Deshayes as a candidate for the medal arose from objections to Deshayes' broad concept of the variability of species. Lyell wrote later to Henry de la Beche that:

95. C. L., Jr. to R. I. M. 30 Oct. 1835. Murchison mss.
96. E. Charlesworth, "On the Crag-formation and its organic remains" (1835).

Deshayes may earn a still higher title to the medal by answering them, as I know he can for I have gone into the question, which is one of the '*haute philosophie*' of conchology & Nat.[1] Hist.[y]—viz. the additional element in the variability of a species which *time* gives & the necessity of allowing a greater range to the variations in proportion as there is more time to multiply the differences of local circumstances capable of acting thro' generations on the same species.—Deshayes has accumulated an enormous body of facts on this subject—no mere conchologist of recent species can do it. All the races of man that have existed & that do & will exist must of course outnumber those which exist at this particular moment in the world—so of any species.[97]

Meanwhile the servants at 16 Hart Street tended to be sickly. On 15 November Mary wrote:

Hall has had a very bad cough, & Jane [the maid] is ill with face ache & Sophy has had rheumatism. I shall become quite a learned doctor in time with so much practice as I prescribe for them all & they all take whatever I give them.[98]

In the evenings she read aloud to Lyell, Gibbon's *Decline and Fall of the Roman Empire,* a work which she had read through twice before but which was new to him. Dr. Beck came frequently to dine as well as to work at Lyell's collection. Mary described him.

Dr. Beck, Frances [her sister] says, lives in our house, & he certainly has been a great deal with us & we like him very much. He is 39, but looks older, has a rough exterior & not elegant manners, but perfect simplicity of character, which gives him a refinement of mind above his station, which is not high, and he has been obliged to work for his bread. But he has one great merit, that he has no servility of character which, living as a sort of dependent on a court, must be difficult not to gain. He is one of the finest conchologists of the day & we have learned much from him.

At Christmas the Lyells went as usual to the Mallets at Hampstead and on New Year's Eve they went to their friends the Door-

<hr />

97. C. L., Jr. to H. de la Beche. 6 April 1836. De la Beche mss. National Museum of Wales.

98. M. E. L. to her sister Frances. 15 Nov. 1835. Kinnordy mss.

mans, a German family living in London. The weather was very
cold. Mary wrote:

> We were well wrapped up going to the Doormans'; otherwise
> we should have felt the cold much as we walked both ways. The
> streets [were] one continued slide which Charles could push me
> into & he slid himself all the way back, so I was afraid the police
> might take us up.[99]

In February 1836 Lyell gave his first anniversary address as
president of the Geological Society. He could announce the establishment of a geological survey of England under the Board of
Ordinance and the appointment of Henry de la Beche as director
of the new survey. He gave a brief obituary of Dr. John Macculloch, who died on 20 August 1835 just as his geological map of
Scotland was about to be published. As was the custom Lyell
summed up the contributions to geology which had appeared during the preceding year. He mentioned Sedgwick's paper on cleavage planes and Murchison's *Silurian System,* then approaching
publication. One important discovery which he could announce
was that Lonsdale, on examining the common white chalk of England, had found it "full of minute corals, foraminifera, and valves
of a small entomostracous animal resembling the Cytherina of
Lamarck. . . . They appear to the eye," said Lyell, "like white
grains of chalk, but when examined by the lens are seen to be fossils in a beautiful state of preservation."[100] The improved micro-
scopes, which had begun to be available in the eighteen-thirties,
were already exerting an influence in geology. He referred to
Charles Darwin who was then on the *Beagle,* sailing homeward
bound from Hobart, Tasmania to King George's Sound at the
southwest corner of Australia:

> Few communications have exerted more interest in the Society
> than the letters on South America addressed by Mr. Charles
> Darwin to Professor Henslow. Mr. Darwin has devoted four
> years from 1832 to 1835 inclusive to the investigation of the
> natural history and geology of South America.[101]

Lyell then went on to give a brief resumé of the evidence which

99. M. E. L. to her sister Katherine. 1 Jan. 1836. Kinnordy mss.
100. "Anniversary address to the Geological Society . . . 19 February, 1836"
(1838) p. 365.
101. Ibid., p. 367. Henslow had published excerpts from these letters. C. Darwin,
Extracts From Letters addressed to Professor Henslow (1835).

Darwin had found to show that the whole of the southern part of South America had been gradually uplifted. The uplift of the Andes had begun before the commencement of the Tertiary period and had continued throughout the whole of that period. Darwin had observed in the western chain of the Andes stratified sedimentary rocks, containing fossils, at an altitude of 13,000 feet. These much disturbed sedimentary strata became crystalline as they approached the subjacent granite. The geology of the Andes therefore was very similar to that of the high Alps, which Lyell had examined the previous summer, and offered additional evidence for his metamorphic theory. In Patagonia Darwin had found that uplift had occurred on a tremendous scale within times geologically very recent.

> Scattered over the whole, and at various heights above the sea, from 1300 feet downwards, are recent shells of *littoral* species of the neighbouring coast, so that every part of the surface seems once to have been a shore, and Mr. Darwin supposes that an upheaval to the amount of 1300 feet has been owing to a succession of small elevations, like those experienced in modern times in Chili.[102]

All of this enormous elevation, then, Darwin attributed to the gradual and cumulative effect of causes still in action. For one who had been so alone, and must often have felt so lonely, in combating catastrophic explanations in all their diverse forms, this was to Lyell very refreshing reinforcement. Well might he write to Sedgwick "How I long for the return of Darwin!"[103] There were a thousand questions he wanted to put to him.

Lyell also presented some of the observations which Captain Fitzroy of the *Beagle* had made of the results of the great earthquake which occurred along the coast of Chile on 20 February 1835, when the land had in many places been uplifted several feet. Because a Mr. Hugh Cuming, formerly resident at Valparaiso, had recently questioned whether any uplift had in fact occurred during the great Chilean earthquake of 1822, Lyell was glad of this circumstantial and detailed evidence of uplift occurring in association with earthquakes. Lyell made additional brief mention of a wide range of papers which had been read before the Society and concluded by affirming his "confidence in the future progress of Geology," which had "risen into such importance as to excite

102. Ibid. Cf. Darwin, *Letters to Henslow*, p. 20.
103. C. L., Jr. to A. Sedgwick. 6 Dec. 1835. *L. & L.* I, 460–61.

a general interest in every nation . . . where the works of nature are studied."[104]

The duties of president and the pursuit of a variety of scientific interests seem to have occupied Lyell during the early months of 1836. Toward the end of May, however, he learned from Murray that the fourth edition of the *Principles,* of which two thousand copies had been printed, was selling so rapidly that it would be out of print within a few months. Although he had long since begun to plan revisions and additional illustrations for a fifth edition, he now had to step up the pace of his preparations. About this time he received letters from John Herschel at Capetown, and from Professor Silliman of Yale College at New Haven, Connecticut, both complimenting him on the *Principles.* Silliman also informed him that an American edition of the *Principles,* reprinted from the third London edition, was to be issued at Philadelphia by Lea. Since there was then no international copyright agreement, Lyell had no means of preventing his work from being thus pirated in America. Silliman wrote, "Your writings are producing a great change in geological opinions. I quote them continually . . ."[105] A few weeks later Silliman wrote again about the interest in the *Principles* in the United States.

> About a year since I was consulted in Boston by a most reputable house as to an edition which they proposed to publish of the *Principles* & they wished to obtain from me the copy of the 3d edition, which you so kindly sent me, as they could not find a copy in the market. I was unwilling to part with my copy both because it was your gift & because I was using it almost daily in my popular & university courses. Subsequently, however, the contemplated edition was abandoned on account of the expense of the cuts which it was ascertained would exceed 600 dollars.

Silliman went on to say that he had also been approached by the firm of D. Appleton and Co. of New York, who had asked him to superintend an edition of the *Principles.*

> I have to add that there would have been a large sale of your work could it have been obtained in New York during a course of public lectures which I have recently finished there on geology. I received from one of the most exclusively commercial

104. "Anniversary address," p. 390.
105. Quoted by Lyell in C. L., Jr. to J. M. 9 June 1836. Murray mss.

cities in the world (money-loving, money-seeking & money-get-ting) a respectful invitation to give this course which occupied 12 evenings with lectures of two hours in many instances & the result was a degree of enthusiasm which, especially in such a city, surprised & gratified me. But I was about to mention that it was manifested by an earnest & general enquiry for your work & for that of Mr. Bakewell while scarcely a copy of either could be obtained. . . . The room was filled holding 800 to 1,000 people & great numbers were refused tickets because there was not room.

Silliman then explained the economics of making Lyell's book available in America.

Your Principles, last edition, I am told has sold for seven & a half dollars and from the London price of 24 s/ it could not sell for much less & afford the bookseller here any profit. The duty on importation into this country is by weight (not of sense or fact) but of paper: the duty is 26 cents a pound—a trifle over a quarter of a dollar. Your copy—4th ed.—I find weighs 3¾ lbs., but it might come in sheets & thus save the weight of the covers & then be done up here. Now as your London editions of course pay publisher & author according to the scale of profit which they have adopted, any number of copies beyond the contem-plated edition can be printed with a comparatively small ex-pense as the composition & cuts are paid for. If therefore you & Mr. Murray can afford the work so that it will sell in this coun-try at a price certainly not exceeding & indeed to make sure of votes it ought to be below that of the London edition then I think you might supply & command the market. But our people are not in general willing to pay high prices & to be candid & to quote the opinion of one of our most sagacious booksellers, with whom I conferred confidentially on receiving your letter, I think your Principles would go in this country promptly at 5 dollars & would not be dead stock at six dollars, but beyond this the sale would probably be slow. I should be greatly gratified if your successive London editions might appear simultaneously in this country at a rate that would insure their sale & in your beautiful getting up without being degraded by an inferior dress.[106]

106. B. Silliman to C. L., Jr. 15 June 1836. Kinnordy mss.

When Lyell received this advice from Silliman he immediately wrote to Murray, sending him a copy of the relevant portions of Silliman's letter, and urging that they, in effect, take Silliman's advice for the new fifth edition.[107]

To his letter Silliman had added news of his own activities:

> ... in Boston (a fine intellectual city of 80,000 people), by invitation of many of their first citizens, I gave in March & April two parallel courses of experimental chemistry to audiences collectively of 1300 to 1500 & I applied the chemistry, especially as regards the composition of the earth & the causes of its heat, to the illustration of the geology of the preceding year.[108]

Silliman had begun to give public lectures on scientific subjects two years earlier and had been very successful at it. He did much to make scientific lectures widely popular in the United States.[109] His success in this venture was to lay the foundation for Lyell's first visit to the United States several years later.

In the end Lyell did not proceed with any haste with his new edition. Perhaps he felt that it would be as well to allow the *Principles* to go out of print for a few months. At the end of June 1836 he went to Scotland for three months. From Kinnordy he wrote to Mantell:

> Here I am rusticating in a very beautiful country not too hot but with much weather like a fine English spring. I am now & then devoting some stray hours to my "Elements," like Buckland's "Bridgewater" long promised but not yet reviewed thank heaven. . . . I am glad to escape awhile from the excitement of London.

Lyell concluded with, "I have been riding today over an old haunt & seeing some points of alluvial & *diluvial* geology with new eyes after my Swedish tour."[110]

On 16 July Lyell's younger brother Henry, whose furlough home from the army in India had been extended on account of an attack of deafness, left Kinnordy to go out again to India; his departure depressed his family.[111]

On 1 August Lyell and Mary went to Edinburgh, where the

107. C. L., Jr. to J. M. 23 July 1836. Murray mss.
108. B. Silliman to C. L., Jr. 15 June 1836. Kinnordy mss.
109. J. F. Fulton and E. H. Thomson, *Benjamin Silliman* . . . (1947) p. 173.
110. C. L., Jr. to G. A. M. 6 July 1836. Mantell mss. *L. & L.* I, 470–71.
111. M. E. L. to her sister Frances. 17 July 1836. Kinnordy mss.

Horner family was staying at their house in Melville Street, and
then to Glasgow, where they took a steamer down the Clyde to the
isle of Arran. On the boat Mary fell into conversation with a
young man sitting beside her who was reading a copy of the *Principles* which he had won as a prize in the chemistry class at Glasgow University. When she found that he was very much impressed
with the work she took him to meet her husband, the author. It
was thus that Lyell first met Lyon Playfair who in later life was
to play an important role in the development of scientific education in Britain.[112] Mary described him as "a young Glasgow student who was very civil to me." He was going to Arran for his vacation. Mary described their arrival:

> It put us quite in spirits as we reached Arran to see so lovely a
> country & one so interesting for geology. As there is no harbour
> at Brodick we were obliged to land in a small boat & it was no
> small exposé for three ladies without *calaçons* to get down the
> side of the vessel. We had then to clamber over rocks. We were
> fortunate in finding a room in the inn as there are an unusual
> number of travellers here. Everything is in the smallest plainest
> way except the food which is excellent. The people of the inn
> wait on us themselves which is much pleasanter than waiters. . . .
> This morning Charles set out with a guide after breakfast on a
> long expedition which he thought would be too fatiguing for
> me so I have been rambling on the seashore collecting treasures
> for him & also a few plants. . . . I never saw a more enjoyable
> looking country. I should like to spend a summer here. It must
> be famous bathing; the water is so perfectly transparent & nice
> sand.[113]

A few days after their arrival Lyon Playfair's friend and fellow
student, Andrew Ramsay, also came to Arran for his vacation.
Since Playfair was helping Mrs. Lyell with her shell collecting,
Ramsay offered to accompany Lyell on his geological field trips
over the island; this experience of geologizing with Lyell seems
to have stimulated Ramsay's interest in geology. His first geological work was on the geology of Arran.[114]

112. A. Geikie, *Memoir of Sir Andrew Crombie Ramsay* (1895) p. 15. Cf. W.
Reid, *Memoirs and correspondence of Lyon Playfair* (1899) pp. 35–36.
113. M. E. L. to her mother. 11 Aug. 1836. Kinnordy mss.
114. A. C. Ramsay, *The geology of the Island of Arran* . . . (1841). He was to become Sir Andrew Crombie Ramsay, director of the Geological Survey of Great Britain. See Geikie, *Ramsay*, p. 15.

Arran is a remarkably beautiful island of green hills lying in the mouth of the firth of Clyde, seemingly remote from the industrial life of Scotland and still undisturbed by it. The geology of Arran was of particular interest to Lyell because Arran embodied an extraordinarily broad range of the geology of Scotland in one place, especially of granite and trap rocks intruded among disturbed and altered stratified rocks. In the northern part of the island there were mountains of granite rising in peaks to an altitude of 3,000 feet and on the sides of these mountains were steeply inclined strata of chloritic schist and blue roofing slate which had been considered by James Hutton and many later observers as primitive rocks. In 1787 Hutton had discovered a place at the northern tip of Arran where strata of red sandstone conglomerate overlay the edges of the nearly vertical strata of primitive schist. The beds of red conglomerate at that point dipped northward into the sea. Similar beds of red conglomerate and sandstone occurred at other points around the shores of Arran and always rested unconformably on the edges of the primitive strata. On the eastern shore of Arran, near the village of Corry, the strata of red conglomerate and sandstone appeared as the ridge of an anticlinal fold, exposed at low tide, with the beds dipping away from the ridge to both north and south. On either side of the anticline on the beach at Corry the strata of red conglomerate and sandstone were overlain by a series of shales and limestones which contained the remains of coal plants and other fossils of the Carboniferous period, and above them again were even younger secondary strata. In the southern part of Arran the secondary strata, which were steeply inclined at Corry and everywhere else in the vicinity of the granite mountains, tended to be more horizontal but they were intersected by numerous dikes of traprock. In fact all the formations of Arran, including even the granite, were intersected by trap dikes indicating that volcanic activity had occurred extensively in the island after its principal geological features had been established. Veins and dikes of granite extended through the schist strata but not into the overlying beds of conglomerate.

After Dr. Hutton's visit in 1787, many other geologists had studied Arran. Robert Jameson had published an account of the island in 1798[115] and John Macculloch a further account in 1819.[116] A number of foreign geologists had visited Arran also, and

115. R. Jameson, *An outline of the mineralogy of the Shetland Islands, and of the island of Arran* ... (1798).

116. J. Macculloch, *A description of the western islands of Scotland* ... (1819).

Lyell had studied von Dechen and Oeynhausen's account of the island.[117]

Robert Jameson, a stalwart Wernerian, had naturally assumed that the granite mountains of Arran were the oldest rock formation on the island and that the stratified rocks had been deposited later. Dr. Macculloch, however, had noted that the secondary red conglomerate of Arran contained, or even largely consisted of, pebbles of the primitive schist strata, but that it contained no pebbles of granite. This curious fact showed that the vertical schist strata had been present when the beds of gravel, which were later to form the red conglomerate, had been laid down, but the granite had not been present or at least not exposed. In 1828 Sedgwick and Murchison had confirmed Macculloch's observation of the absence of granite pebbles in the red conglomerate of Arran.[118] Lyell noted that:

> The total absence of such pebbles has justly been a theme of wonder to those who have visited Arran and have seen that the conglomerates are several hundred feet in thickness and that they occur at the base of the granite mountains, which tower above them in far bolder and more picturesque forms than those of similar composition in other parts of Scotland.[119]

The granite, therefore, instead of being the oldest rock on the island, must have become exposed after the secondary red conglomerate had been laid down. Because the granite mountains had not overflowed the stratified rocks on their sides, Sedgwick and Murchison suggested that the granite had been pushed up from below as a solid mass, rather than as a molten one. They showed that at the lines of junction of the bodies of granite with the stratified rocks the latter tended to be broken and crushed ino a rubble, but had not been fused.

With its granite mountains and numerous dikes of traprock intersecting and altering stratified sedimentary rocks, Arran was a veritable laboratory for Lyell's study of hypogene rocks and for the confirmation of his metamorphic theory.

On 23 August, after nearly two weeks on Arran, the Lyells left to return to Kinnordy where they remained until 28 September. It was a long rest and summer vacation—a complete break from

---

117. H. von Dechen and K. von Oeynhausen, "Die insel Arran" (1829).

118. A. Sedgwick and R. I. Murchison, "On the geological relations of the Secondary strata in the isle of Arran" (1835).

119. *Elements of Geology* (1838) p. 508.

London, foreign travel, and scientific meetings. During the preceding four years Lyell had worked through three editions of the *Principles,* three tours on the continent, one long trip through Sweden, and all the duties and demands of the foreign secretaryship and presidency of the Geological Society. Mary had acted in part as his secretary and assistant. She wrote many of his letters, helped to catalogue shells, and protected him from visitors. She had accompanied him on his excursions on the continent, often under extremely primitive conditions; she had been abandoned in hotel rooms while Charles was off geologizing; she was often lonely. The vacation was for her too a chance to revitalize. When they arrived back at 16 Hart Street Lyell wrote to his father, "Everyone is quite struck with the improvement in Mary's health & appearance."[120] Now they were both rested and ready for fresh campaigns.

120. C. L., Jr. to his father. 4 Oct. 1836. Kinnordy mss.

CHAPTER 13

Darwin and Lyell, 1836–1841

There were the friends Lyell and Charles Darwin, after the return of the latter from his four years' voyage round the world;—Lyell with a Scotch prudence which gave way more and more as years passed on, to his natural geniality, and to an expanding liberality and freedom of speech; and the simple, childlike, painstaking, effective Charles Darwin, who established himself presently at the head of living English naturalists.

Martineau, *Autobiography*[1]

On 2 October 1836 H.M.S. *Beagle* dropped anchor at Falmouth in Devonshire. She was returned from a survey voyage to the coasts of South America which had lasted nearly five years, and on her way home she had circumnavigated the globe. Mr. Charles Darwin, naturalist aboard, came ashore and took the mail coach for Shrewsbury. The landing in England of this tall weather-beaten young man, on a stormy autumn night at a remote harbor, was an event of the first magnitude in the history of science. The scientific world at London in a sense was awaiting him. Of those who waited, none was more eagerly expectant than Charles Lyell.

On 5 October Darwin reached his home at Shrewsbury, where he immediately began to make plans for his scientific work. On 20 October, however, he was at London and at the end of the month he went to Greenwich, where the *Beagle* arrived on the 28th, and began to unpack his specimens. He had already met Lyell who, he told Henslow, "has entered in the *most* good natured manner, and almost without being asked, into all my plans." A few days later he dined with the Geological Society and was immediately proposed for membership. The kindness and helpfulness of Lyell and William Lonsdale, secretary of the Geological Society, stood out so much in contrast to the cool indifference of various naturalists that Darwin said that if he were not already "much more inclined for geology than the other branches of

1. H. Martineau, *Autobiography* (1877) vol. I, p. 268.

Natural History, I am sure Mr. Lyell's and Lonsdale's kindness ought to fix me." Lyell discussed with Darwin his best course for the future. "You cannot conceive [Darwin wrote to Henslow] anything more thoroughly good natured than the heart & soul manner, in which he [Lyell] put himself in my place & thought what would be best to do."[2] Lyell thought that London was the best place to do scientific work, but that next to London, "there was no place in England, so good for a naturalist as Cambridge." Lyell also offered to read some of Darwin's rough papers. To his cousin, W. Darwin Fox, Darwin wrote, "Amongst the great scientific men, no one has been nearly so friendly and kind as Lyell. I have seen him several times and feel inclined to like him much."[3]

On Saturday 29 October the Lyells held "an early tea party" to which Lyell invited Richard Owen and promised him, "you will meet Mr. Charles Darwin."[4] Owen was then a young assistant to William Clift at the Hunterian Museum of the Royal College of Surgeons. Since 1834 he had been giving Lyell occasional advice and instruction in zoology and Lyell had formed a high opinion of his abilities. When Darwin showed his fossil bones to William Clift, Clift thought he should have Professor Buckland examine them because some of them belonged to forms which he, Clift, did not know at all.[5] By contrast, Owen seems to have been eager to examine the bones and Darwin in December 1836 decided to deposit them at the Royal College of Surgeons.[6]

On 10 December, after little more than a month at London, Darwin went to Cambridge and remained there until early in March of 1837, when he returned to London and took up lodgings at 36 Great Marlborough Street. There he began to write up his *Journal*.

Apparently during his first sojourn at London or soon afterward Darwin had written the draft of a paper on the elevation of South

2. C. Darwin to J. S. Henslow. 30 Oct. 1836, in *Darwin and Henslow* . . . (1967) pp. 118–23.

3. C. Darwin to W. D. Fox. 6 Nov. 1836, in F. Darwin, *The Life and Letters of Charles Darwin* (1887) I, p. 277.

4. C. L., Jr. to R. Owen. 26 Oct. 1836. Owen mss.

5. C. Darwin to J. S. Henslow. 30 Oct. 1836, in *Darwin and Henslow*, pp. 118–23.

6. Lyell sent the news to Mantell, "The College of Surgeons are to have Mr. Darwin's South American fossil bones, a new gigantic rodent quadruped & anteater & other wonders which Owen & Clift are to describe." C. L., Jr. to G. A. M. 31 Dec. 1836. Mantell mss.

America and sent it to Lyell who wrote to him about it on 26
December 1836.[7] Lyell also invited Darwin to come up from Cambridge to dine with them at 16 Hart Street and spend the evening
on Monday 2 January; he would be coming to London anyway for
a meeting of the Geological Society on Wednesday the Fourth,
when he was to read a paper on his observations of recent elevations of the coast of Chile. Darwin had already sent the manuscript of his paper to Lyell who wanted to discuss it with him.
They evidently spent considerable time going over this paper
together because on 6 January Lyell wrote to Babbage, "I have
been working so hard both with Darwin's paper & since with his
new views on Coral reefs, then with the Geol. Soc. Council" that
he had not had time to do more than begin Babbage's Ninth
Bridgewater treatise.[8]

Darwin's paper was of considerable interest because it confirmed, once and for all, that there had been an uplift of the
Chilean coast as a result of both the earthquake of 1822 and that
of 1835. But more than this, Darwin showed that all the land along
the coast of Chile bore the marks of being a recently uplifted sea
bottom. He told the Geological Society:

> Along the bold granitic coast south of the promontory which
> forms the bay of Valparaiso, are numerous level and horizontal
> beds of shells, constituting an almost continuous band, elevated
> from 60 to 230 feet above the level of the sea. The shells are
> brittle, but of various kinds, and are all similar and in similar
> proportional numbers to those on the beach.[9]

Darwin also demonstrated that while abrupt upheavals of the land
occurred as a result of earthquakes there must also be occurring a
gradual and insensible rise of the land in South America; this
gradual rise, he thought, extended over a far wider area than that
subjected to earthquakes. The pampas around Buenos Aires and
the whole eastern coast of South America had been elevated in
times geologically very recent, yet this vast area was not subject
to earthquakes.

The following month, in his presidential address to the Geological Society, Lyell commented both on Darwin's observations on

7. C. L., Jr. to C. Darwin. 26 Dec. 1836. *L. & L.* I, 474–75.
8. C. L., Jr. to C. B. 6 Jan. 1837. Babbage mss.
9. C. Darwin. "Observations of proofs of recent elevation on the coast of Chili
. . ." (1838).

the rise of land in South America and his own on the rise of land in Sweden and added:

> I cannot take leave of this subject without remarking that the occurrence in various parts of Ireland, Scotland, and England, of recent shells in stratified gravel, sand and loam, confirm the opinion which I derived from an examination of part of Sweden, namely, that the formations usually called diluvial have not been produced by any violent flood or débacle, or transient passage of the sea over the land, but by a prolonged submersion of the land, the level of which has been greatly altered at periods very modern in our geological chronology.[10]

Lyell was here dismissing the old catastrophism, but at the same time he was adopting a new theory which was to prove embarrassing in its consequences. The rapid and large-scale changes of level which had occurred and were occurring in South America and Sweden were peculiar to those countries, and the consequences inferred from them could not be extended universally.

In the meantime Owen had been studying Darwin's collections of fossil bones from South America. Darwin was already familiar with the more striking features of these fossil animals. Of some bony polygonal plates which he found on the pampas he wrote, "Immediately I saw this I thought they must belong to an enormous armadillo, living species of which genus are so abundant here."[11] However, Owen was able to identify the bones more completely. In response to a query from Lyell, Owen sent him a list of Darwin's fossils, which he had by then identified, on 23 January 1837:

College of Surgeons
Jan.ʸ 23.ᵈ 1837
    My dear Sir,
        I have again compared in a general manner the bones of extinct mammalia collected by Mr. Darwin in South America, and would refer them to the following orders & families:

    Or: *Edentata*
       Fam. *Dasypodidae,* or family of Armadillos

10. "Anniversary Address to the Geological Society, . . . 17 February, 1837" (1838) p. 507.
11. C. Darwin to J. S. Henslow. 24 Nov. 1832 in *More Letters of Charles Darwin* (1903) vol. I, pp. 11–14.

1. cranium (great part of), cervical & part of dorsal vertebrae, sacrum, humerus, ulna & radius, patella & astragalus of a *gigantic species of Armadillo.*
2. Portions of jaws, femur, astragalus & portions of armour
   of an animal, somewhat less than, but allied to *Megatherium.*
3. Part of the cranium, with teeth, of the *Megatherium.*

RUMINANTIA
   Fam: *Camelidae*
   2 cervical vertebrae, portions of femur, & fragments of a
   Gigantic Llama! as large as a Camel, but an *Auchenia*
   (from the plains of Patagonia)

RODENTIA
   Great portion of the Cranium of a *Gigantic Rodent;*
   (size of a Rhinoceros) with some modifications resembling those presented in the cranium of the Wombat.

I regret my absence from home yesterday when you called;
should you be tempted out this evening you will find me disen-
gaged from ½ past 6. What is the best book with figures for working out Ammonites & other fossil Cephalopoda?

With many thanks for your kind enquiries after our health,
believe me with best respects to Mrs. Lyell. My dear Sir

> Faithfully yours
> Rich.[d] Owen.

Lyell seems to have taken advantage of Owen's invitation to call,
because he had a number of questions to ask about the fossil animals. He learned from Owen that the armadillos were a family confined exclusively to South America and the gigantic fossil species
had been as large as a tapir. The animal related to *Megatherium*
had been as large as an ox. Lyell noted on Owen's letter the following queries:

1st   Localities of animals or habitats.
2[dly]   Genus Auchenia?
3.[d]   All new but the Megatherium
4   *Molars* in cranium of   "
5th   Any living rodent in S. America of large size?

He also noted the substance of Owen's answer to his fifth query:

"Largest rodent now known living in S. America is Capybara, a swamp & water animal wh. is large as [a] hog."[12]

In his anniversary address to the Geological Society Lyell described the initial results of Owen's study of Darwin's fossils and then said:

> These fossils . . . establish the fact that the peculiar type of organization which is now characteristic of the South American mammalia has been developed on that continent for a long period, sufficient at least to allow of the extinction of many large species of quadrupeds.[13]

Lyell went on to point out that this close relationship between the fossil and living forms peculiar to South America also existed between the fossil and living forms peculiar to Australia. The proportion of his address that Lyell devoted to Darwin's South American discoveries is an indication of the success that Darwin had already achieved both by his own first paper and by Owen's study of his fossil bones. One of Lyell's final acts as president of the Geological Society was to nominate Darwin to the council.

Lyell's query to Owen whether there was any large living species of South American rodent shows that in January 1837 he was sensitive to the fact that Darwin's fossils demonstrated a close relationship between living and extinct species in South America. It raises the question of his own view of the origin of species in 1837. In 1836 John Herschel had written to Lyell from Capetown to thank him for a copy of the fourth edition of the *Principles* which Lyell had sent him. Herschel described the *Principles* as "one of those productions which work a complete revolution in their subject by altering entirely the point of view in which it must thenceforward be contemplated." He went on:

> You have succeeded too in adding dignity to a subject already grand by exposing to view the immense extent and complication of the problems it offers for solution and by unveiling a dim glimpse of a region of speculation connected with it. . . .
>
> Of course I allude to that mystery of mysteries the replacement of extinct species by others. Many will doubtless think your speculations too bold—but it is as well to face the difficulty at once. For my own part I cannot but think it an inadequate

12. R. Owen to C. L., Jr. 23 Jan. 1837. APS mss.
13. "Address . . . 1837" pp. 510–11.

conception of the Creator to assume it as granted that his combinations are exhausted upon any one of the theatres of their former exercise—though in this as in all his other works, we are led by all analogy to suppose that he operates through a series of intermediate causes & that in consequence, the origination of fresh species, could it ever come under our cognizance, would be found to be a natural in contradistinction to a miraculous process—although we perceive no indications of any process actually in progress which is likely to issue in such a result.[14]

In reply Lyell had written on 1 June 1836:

In regard to the origination of new species I am very glad to find that you think it probable that it may be carried on through the intervention of intermediate causes. I left this rather to be inferred, not thinking it worthwhile to offend a certain class of persons by embodying in words what would only be a speculation. . . . When I first came to the notion, which I never saw expressed elsewhere, though I have no doubt it had all been thought out before, of a succession of extinction of species, and creation of new ones, going on perpetually now, and through an indefinite period of the past, and to continue for ages to come, all in accommodation to the changes which must continue in the inanimate and habitable earth, the idea struck me as the grandest which I had ever conceived so far as regards the attributes of the Presiding Mind. For one can in imagination summon before us a small part at least of the circumstances that must be contemplated and foreknown, before it can be decided what powers and quantities a new species must have in order to enable it to endure for a given time. . . .

. . . Now if it be an insect it may be made in one of its transformations to resemble a dead stick, or a leaf, or a lichen, or a stone, so as to be somewhat less easily found by its enemies; or if this would make it too strong, an occasional variety of the species may have this advantage conferred on it; or if this would be still too much, one sex of a certain variety. Probably there is scarcely a dash of colour on the wing or body of which the choice would be quite arbitrary, or which might not affect its duration for thousands of years. I have been told that the leaf-like expansions of the abdomen and thighs of a certain Brazilian

14. J. F. W. Herschel to C. L., Jr. 20 Feb. 1836. APS mss.

Mantis turn from green to yellow as autumn advances, together with the leaves of the plants among which it seeks for its prey.

Now if species come in succession, such contrivances must sometimes be made, and such relations predetermined between species, as the Mantis, for example, and plants not then existing, but which it was foreseen would exist together with some particular climate at a given time.[15]

That Lyell really believed that new species were being formed in the modern period is evident from a letter he wrote to Adam Sedgwick on 20 January 1838. The week before, Sedgwick had delivered a lecture at Norfolk in which he had referred to the theories of both Lamarck and Lyell. In reporting his lecture, the *Norfolk Chronicle* for 13 January 1838 said that Sedgwick described Lamarck's theory as false and added that "Mr. Lyell's theory that the creation of new species is going on at the present day was also condemned as rash and unphilosophical." Lyell wrote to Sedgwick:

> Now touching my opinion I have no right to object, as I really entertain it, to your controverting it; at the same time you will see, on reading my chapter on the subject that I have studiously avoided laying the doctrine down dogmatically as capable of proof. I have admitted that we have only data for *extinction,* & have left it rather to be inferred, instead of enunciating it, even as my opinion, that the place of lost species is filled up (as it was of old) from time to time by new species. I have only ventured to say that had new mammalia come in we could hardly have hoped to verify the fact. . . .
>
> You will I hope allow that to assume that there have been no new creations since man appeared is at least as "rash and unphilosophical" as modestly to limit the possibility of such occurrences, which is all you will find I have done.[16]

These letters show that, at least for his more perceptive readers, Lyell's *Principles of Geology* demonstrated that new species were coming into being in the modern period and raised the question of *how* they originated. The letters also show how discreet Lyell felt he had to be in treating the species question.

On 19 April Richard Owen read to the Society a detailed anatomical description of the *Toxodon* skull which Darwin had

15. C. L., Jr. to Sir J. F. W. Herschel. 1 June 1836. *L. & L.* I, 464–69.
16. C. L., Jr. to A. Sedgwick. 20 Jan. 1838. [copy] Kinnordy mss.

brought from Uruguay and which, Owen showed, possessed simi-
larities to the modern water hog (*Hydrochaerus capybara*) of
South America.[17] Lyell was delighted with the new information
provided by Darwin's discoveries. Moreover, he had found in
Darwin a new and close friend. To Sedgwick he wrote:

> . . . it is rare, even in one's own pursuits to meet with congenial
> souls & Darwin is a glorious addition to my society of geologists
> & is working hard & making way both in his book & in our dis-
> cussions. I really never saw that bore Dr. Mitchell so successfully
> silenced or such a bucket of cold water so dexterously poured
> down his back as when Darwin answered some impertinent &
> irrelevant questions about S. America.[18]

Then on 3 May Darwin presented his own report of his South
American fossil bones. He first described the red earth formation
of the pampas; and then presented evidence to show that the basin
of the Plata had recently been uplifted to its present level. The
area of the pampas and the lower parts of Banda Oriental province
had therefore once formed a great bay and "into the bay the several rivers which now unite to form the Plata poured down reddish sediment." Darwin suggested that the ancient rivers had carried down the carcasses of land animals just as modern rivers do,
and the bodies of these animals then became buried in the mud
of the sea bottom. After describing the various fossils and the locations where he found them:

> The author finally remarked, that although several gigantic
> land animals, which formerly swarmed in South America, have
> perished, yet that they are now represented by animals, confined
> to that country; and though of diminutive size, possess the pecul-
> iar anatomical structure of their great extinct prototypes.[19]

Darwin afterwards dated the beginning of his views on the
transmutation of species from the month of March 1837, that is,
from the time when he had just returned to London from Cambridge and must have been beginning to write this paper, delivered on 3 May.[20] Lyell had remarked on the distinctive South Amer-

17. R. Owen, "A description of the cranium of the *Toxodon Platensis* . . ."
(1838).
18. C. L., Jr. to A. Sedgwick. 25 April 1837. [copy] Kinnordy mss.
19. C. Darwin, "A sketch of the deposits containing extinct Mammalia in the
neighbourhood of the Plata" (1838).
20. C. Darwin, "Darwin's Journal" (1959) p. 7.

ican characteristics of the fossil as well as the living forms in his anniversary address on 17 February, but he did not then state it in terms of a direct comparison between fossil and living species as Darwin did on 3 May.

Darwin was at this same time actively writing his *Journal of Researches,* in which also he discussed these South American fossils. He wrote that he was puzzled by the large bones which he had found in a bed of reddish earth atop the ninety-foot cliff at Bahia Blanca because "how could any large quadruped have subsisted on these wretched deserts in lat. 49° 15?" He also mentioned that he had no idea what kind of large animal these bones represented before Owen examined them. Owen found that they belonged to "an animal allied to the guanaco or llama, but fully as large as the true camel."[21] Since the camel was capable of living in desert countries, Darwin thought that this large extinct camel-like animal must have been able to do so too. The puzzle posed by the large bones from Bahia Blanca was therefore less mysterious.[22]

In his *Journal of Researches* Darwin wrote of Owen's demonstration that the large fossil bones of Bahia Blanca were those of a gigantic llama.

> The most important result of this discovery, is the confirmation of the law that existing animals have a close relation in form with extinct species. As the guanaco [i.e. llama] is the characteristic quadruped of Patagonia, and the vicuna of the snowclad summits of the Cordillera, so in bygone days, this gigantic species of the same family must have been conspicuous on the southern plains.[23]

Thus Darwin's awareness of Owen's discovery seems to have coin-

21. C. Darwin, *Journal of Researches* . . . (1839) pp. 152–55, 208–11. Owen seems to have made his first serious examination of Darwin's fossil bones in January 1837 and his first communication of his findings was his letter to Lyell on 23 January. Darwin recorded in his *Journal* that he paid two short visits to London in January 1837, but one of these was to deliver his paper on the elevation of Chile at the Geological Society on 4 January and the other visit may have been before Lyell received Owen's letter of the 23rd. Lyell wrote to Darwin on 13 February urging him to attend the anniversary meeting of the Geological Society on 17 February and mentioning their earlier discussion of Darwin's coral reef theory, but he said nothing about Owen's work on the fossil bones. In any event Darwin seems not to have come to London from Cambridge at all during February 1837 and his first awareness of Owen's results may have come after he moved permanently to London on 6 March.

22. F. Darwin, *Life and Letters* I, p. 282.

23. C. Darwin, *Journal of Researches,* p. 209.

cided with his first deep conviction of the reality of the transmutation of species.

During the spring of 1837, when Darwin was having increasing doubts as to the fixity of species, Lyell was also deeply concerned with the question of defining species because Dr. Beck of Copenhagen, and George Sowerby of London differed so widely from Gérard Deshayes of Paris concerning the limits of species. Whereas Deshayes considered that a large proportion of the fossil shells of the crag were identical with living species, Beck and Sowerby thought that all of them were distinct. Because Lyell had based his whole classification of Tertiary strata on the proportion of living species among the fossil shells of each formation, the question of the proper identification of species was a fundamental one. He knew that Deshayes' opinion was based on a broad knowledge of Tertiary fossil shells and of their variability through time. On 6 June 1837 he and Mary set out from London for Copenhagen to learn the points used by Beck in distinguishing species and, apart from a visit to Norway, they remained at Copenhagen until 28 August.

Lyell understood that the question was larger than merely that of the characteristics by which species should be distinguished, because soon after his arrival at Copenhagen he discussed with Beck an instance described by Captain Parry of a bitch having mated with wolves, an instance which seemed "to favour notion of wolf & dog being same species." Beck, Lyell noted, "suggests that the jackall & wolf & others of genus Canis may be wild progenitors of the diff.ᵗ races of dog?"[24] They also discussed the possible origin of the Chinese pig from the wild pig, which Beck thought had not yet been sufficiently studied. Lyell asked Beck what he thought of Darwin's discovery of fossil bones of extinct mammals such as *Megatherium* and *Toxodon* in the red mud of the pampas together with shells identical with species living in the estuary of the Plata. This fact seemed to show that species of shells lived longer than those of mammals. Lyell noted the following queries which he put to Beck:

1. If he admits that there are true cosmopolite species, may there not also be among these some which vary much accord.ᵍ to localities?—more than it is possible for non-cosmopolites to do?

24. Ms. Notebook 64, p. 61. Kinnordy mss.

2. May not time when added as an element cause new varieties to arise from gradual change of circumst.ˢ? Thus all the var.ˢ of the human race in 5,000 years are more than those now existing—extinct varieties of Man, therefore, there may be extinct varieties of any variable species.

Many existing var.ˢ of Man will certainly die out, but others may arise, & so of the dog?—so of Venus divaricata?—

3. Is it not true that a cosmopolite species will probably out-last others?[25]

They discussed *Buccinum undatum,* a cosmopolitan species of which Deshayes had shown Lyell a number of varieties from different parts of the world. Beck considered all of these to be distinct species. Lyell observed:

Here then is the question. Are there one or 10 species of Buccinum undatum—one or 7 species of Lucina divaricata? If one of the latter, then the Paris & Touraine & Maryland fossils will be identical, if many then all distinct.

Beck does not admit that the argument founded on permanent varieties in natural history nor that on time changing species in Geology [is valid].

He says that you cannot stop between Lamarck's transmutation of species theory & any one which would bring the 7 species of Lucina divaricata, & as many fossils, from one primitive species, the foundation of the whole group.[26]

As his discussions with Beck proceeded, Lyell came to the conclusion that, while Beck was a somewhat more accurate conchologist than Deshayes, he was prejudiced against the possibility of discovering fossil species identical with living ones.

While he was at Copenhagen in August 1837 thus pondering the range of species of shells in space and time, Lyell received a letter from Charles Darwin written from 36 Great Marlborough St., London, and dated 30 July 1837. Darwin was at this time still writing his *Journal of Researches.* He seems to have been working on the chapter on the Galapagos Islands and he had also recently begun his first notebook on the transmutation of species. He wrote:

25. Ibid., p. 101.
26. Ms. Notebook 65, p. 49. Kinnordy mss. Abbreviations extended for clarity.

I believe there are 27 land birds from the Galapagos, all new except one, (a species of very wide range) yet of an American form, some north, some south. Now as the Galapagos is on the Equator is this not curious? Reptiles the same.

Has your late work at shells startled you about the existence of species? I have been attending a very little to species of birds, & the passages of forms do appear frightful—everything is arbitrary; not two naturalists agree on any fundamental idea that I can see.

I had a most interesting morning with Owen (who is gone to rest for a month in the N. of England) at the Coll. of Surgeons. We made out the rem.ˢ of 11 or 12 great animals, besides these some rodents, one of wh. is a distinct species, but most strictly S. American genus. At Bahia Blanca there were no less than *five great* Edentata! What could those monsters have fed upon? I am well convinced, like the present Armadillo they lived on land nearly desert. I have worked out the *non*-relation of bulk of animals & luxuriance of vegetation, & I have been perfectly astonished at some of the facts given me by Dr. Smith.[27] If it would be any satisfaction to you I think it could be proved rhinoceroses live upon air, certain it is they must be light feeders. What will you say to the tusk of a boar like the African species being imbedded with the Edentata. Lastly I am sure when you read my evidence (& see the tooth) you will be as much convinced as I am that a horse was formerly common on the Pampas as at the present day. What an extraordinary mystery it is, the cause of the death of these numerous animals so recently, & with so little physical change.[28]

Lyell's reply to this letter has been lost. He thought the passage sufficiently interesting to transcribe into his notebook. It would have been unlike him not to answer and in his answer to discuss Darwin's questions fully. Darwin seems to have told Lyell that he had begun to collect facts which might bear on the question of the possible transmutation of species, and they possibly discussed the species question occasionally during the winter of 1837–38. On 13 September 1838 he wrote to Lyell, who was then at Kinnordy:

27. Sir Andrew Smith (1797–1872), ornithologist and African traveler, was a friend of Darwin whom he had met at Cape Town during the voyage of the *Beagle*.

28. Ms. Notebook 69, pp. 140–42. Kinnordy mss.

I have lately been sorely tempted to be idle, that is as far as past geology is concerned, by the delightful number of new views, which have been coming in, thickly and steadily, on the classification & affinities & instincts of animals—bearing on the question of species—note book after note book has been filled with facts which begin to group themselves clearly under sub-laws.[29]

By this time Darwin was making entries in his third transmutation notebook and he had developed a preliminary theory of the transmutation of species. His theory held that when a population of a species became isolated geographically or otherwise, it became subject to variation and gradually, through many generations, diverged from the other members of the species to form a new and distinct species which did not interbreed with the old. Thus he united what he knew of the geographical distribution of closely related species, the succession of types in South America and other places, and the variation which accompanied sexual reproduction, to form a coherent if as yet incomplete theory.

In his third transmutation notebook, which he began in July 1838, Darwin revealed an increased interest in the breeding of domesticated animals which he began to see had a direct bearing on the species question. On 7 September 1838 he noted the resemblance between the hump of Indian cattle and that of bison and asked himself whether "*variation* in one was analogous to specific *character* of *other species in genus.*"[30]

On 3 October 1838 Darwin began to read Thomas Robert Malthus, *Essay on the Principle of Population,* a book which had an electrifying effect on his ideas. Malthus showed that populations of living things tended to increase in geometric progression, or had the potential to do so, whereas their food supply was constant or increased, in the case of the human population, only in arithmetic ratio. He thereupon attempted to determine for human populations the factors which prevented them from increasing.

Malthus' book had the effect of forcing on Darwin's attention the intense and unremitting struggle for existence in nature. He realized that the population of a species was being constantly and rigorously decimated. From his interest in animal breeding he concluded that this constant elimination of individuals would be selective and would tend to select for characters which favored

29. C. Darwin to C. L., Jr. 13 Sept. 1838. APS mss.
30. "Darwin's Notebooks on transmutation of species . . ." (1960) p. 137.

individuals in the struggle for existence. Thus he saw active in every species a constant process of natural selection which could modify the species through time.

Lyell and Darwin met frequently to discuss geology. Seldom can there have been a more fruitful interaction of scientific minds. Darwin had found the *Principles of Geology* an indispensable guide in interpreting the geology of South America and one which illuminated the meaning of the country for him. On 10 April 1837 he wrote to Leonard Jenyns, "I have a capital friend in Lyell, and see a great deal of him, which is very advantageous to me in discussing much South American geology."[31] In turn, Lyell found that Darwin's South American geology presented striking and massive new evidence for the theories which he had developed in the *Principles*. He found too that Darwin was extending the application of his concepts of uplift and subsidence brilliantly.

In January 1837 Darwin had explained to Lyell his theory of the origin of coral reefs and atolls. In the *Principles* Lyell had argued that atolls represented tops of volcanic craters in the ocean, capped with coral.[32] However, he had also suggested that the absence of any extensive tract of land in the Pacific, where coral islands were very numerous, "seems to show that the amount of subsidence by earthquakes exceeds in that quarter of the globe at present the elevation due to the same cause."[33] In South America Darwin had discovered evidence for the large-scale uplift of that whole continent and he had also concluded that where great thicknesses of sediment were uplifted there must previously have been an amount of subsidence roughly equal to the depth of sediment deposited. He was therefore prepared to consider the possibility of extensive subsidence as well as extensive elevation. Darwin was also troubled by Lyell's theory of coral islands as simply the tops of volcanic craters, because the coral islands were scattered on the surface of a very deep ocean. Each island was surrounded on all sides by water of great depth, yet none of the coral islands rose significantly above sea level. Darwin found it difficult to conceive how, if coral islands represented the tops of volcanic craters, so many volcanic mountains distributed over thousands of square miles had been elevated from the sea bottom, or sunken, so exactly to the same level. At the same time Darwin knew that coral grew

31. Darwin, *Life and Letters* I, p. 282.
32. *Principles* II (1832) p. 290.
33. Ibid., p. 296.

only in relatively shallow water, not more than 120 feet deep. This fact raised a particular question in the case of encircling reefs, that is, reefs which encircled a high island such as Tahiti, at a distance of two or three miles from the shore. Darwin wrote:

> We will take as an instance, Vanikoro. . . . The reef there runs at a distance of nearly two, and in some parts three miles from the shore, and is separated from it by a channel having a general depth between thirty and forty fathoms, and, in one part, no less than fifty, or three hundred feet. Externally the reef rises from an ocean profoundly deep. Can anything be more singular than this structure? It is analogous to that of a lagoon, but with an island standing like a picture in its frame, in the middle. . . . We cannot suppose these encircling reefs are based on an external crater, for the central mass sometimes consists of primary rock.[34]

If the rock of the mountainous central island continued to descend beneath the sea with the same slope as it showed at the shore, then the depth of coral which overlay the foundation rock at a distance of two miles from the shore was far greater than the greatest depth at which coral could live. The solution, Darwin decided, was that the island had subsided and at the same time the corals had grown so as to maintain the encircling reef at or near the surface of the sea. As the island subsided it grew smaller and the encircling reef more distant from its shores. If the subsidence continued long enough the whole central island would disappear beneath the sea and the former encircling reef, with no island left to encircle, would become an atoll enclosing only a large lagoon.

A further consequence of Darwin's theory was that those areas of the Pacific which contained coral atolls and encircling reefs must be areas of subsidence and he was thus able to map out great bands of subsidence on the floor of the Pacific. In addition there was a third class of coral reefs, the fringing reefs, which very closely surrounded islands with often a band of dead coral between the reef and the island. Fringing reefs, Darwin concluded, occurred around islands undergoing elevation, and the areas of the Pacific containing islands with fringing coral reefs must therefore be areas of elevation of the ocean floor. However, in the Pacific the areas of elevation so determined were relatively small in comparison with the vast areas of subsidence.

34. C. Darwin, *Journal of Researches* (1839) p. 555.

Darwin apparently explained his theory of coral reefs to Lyell when he was in London in January 1837. On 13 February Lyell wrote to him to urge him to attend the anniversary meeting of the Geological Society on 17 February, to hear Lyell's announcement of the new fossil animals from South America, and said:

> I could think of nothing for days after your lesson on coral reefs, but of the tops of submerged continents.
>
> It is all true, but do not flatter yourself that you will be believed, till you are growing bald, like me, with hard work & vexation at the incredulity of the world.[35]

On 24 May Lyell wrote to Herschel, who had entertained Darwin at the Cape of Good Hope:

> I am very full of Darwin's new theory of coral islands & have urged Whewell to make him read it at our next meeting. I must give up my volcanic crater theory for ever, tho' it cost me a pang at first, for it accounted for so much—the annular form, the central lagoon, the sudden rising of an isolated mountain in a deep sea all went so well with the notion of submerged, crateriform & conical volcanoes of the shape of South Shetland & with an opening into which a ship could sail—& then we had volcanoes inside, some circular reefs as in Dampeir's island, & then we knew that it was not the corals which had any inclination of their own to build in a ring, like mushrooms & funguses in fairy circles on the green, for the very same species of corals will form a long barrier reef or grow in any shape the ground permits—& then the fact that in the Pacific we had scarcely any rocks in the region of coral islands, save two kinds, coral limestone & volcanic! Yet, in spite of all this, the whole theory is knocked on the head & the annular shape & central lagoon have nothing to do with volcanoes nor even with a crateriform bottom.— Perhaps Darwin told you when at the Cape what he considers the true cause—? Let any mountain be submerged gradually & coral grow in the sea in which it is sinking & there will be a ring of coral & finally only a lagoon in the centre.—Why? For the same reason that a barrier reef of coral grows along certain coasts, Australia etc.[36]

Lyell went on to explain with the aid of a diagram the detailed working of Darwin's theory.

35. C. L., Jr. to C. Darwin. 13 Feb. 1837. [copy] Kinnordy mss.
36. C. L., Jr. to J. F. Herschel. 24 May 1837. *L. & L.* II, 11–13.

On 31 May 1837 Darwin presented his theory to the Geological Society.[37] He showed that if, as his theory indicated, the broad area of the South Pacific containing coral islands was an area of subsidence, there were other areas such as that in the vicinity of Sumatra where elevation had occurred. Darwin seems originally to have inferred the probability of large-scale subsidence as a necessary consequence of the kind of large-scale elevation which, he saw, had occurred in South America. He said in fact that he had developed his coral island theory almost in its entirety before he left the coast of South America.

In South America Darwin had found first in the region of the Rio de la Plata elevated beds of fossil shells of the same species as those living along the coasts. These showed the very recent elevation of the area of the pampas. Then as he had cruised with the *Beagle* southward along the coast he had observed in Patagonia a series of terraces which extended continuously along the coast from the Rio Colorado to the Rio Negro, a distance of 800 miles. He was astonished to find that these terraces, of which he could distinguish seven, were always within a few feet of the same level wherever he measured them along some 600 miles of coast. The principal ones stood at elevations of 100 feet, 250 feet, 350 feet, and 580 feet above the sea. Each terrace was capped with a gravel formed of pebbles of porphyry. In fact, the plains of Patagonia were wholly covered with this coarse porphyritic gravel, a fact which made them remarkably barren.

> At first [Darwin wrote] I could only understand the grand covering of gravel, by the supposition of some epoch of extreme violence, and the successive lines of cliff, by as many great elevations, the precise action of which I could not however follow out. Guided by the "Principles of Geology," and having under my view the vast changes in this continent, I came to another, and I hope more satisfactory conclusion.[38]

His conclusion was that each line of cliff represented not a period of abrupt elevation, but rather a long period of repose during which the sea had eaten back into the land. The nearly level plains, however, represented periods of gradual elevation during which each portion of the plain had successively formed a line of shingle beach.

37. C. Darwin, "On certain areas of elevation and subsidence . . ." (1838).
38. C. Darwin, *Journal of Researches* (1839) p. 204.

In explaining the widely-spread bed of gravel, [Darwin wrote] we must first suppose a great mass of shingle to be collected by the action of innumerable torrents, and the swell of an open ocean, at the submarine base of the Andes, prior to the elevation of the plains of Patagonia. If such a mass should then be lifted up, and left exposed during one of the periods of subterranean repose; a certain breadth, for instance a mile, would be washed down, and spread out over the bottom of the invading waters. . . .

If this part of the sea should now be elevated, we should have a bed of gravel, but it would be of less thickness than in the first mass, both because it is spread over a larger area, and because it has been much reduced by attrition. This process being repeated, we might carry beds of gravel, always decreasing in thickness (as happens in Patagonia) to a considerable distance from the line of parent rock.[39]

Darwin does not indicate just when he developed the theory for the distribution of Patagonian gravel outlined above, but it was essential to his understanding of the recent geological history of the southern tip of South America. When he reached Chile in September 1834 he visited the elevated beds of shells along the coast north of Valparaiso. "They nearly all consist of one species of Erycina," Darwin wrote, "and these shells at the present day live together in great numbers on the sandy flats. So wonderfully numerous are those forming the beds, that for years they have been quarried, and burnt for the lime, with which the large town of Valparaiso is supplied."[40] He was also surprised to find elevated plains south of Santiago. "Never having heard of these plains," he wrote, "I was much surprised at meeting with such scenery in Chile. The plains belong to more than one series of different elevations, and they are traversed by broad flat-bottomed valleys; both of which circumstances, as in Patagonia, bespeak the gentle retreat of the ocean."[41] Then on 4 March 1835, when the *Beagle* sailed to Concepción from Valdivia, they found the city entirely destroyed by a great earthquake which had occurred on 20 February. As a result of this earthquake the coast line had been permanently elevated nearly two feet, and the island of Santa Maria elevated between two and three feet.

39. Ibid., p. 206.
40. Ibid., p. 310.
41. Ibid., p. 327.

All of these facts showed that Chile had undergone elevation during the recent past and that it was being elevated at present through a series of small successive elevations which accompanied each earthquake.

Two weeks after seeing the effects of the great earthquake at Concepción, Darwin rode across the Andes. He found the core of these mountains to be a red granite which had pushed upward, into a series of anticlinal ridges, an enormous thickness of stratified rocks. In these strata he found fossils of the secondary period at altitudes of more than 13,000 feet. On the eastern side of the Andes he found that as he rode north to Mendoza he was riding across a plain of porphyritic gravel similar to that of Patagonia and very different from the rich plains of the pampas to the east. On his return from Mendoza he crossed first a lower range of mountains, the Uspallata, separated from the Andes by a narrow plain. The rocks in it consisted of various submarine lavas alternating with sedimentary strata. In these rocks at an elevation of about 7,000 feet he found a fossil forest of petrified trees. Robert Brown later identified the wood as that of one of the *Araucarian* family, to which the South Chilian pine also belonged. The bed containing the trees was overlain by other sedimentary strata and by submarine lavas a thousand feet thick. Darwin's imagination was deeply struck by the enormous changes in level which had occurred since these trees had "waved their branches on the shores of the Atlantic." The bed containing the trees had sunk beneath the ocean to a great depth in order to be covered over with the sedimentary beds and submarine lavas and then had been re-elevated from the depths of the sea to an altitude of 7,000 feet above sea level. He reasoned that at an earlier period the Andes were probably a chain of islands, and since, then, the eastern side would not be cut off from the moisture-bearing westerly winds, they would be richly forested.

Darwin outlined these general conclusions concerning the subsidence and re-elevation of South America in his *Journal of Researches*. He began to send it to press in August 1837 and it was printed between August and November of 1837, but publication was delayed until Captain Fitzroy completed his account of the voyage. However, Darwin gave a copy in printed sheets to Lyell, and Lyell had begun to read it in October. Mary seems to have read it to him in installments in the evenings during the winter of 1837–38. On 10 March 1838 she wrote to her father, "We have not been reading anything very particular lately since we finished Mr. Darwin's journal which is most interesting to the last."[42] Lyell was thus made aware, quite early, of the broad outlines of Darwin's geological discoveries on the voyage of the *Beagle* and doubtless continued to urge him to present his results to the scientific world.

At a meeting of the Geological Society on 7 March 1838, Charles Darwin read a remarkable paper in which he connected the phenomena of earthquakes and volcanic action to show that they were both manifestations of the internal forces of the earth which had worked and were working to elevate the continent of South America.[43] He showed that in the great earthquake of 1835 on the western coast of South America, the quakes had occurred from Concepción to the island of Juan Fernandez 720 miles to the north and that they had been accompanied by extensive volcanic action. Darwin said:

> To form a just idea of the scale of this phenomenon, we must suppose, during the same hour, Europe to be shaken from the North Sea to the Mediterranean,—a large tract of the eastern coast of England to be permanently elevated,—a train of volcanoes on the northern coast of Holland to burst forth in action,—an eruption to take place at the bottom of the sea, near the northern extremity of Ireland, and the ancient vents of Auvergne, Cantal, Mont d'Or, and others, so long extinct, each to send up to the sky a dark column of smoke. [p. 607]

He added:

> In a geological point of view, it is of the highest importance thus to find three great phenomena,—a submarine outburst, a period of renewed activity through many habitual vents, and a permanent elevation of the land,—forming parts of one action, and being the effects of one great cause, modified only by local circumstances. [p. 609]

Darwin reproduced two tables compiled by Alexander von Humboldt of earthquakes and volcanic phenomena which had occurred over very wide areas in 1796–97 and 1811–12. He added a third

42. M. E. L. to her father. 10 March 1838. Kinnordy mss.
43. C. Darwin, "On the connexion of certain volcanic phenomena . . ." (1840). Specific page references given in the text. Cf. *Proc. Geol. Soc. Lond.* 2 (1838): 654–60.

table of his own of earthquakes and volcanic activity in 1834–35 which had extended from Concepción in Chile to Jamaica (p. 610). Darwin noted that violent eruptions of Osorno and Aconcagua in Chile, and Coseguina in Central America had all occurred within six hours on 19 and 20 January 1835 although Aconcagua was 400 miles north of Osorno and Coseguina 2700 miles to the north. "It may be asked," Darwin said, "were these three eruptions, which burst through the same chain of mountains, in any respect connected, or was the coincidence accidental–" (p. 612).

Darwin attributed the earthquakes which occurred along the coast of South America to the forcing of molten rock between masses of strata. He noted that in the vicinity of volcanoes which had been in eruption at the time of the great earthquake which destroyed Concepción, the effects of the earthquake were barely felt. The volcanoes, therefore, seemed to be acting as escape valves which released the pressures that elsewhere produced earthquakes. Earthquakes, he noted, generally were felt along long narrow bands, which in the case of the Chilian earthquakes extended north and south along the coast but did not extend inland across the Cordillera. Thus "when earthquakes follow coast lines they may be said to extend parallel to the littoral chain of mountains." Darwin continued his argument:

Now, what constitutes the axis, where visible, of most great mountain chains? Is it not a wedge-formed linear mass of rock, which scarcely any geologist disputes was once fluid, and has since cooled under pressure? Must not the interjection of such matter between masses of strata have relieved the subterranean pressure in the same manner, as an ejection of lava and scoriae through a volcanic orifice? [p. 619]

He thought that the interjection of fluid rock between masses of strata would produce an earthquake; therefore, an earthquake such as the one which destroyed Concepción in 1835, was the result of the rending of strata and the forcing of fluid rock between them. This earthquake, then, was one small step in the elevation of the line of the Cordillera. Furthermore, if this theory were true, Darwin said, one might expect "to find proofs of successive formation in the many parallel ridges, of which the Cordillera is composed." These he had found. He had also concluded from his observations of large-scale elevation in South America "that mountain chains are only subsidiary and attendant phenomena on continental elevations" (p. 623). This conclusion also followed from mathematical studies of the mechanics of earth movements made by William Hopkins of Cambridge. Darwin suggested that as each injection of molten rock was allowed to cool and solidify, it would offer a greater resistance to later injections. "Would not the crust in such case yield more readily on either flank, as I believe it must have done in the Cordillera," asked Darwin, "than on the line of an axis composed of solidified rocks" (p. 624). This would account for the formation of subordinate parallel ridges.

The most impressive feature of Darwin's theory was that he showed how the highest and longest mountain chains could be elevated gradually.

> The important fact [he said] which appears to me proved, is that there is a power now in action, and which has been in action with the same average intensity (volcanic eruptions being the index) since the remotest periods, not only sufficient to produce, but which almost inevitably must have produced, unequal elevation on the lines of fracture. [p. 625]

This was the most extensive and strongly supported argument yet to be launched against Élie de Beaumont's theory of the paroxysmal elevation of mountain chains, and it had the great advantage of being based on the detailed examination of an important mountain chain, the Andes. Lyell was impressed by such powerful support arrayed in favor of his doctrine of the gradual action of existing causes. He wrote to Leonard Horner:

> . . . about the last meeting of the G.S. where Darwin read a paper on the connexion of volcanic phenomena & elevation of mountain chains in support of my heretical doctrines; he opened upon de la Bêche, Phillips & others, for Greenough was absent, his whole battery of the earthquakes and volcanos of the Andes & argued that spaces at least a thousand miles long were simultaneously subject to earthquakes & volcanic eruptions & that the elevation of the whole Pampas, Patagonia etc. all depended on a common cause & also that the greater the contortions of strata in a mountain chain the smaller must have been each separate and individual movement of that long series which was necessary to upheave the chain. Had they been more violent he contended that the subterranean fluid matter w.^{d} have gushed out & overflowed & the strata would have been

blown up & annihilated. He therefore introduced a cooling of one small underground injection & then the pumping in of other lava or porphyry or granite into the previously consolidated & first formed mass of igneous rock.

A considerable discussion followed. Henry de la Bêche, John Phillips, Dr. Fitton, and William Whewell spoke. Lyell added:

I was much struck with the different tone in which my gradual causes were treated by all, even including de la Bêche from that which they experienced in the same room 4 years ago when Buckland, de la Bêche, Sedgwick, Whewell and some others treated them with as much ridicule as was consistent with politeness in my presence.

A day or two later he added a postscript to this letter:

Monday—I found that Darwin, who was with us yesterday evening, had felt very differently in regard to Wed'y's discussion for not being able to measure the change of tone in the last 4 years he translated de la B's & Co.'s remarks into a vigorous defiance instead of a diminishing fire & an almost beating of a retreat. But I have restored him to an opinion of the growing progress of the true cause.[44]

During the spring months of 1838 Darwin was also reading and criticizing the manuscript of Lyell's *Elements* before it went to the printer, a service he continued to perform for Lyell until he set off for Glen Roy in June.

Darwin's Glen Roy paper, which in later life he regarded as a reprehensible blunder and which did prove mistaken in its central thesis, was the product of the various influences that had entered into his development as a scientist. It reflected his experience in South America where he had seen proofs of the recent, and still continuing, elevation of an entire continent. Lyell had demonstrated in 1834 that Scandinavia was rising slowly and imperceptibly in the modern period and had risen as much as several hundred feet during the recent geological past. Then James Smith of Jordanhill had discovered in the neighborhood of Glasgow elevated beds containing fossil shells of living species and

44. C. L., Jr. to L. Horner. 12 March 1838. Kinnordy mss. *L. & L.* II, 39–41. Postscript not included in *L. & L.*

had demonstrated from them that the coast of Scotland had been elevated during the period of existing shell species. This was the same kind of evidence which Darwin had seen on the coast of Chile to indicate elevation of the land. All of these pieces of evidence suggested that Scotland had been elevated in some measure during the recent geological past. When Darwin concluded that the parallel roads of Glen Roy indicated the levels at which water had once stood in the Glen, he decided that Glen Roy must once have been a narrow bay, or fiord, of the sea. He rejected the idea that it could have been a freshwater lake because he could conceive of no possible barrier which would retain a lake in the Glen-at the several levels at which the water stood. He could find no remains of sea shells in the thin layer of gravel along the parallel roads, but thought that in such circumstances the preservation of shells would be the rare exception rather than the rule.

The close relation between Darwin's Glen Roy paper and the influence on him of Lyell's *Principles* is seen in his remarks on John Macculloch's paper on Glen Roy.[45] Macculloch had argued that parallel roads represented the shorelines of a lake and Darwin commented:

> The idea of a continent slowly emerging from beneath the sea, appears, and it is a very curious point in the history of geology, never to have occurred to him as a possibility, although he was so bold and ingenious a speculator. His paper was read in the beginning of 1817, and when we reflect that during the few latter years, proofs of such movements have accumulated from all quarters of the world, we must recognize how much of this important change (the foundation stone, I may add, of this paper) is due to the Principles of Geology by Mr. Lyell.[46]

Scotland has undergone elevation since the glacial period, although not nearly as much as Darwin thought, and in 1862 the parallel roads of Glen Roy were shown conclusively to be the former shorelines of a glacial lake, but the above passage demonstrates again the close relationship between Darwin's interpretation of continental elevation in South America and his reading of Lyell's *Principles*.

Lyell and Darwin continued to see each other frequently. On 13 September 1838, Darwin, in writing to Lyell who was at Kin-

45. J. Macculloch, "On the 'Parallel Roads' of Glen Roy" (1817).
46. C. Darwin, "Observations on the Parallel Roads . . ." (1839) p. 68.

nordy and had mentioned that he intended to stay there until the
end of November, wrote:

> I hope this is a mistake & you meant to say October.—I shall be
> grieved if it is true; I trust you will want books; or something
> will bring you back before then.—Remember what I have often
> heard you say, the country is very bad for the intellects, the
> Scotch mists will put out some volcanic speculations.[47]

On 13 November Darwin wrote Lyell from Shrewsbury to tell
him of his engagement to Emma Wedgwood, and after his return
to London, wrote to his fiancée:

> On Saturday [17 Nov.] I dined with the Lyells and spent one
> of the pleasantest evenings I ever did in my life. Lyell grew
> quite audacious at the thoughts of having a married geological
> companion, and proposed going to dine at the Athenaeum to-
> gether and leaving our wives at home. Poor man, he would as
> soon "eat his head" as do such an action, whilst I feel as yet as
> bold as a lion. We had much geological and economical talk,
> the latter very profitable.[48]

The Lyells advised Darwin that he and Emma should furnish
slowly a house for themselves because it would be more economical, though less comfortable at first.

On 30 November 1838 Darwin described to Emma Wedgwood
his unsuccessful efforts at househunting and added:

> I called, however, to-day on the Lyells. I cannot tell you how
> particularly pleasant and cordial Lyell's manner has been to
> me: I am sure he will be a steady and sure friend to both of us.[49]

On New Years Day, Darwin moved into his new house where he
was to bring his bride. On Sunday 20 January he wrote to Emma:

> The Lyells called on me today after church, as Lyell was so
> full of geology he was obliged to disgorge; and I dine there on
> Tuesday for an especial conference. I was quite ashamed of my-
> self today, for we talked for half-an-hour unsophisticated Geol-
> ogy, with poor Mrs. Lyell sitting by, a monument of patience.

47. C. Darwin to C. L., Jr. 13 Sept. 1838. APS mss.
48. C. Darwin to Emma Wedgwood. [23 Nov. 1838] in *Emma Darwin* . . .
(1915) vol. II, pp. 13–15.
49. C. Darwin to E. Wedgwood [30 Nov. 1838] in *Emma Darwin* vol. II, p. 15.

I want *practice* in ill-treating the female sex. I did not observe Lyell had any compunction; I hope to harden my conscience in time: few husbands seem to find it difficult to effect this.[50]

Charles Darwin and Emma Wedgwood were married on 29 January 1839 and came to live at 12 Upper Gower Street (Fig. 51). On 1 April they gave their first dinner party. J. S. Henslow and his wife were staying with the Darwins; the other guests were the Lyells, Mary Lyell's sister, Leonora Horner, and Dr. Fitton and Robert Brown. The party seems to have been an ordeal for Emma Darwin who wrote to her sister:

We had some time to wait before dinner for Dr. Fitton, which is always awful, and in my opinion, Mr. Lyell is enough to flatten a party, as he never speaks above his breath, so that everybody keeps lowering their tone to his. Mr. Brown, whom Humboldt calls "the glory of Great Britain" looks so shy, as if he longed to shrink into himself and disappear entirely; however, notwithstanding these two dead weights, viz. the greatest botanist and the greatest geologist in Europe we did very well and had no pauses. Mrs. Henslow has a good loud sharp voice which was a great comfort, and Mrs. Lyell has a very constant supply of talk.[51]

Darwin's friendship with Lyell was perhaps not greatly encouraged after his marriage. An additional difficulty was Darwin's increasing ill health. He became ill on 10 March 1839 and seems to have been frequently unwell thereafter. On his part Lyell admired Darwin and was fond of him. He described him as "the most candid of men & if anything is new, says at once he never had thought of it."[52]

In 1841 when Lyell was about to leave for a year's absence in America, Darwin, who had been during the preceding four and a half years probably Lyell's closest friend and certainly his most congenial scientific associate, was planning to move into the country. Darwin had gone to visit his father at Shrewsbury during July so that he was away from London when Lyell was preparing to depart. Lyell wrote to him:

50. C. Darwin to E. Wedgwood. [20 Jan. 1839] in *Emma Darwin* vol. II, pp. 23–24.
51. E. Darwin to her sister Elizabeth Wedgwood. 2 April 1839 in *Emma Darwin* vol. II, pp. 40–41.
52. C. L., Jr. to his sister-in-law, Susan Horner. [September 1838?] Kinnordy mss.

My dear Darwin

I have no doubt that your father did rightly in persuading you to stay, but we were much disappointed in not seeing you before we start for a year's absence. I cannot tell you how often since your long illness I have missed the friendly intercourse which we had so frequently before and on which I built more than ever after your marriage. It will not happen easily that twice in one's life even in the large world of London a congenial soul so occupied with precisely the same pursuits, and with an independence enabling him to pursue them, will fall so nearly in my way and to have had it snatched from me with the prospect of your residence somewhere far off, is a privation—I feel as a very great one—I hope you will not like Herschel get far off from a railway.[53]

When Lyell returned to England on 27 August 1842 Darwin had already purchased the house at the village of Down in Kent where he moved on 14 September and where he lived thereafter.

53. C. L., Jr. to C. Darwin. July 1841. Darwin mss. Printed in *More Letters of Charles Darwin* (1903) vol. I, p. 31.

CHAPTER 14

The Crag Question and the Classification of Tertiary Formations, 1836–1840

DURING the winter of 1836–37 Lyell was preparing for the press the fifth edition of the *Principles*. He was also writing the *Elements,* a work which he had been developing off and on since 1834. In March he and Mary attended a dinner at Miss Rogers' house. One of the subjects of discussion was the Rev. William Buckland's Bridgewater treatise *Geology and Mineralogy* which had finally appeared in 1836. It was the sixth in the series of works published under the will of the Rev. Francis Henry Egerton, eighth Earl of Bridgewater, who had died in 1829. Each treatise was intended to demonstrate "the Power, Wisdom and Goodness of God, as manifested in the Creation" in its particular field of science.

> After the ladies were gone Lord Holland asked me about Buckland's book & whether he knew much of geology. He seemed not to have formed a high estimate of the said Bridgewater & so I spoke up in favour of the body of the work on fossils. This led to a talk on new species & that mystery of mysteries, the creation of man. Lord H. said that we were no further on that point than Lucretius out of whom he could take mottos which would have done for each of my volumes.[1]

A very different work was Charles Babbage's *Ninth Bridgewater Treatise,* not commissioned by the trustees of the Earl of Bridgewater and written in parody of the other eight. One of Lyell's activities in 1837 was to read it in proof sheets and, together with Dr. Fitton, try to persuade Babbage to delete some passages that would likely be offensive to his readers.[2] Babbage was unwilling to make the deletions so Lyell persuaded him to send some of the proofs to Adam Sedgwick at Cambridge, with the objectionable passages unmarked, to see whether Sedgwick would react to the same statements.[3] "As I had told him to deal with it freely as if my

1. C. L., Jr. to his sister Sophia. 19 March 1837. Kinnordy mss. *L. & L.* II, 7–9.
2. C. L., Jr. to C. B. 13 March 1837. Babbage mss.
3. C. L., Jr to A. Sedgwick. 5 April 1837. [copy] Kinnordy mss.

M.S. (which he has many a day cut up before now)," Lyell wrote Babbage, "& not knowing whether you belonged to the small minority of pachydermatous authors he prudently fired his shot at an anonymous writer."[4] Sedgwick's criticisms finally convinced the obstinate author. Babbage had valued the two-page critique which Sedgwick sent and, Lyell wrote to Sedgwick, "I hardly know anything else which would have induced him to leave out the most offensive passages." Lyell added a note on his own activities:

> I have been working pretty steadily on conchology, & with Owen's help at comparative anatomy & osteology, desultory work, at least most of it, not bearing immediately on a sort of "supplement to the Principles" which I am writing to serve as an "Elements of Geology."[5]

In May Gideon Mantell came to London to deliver a lecture at the Royal Institution and Lyell invited him to dine at 16 Hart Street to meet Darwin, who was going to attend the lecture.[6]

Lyell's plan for the summer of 1837 was to make a long visit to Copenhagen and to Christiania in Norway. He wished to study with Beck the large collection of shells in Prince Christian's museum at Copenhagen. Lyell wanted to form a clearer idea of the differences of opinion which existed between Deshayes and Beck as to the identity of recent and fossil species of shells. In 1830 Deshayes had drawn up the tables of shells which were published at the end of the third volume of the *Principles* in 1833. These tables were based on his examination of about five thousand species of recent shells then in the collections at Paris. In the intervening seven years the number of shell species in European collections had grown to between eight and nine thousand. And, wrote Lyell:

> What is of no less consequence, individuals of species which before that time were extremely rare, have been supplied in abundance. Fossil shells also have been collected with equal zeal and success; and thus the facility of discriminating nice distinctions in closely allied species, or of deciding which characters are constant and which variable has been greatly promoted; and the study of these more ample data has led all conchologists

4. C. L., Jr. to C. B. 9 April 1837. Babbage mss.
5. C. L., Jr. to A. Sedgwick. 25 April 1837. [copy] Kinnordy mss.
6. C. L., Jr. to G. A. M. 6 May 1837. Mantell mss.

to separate many species, both of fossil and recent shells, which before they had confounded together.[7]

What made Lyell wish to consult Beck with some urgency, however, was that he had become involved in a controversy over the crag formation, and this controversy turned on the identity of the species of fossil shells in the crag. A dispute over the relative age of a single geological formation ought not of itself to have been so important, but his opponent had also called in question the basis for Lyell's whole classification of the Tertiary strata—namely, the proportion of living to extinct fossil species.

In the first edition of the *Principles* Lyell had described the characteristics and distribution of the crag, a formation which he had studied in 1829 in the course of his tour along the Suffolk coast.

The crag consisted of various groups of beds of sand, gravel, and blue or brown marl which were revealed along the coast of Suffolk and Norfolk. R. C. Taylor had reported in 1827 that in a few places the strata formed a soft rock containing multitudes of corals, sponges, and echini.[8] In quarries in these beds, where the rain had an opportunity to wash away the sand, the corals were revealed in the quarry wall in all their beautiful and varied forms. Between Dunwich and Yarmouth the crag consisted of alternating beds of nonfossiliferous sand and coarse gravel, more than 200 feet thick. In the neighborhood of Norwich the crag contained bones of large land animals embedded in sand, loam, or clay, sometimes in regular strata and sometimes in a confused mass. In this area, the crag overlay chalk strata and sometimes contained bits of chalk and flint. In still other exposures, for example, the crag was found to overlay the London clay formation. There was some question whether all these diverse beds, termed crag, belonged to the same geological period, but Lyell wrote that, "after examining in 1829, the whole line of coast of Essex, Suffolk and Norfolk, I found it impossible to draw any line of separation between the different groups. Each seemed in its turn to pass into another.[9] The diffi-

7. *Elements of Geology* (1838) p. 287.
8. R. C. Taylor, *On the Geology of East Norfolk* . . . (1827). Richard Cowling Taylor (1789–1851) was until 1826 a land surveyor at Norwich. He had studied geology with William Smith, also a surveyor, and worked for the Ordinance Survey of Great Britain. He later came to America where he surveyed coal mines and wrote on American geology.
9. *Principles* (1833) vol. III, p. 172.

culty in studying the crag lay in the very confused and variable pattern of stratification revealed particularly in the coastal cliffs.

As early as 1811 James Parkinson had noted that some of the fossils of the crag were identical with species of shells living in the North Sea.[10] Lyell had placed the crag in the older Pliocene period on the basis of Deshayes' identification of 111 species of crag shells, of which he considered 66 extinct and 45 identical with species living in the North Sea. Since Lyell thought that the crag strata formed a single series and had been laid down within a single geological period, he thought that essentially the same assemblage of fossil species existed in all the crag strata, although he recognized that in some places the fossils consisted "almost entirely of corals, sponges, and echini," and in others "of sand, loam, and clay, containing bones of terrestrial quadrupeds and drift wood."[11]

At a meeting of the Geological Society on 27 May 1835, Edward Charlesworth of Suffolk pointed out that in parts of Essex and Suffolk the crag consisted of two distinct beds. Charlesworth said that some years before he had seen at Tattingstone, Suffolk, in a quarry worked to a deeper level than usual, that the crag was underlain by a different bed, lacking the characteristic reddish color of the crag and containing shells new to him. He had later discovered this same bed at several places near Ramsholt, Suffolk on the east bank of the river Deben. In quarries at Sudbourne and Orford, Charlesworth found this distinct lower stratum particularly rich in corals. He therefore called the upper reddish deposit the red crag and the lower stratum, characterized by an abundance of corals, the coralline crag. The coralline crag was much more uniform than the red crag, which varied greatly in both color and stratification. Charlesworth also argued that these two beds belonged to distinct geological periods. He said that earlier descriptions of the crag by R. C. Taylor and by Samuel Woodward had been based solely on a study of the crag of Norfolk, which contained relatively few fossils. Mr. Searles Wood (1798–1880) of Hasketon, Suffolk, had collected some 450 species of fossils from the crag, of which 80 belonged exclusively to the red crag, 200 to the coralline crag, and the remaining 150 were common to the two formations. Altogether they included nearly 400 species of fossil shells. Mr. Wood had also told Charlesworth, "That there are two distinct beds in Suffolk is an observa-

10. J. Parkinson, "Observations on some of the strata in the neighbourhood of London . . ." (1811).
11. *Principles* (1833), vol. III, p. 172.

tion that has long been made." Charlesworth said that the assignment of the crag to the older Pliocene had been based on Deshayes' examination of only 111 species of which he considered 66 to be extinct. He regretted that no such separation of extinct from living species had been made for Wood's collection, but he thought that this much larger number of fossils would show a larger proportion of extinct species and that the crag would prove to be older than the Pliocene.[12]

Charlesworth's paper was published in the *Philosophical Magazine* for August 1835. It was a thoughtful paper based on the observations of several years and on the large collection of crag shells of Searles Wood; it was not very favorably received. In the *Philosophical Magazine* for November 1835 Samuel Woodward published a letter in reply to Charlesworth. Woodward, who had written on the topography, archaeology, and geology of Norfolk, was a self-educated man. He had established himself by his ability and learning, and now earned his living as a clerk in Gurney's Bank at Norwich. Woodward wrote:

> In the first place, his red crag is decidedly diluvium or disrupted crag, with an admixture of the oxide of iron, precisely similar to what we witness in the gravel of Norfolk. . . .
>
> Secondly, his term "coralline crag" is not appropriate, as it leads us to suppose that it is composed of corallines, when in fact, there are none in the Ramsholt bed, which is chiefly adverted to.

Woodward said that he had visited Ramsholt and considered the lower bed there to be "undisturbed crag" and the upper ones "transported." He considered them to be of the same age, "and that the red crag, by diluvial agency, has been superimposed upon the undisturbed bed." He thought however that the Norfolk crag was a newer deposit than that of Suffolk because it lacked many of the shells characteristic of Suffolk.[13]

Woodward's flat contradiction of both Charlesworth's evidence and his conclusions was not very courteous and furthermore he

12. E. Charlesworth, "On the Crag of part of Essex and Suffolk" (1835). This is but an abstract; the complete paper was published as: "Observations on the Crag-formation . . ." (1835). Cf. R. C. Taylor, *Geology of East Norfolk* (1827) and S. Woodward, *An outline of the geology of Norfolk* (1833). Edward Charlesworth (1813–93) was the son of a Suffolk clergyman; he had been educated for the medical profession, but turned to geology and natural history.

13. S. Woodward, "Some remarks upon the Crag . . ." (1835).

was wrong in his facts. In the next issue of the *Philosophical Magazine* appeared a letter from Robert Fitch of Norwich. Fitch said that he had read Woodward's letter with some surprise because during the previous summer he had visited Ramsholt to collect fossils. He wrote:

> Besides a great variety of shells, I found several species of coral, so abundant, that in the course of a few hours, I obtained from the stratum itself, and the beach below it, more specimens than I could carry away without assistance. I have since compared some of these corals with those from the other localities described by Mr. Charlesworth, and they appear precisely to correspond.[14]

Charlesworth himself also replied immediately to Woodward's letter.[15] He reaffirmed that the red crag was a gradual deposit, undisturbed and not diluvial, and then went on to defend himself with rather more zeal than was necessary since the editor of the *Philosophical Magazine* had already appended three footnotes to Woodward's letter pointing out his inaccuracies. Charlesworth's reply revealed his great sensitivity to criticism. He also suggested the importance of the possibility that fossil shells might have been washed out of one Tertiary stratum and deposited in another and this transfer would be unnoticed because, both before and after, a Tertiary fossil would have been present in a Tertiary bed. That such transpositions of fossils might occur, Charlesworth argued, was suggested by the fact that various species of *Terebratula* and other chalk fossils had been washed out of the chalk and redeposited in the Norfolk crag. They could be distinguished from the other fossils of the crag *by the fact that they were chalk fossils.* If such transpositions of fossils had occurred from one Tertiary bed to another it would be much less easily detected, but it would alter the proportion of extinct to living species in the formation. Yet this proportion of extinct to living species of fossils was the basis for Lyell's classification of Tertiary formations.

Charlesworth raised this point because in the fourth edition of the *Principles* Lyell had argued that, because there were 150 species of shells common to the upper and lower portions of the crag, they must both have been deposited during the same geological period of time. Lyell also noted that the much larger number of

14. R. Fitch, "On the Coralline Crag . . ." (1835).
15. E. Charlesworth, "Reply to Mr. Woodward's remarks . . ." (1835).

fossils in Wood's collection might possibly alter the proportion of recent to extinct species, but he declined to change his opinion that the formation belonged to the older Pliocene until the fossils had been more thoroughly studied. He admitted that most of the shells that Deshayes had identified for him had come from the red crag, but because they had so many species of fossils in common, he did not think that the red crag had been deposited at a different period of time from the coralline crag. The two crags might simply have been deposited in different parts of the sea during the same period:

> Thus we may suppose one region, where the water is deep and tranquil, to be favourable to the growth of coral, sponges, echini, and microscopic cephalopods, such as characterize the lower crag; whilst in another and somewhat shallower region, where currents prevailed, and to which sand and shingle were often drifted no zoophytes might exist, although certain kinds of testacea abounded.[16]

In his first paper of 1835 Charlesworth had suggested that, since bones of land animals were either very rare or completely lacking in the red crag and coralline crag of Suffolk, the numerous bones of mammals reported from the crag of Norfolk must have resulted from a confusion of the crag with diluvium. During the summer of 1836, however, he visited Norfolk and almost immediately changed his opinion. He found:

> . . . that not only are the bones of land animals constantly found in the so-called crag of that county, but that they are of most frequent occurrence in those particular beds which furnish the strongest evidence of tranquil deposition; and further, the bones strictly belonging to these beds of marine origin can be at once distinguished from those of the overlying diluvial or lacustrine deposits by the peculiar chemical change which the former have undergone.[17]

The Norfolk crag contained the bones of six or eight species of mammals plus the teeth of elephant, hippopotamus, and mastodon.

Charlesworth decided that the Norfolk crag was a formation dis-

16. *Principles* (1835) vol. IV, pp. 87–88.
17. E. Charlesworth, "A notice of the remains of vertebrated animals . . ." (1836).

tinct from both the red crag and the corralline crag of Suffolk and younger than both. It extended from Norwich to Aldborough in Suffolk at which place it immediately overlay the coralline crag. There were, therefore, now three distinct formations in what had formerly been considered one crag formation, and Charlesworth was convinced that they had been deposited during three successive periods of time.

Charlesworth had perhaps been annoyed by Lyell's suggestion in the fourth edition of the *Principles* that the red crag and coralline crag might have been laid down during the same geological period in different parts of the same ocean. He was certain that the coralline crag extended over a wide area in Suffolk and Norfolk and was uniform in its thickness, color, and fossils throughout. The period of its deposition must, therefore, have been quite distinct from that of the red crag which overlay it. Moreover, by referring to the question again in his address to the Geological Society on 19 February 1836, Lyell may have aggravated any damage he had done to Charlesworth's feelings in the 1835 edition of the *Principles*. In the address, Lyell said that Charlesworth had laid before him some sixty species of shells from the coralline crag, and that Lyell had taken them to Paris to Deshayes who thought the proportion of living to extinct species was slightly higher than that in the 111 species which he had examined previously. At the same time Lyell mentioned that Dr. Beck of Copenhagen, who had been in London during the autumn of 1835, had examined 260 species of shells in Charlesworth's collection and "that although a large proportion of the species approach very near to others which now live in our northern seas, he regards them as almost all of distinct species."[18]

However, Charlesworth knew that Lyell had written and spoken without having reexamined the country since his tour along the coastal cliffs in 1829. He, therefore, retaliated by delivering before the meeting of the British Association at Bristol in August 1836 a second paper which attacked Lyell's classification of the Tertiary strata on the basis of the simple percentage of extinct species. He said that whereas Deshayes had identified forty per cent of the crag shells with living species, Dr. Beck of Copenhagen, on examining the crag shells in his own collection during a visit to London, had found all of them to be extinct. This was also the

18. "Anniversary Address to the Geological Society, 19 February 1836" (1838) pp. 372–73.

opinion of George Sowerby. Louis Agassiz thought all the fossil fishes of the crag were of extinct species and Milne-Edwards was of the same opinion concerning the fossil corals. Dr. John Fleming, however, thought that the proportion of living species in the crag fossils had been underestimated by Deshayes. With such wide disagreement about its fundamental basis, Charlesworth implied, there could be little consistency in the system of classification. Charlesworth suggested that a better way to judge the relative age of these deposits would be "by a general estimate of the amount of resemblance borne to existing species, by the entire series of crag or London clay-fossils taken collectively." He did not say how this was to be done.[19]

Charlesworth also repeated his suggestion that fossil shells could be washed out of one deposit and laid down in another sediment being newly formed. Thus the fossils incorporated in a stratum need not all represent the same geological period. Some may be fossilized for a second time. This was doubt with a vengeance. However, Charlesworth made this suggestion principally to account for the large number of species which were common to the red crag and the coralline crag.

Charlesworth published a third paper to sustain his argument that the red crag and coralline crag were distinct beds and, in particular, that they had been formed at distinct periods of time. This paper tended occasionally to be polemical in tone. He noted that, in addition to Beck and Sowerby, who thought that most of the crag species were extinct, John Phillips had considered, after examining a large collection of crag shells in the museum at York, that the crag was of Miocene age. Charlesworth then suggested that if, on the basis of the percentage of extinct species, these different conchologists were to decide in which division of the Tertiary the crag should be placed, it might be "*eocene* in Denmark, *miocene* in England, and *pliocene* in France."[20]

Lyell took this attack upon his classification very seriously and he therefore determined to go to Copenhagen to make himself thoroughly familiar with the criteria by which Beck distinguished between living and extinct species of fossil shells and between species and varieties. When he had mastered this thorny subject he

19. E. Charlesworth, "On some fallacies involved . . ." (1837). Cf. *Brit. Assn. Rep.* 6 (1837): 86.
20. E. Charlesworth, "Observations on the Crag and on the Fallacies involved in the present System of Classification of Tertiary Deposits" (1837).

would do his best to reconcile Beck's results with those of Deshayes.

On 6 June 1837 the Lyells sailed from London for Hamburg, where they arrived on the ninth. They proceeded by coach to Kiel and there took another steamboat for Copenhagen, which they reached on Sunday 11 June. The following Tuesday they both went to the Prince's museum. "Charles & Dr. Beck work in one little room," Mary wrote, "& I sit in the other & may look at all the drawers I please which is a great privilege as it is the best collection of recent shells in Europe & every now & then Dr. Beck comes in & I get a question answered."[21] Lyell explained the importance of the Danish collection to his sister Eleanor:

> In the time of Linnaeus this city contained finer collections of shells & finer works were published here by Chemnitz (12 vols.)[22] & others than in any other country of Europe.—It is not wonderful, therefore, that even now some of the Danes should be far ahead & that as Prince Christian had a taste for Nat. Hist. he should have a splendid private collection & that the Curator of his Museum, (containing above 8000 spec.ˢ of living shells) Dr. Beck, should be one of the 2 or 3 best conchologists in the world. —But besides this, Copenhagen possesses in its different museums most of the identical shells which Linnaeus described in the Ed.ˢ of his *Systema Naturae* publ.ᵈ during his life & here, therefore, alone, we can verify incontestably the species which he really described & named. As Lamarck & others have in very many cases mistaken the shells which Linnaeus meant, great confusion has arisen & it is here alone that this confusion can most readily be cleared up.[23]

Their stay at Copenhagen was very pleasant. Lyell renewed his acquaintance with Dr. Forchhammer; they dined at his house. They went walking in the parks and gardens, and for occasional drives. Mary described some of their activities:

> Saturday afternoon Mr. Oersted called, but did not stay long as we were just preparing to go out. We took a walk that evening in the Citadel, which is very pretty, surrounded with grassed

21. C. L., Jr. and M. E. L. to his sister Caroline. 13 June 1837. Kinnordy mss.

22. F. H. W. Martine et al., *Neues systematisches Conchylien-Cabinet* (1769–1829). Johann Hieronymus Chemnitz (1730–1800) had prepared volumes 4 to 11, published 1780–95.

23. C. L., Jr. to his sister Eleanor. 2 July 1837. Kinnordy mss.

ramparts overlooking the sea & planted with trees. On Sunday we went to the German Lutheran Church & heard a most excellent sermon. The preacher was dressed in a long black gown with a white frill round his neck just like one of the early reformers.[24]

On 21 June Prince Christian, who had been away when they arrived, returned to Copenhagen and next morning Lyell attended the court to pay his respects. Mary wrote that Prince Christian's return was, ". . . no small event, I assure you, in the eyes of his household & dependents of every kind. Charles & I cannot help smiling sometimes at finding our actions & plans controlled by the will of a Prince, we who are so much used to have our own way." Lyell described how he was spending his time in the Prince's collection.

I am working steadily at the grand controverted question as to the specific identity of a great many tertiary shells & acquiring the means of forming an independent opinion, but it will require time, more especially as the collection of the Prince is not at Paris, or that of Deshayes here, which might be wished. Even with the aid of Beck & all the books & specimens at hand it often takes us a day to go through the evidence relating to a single species, of which you can rarely form an opinion till you have compared many species of the same genus & many individuals of each, of different ages, sexes & countries so as to appreciate the true laws of specific distinction in the group, whether it be called genus or sub-genus, to which the species in question belongs. I have already learned how to correct many errors which Deshayes has made & to doubt some of his determinations, but I shall of course hear what he can say in their defence.[25]

A few days later they received the news of the death of King William IV of England and the ascent of the young Queen Victoria to the throne. Mary Lyell was obliged to buy a black silk gown for mourning in order to be able to attend the court because William IV had been a close relation of the Danish royal family.

On Monday 25 June Prince Christian invited Lyell to dine with him at Copenhagen and then invited him to go on a long geological excursion the following day. The Prince arranged that they

24. C. L., Jr. and M. E. L. to his sister Caroline. 21 June 1837. Kinnordy mss.
25. M. E. L. and C. L., Jr. to her father. 23 June 1837. Kinnordy mss.

should dine at his country house *Sorgenfrei* and that Mary should also come there in the afternoon to meet the Princess and other ladies and to dine. Next morning Lyell and Beck left Copenhagen soon after seven o'clock and went to *Sorgenfrei* where they met the Prince.

> A landau & four nice horses was in waiting & away we drove over a very fair macadamized road thro' woods as wild & natural as any part of the New Forest, having at our left a remarkable chain of small lakes, far below us, that is to say we looked down almost a precipice covered with wood upon the lakes. We discussed the probable origin of the lake-hollows, whether by depressions of the soil or by water etc., but the Prince not forgetting here & there to stop the carriage & take me to points slightly elevated where beautiful views are seen. In one of them we saw the towers of Copenhagen about 8 miles off to the South & from another the ancient abbey church of Roskilde about 10 or 12 miles to the South. We then passed between lake Fure & a smaller lake to the village of Farum & some miles beyond this came to where the soil is composed to a great depth of innumerable rolled blocks of chalk with a few of granite intermixed. Fossils were very numerous in the chalk & I hammered out many & Beck found a finer fossil fish than had ever been found before in Denmark. Prince Christian set 4 men to work, while the horses were baiting, to clear away the talus & make a section for me by which I saw that the boulders of chalk were in fact in beds with occasional layers of sand between.[26]

After this excursion and some fishing during the afternoon, they returned for dinner to *Sorgenfrei,* where Mary Lyell had come in the meantime and was with the Princess.

On 7 July Lyell and his wife left Copenhagen for Christiania in Norway. They stopped a second time for dinner with Prince Christian at *Sorgenfrei* and then proceeded by carriage to Elsinore. Mary described the journey:

> The road great part of the way along the shore was beautiful. We saw the opposite coast of Sweden most distinctly & the sight of mountains was really quite delightful again. The island of Hveen lies very near, where Tycho Brahe's observatory was placed. After depositing our luggage in the Inn at Elsinore we set out to see the castle of Kronborg & ascended the light tower

26. C. L., Jr. to his sister Eleanor. 2 July 1837. Kinnordy mss. *L. & L.* II, 15–18.

which is lined with brass reflecting plates. The view is quite splendid in each direction, ships in full sail of all nations coming in & out of the Sound.

After dining at the inn they boarded a steam-boat to take them to Norway. "We had scarcely landed," at Christiania, Mary went on, "before Professor Keilhau (Prof^r of Mineralogy) & his wife came to see us. Charles had never seen him but had written to him from Copenhagen." Professor Keyser, the professor of physics, whom they had met two years before in London, also came to call on them.[27] While Lyell and Professor Keilhau were away on a geological expedition, Professor Keyser took Mary for drives in the country, introduced her to his three little girls and to a number of his friends. His wife, who had died some years before, had been from Edinburgh so that Mary had already known of him through her Edinburgh acquaintance. "He is a very gentlemanlike agreeable old man & speaks English perfectly," Mary wrote. "He brought us an invitation from the governor of Norway, Count Wedel Jarlsberg, to dine with him next day."[28]

Lyell's purpose in visiting Christiania was to study the relationship between the granite and the transition strata of the neighborhood. Leopold von Buch had described the granite as overlying the transition strata in the vicinity of Christiania, where the two kinds of rock came together. Professor Keilhau, who had studied the junction of the transition limestone with the granite, was able to show Lyell that the granite in some places did extend slightly over the edges of the transition strata, but not for more than a few yards and always in such a way as to be consistent with the granite's having been intruded in a molten condition from below. Von Buch had thought that the granite might have spread over the stratified rocks in sheets in the same way as a sheet of lava might spread out over sedimentary strata, but this was not so. Von Buch had inferred this idea from the fact that, at their line of contact, the transition strata dipped toward the granite. Professor Keilhau showed Lyell that while this was true, nevertheless all of the transition strata were cut off abruptly at the line of contact with the granite and did not pass under it.[29]

27. Baltazar Mathias Keilhau (1797–1858) had been since 1834 professor of mineralogy in the University of Christiania; Jens Jacob Keyser (1780–1847), since 1814 professor of physics in the University of Christiania.

28. M. E. L. to Eleanor Lyell. 12 July 1837. Kinnordy mss.

29. "On certain phaenomena connected with the junction of granitic and transition rocks, near Christiania in Norway" (1838).

Oddly enough, from his observations around Christiania Keilhau was inclined to doubt the Huttonian theory of the igneous origin of granite. In places there were masses of transition strata isolated and completely surrounded by granite, but in such instances these isolated strata preserved exactly the same dip and strike as the main body of transition strata with which they had once been continuous. Keilhau did not see how, if the forceful intrusion of molten granite had isolated these masses of strata, it could have done so without at all disturbing the position of the strata, as indicated by their dip and strike. Lyell decided that the answer to this puzzle was probably that the granite had invaded fissures and gaps which had already existed in the hardened transition strata.[30]

Lyell also observed that in the district on the west side of the fiord of Christiania, where granite and syenite protruded in mountain masses through the fossiliferous transition strata, that these strata had been metamorphosed. Near the granite the blue earthy limestone, containing many corals, became a white granular marble; the zone of marble often extended as much as 400 yards from the junction with the granite.[31]

Apart from these geological excursions with Professor Keilhau the Lyells enjoyed several pleasant social occasions at Christiania. On Sunday 16 July they dined at Count Wedel's country house. On 20 July they left Christiania to go by horse and carriage to Drammen. Mary described their journey:

It was a beautiful drive over many hills, among others Paradise Hill, celebrated for its view which is very extensive, but we preferred some other views a little lower down. Numbers of children came out on the road with strawberries for us in little bags made of the birch tree bark sewed together with twigs. Drammen is a thriving & annually increasing town on a fine river, & the great place in Norway for exporting timber. There was a great appearance of activity in the town & shipping.

From Drammen they went to Holmstrand where they spent three days and went along the fiord in a boat to study the geology of the shore, stopping at noon to eat their luncheon "under fir trees in the shade." Mary wrote:

30. Ibid., p. 69. Cf. B. M. Keilhau, Ed., *Gaea Norvegica von mehreren verfassern* (1838–50); B. M. Keilhau, "Granitens og de ovrige saakeldte massive Bjergarters samt de Krystalliniske Skiferes Theorie" (1838–40).

31. *Elements*, pp. 243–44.

The fiord was as smooth as a looking glass in the morning, but the southerly wind always rises about twelve o'clock & we were finely tossed about on our return. However, neither of us were ill & next morning we set out again on rather a shorter expedition to one of the islands where we collected fossils in great abundance, corals chiefly as these are the older rocks.[32]

From these fossils Lyell determined later that the strata of Christiania corresponded in age to Murchison's lower Silurian formation in England.[33] At Frederikshavn they boarded the steamboat which carried them back to Copenhagen, where they arrived on Thursday 27 July.

They spent the next three weeks at Copenhagen going over Tertiary shells with Dr. Beck. The trip to Christiana had been in a sense a holiday from the main work. The problem of the crag shells was by itself less important than the degree of certainty with which fossil shell species could be identified or distinguished. In this respect the results of their stay at Copenhagen satisfied Lyell. From Paris he wrote to Charles Darwin, who was to attend the meeting of the British Association at Liverpool:

> Last year when Charlesworth spoke at Bristol about Crag, and the numerical percentage of recent tertiary shells, Sedgwick and Buckland gave some useful impromptu replies, stating that I was aware some modifications would be required etc. but they would not affect this classification in the main. Now if he should again, as I expect, speak on this subject, and if he should cite Beck, will you state that you happen to know from correspondence which you have had with me this summer, that I have been engaged with Dr. Beck in a careful examination of the species of fossil shells of the Crag and other tertiary formations which have been identified with recent species; that you have learnt from my letters that Dr. Beck by no means denies the absolute identity of a certain number of Crag species, though he thinks a large proportion of those identified by Deshayes to be distinguishable. Also that I consider that Dr. Beck's views of the conchological fauna of the Crag, drawn from the consideration of 260 species, tend to confirm the classification which places the Crag as older Pliocene and on a parallel with the Sub-Apennine beds, and dis-

32. M. E. L. to Eleanor Lyell. 18–27 July 1837. Kinnordy mss.
33. "Notes on the Silurian strata in the neighbourhood of Christiania, in Norway" [1841].

tinct from and more modern than the Touraine, Bordeaux, and other Miocene deposits. Also that I am convinced that independently of the relative percentage of recent shells, about which naturalists may differ according to their notions of what constitutes a specific difference, there are other characters in the entire assemblage of forms of shells belonging to each great Tertiary epoch, which will enable us to classify the deposits according to the approach which they make to the type of organisation now existing in the neighbouring seas; and that this approach will serve as a chronological test of the eras to which Tertiary deposits may respectively belong. I mean the degree of approach to or departure from the assemblage of living shells in the neighbouring seas will be a test of the relative newness or antiquity of the several deposits. . . .

I wish you to know that my conviction is stronger than ever, that rules may be given for measuring the approximation of different groups of Tertiary shells, and that the degree of this approximation may be used as a test of age, and may lead to the same classification as that which I have adopted in the "Principles." I am fully prepared to defend all that is essential in my system of Tertiary classification as founded on fossil shells.[34]

Toward the end of August the Lyells left Copenhagen and went by steamer to Lubeck, crossing from there by carriage to Hamburg. At Bremen, Osnabruck, and Munster, Lyell met various German scientists who, having read one or other of his works, greeted him warmly. From Wesel they ascended the Rhine by steamboat to Dusseldorf and thence went by diligence across Belgium to Paris, where they were on 5 September. Lyell wanted again to consult with Deshayes and to attempt to reconcile his identifications of Tertiary fossil shell species with those of Beck. Unfortunately Deshayes was absent from the city. They saw Mrs. Byrne, one of Mary's aunts who had moved to Paris from Switzerland. Mary described her:

Dear Aunt Fanny is as kind as possible . . . . but is the most ultra radical I ever knew, & it is so constantly the uppermost subject in her mind that it is impossible to keep from something political for ten minutes together. She belongs to a school in France

34. C. L., Jr. to C. Darwin. 29 Aug.–5 Sept. 1837. *L. & L.* II, 20–23.

such as I hope & believe there are but few of yet in England who think everything old & established must be bad & everything sanctified by the name of revolution.[35]

Mrs. Byrne and her husband lived comfortably on their capital.

The Lyells remained at Paris nearly three weeks. Lyell spent every day at work on shells either at the Jardin du Roi or in private collections. He met for the first time Alcide d'Orbigny (1802–57) who had spent eight years from 1826 to 1834 traveling in South America and was in Argentina and Patagonia shortly before Darwin. The Lyells also met Captain Sander Rang whose *Manuel des Mollusques* Mary wrote "has been our constant companion both at home & on our travels for the last three years."[36] From Felix Dujardin[37] Lyell obtained some 212 species of Touraine fossil shells to take back to London. They were of special value to him because they would allow him to compare in detail the Touraine fossils with those of the crag. On 24 September they took the new railroad from Paris to St. Germain. This railroad was a great sensation, "une gloire nouvelle" for Paris and each day thousands of people rode back and forth upon it for pleasure. Fortunately, Lyell noted, the locomotives and engineers were all English. "What a good thing," he wrote, "for our own machinery makers to supply the continent. All the steam-boats I am told in the Mediterranean have English men & machinery & so I found it in the Baltic & in Norway.[38] It was a portent for the opening of Victoria's reign. They went on by steamboat down the Seine to Le Havre and thence by another steamboat to London. Travel by water they found better both for themselves and for Lyell's collection of fossil shells. On 28 September they arrived at 16 Hart Street.

Shortly after their return Lyell received from his father a present of fifty pounds and he decided to use it "to make a thorough examination of 'the Crag' in parts of Norfolk & Suffolk & to collect the fossils of it & publish a description of them in the Geological

35. M. E. L. to her mother. 8 Sept. 1837. Kinnordy mss.

36. Paul Karel Sander Leonard Rang (1784–1859), *Manuel de l'histoire naturelle des mollusques* ... (1829). M. E. L. to Sophia Lyell, 15 Sept. 1837. Kinnordy mss.

37. Felix Dujardin (1801–62), French naturalist and geologist coined the term *sarcode* to describe the living contents of Protozoa.

38. C. L., Jr. to his sister Sophia. 23–29 Sept. 1837. Kinnordy mss. *L. & L.* II, 24–27.

Transactions." He would use the money, he said, "for some books on recent & fossil shells, a new cabinet (besides one now building to receive the fruits of this summer's campaign), money to collectors, *drawings* from which the Geol. S. might engrave & some other outlays."[39]

During the winter of 1837–38 Lyell worked steadily to complete the *Elements*. On 20 January he wrote to Adam Sedgwick that he had just finished abstracting from the sheets of Murchison's as yet unpublished *Silurian System* a brief account of the Silurian rocks and asked Sedgwick for some drawings of the typical fossils of his Cambrian rocks.[40] On 26 January he wrote to Dr. Fleming that he was "just finishing a Chapter on igneous rocks" and asked him for information about the trap tuffs of Fife.[41] He was extending here and there, and polishing his manuscript of 1836. In February 1838 he made a field excursion into Suffolk for about a week to study the geology of the crag. This was a preliminary reconnaissance. In April after Lyell had corrected the first sheet of proofs of the *Elements*, the Lyells went to Suffolk to make the long awaited field study of the crag (Map 16).

On 17 April they took a steamboat from London to Ipswich and thence went by chaise to Woodbridge. The following day, Lyell wrote:

We went off in a chaise & pair by 8 o' ck. to the village of Melton & found Mr. Wood, Solicitor disappointed that we would not stay & take a 2ᵈ breakfast, so I took a rusk & some noyeau & Miss Wood tried to persuade Mary to take some & also brandy or "perhaps Hollands"—Mr. Wood's servant William who formerly served under Searles Wood Esq., aspirant to G. S. curatorship, in that learned gentleman's successful campaign in the crag district, was mounted on a fine pony to serve as guide & outrider to your humble servants—Off we drove to Sutton to a nice farm of Mr. Colchester who lionized me over the county seeing the pits of Shottesham & others. Mary went to almost all in the carriage, making great rounds thro' a very nice rural country while the gentleman farmer & I trudged by short cuts over hedges, marshes & fields—. The hedges are, some few of them, getting green, but with the exception of numerous lambs &

39. C. L., Jr. to his father. 5 Oct. 1837. Kinnordy mss.
40. C. L., Jr. to A. Sedgwick. 20 Jan. 1838. *L. & L.* II, 35–37.
41. C. L., Jr. to J. Fleming. 26 Jan. 1838. [copy] Kinnordy mss.

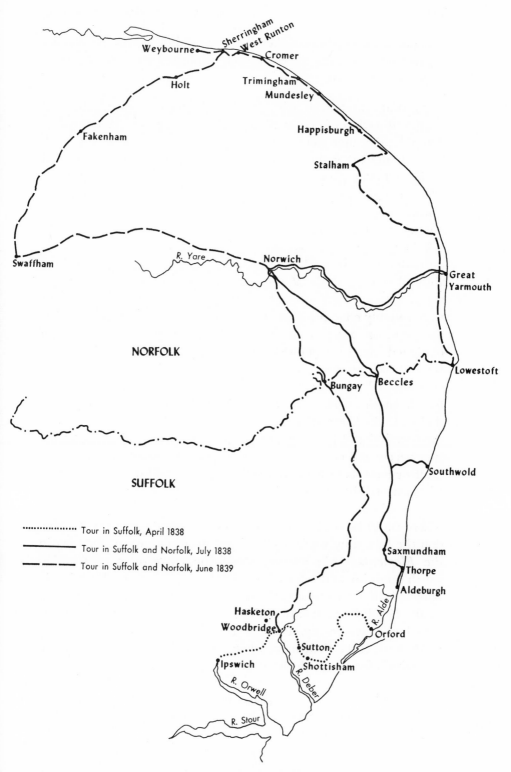

16. Lyell's tours in Suffolk and Norfolk to study the Crag

primroses everything looked like the dead of winter. . . . I did a great day's geology & the carriage protected us from the occasional rain & cold.[42]

They dined at Sutton with Mr. Colchester's brother, who had a large collection of crag shells, and then returned to Woodbridge. The next day they went to Orford. From his first day's field work Lyell thought that the coralline crag belonged to the same period as the red crag, though marked by many "peculiarities in the sea where it was formed." However, he was to return to Sutton in a couple of days to examine a section which Mr. Colchester was going to have laid open for him.

When Lyell examined this section he found a state of affairs quite different from what he expected. The beds of red crag there abutted against those of the coralline crag instead of overlying them, a fact which might have suggested that the two deposits were roughly contemporary. However, the evidence was clear that the coralline crag was the older of the two and, in fact, had been hardened into rock before the red crag had been deposited. The vertical face of the coralline crag against which the beds of red crag abutted was, Lyell wrote, "perforated to the depth of 6 or 8 feet from the surface by the tortuous borings of pholades, the shells of which are frequently found at the bottom of the tubes, the remainder of the perforations being filled with the sand of the superjacent red crag."[43] Thus this vertical face had been a coastal bluff or bank before the red crag had been laid down. Therefore Charlesworth had been right in considering the red and coralline crag as distinct deposits laid down at different periods of time. There could be no further argument and after his return to London the following week Lyell revised his discussion of the crag in the *Elements*.[44] He acknowledged the correctness of Charlesworth's opinion and referred to the latter's 1835 paper, but his acknowledgement was not perhaps particularly conspicuous nor generous. He did not mention that his own earlier account of the crag had been wrong. Perhaps Darwin was hinting that Lyell might have said a little more when he wrote the following September, with reference to the *Elements*:

42. M. E. L. and C. L., Jr. to her mother. 18 April 1838. Kinnordy mss.
43. "On the relative ages of the tertiary deposits commonly called Crag in Norfolk and Suffolk" [1838] p. 127.
44. *Elements*, pp. 300–02.

Charlesworth, I think, is annoyed that you have not quoted him more about the embedding of the older shells in the newer beds. But poor Charlesworth is of an unhappy discontented disposition.—He is, moreover, very much to be pitied. The Zoological Soc. are going to give up the Ass't Secretary's place & it is feared that he has a disease of the heart, so that altogether he is greatly to be pitied.[45]

When Lyell finished seeing the *Elements* through the press at the end of July 1838, he and Mary again went on a tour through Suffolk and Norfolk to examine the crag. Lyell wanted to determine whether Charlesworth was right in his view that the beds of the Norfolk crag, containing bones of mammals, had been laid down under water in tranquil conditions and were not contained in intermixed diluvium. He also wanted to determine whether the Norfolk crag was, as Charlesworth believed, younger than the red crag of Suffolk.

Lyell first examined the Norfolk crag at Thorpe, near Aldborough on the coast of Suffolk, where these beds extended to the sea and were revealed in the coastal cliffs. At Southwold, ten miles north of Thorpe, the beds of Norfolk crag formed a continuous sea cliff, revealing a section about forty feet thick. Captain Alexander acted as Lyell's guide in his examination of these beds and told him of the fossils collected from them. The fossils included land and freshwater shells, and marine shells; rolled fish bones and the bones and teeth of such mammals as the elephant, mastodon, rhinoceros, horse, and deer. Captain Alexander had frequently found the bones of mammals in the same stratum with fish bones, seashells, and crustacea. In a gravel pit at Henham, near Southwold, Lyell himself picked up mammalian bones and teeth from a bed containing seashells together with freshwater and land shells.

At Norwich, Lyell found that the crag consisted of beds of sand, loam, and gravel containing seashells, freshwater shells, fish bones and bones of mammals. Thus the beds of crag at Norwich were very similar to those on the coast at Southwold and the whole formation seemed to have been deposited in a great bay of the sea into which large rivers had poured much fresh water. The conditions in the bay or estuary had thus ranged from those of brackish water to those of the open sea. The freshwater shells were rela-

45. C. Darwin to C. L., Jr. 13 Sept. 1838. APS mss.

tively few in comparison with the number of marine shells. Captain Alexander had found in the crag a fossil elephant's tusk covered with *Serpulae* indicating that it had lain for a long time on the sea bottom before being embedded. This fact demonstrated, Lyell wrote, "that the bones of quadrupeds were really washed down into the sea of the Norwich Crag, and were not introduced afterwards by diluvial action, as has been sometimes suspected."[46]

At Norwich Lyell talked with various men who had collections of crag fossils. A Mr. J. B. Wigham gave him the left side of the upper jaw of a mastodon containing one complete molar tooth and a fragment of another. Richard Owen later identified this jaw as that of *Mastodon longirostris*, also found at Eppelsheim in Germany. Mr. Wigham also provided Lyell with a large number of fossil shells from the Norwich crag and he got others from Robert Fitch of Norwich; Captain Alexander gave him a collection of fossil shells from the crag beds at Southwold.

All told, Lyell obtained from Mr. Wigham and other collectors 111 species of shells from the Norwich crag and of these, 92 were marine and 19 were freshwater shells. Among the marine shells he recognized immediately a very large number of species which also occurred in the red crag of Suffolk. This fact, he wrote, "struck me so forcibly when collecting at Southwold and Norwich, that I at first began to suspect, that by increasing our knowledge of the fossils of the Norwich beds we should eventually prove them and the red crag to be nearly, if not wholly of the same age."[47] Thus, although Lyell had confirmed Charlesworth's opinion that the bones of mammals had been embedded in the Norwich crag strata at the time these strata were first laid down, he was inclined to disagree with Charlesworth that the Norfolk crag beds were younger than those of Suffolk. On 1 September 1838 he wrote to Leonard Horner:

> I ascertained during my tour in Suffolk and Norfolk two points respecting the Crag which I had never made out before, at least to my own satisfaction. First, that the mammalia, such as mastodon, elephant etc. were really coeval with the true Crag shells. 2.dly, that the Crag of Norfolk was not as some have supposed of a newer date than that of Suffolk.[48]

46. "On the relative ages of the Tertiary deposits commonly called 'Crag' in the counties of Norfolk and Suffolk" (1839) p. 317.

47. Ibid., p. 319.

48. C. L., Jr. and M. E. L. to her father. 1 Sept. 1838. Kinnordy mss. *L. & L.* II, 41–43.

From Norwich the Lyells went by steamboat down the river Yare to Yarmouth and thence by another steamboat to Hull to attend the annual meeting of the British Association, which opened at Newcastle on 20 August 1838. After the meeting they went to Kinnordy. Lyell was astonished to see the changes occurring in his native county; fifty-six miles of railroad would be completed in Forfarshire by the end of 1838 and at a cost of nearly £400,000. Apart from a visit to St. Andrews, where Lyell examined the rocks along the coast, the Lyells remained quietly at Kinnordy until his birthday, 14 November, when they took the steamboat from Dundee to London, arriving on the sixteenth. During the winter of 1838–39 Lyell continued to work at the revision of the *Principles* for the sixth edition. He also worked at the collection of crag fossils which he had made in Suffolk and at Norwich during the preceding August, "trying to make out the relations of the coralline crag, red crag, Norfolk or fluvio-marine crag with Mammalian remains & freshwater & land shells & lastly the freshwater deposits of the basin of the Thames, with mostly recent shells & many extinct quadrupeds."[49]

In order to make a detailed comparison of the 111 species of shells he had obtained from the Norfolk crag with those of the Suffolk crag, Lyell obtained representative specimens of the fossil shells of both the red crag and the coralline crag of Suffolk from Mr. Searles Wood and had them compared by George Sowerby[50] of London. Of the ninety-two marine shells in the Norwich crag, Searles Wood had already recognized that seventy-three also occurred in the red crag of Suffolk—the fact which had led Lyell to think that the two formations were of the same age. However, when George Sowerby determined the proportion of recent species in the two formations, the results were very different. The Norwich crag shells contained between fifty and sixty per cent of recent species, whereas the red crag contained only thirty per cent of recent species, and the coralline crag only nineteen per cent. The irony of this finding was that Lyell's percentage system for determining the relative age of Tertiary strata, a system which Edward Charlesworth had attacked, now confirmed Charlesworth's opinion that the Norwich crag was younger than the red

49. C. L., Jr. to J. Fleming. 15 Feb. 1839. [copy] Kinnordy mss.
50. George Brettingham Sowerby (1788–1854) conchologist and artist, was the second son of James Sowerby and had contributed largely to his father's *Mineral Conchology*. He was a dealer in shells and natural history objects and was a very skilled conchologist.

crag and contradicted Lyell's own initial impression that the two formations were of the same age.

The fact that so many species were common to the red crag and Norwich crag raised the question whether some of them might, as Charlesworth had suggested, have been first deposited as fossils in the red crag and later washed out of that formation and reembedded in the Norwich crag. Lyell noted that some of the commonest shells of the Norwich crag also occurred in the red crag, "yet no one can doubt that these lived in the sea of the Norwich crag, as they abound in it in a good state of preservation, although some of them are fragile shells, and the *Acephala* have occasionally both valves united."[51] Charlesworth had mentioned that various species of *Terebratula* and other chalk fossils occurred commonly in the Norfolk crag and he thought that they had been washed out of the chalk and redeposited in the crag. Lyell also collected many *Terebratulae* from the crag in Norfolk, but of a species different from that of the chalk and one, in fact, still living. He found no true *Terebratulae* of the chalk in the crag and thought that their introduction was a "local accident."[52] The transfer of fossils from one formation to a later one seemed, therefore, of very rare occurrence.

The results of Lyell's studies on the crag, carried out with the help of Searles Wood and George Sowerby, may be summarized as follows:

Norwich crag	60% recent species
red crag	30% recent species
coralline crag	19% recent species

On the basis of the rules which he had previously established for the classification of Tertiary formations, Lyell had to consider the Norwich crag as older Pliocene and the coralline crag and red crag as belonging to two successive periods of the Miocene.

When he was at Norwich in August 1838 Lyell had also obtained from Robert Fitch a collection of shells from certain deposits at Cromer and Mundesley on the north coast of Norfolk, and during the following winter he compared them with fossils from other deposits at Stutton, Grays, and Ilford in Essex. Among these fossils the proportion of recent species was of the order of ninety to ninety-five per cent, much higher than that of the Norwich crag. Lyell, therefore, considered these beds to be newer Pleiocene

51. "On the relative ages of the . . . 'Crag'" (1839) p. 320.
52. Ibid., p. 321.

or Pleistocene. He had first introduced the term "Pleistocene" in an appendix to the French translation of his *Elements of Geology*. As the number of subdivisions of the Pleiocene period had increased, he had found himself in the uncomfortable position of referring to the upper and lower "older Pleiocene" and the awkwardness of this suggested the need for new terms. Then Charles Darwin had pointed out the need for a term to designate a formation like that of the pampas, which contained the bones of extinct mammals embedded with fossil shells entirely belonging to recent species. The discovery of a Pleistocene formation on the coast of Norfolk meant that the crag, which had a short while before been thought of as a single formation of little thickness or importance, was now distinguished into four formations of successive ages, the oldest, the coralline crag, extending far back into the Tertiary period.

At a meeting of the Geological Society in April 1839 Lyell presented the results of his researches on the crag.[53]

After delivering this paper, Lyell prepared it for publication in *The Magazine of Natural History*, edited by Charlesworth, and it appeared in the issue for July 1839. By publishing it in Charlesworth's own journal Lyell seems to have wished to compensate a little for his slightly frugal acknowledgment in the *Elements* of Charlesworth's contribution to the understanding of the crag. Lyell pointed out that Charlesworth had given the correct order of succession of the crag formations in his paper before the British Association in 1836. "It is now satisfactory," Lyell wrote, "to find that the palaeontological test of age, as derived from the relative approach to the recent Fauna, is perfectly in accordance with the independent evidence drawn from superposition, and the included fragments of older beds."[54]

These facts provided a beautiful confirmation of the validity of the percentage test in determining the relative age of strata because Lyell showed that his original assignment of the crag to the older Pliocene was based on the examination of fossils chiefly from the Norwich crag and on the assumption that he was dealing with a single formation deposited within one period of time. Based on this much more thorough examination of fossil shells, the Norwich crag still belonged to the older Pliocene, while the red crag and coralline crag belonged to two successively older periods of the

53. "On the relative ages of the . . . 'Crag' " [1839]. This is an abstract of the paper only.
54. "On the relative ages of the . . . 'Crag' " (1839) p. 323.

Miocene. The superficial lake and river deposits at Cromer and Mundesley in Norfolk and various other places contained more than seventy per cent of recent shells and therefore, as Edward Charlesworth had shown in 1836, were still younger than the Norwich crag. In other words, the percentage test, when applied by a thorough examination of fossil shell species, gave precisely the same results as Charlesworth had obtained by studying the order of superposition of the beds.

In 1825 Jules Desnoyers had published an account of the crag in which he had considered it to be of the same age as the faluns of the Loire in Touraine. When he had visited England he had shared the opinion, then universal, that the crag was a single formation; the locality which he visited and on which his opinion of the age of the crag was later based, was at Aldborough, Suffolk, where the coralline crag was exposed on the sea coast. Lyell disagreed with Desnoyers' opinion because identifications of the 111 species of crag shells, collected indiscriminately from the Norwich crag and red crag, which Lyell had taken to Deshayes at Paris, suggested that the crag was of Pleiocene Age, whereas the faluns of Touraine were of Miocene Age. Also the fossil species of Touraine described by Desnoyers differed almost entirely from those of the crag. However, when George Sowerby examined the 240 species of Touraine fossil shells which Lyell had obtained at Paris from Felix Dujardin in September 1837, he determined the proportion of recent species among them to be twenty-six per cent. This was very close to the nineteen per cent of recent species among the fossil shells of the coralline crag. However, when Searles Wood compared Dujardin's shells with his own large collection of crag shells there were less than ten percent of species common to the two. Furthermore, the fossil shells of the crag tended to be of northern species whereas those of Touraine belonged to southern and even subtropical species. Lyell decided that during the Miocene period there must have been a continuous land barrier extending across the straits of Dover to the coast of France. The crag was, therefore, probably laid down in a great bay of the sea opening only to the north, while the faluns of Touraine had been laid down in the bay of a warmer sea on the far side of a barrier of land to the south.

In June 1839 Lyell made yet another geological excursion into Suffolk. He wished to continue his examination of the crag which was providing so much new information about the Tertiary period. He wrote to Leonard Horner:

I have got so many new lights respecting Tertiary & recent fossil shells that I am more & more desirous of completing an extensive re-examination of all the evidence on which I built in 1830, since which time I have never had a respite from printing, or preparing for the press, sufficiently long to enable me to go fairly into the subject as now.[55]

On Sunday 16 June 1839 the Lyells took a steamer from London to Yarmouth, but as one of the boilers sprang a leak, the boat limped along at four miles an hour, so they landed at Lowestoft and took a chaise to Yarmouth and afterwards to the village of Stalham, a "most rural little place" where they stayed. From Happisburgh Mary wrote:

The lanes are in great beauty, smelling so deliciously of may & the fields of white clover. I think Norfolk much libelled when it is called ugly. I never saw anything so pretty as the farmhouses & gardens, and such numbers of small gentlemen's houses that might belong to people of £500 a year. Then the old church towers are so picturesque. Charles & I have been all the morning snuffing up the air & exclaiming at some new cottage at each turn. We breakfasted early & left soon after light & went to Eccles where there is a line of sand hills & the tower of an old church which was buried time out of mind. The sea is making great encroachments at Nuant. We sauntered about nearly an hour making sketches & Charles examining the cliffs & then on to Happisburgh lighthouse where Charles left me & I came on here in the chaise.[56]

They spent two days at Mundesley and at Cromer making excursions along the coast as far as Weybourne where the cliffs ended. They then traveled inland through Holt and Fakenham to Swaffnam, where they gave up their chaise and took a coach to Norwich. Mary wrote:

We have collected a good deal as you will believe when I tell you that we sent home, or brought with us, four hampers & a large deal box full of our collectings, chiefly fossil shells. We saw a great many kind people & met with various adventures dining in little ale houses.

She also remarked on:

55. C. L., Jr. and M. E. L. to her father. 13 June 1839. Kinnordy mss.
56. M. E. L. to her mother. 18 June 1839. Kinnordy mss.

. . . the beautiful hedges covered with dog roses & honeysuckles, with the banks on each side perfectly enamelled with flowers, the fine trees of different kinds, *multitudes* of singing birds, fine ancient towers of the churches & the neatest cottages & brick farm houses with old twisted chimneys each quite a picture & before every cottage or farm was a beautiful garden full of flowers & making the air quite deliciously scented, not to mention the many bean fields in blossom. The people are great florists & in all the little towns there are horticultural shows.[57]

On their return journey they spent five days at Mr. William Colchester's farm at Sutton in Suffolk, collecting fossils from the crag formations there. On this occasion Lyell obtained from Colchester a large tooth which had been found in the red crag. Richard Owen identified it as being the tooth of a leopard. Lyell obtained from the crag other teeth which Owen identified as having belonged to an extinct species of bear, a hog, and a small ruminant about the size of a red deer.[58] Mr. Colchester also showed Lyell yet another tooth, which seemed to be mammalian, and which he had found in a sandpit belonging to the London clay formation at Kyson, near Woodbridge in Suffolk. At Lyell's request Colchester took him to this pit; there they found more of these apparently mammalian teeth mingled together with many shark's teeth. When Lyell showed these peculiar mammalian teeth to Owen the latter at first thought that they were molars of the lower jaw of the North American opossum, a marsupial; but on closer examination Owen decided that they were the molars of a monkey of the genus *Macacus*. Since this was the first land mammal to be found in the London clay and the first primate to be found as early as the eocene, its discovery was something of a sensation. Later a complete lower jaw of *Macacus* was found in this pit and on further search another jaw, this time really of an opossum, turned up. The mammals, as a large and varied group of genera and species, were therefore at least as old as the beginning of the Tertiary period.[59]

57. M. E. L. to her sister Katherine. 9 July 1839. Kinnordy mss.
58. "On the remains of Mammalia . . ." (1840). Cf. "On the discovery of fossil teeth of a Leopard, Bear and other animals . . ." (1840).
59. "On the occurrence of Fossil Quadrumanous, Marsupial and other Mammalia . . ." (1840). Cf. S. W. Wood, "The discovery of fossil quadrumanous remains . . ." (1839); R. Owen, "Description of the fossil mentioned in the preceding letter" (1839). In 1862 Owen found that his identification of the fossil jaw as that of a *Macacus* was mistaken and that the fossil jaw was that of a *Hyracotherium*. There was no *Macacus* in the Eocene.

During his excursion into Suffolk and Norfolk in June 1839 Lyell also reexamined the mud cliffs of Norfolk which he had first studied during the summer of 1829. He wished to see what changes had occurred as a result of the action of the sea during the intervening ten years. These cliffs, which extended for about twenty miles from Happisburgh lighthouse to near Weybourne, were composed of two kinds of deposits, "drift" or "diluvium," actually glacial in origin, and freshwater strata, both resting on chalk. The sections in these cliffs revealed many confusing features. In places the freshwater strata were extremely folded, bent, and contorted as if by lateral pressure exerted on the surface; they rested on other strata which showed no signs of disturbance. The origin of the "drift" was a puzzle to Lyell. He noted that:

> The regularly stratified arrangement of a large part of it, and the different materials of the alternating strata, clearly demonstrate that it was formed gradually, and not by any single or sudden flood. The boulders which it contains, some of large size, seem to imply, that while a great proportion of the mass may have been derived from neighbouring regions, part at least has come from a great distance.

He saw clearly that the boulder formation of Norfolk was very similar to "the boulder formation which I have seen in Sweden, Denmark, Holstein and other countries." Since he had concluded in Sweden that coast ice and icebergs had much to do with the transportation of boulders and loose deposits of clay, sand, and gravel, he concluded that the drift of Norfolk must also have resulted from ice action and that the momentum of large icebergs coming aground could disturb the superficial strata in the manner revealed in the Norfolk cliffs.[60]

On Monday 29 August 1839, the meeting of the British Association opened at Birmingham. Lyell was present as one of the vice-presidents of the geological section. He also delivered two papers, one on tubular cavities filled with sand and gravel, which he had observed in a chalk quarry near Norwich,[61] and another on the fossil mammals discovered in the crag and London clay of Suffolk.[62] After the business of the section was over on Tuesday, he went with a group of other scientists to stay overnight at Tam-

60. "On the Boulder Formation . . ." (1840).
61. "On the origin of the tubular cavities . . ." (1840).
62. "On remains of Mammalia . . ." (1840).

worth Castle, the country home of Sir Robert Peel, then prime minister of Great Britain. While on the train they traveled at twenty-two miles an hour, which seemed a great speed. When they turned off from the main London to Birmingham line onto the road to Derby they had to wait to see if there were any passengers for Derby on the train from London. Lyell described the pageantry of the railroad:

> During this stop we had a fine view of the great luggage train, in which there were no passengers, but forty-eight waggons laden with baggage covered with canvas. It seemed an interminable length, was preceded by two locomotives, and passed us at full speed, having to keep clear of a train only ten minutes behind it. To prevent this train from running into it the last carriage contained a huge red lamp which looked like a conflagration.[63]

At dinner Lyell sat beside Sir Robert Peel and talked with him at length. Peel had little knowledge of science but he knew enough to realize its importance, a quality extremely rare among British prime ministers.

During the winter of 1839–40 Lyell wrote a paper on his observations made in June 1839 of the cliffs between Mundesley and Weybourne.[64] He also worked at the revision of the *Principles* for the sixth edition, which he completed in June 1840. In July he set off for France to make his own first-hand study of the faluns of the Loire. He wished to check the localities and geological position of some of the fossil shells reported from the faluns and in general make a detailed comparison of the fossils of the faluns with those of the coralline crag and red crag of Suffolk so as to determine the geographical distribution of Miocene shell species.

The Lyells went first to Le Havre, where Lyell studied the chalk cliffs which in some places mark the boundaries of the lower valley of the Seine in Normandy[65] (Map 17). Although the chalk itself did not contain salt, in some places the chalk of the cliff face was encrusted with common salt. This phenomenon, which possibly was the result of the evaporation on the chalk surface of water containing quite minute quantities of salt, seems to have puzzled Lyell. It was, however, compatible with his belief

63. C. L., Jr. to his sister Sophia. 1 Sept. 1839. *L. & L.* II, 50–53.
64. "On the boulder formation . . ." (1840).
65. "On ancient sea-cliffs . . ." (1841).

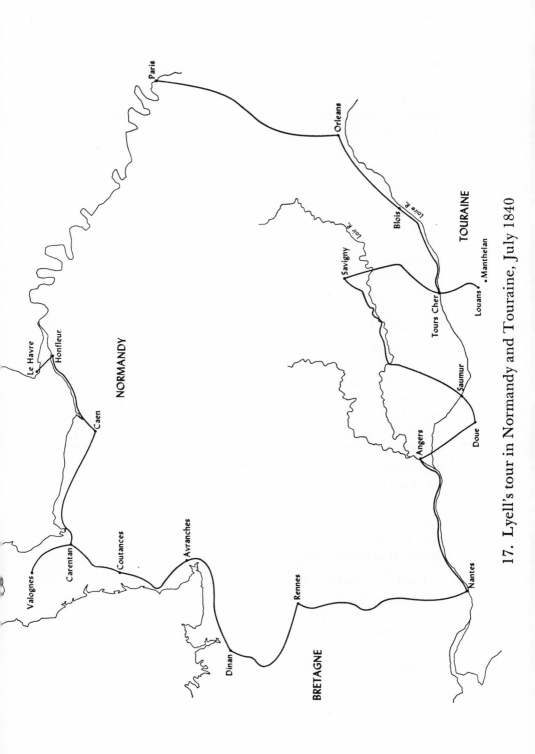

Paris

Orleans

Loire R.

Blois

TOURAINE

Savigny

Loir R.

Tours Cher

Louans •Manthelan

Saumur

Le Havre

Honfleur.

Caen

NORMANDY

Doue

Angers

Valognes

Carentan

Coutances

Avranches

Dinan

Rennes

BRETAGNE

Nantes

17. Lyell's tour in Normandy and Touraine, July 1840

that these chalk escarpments represented ancient sea cliffs and that the present valley of the Seine had once been an inlet of the sea.

At Caen Lyell was able to confirm a kind of fact which never failed to delight him because it revealed the great persistence of fossil genera through immense periods of geological time. In the collection of Professor Deslongschamps he saw two species of shells belonging to the genus *Conus*. Shells of this and related genera were abundant in Tertiary strata, but Deslongschamps told Lyell that these two species had come from strata belonging to the lias or inferior oolite and therefore dated from far back in the secondary period. The fact was so startling that Lyell went with Deslongschamps to check the age of the quarry from which the shells had come, but from the associated fossils there could be no doubt that the strata were at least as old as the inferior oolite.[66]

From Caen the Lyells travelled into the Cotentin peninsula to Valognes. Lyell visited a marl pit on a farm near Ranville La Place, eight miles southwest of Valognes, where he found the marl abounding in the same shells as the Suffolk crag. Five miles southwest of Carentan he found another bed containing Suffolk crag fossils; near Sainteny he found more crag fossils. This was the last place where he found a characteristic group of crag fossils; the next Tertiary deposit he came to, in a depression of the granitic rocks of Brittany near Dinan, contained the fossils characteristic of the faluns of the Loire. However, the presence of the crag in the Cotentin showed that the Miocene land barrier, which Lyell thought must have separated the crag sea from that in which the faluns were laid down, had been in the latitude of Brittany and Cornwall, far south of the straits of Dover. Of the neighborhood of Dinan Mary wrote:

> Charles considers the tertiary deposit there as agreeing with the faluns of the Loire altho' almost all the shells, instead of being in the full & perfect state in which they are so often taken from the sand of the faluns are mere casts & but for their specific characters might be taken as fossils of the oolite or any older rock. There are also abundance of small corals . . . besides large teeth of fish & other curious remains.

On 7 July they went from Dinan to Rennes, where they made two geological excursions and sent a box containing the fossils col-

66. "On the occurrence of . . . *Conus* . . ." (1840).

lected to Le Havre by diligence, "being the fourth already dispatched," Mary wrote, "towards filling up every cranny in Hart St., or at least of a new cabinet just ordered." From Rennes they travelled south to Nantes, "a most beautiful town & very flourishing & increasing—new buildings on all sides."[67] M. Caillaud, curator of the natural history museum at Nantes, showed them his collection of shells and gave them some specimens.

From Nantes they went up the Loire by steamboat. Mary wrote:

> We left Nantes on the Monday morning [13 July] in a small steamer christened the *Inexplosible* & had a most ridiculous scene, by a rival steamer running close up to us, everybody so terrified, such running & chattering, & we found afterwards it was not lest we should be run aground, which was the only thing there was the slightest chance of, but lest their boiler should explode against us, while we being *inexplosible* could not injure them!

Since the weather was rainy they kept below, but the Loire proved on the whole less scenic than the Seine. Mary continued:

> We stopped in the evening at Angers which is a curious old town with a very remarkable castle, surrounded with round towers, a moat & drawbridge. We walked up there just at sunset & it commands a very fine view. Here we found a M. Millet, a naturalist, who gave us some fossils in exchange for some British shells we brought.

They then spent two days collecting at Doué, southwest of Angers, where they found a limestone very rich in corals. Afterwards they went to Saumur where they hired a *voiturier*. Mary recounted:

> We first made a little tour to the north of the Loire to Savigné sleeping at very small villages. It was a very pretty country, well cultivated & hills & vales, the nicest country I think we have been in altogether. . . . We had a grand collecting of fossils close to Savigné with a tribe of children to help.

At Savigné Lyell obtained eighteen species of corals, two of echinoderms, seventy-six species of shells and four of fishes. On 18 July they reached Tours. Mary continued:

67. M. E. L. to her sister Katherine. 12 July 1840. Kinnordy mss.

We left Tours on Sunday afternoon [19 July] intending to go to Montelan, but learning at a village where we stopped by the way, that there was a great place for fossils at Louans we turned off through the most detestable country roads you ever saw, which almost shook us to pieces, to the very small village of Louans. We found however clean accommodation in a little cabaret where they took great pains to please us. We visited the curé, who was a very pleasing gentlemanlike young man who had collected fossils. His mother who was with him had quite a good manner, but was dressed in the peasants' costume & we found she could not read.[68]

In a marl pit at Louans Lyell obtained 180 species of shells, many of them very small and previously unknown. The result of their collections there and at other places was that they returned to Tours with boxes of fossils. Mary wrote:

Charles is so perfectly satisfied with his campaign this year. It was downright hard work while it lasted & we both confessed when we got to Blois & had no more geology to do that we were glad of a little holiday.[69]

However, they were both brown and healthy. From Blois they took the diligence to Paris and after a few days there went down the Seine to Le Havre, where all their boxes of fossils had been sent. On 30 July they sailed for London.

During the following winter Lyell studied his collections of Touraine fossil shells with the help of George Sowerby and Edward Forbes.[70] William Lonsdale, curator at the Geological Society, identified the corals. The general result was to show that the fossils of the faluns of Touraine formed a single fauna of Miocene age and, although only isolated portions of its sediments remained, the whole valley of the Loire had been a single basin in the Miocene sea. The large number of corals, compared with the few shells in the limestone at Doué, corresponded perfectly to the coralline crag, but only fifteen per cent of the species agreed with those of the crag. Lyell considered that this wide difference in species was similar to that which existed between the Red Sea and the Medi-

68. M. E. L. to her sister-in-law Marianne. 20 July 1840. Kinnordy mss.
69. M. E. L. to her sister-in-law Marianne. 28 July 1840. Kinnordy mss.
70. Edward Forbes (1815–54), naturalist and paleontologist, spent some time in London during 1840–41 preparing for publication his book on British starfish.

terranean or between the two sides of the isthmus of Panama in the modern period. The fossils of both the faluns and the crag were almost entirely different from those of the Eocene strata of the London and Paris basins and they contained about one-fifth of recent species.[71]

71. "On the Faluns of the Loire . . ." [1841].

CHAPTER 15

The Glacier Theory, 1840

AFTER HIS RETURN from the Loire valley, Lyell remained at 16 Hart Street until September, when he went to Scotland first to attend the meeting of the British Association at Glasgow and then for a holiday at Kinnordy. At this meeting Louis Agassiz presented a report of his discoveries on the movements of glaciers. As a result of his studies of glaciers in Switzerland, Agassiz had concluded that the tendency of water to run into all cracks and fissures of the glacier and there to freeze caused the mass of the glacier to expand continually. The repeated expansion of the mass of the glacier caused it to move. Agassiz also described the effects of glacial movement, the polishing and furrowing of the underlying rocks, and the medial and lateral moraines resulting from fragments of rocks and gravel which fall upon the glacier and are carried along by it. Agassiz said:

> As the glaciers are continually pressed forwards, and often in hot summers melted back at their lower extremity, it results that the polished surfaces, occasioned by friction on the bottom and sides, are left uncovered, and that terminal *moraines,* or curvilinear ridges of gravel and boulders, remain upon the rocks formerly covered by the ice. Thus we can discover, by the polished surfaces and the *moraines,* the extent to which the glaciers have heretofore existed, which is much beyond the limits they now occupy in the Alpine valleys.[1]

Agassiz had just published his *Études sur les Glaciers de la Suisse,* in which he presented the results of his studies of glaciers during the preceding three summers. He had first become interested in glaciers during the summer of 1836 when he had accepted the invitation of Jean de Charpentier to visit him at Bex in the valley of the Aar. The year before, Charpentier had attributed the distribution of erratic blocks in the lower Swiss valleys and on

---

1. L. Agassiz, "On glaciers and boulders in Switzerland" (1841).

the Jura to a former wider extent of the Alpine glaciers.[2] When
Agassiz saw glacial phenomena at first hand, he very quickly became converted to Charpentier's views. In fact, he went even further and proposed to explain the occurrence of erratic blocks
throughout all of northern Europe by postulating that a great ice
sheet had extended over the whole area. In 1837 Agassiz had announced his ice-age theory to a meeting of the Swiss Natural History Society. Agassiz noted that below the lower ends of the glaciers a succession of curvilinear moraines occurred, each exactly
similar to the moraine immediately beneath the glacier itself. He
suggested that prior to the elevation of the Alps, a great sheet of
ice, extending from the north pole to the shores of the Mediterranean, had covered all of Europe. The Alps had then been upheaved in a great cataclysm and in so doing had both elevated and
broken the ice sheet. At the same time, as a result of these upheavals, many fragments of rock had been broken off from the jagged
edges of the protruding Alps and had slid down the smooth slope
of the ice sheet which clothed them. When the ice melted, these
fragments were left as lines of erratic boulders on the Jura and
those erratic boulders scattered more widely across the surface of
Europe. This was imaginative geology on a grand scale; it was
also unabashed catastrophism. Agassiz said that this great ice age
had produced the extinction of "the animals of the diluvial epoch
of the geologists" including the Siberian mammoths.[3]

It was perhaps the catastrophic implications of glaciation which
had made Lyell slow to take an interest in it. In his presidential
address to the Geological Society in 1836 he had noted Charpentier's theory "which he informs us is merely a development of one
first advanced by M. Venetz."[4] Charpentier argued that the erratic
blocks on the Jura had been carried there by ice and could not
have been carried by water. However, Charpentier linked his theory to Élie de Beaumont's theory that the Alps had been elevated
at a comparatively modern period and had at first been upheaved
to a greater height than now so that their snow fields and glaciers
were then more extensive. In his theory Agassiz had retained
Beaumont's concept of the relatively sudden modern elevation of

2. J. G. F. de Charpentier, "Notice sur la cause probable du transport des
blocs erratiques de la Suisse" (1835).
3. L. Agassiz, "Discours . . . à Neuchâtel le 24 Juillet 1837" (1837).
4. "Anniversary Address . . . 19 February 1836," p. 383.

the Alps and had added to it his own theory of a preceding universal ice age in Europe. Since Lyell knew that the elevation of the Alps dated at least from the beginning of the Tertiary period and since he was perfectly confident that they had been upraised very slowly and gradually, he was not prepared to accept Agassiz's conclusions.

However, during each of the summers from 1838 to 1840, Agassiz had been making detailed studies of the effects of glaciation in the Alps and had established a camp on the glacier of the Aar. "There," he wrote to Sir Philip Egerton, "I ascertained the most important fact that I now know concerning the advance of glaciers, namely, that the cabin constructed by Hugi in 1827, at the foot of the Abschwung, is now four thousand feet lower down."[5] The fact that glaciers moved at so considerable a rate was a startling idea and Agassiz's studies thenceforward were devoted to the study of this motion. Saussure had suggested that the accumulation of snow above and the discharge of snowy avalanches from steep mountain slopes not only formed the glacier but created a pressure which forced it downward. The melting of ice on its lower surface tended to lubricate its motion, so that in effect the glacier, pushed from above, slid down its valley.[6] An alternative theory, originated by Scheuchzer in the eighteenth century and developed by Jean de Charpentier, stated that the glacier moved as a result of diurnal freezing and thawing. During the day some of the snow and ice melted and the water trickled into cracks and fissures in the glacier. At night when it froze, it expanded and thereby created a pressure which pushed the glacier forward slightly. It was this theory which Agassiz expounded before the meeting of the British Association at Glasgow in September 1840.

The distribution of erratic blocks and moraines in Switzerland had convinced Agassiz that the glaciers had gradually retreated to their present position. It was this fact which had led him to postulate an ice sheet formerly extended over Europe. After the meeting at Glasgow, therefore, he went with the Reverend William Buckland on a tour through the highlands of Scotland to look for signs of former glaciation there. In 1838, when Buckland had visited Agassiz at Neuchâtel, the latter had shown him the "pol-

5. L. Agassiz to P. Egerton. 10 Sept. 1839, in E. C. Agassiz, *Louis Agassiz* (1886) vol. I, pp. 294–95.
6. H. B. de Saussure, *Voyages dans les Alpes* . . . (1779–96) vol. I, pp. 436–65, esp. p. 454.

ished, striated and furrowed surfaces" of the rocks on the southeast slope of the Jura as well as the erratic boulders, and had convinced him that these were the effects of ice. Buckland then went
to examine the glaciers of Rosenlaui and Grindelwald and on his
return to Neuchâtel told Agassiz "that he had noticed in Scotland
and England phaenomena similar to those he had just examined,
but which he had attributed to diluvial action."[7] If Scotland had
been glaciated there should once have been glaciers extending
down each of the valleys of the Grampians, and at the mouth of
each valley there should be the remnants of a terminal moraine.
This was what Agassiz was looking for and this was what he
found. "As we approached the castle of the Duke of Argyll, standing in a valley not unlike some of the Swiss valleys," Agassiz wrote,
"I said to Buckland: 'Here we shall find our first traces of glaciers';
and as the stage entered the valley, we actually drove over an ancient terminal moraine, which spanned the opening of the valley."[8] Agassiz found moraines at Inverary, at Muc Airn at the out-
let of Loch Treig, at Strankaer, and on the shores of the bay of
Beauley.

In addition to moraines, glaciers leave behind quantities of
waterwashed pebbles and boulders which are similar to the materials of the moraine but spread out in stratified deposits rather
than heaped up. Agassiz found such deposits also associated with
moraines. But the most distinctive effect of glaciation was the
grinding of polished and striated surfaces on the underlying solid
rocks. This effect was produced only by glaciers; Agassiz had observed it at the foot of the glacier of the Aar, in the valley of the
Rhone and at Chamonix. He now observed it in Scotland on the
banks of Loch Awe and Loch Leven. The most striking feature of
the lines of striation on the underlying rocks was the way in which
they radiated from the outlets of valleys. Agassiz argued that the
glaciers which had existed in the valleys of the highlands had been
the remaining portions of a sheet of ice which at an earlier time
had covered the whole country. Agassiz told the Geological Society:

> . . . if the glaciers descended from high mountains, and extended
> forward into the plains, the largest moraines ought to be the
> most distant, and to be formed of the most rounded masses;

7. W. Buckland, "Memoir on the evidences of glaciers . . ." (1841) p. 332.
8. E. C. Agassiz, *Louis Agassiz*, vol. I, p. 307.

whereas the actual condition of the detrital accumulations is the reverse, the distant materials being widely spread, and true moraines being found only in valleys connected with great chains of lofty mountains.[9]

He compared these ice sheets formerly spread over the British Isles and the continent of Europe to the great ice sheet present today over Greenland.

From Inverary, Agassiz and Buckland went north through the center of the highlands to Glen Roy where they studied the famous parallel roads. Agassiz decided that a glacier extending from a lateral valley into a main valley could in effect dam up the main valley to create a lake. This, he suggested, had occurred in Glen Roy. As the glacier gradually melted, the lake stood at successively lower levels each of which was marked by one of the terraces or parallel roads of Glen Roy. At Glen Roy Agassiz and Buckland apparently separated, Agassiz to go to Ireland to visit with Lord Cole at Florence Court, the home of his father, the Earl of Enniskillen, Buckland to go across Scotland to Aberdeen in search of further traces of glaciers. Their joint excursion had already been very fruitful. Agassiz later wrote:

> It was in Scotland that I acquired precision in my ideas regarding ancient glaciers. The existence in that country of so considerable a network of these traces, enabled me to appreciate better the geological mechanism of glaciers and the importance of many facts of detail observed in the neighbourhood of those which now exist.[10]

Buckland continued to find additional evidences of the effects of glaciers in eastern Scotland. Between Aberdeen and Stonehaven he found gravel and sand which he interpreted to be the detritus of moraines. When he reached Forfar in early October he went on to Kirriemuir where he stayed as the guest of Mr. Lyell at Kinnordy and where Charles and Mary Lyell also had come after the Glasgow meeting. Buckland immediately took Lyell out in search of glacial moraines, and they soon found some. The valley of Strathmore, on the north slope of which Kinnordy lies, is a broad shallow valley running roughly east–west. The mass of the Gram-

9. L. Agassiz, "On glaciers and the evidence of their having once existed in Scotland, Ireland and England" (1841).
10. L. Agassiz, "The Glacial Theory and its recent progress" (1842) p. 240.

pians rises to the north, and descending from these hills are a number of narrow steep-sided glens or valleys. In the vicinity of Kinnordy, opposite the lower ends of Glen Prosen and Glen Carity, whose streams enter the South Esk about a mile apart, were broad terraces or lateral mounds of boulder till. These, Buckland pointed out, must be the lateral moraines of glaciers. A half mile southwest of the house of Pearsie, Buckland pointed out the surface of a porphyry rock which was "polished, furrowed and scratched." Buckland wrote to Agassiz in jubilation:

> Lyell has adopted your theory *in toto!!!* On my showing him a beautiful cluster of moraines within two miles of his father's house, he instantly accepted it, as solving a host of difficulties that have all his life embarrassed him. And not these only, but similar moraines and detritus of moraines that cover half of the adjoining counties are explicable on your theory, and he has consented to my proposal that he should immediately lay them all down on a map of the county and describe them in a paper to be read the day after yours at the Geological Society.[11]

Lyell did prepare this paper and read it to the Geological Society at the meetings of 18 November and 2 December in immediate succession to the papers of Agassiz and Buckland.[12] The declarations of Buckland and Lyell in favor of Agassiz's glacial theory created a sensation. Adam Sedgwick attacked the glacial theory vigorously and the discussion lasted until near midnight. After the second occasion Mary wrote to Kinnordy:

> They had a capital meeting at the G. S. on Wednesday, a great fight and I hear (not from himself) that Charles spoke extremely well. There was a sort of renewal of the discussion at Mr. Greenough's where we dined next day and met the Murchisons, Dr. Buckland, Prof[r] Phillips, Mr. Agassiz, Mr. Stokes & some others. It was a pleasant lively party.[13]

Lyell had been prepared by his tour in Sweden to think that ice was the probable means by which erratic boulders had been transported, and he must have welcomed the glacier theory to ex-

11. W. Buckland to L. Agassiz. 15 Oct. 1840, in E. C. Agassiz, *Louis Agassiz*, vol. I, pp. 309–10.
12. "On the geological evidence of the former existence of glaciers in Forfarshire" (1841).
13. M. E. L. to her sister-in-law Marianne. 5 Dec. 1840. Kinnordy mss.

plain many features of the geology of Scotland, because it would remove the need for a catastrophic diluvial wave passing over the whole country. This latter explanation had been put forward in 1814 by Sir James Hall to account for deposits of glacial till in the neighborhood of Edinburgh and glacial scratches and furrows in the underlying rocks. Yet glacial phenomena were very complex and it would be a long time before Lyell or his contemporaries comprehended the wider effects of glaciation.

CHAPTER 16

The *Elements of Geology* and the Sixth Edition of the *Principles of Geology*, 1838–1841

WHEN LYELL completed the first draft of the manuscript of the *Elements of Geology* at Kinnordy in September 1836, he realized that the *Elements* would overlap in part the subject territory of the *Principles*. He wrote to John Murray:

> You are aware that out of four vols., of which the "Principles" consists, nearly three (i.e. two & ¾) are occupied first with the History of the progress of the science & 2dly with treatises on the modern changes in the inorganic & organic worlds.—Now all this, which is the part of my book most read & relished, is not strictly & properly *Geology*. The 4th vol. is on Geology proper & is to a great extent really an "Elements" & might be made more so by a moderate expansion & by the incorporating into it much which I have written for the "Elements."

Lyell thought that the *Elements* might tend to interfere with the sale of the *Principles,* both because the public would not realize that they were for the most part separate and independent works, and because "most people, after getting the smaller, cheaper & necessarily *dryer* work first, would not afterwards be led on to the more entertaining, attractive, diffuse, voluminous & costlier work."[1] He therefore proposed to put his manuscript of the *Elements* to one side for the present with the intention of taking up his work on another book which he proposed to call *Introduction to the study of fossil shells and their application to Geology*—a book he was never to complete.

In writing to Murray Lyell was seeking his advice as to what to do with the *Elements,* for despite his occasional complaints about Murray, he had come to trust Murray's judgment in matters of publication. Murray concurred in Lyell's proposal to lay the *Elements* aside for the time being and encouraged him with the work on fossil shells.[2] There may have been little else that Lyell could

1. C. L., Jr. to J. M. 21 Sept. 1836. Murray mss.
2. C. L., Jr. to his father. [4 Oct.] 1836. Kinnordy mss.

do in any case because during the autumn and early winter of 1836–37 he was occupied for long periods in writing his presidential address for the anniversary meeting of the Geological Society. After this address was delivered on 17 February 1837 and printed, Lyell was preoccupied with the publication of the fifth edition of the *Principles* in March 1837, talks with Darwin, correspondence with Sir John Herschel at Cape Town and the question of the proper delimitation of the species of Tertiary fossil shells. For three and a half months during the summer of 1837 this last problem took Lyell first to Copenhagen and then to Paris. Before he left London in June 1837, however, Lyell had worked out with Murray a plan for publishing the *Elements* together with the sixth edition of the *Principles*. This plan called for the transfer of Book IV of the *Principles,* that section in which Lyell discussed the succession of Tertiary formations, from the *Principles* into the *Elements*. "Those parts," Lyell wrote, "most strictly geological in the 'Principles,' which were addressed to beginners are to be transferred to the smaller and one volume book, & dished up in an easier form with more full explanations & illustrations."[3] In June 1837 John Murray thought that the fifth edition of the *Principles* would be sold out by February 1839, so that on his return to London in October, Lyell had only seventeen months in which to prepare the two works; since they would take five months to print, he had only a year for writing.

On 30 October 1837 Lyell made a new calculation, based on the rate of sale of the fifth edition of the *Principles,* then published nearly eight months, and found that the 2,000 copies printed should last until September 1839.[4] If he allowed it to remain out of print a few months before the appearance of the sixth edition, that would mean that the sixth edition would not appear until 1840. He seems, then, to have decided not to hold up the *Elements* any longer but to prepare it for publication in a form that would overlap the fifth edition of the *Principles* as little as possible. He therefore began to revise and rewrite the manuscript of the *Elements,* which he had laid aside in September 1836.

During the winter of 1837–38 Lyell was also collaborating with George Sowerby and Searles Wood on the study of crag shells, but his main work was the *Elements*. On 14 February 1838 he wrote to John Murray about a French translation of the *Principles* and

3. C. L., Jr. to his father. 5 Oct. 1837. Kinnordy mss.
4. Ms. Notebook 69, p. 142. Kinnordy mss.

added, "I am getting on with the Elements & feel confident of being out in June."⁵ On 12 March he wrote to Leonard Horner:

> I have just corrected the first sheet of proofs, 24 pp., of Elements—more elementary I think than any book yet out, but of necessity lamentably inferior in interest to the Principles. How fortunate for me that I did not begin with Geology proper! I am in good hopes of it as a teaching & selling school-book, but nothing of this kind would have earned me the literary reputation which the Principles gave me.⁶

Through the spring months of 1838 Lyell continued to work at the *Elements*. Charles Darwin read the manuscript and criticized portions of it. Leonard Horner helped to correct the proof sheets. Lyell could not finish printing the work in June and by 8 June thought he would be lucky to complete it by mid-July.⁷ At the end of June Lyell attended with Mary the coronation of Queen Victoria in Westminster Abbey where they had "a splendid view."⁸ On 8 July Lyell was working on the last chapter of the *Elements*.⁹ On 24 July he was correcting the index and a week later he and Mary left London to go first to Norfolk, then to the British Association at Newcastle, and finally to Kinnordy for a holiday. They were to be away for three months.¹⁰ The *Elements* was published while they were gone.¹¹

A few days after Lyell and his wife left London, Charles Darwin returned there from his expedition to Glen Roy. He found waiting for him a copy of the *Elements* which Lyell had sent as a gift. On 9 August Darwin wrote to Lyell in part to thank him for the book. He added:

> I have read it through every word & am full of admiration for it.—As I now see no geologist I must talk to you about it. There is no pleasure in reading a book if one cannot have a good talk over it.—I repeat I am full of admiration at it. It is as clear as daylight—in fact I felt in many parts some mortification at thinking how geologists have laboured & struggled at proving

5. C. L., Jr. to J. M. 14 Feb. 1838. Murray mss.
6. C. L., Jr. to L. Horner. 12 March 1838. Kinnordy mss. This portion omitted in the published letter, *L. & L.* II, 39–41.
7. C. L., Jr. to L. Horner. 18 June 1838. Kinnordy mss.
8. C. L., Jr. to J. Fleming. 4 July 1838. [copy] Kinnordy mss.
9. M. E. L. to her sister-in-law Marianne. [8] July 1838. Kinnordy mss.
10. C. L., Jr. to J. M. 24 July 1838. Murray mss.
11. *Elements of Geology* (1838).

what seems, as you have put it, so evidently probable.—I read with much interest your sketch of the secondary deposits. You have contrived to make it quite "juicy" as we used to say as children of a good story. There was also much new to me & I have to copy out some fifty notes & references. It must do good: the hereticks against common sense must yield.[12]

Darwin's estimate of the *Elements* was just. It was a marvel of clear, concise, and accurate exposition. Although the *Elements* was professedly non-theoretical, it was inevitably pervaded with theory. It bears a relationship to the revolution which Lyell had brought about in geology, similar to that which Lavoisier's *Traité de Chemie* had borne fifty years earlier to the chemical revolution. The *Elements,* like the *Traité,* was a textbook written entirely in terms of a new theory, which it also expounded and fortified. Lyell's *Elements of Geology* is the first modern textbook of geology; that is, it is the first systematic treatment of geology written on the assumption that *all* the phenomena of geology can be explained naturally and discussed scientifically. It was founded upon the *Principles* and probably could not have been written, and certainly not accepted by the public, if it had not been preceded by the *Principles.*

The Elements of Geology

The frontispiece to the *Elements* was a colored diagram of a vertical section through a volcanic island surrounded by sea and showing diagrammatically how each of the four great classes of rocks: "the aqueous, volcanic, plutonic and metamorphic" were produced (Fig. 52). The diagram showed streams of molten rock flowing upward from a reservoir deep within the earth, two streams extending to craters at the summit of the volcano while others probed their way into strata of sedimentary rock. Thus Lyell showed in this one diagram (1) the production of volcanic rocks on the surface, (2) the origin of plutonic rocks, such as granite, by cooling at the margins of the interior reservoir of molten rock, (3) the production of metamorphic rocks by alteration of sedimentary strata by finger-like intrusions of hot molten rock into them, (4) the deposition of layers of sediment beneath the sea, and (5) the flow of submarine lavas down the sides of the volcano and out beneath the sea. The whole of the eleven chapters of Part I of

12. C. Darwin to C. L., Jr. 9 Aug. 1838. APS mss.

the *Elements* were taken up with the elucidation of the geological processes illustrated in the frontispiece. Lyell explained in the simplest terms the deposition of sediments beneath the sea, the reasons why they formed layers, the embedding of fossils in them, and their consolidation into rock. He described their elevation and folding and their subsequent denudation. He went on to describe the various volcanic rocks, plutonic rocks, and metamorphic rocks.

In Part II of the *Elements* Lyell treated the question of the age of the four classes of rocks and showed that all four had been produced at every period of the earth's history. He showed how a mass of granite, or trap rock, might be older or younger than the stratified rocks surrounding it and pointed out the criteria for determining their relative age. Finally, in a series of eight chapters, he summarized what was then known of the succession of geological formations, beginning with a single chapter on Tertiary formations and going backward in time through the Cretaceous, Wealden, oolite, etc.

In writing the *Elements* Lyell acknowledged his indebtedness to two books not yet published; one was Darwin's *Journal of Researches,* the other, Roderick Murchison's *Silurian System.* From Darwin he gleaned many facts illustrative of elevation of mountains and volcanic geology and from Murchison an account of the fossils of the Silurian rocks, then almost the oldest known fossil-bearing strata.

When he and Mary reached Kinnordy on 30 August 1838, Lyell was finally able to relax. The life there, together again with his family, amid the green hills and broad expanses of the valley of Strathmore was particularly soothing. Lyell needed a rest. When he had finished the *Elements* Mary commented "I hope he will never work so many months *de suite* again."[13] When they reached Kinnordy his mother noted his "worn, worried look" which a few weeks later she was glad to see had largely vanished. He and Mary went one day with Caroline and Eleanor on horseback to Balintore high on the slope of the Grampians with a view of the small loch of Lintrathen. It was, his mother wrote,

> . . . one of those beautiful kinds of day which I really think we enjoy to greater perfection in the North . . . there is a delightful clear freshness in the air which seems to strengthen both body

13. M. E. L. to Marianne Lyell. July 1838. Kinnordy mss.

and spirits, with a fine hot sun which is making the country look to great advantage and universally in a bustle with harvest.[14]

Lyell was not entirely idle at Kinnordy, for he began to recast the *Principles* for a sixth edition. In order to remove the chapters on Tertiary formations, which had been in Book IV, to include them in a second edition of the *Elements,* he had to do something with the five introductory chapters of Book IV. These had been essays preliminary to a discussion of Tertiary formations, but he now put them together with the preliminary essays of Book I. He hoped that these chapters would "now become more attractive to the general reader." To Murray he wrote:

> Indeed I have frequent misgivings when I feel how much more attractive & entertaining the Principles are, as to the ultimate effect of interposing a cheaper & necessarily dryer book between the beginner & the Principles. But the die is cast.

He thought it would be desirable if the *Principles* could be brought out "in the same open & easy type as the Elements." The difficulty was cost; it would make the work much more expensive. Yet, he wrote:

> If the size of the book & type were ever altered, now would be the time, & as I am bringing the book up to the knowledge of 1838 with much care & "buckling on of armour"—it might serve to mark the distinctness to earlier Editions. But authors are no sound judges of these matters.[15]

At the same time he was cheered, as he went over the early chapters of the *Principles,* to find how sound they still were after an interval of eight years. To Darwin he wrote:

> I really find, when bringing up my preliminary Essays in "Principles" to the science of the present day, so far as I know it, that the great outline, and even most of the details, stand so uninjured, and in many cases they are so much strengthened by new discoveries, especially by yours, that we may begin to hope that the great principles there insisted on will stand the test of new discoveries.[16]

14. Mrs. Charles Lyell, Sr. to Mrs. Leonard Horner. Sept. 1838. Kinnordy mss.
15. C. L., Jr. to J. M. 25 Sept. 1838. Murray mss.
16. C. L., Jr. to C. Darwin. 6–8 Sept. 1838. *L. & L.* II, 43–46.

And Darwin replied:

> You say you *"begin to hope* that the great principles there in-
> sisted on will stand the test of time." *Begin to hope;* why the
> *possibility* of a doubt had never crossed my mind for many a
> long day: this may be very unphilosophical, but my geological
> salvation is staked on it. After having just come back from Glen
> Roy & found how difficulties smooth away under your Princi-
> ples, it makes me quite indignant that you should talk of
> *hoping.*[17]

Except for his brief visit of five days to St. Andrews early in
November, Lyell spent most of his two and a half months at Kin-
nordy during the autumn of 1838 working at the revision of the
Principles. He found the work more than he had expected and
after his return to London on 16 November, wrote to Leonard
Horner:

> I have made such important alterations in the First Book of
> Principles that to complete them, even after all the work I gave
> to it at Kinnordy, will take some time.[18]

During the winter months of 1839, however, Lyell did not
continue his revisions of the *Principles* because he spent much
time with the help of George Sowerby and Searles Wood on the
detailed study of crag fossil shells which finally convinced him that
the Suffolk crag was of Miocene age and at the same time vindi-
cated his percentage system for the classification of Tertiary strata.
He gave an account of this work to the Geological Society in April
and prepared his paper on it for publication in the *Magazine of
Natural History* before he and Mary left London on 15 June 1839
for a tour of Norfolk and Suffolk. Immediately after their return
from this, their third crag expedition, the Lyells set out on 10 July
for Kinnordy for a long summer vacation.

Lyell was at Kinnordy on 1 August when he received the July issue of the *Edinburgh Review* which contained a long article by Dr.
Fitton reviewing the *Elements.*[19] Fitton first devoted some thirty
six pages to a thorough and highly complimentary analysis of the
Elements. Yet he questioned Lyell's introduction of the term "metamorphic" to describe strata which had been changed to a crys-

17. C. Darwin to C. L., Jr. 13 Sept. 1838. APS mss.
18. C. L., Jr. to L. Horner. 15–16 Nov. 1838. Kinnordy mss.
19. [W. H. Fitton]. "Art. V. *Elements of Geology,* by Charles Lyell Esq." (1839).

talline state by heat, because in applying it to a whole class of
rocks Lyell was requiring his readers to accept his theory of their
origin. Similarly Fitton objected to Lyell's introduction of the
terms Eocene, Miocene, and Pliocene, and the value of the percentage system for determining the relative age of Tertiary deposits. He doubted that the use of these terms would be "permanently
expedient."

In the latter part of his review Fitton entered into a full discussion of the theories of Dr. Hutton, whom he credited with origi-
nating that doctrine of metamorphic rocks, the value of which he
had questioned in Lyell's *Elements*. Inconsistency was one of
Fitton's more characteristic qualities. He was a warm advocate of
Dr. Hutton and he would not hesitate to go overboard in his defense. He accused Lyell of not having done "quite sufficient justice to the claims of Dr. Hutton . . . and that in adopting the
metamorphic theory, and the views connected with it, by modern
writers, he ought to have referred more emphatically to the works
of that very remarkable man, as the source from which those doctrines were first obtained."

As soon as he had read Fitton's article, Lyell wrote him a letter
which was a mixture of rueful thanks for the thoroughly intelligent and critical discussion of the *Elements* and an answer to his
criticism that Lyell had done inadequate justice to Hutton. Lyell
said that if Fitton's long "defence and eulogy" of Hutton was presented on the ground of his, Lyell's, neglect of him, Fitton might
have pointed out that whereas Cuvier, von Buch, Humboldt,
Boué, and Brongniart had totally ignored Hutton, he, Lyell, had
discussed Hutton's theories in the *Principles* in his historical sketch
of the development of geology. He had also used quotations from
Playfair's *Illustrations of the Huttonian Theory* on the title pages
of both the first and second volumes of the *Principles*. Since Fitton
had not complained that Lyell's historical sketch was too short in
relation to the general plan of the *Principles*, he must think that
the treatment of Hutton within that sketch had been too brief.
Yet, Lyell argued, he had given "comparatively speaking, full-
length portraits of Werner and Hutton, giving to the latter the
decided palm of theoretical excellence." He had referred to two
outstanding contributions made by Hutton:

First, the igneous origin of granite, secondly that the so-called
primitive rocks were altered strata. I dwelt emphatically on the

complete revolution brought about by his new views respecting
granite, and entered fully on Playfair's illustrations and defence of Hutton, and he is again put prominently forward in
the Elements p. 261 where no other but Lehman and Werner
are mentioned. . . .

Yet, to how many of your readers, who will never see my
work, will your elaborate advocacy of Hutton seem to imply
that I overlooked, or have been unwilling to acknowledge even
in a moderate degree, his just pretensions!

This latter complaint was apparently justified, because Fitton's
review has been referred to by a number of writers as indicating
that Lyell failed to do justice to Hutton.[20] Finally, Lyell said,

> Yet as an admirer of Hutton all I could have wished is, that your
> panegyric on Hutton had appeared as aiding and seconding my
> efforts, since I trust that no book has made the claims of Hut-
> ton better known on the Continent of late years than mine.[21]

The real issue between Fitton and Lyell perhaps does not
emerge fully in this exchange. Fitton believed that Lyell had not
added anything essentially new to Hutton's theory of the earth;
Lyell thought he had. The issue, therefore, was whether the ideas
contained in Lyell's *Principles* and *Elements* had already been
present in essence in Hutton's *Theory of the Earth* and Playfair's
Illustrations. Hutton's theory, as Hutton stated it, explained certain features of a limited range of geological phenomena. It could
not be applied to an immensely wider range of geological phenomena without the elaboration of many additional theories, sub-
theories, and hypotheses. For Hutton the presence of fossils in
strata had simply been evidence that such strata had been sediments deposited in the sea. He was unacquainted with the succession of faunas revealed by the fossil record. Similarly, he was
acquainted with the metamorphosed strata of the Alps only
through Saussure's writing and not by direct study. Thus he was
not aware that strata of all ages could be altered by heat, that
this alteration occurred only in association with igneous intrusives,

20. The relationship between Hutton and Lyell has been discussed very fairly by
V. A. Eyles in "James Hutton (1726–97) and Sir Charles Lyell (1797–1875)"
(1947). Sir Archibald Geikie, on the other hand, wrote of Lyell: "Adopting the
principles of the Huttonian theory, he developed them until the original enun-
ciator of them was nearly lost sight of." *The Founders of Geology* (1905) p. 403.
21. C. L., Jr. to W. H. Fitton. 1 Aug. 1839. [copy] Kinnordy mss. *L. & L.* II, 47–50.

and that the alteration of strata by heat was a process quite different from that of the compaction of loose sediments into solid rock. Lyell's theoretical position was fundamentally similar to Hutton's, but if he had simply rested upon Huttonian doctrine he would have been able neither to convince his contemporaries nor to interpret the immense variety of new geological phenomena which was emerging as a result of his own and others' field studies.

From Kinnordy the Lyells went to attend the annual meeting of the British Association at Birmingham in September, and shortly thereafter returned to London. Lyell was then occupied with "increasing & arranging my collection of tertiary shells, naming them with G. Sowerby's assistance & Mr. Wood's, buying a new cabinet etc."[22] He also continued to revise and reshape the *Principles*. In December, because of the large amount of material which he was transferring to the second edition of the *Elements*, he decided to reduce it to three volumes in size. He wrote to Murray:

> I thought it might be expedient to inform you of the new shape that the Principles will assume in case of your feeling at liberty to speak at your sale of the forthcoming 6th Ed.[n], to the improvement of which I have devoted much time and care in the course of the last nine months.[23]

During the winter of 1839–40 Lyell also prepared his paper, which he read to the Geological Society on 22 January, on the boulder formation and other deposits represented in the mud cliffs of eastern Norfolk.[24]

In June 1840, the sixth edition of the *Principles* came out in three volumes. Lyell might have brought it out in four volumes in a slightly larger and more open type, but the year before Murray had had set in type some two hundred pages of the first volume so that they were committed to the old format. Lyell wrote to his Father:

> I could have made more pecuniary profit if I had got out my new edition sooner as the public were ready for it, but I had resolved to come out first with all the results of my Norfolk expedition,—which, as well as others which preceded it & are yet

22. C. L., Jr. to G. A. M. 2 Nov. 1839. Mantell mss.
23. C. L., Jr. to J. M. 4 Dec. 1839. Murray mss.
24. "On the Boulder Formation . . ," (1840).

to come, are intended to give me the means of correcting & improving certain chapters in my Principles & Elements at the same time that I am contributing my fair proportion of original observation to the general fund. It is necessary to resist the temptation of coining money by simply compiling materials provided by others instead of testing their accuracy by personally examining the facts in the field wherever they are readily come-at. I felt some compunction when printing the Elements at not waiting a year in order first to conclude those investigations which led soon afterwards to my reforming the classification of the Norfolk & Suffolk tertiary strata and which if I had concluded first would greatly have strengthened my confidence in the percentage system.[25]

THE SIXTH EDITION OF THE *Principles*

In preparing the sixth edition of the *Principles* Lyell began to put into effect the plan which he had worked out with Murray in June 1837 for distinguishing the *Principles* from the *Elements*. All purely descriptive geology was to be transferred to the *Elements,* and the *Principles* was to become entirely a discussion of the changes now going on on the earth's surface, for the purpose of interpreting the changes which had gone on during the past. Lyell, therefore, removed from the *Principles* the whole of Book IV. This book contained his account of the succession of Tertiary formations, which he had published originally in 1833 in the third volume of the *Principles*. At the same time Lyell wished to retain in the *Principles* certain portions of Book IV, such as chapter one in which he discussed the various methods of theorizing in geology, and chapter twenty-five in which he treated Élie de Beaumont's theory of the elevation of parallel mountain chains. Accordingly, he added four chapters (chapters ten through thirteen) to Book I of the *Principles* and developed each chapter as an essay on a particular application of the principle of uniformity in geology. In chapter ten he dealt with the theory of deluges, which had been developed to account for the distribution of erratic blocks, and argued that these boulders had been transported by floating ice. In chapter eleven he showed that volcanic action had gone on at all periods in the history of the earth with the same intensity as in the modern period and demonstrated, in contradiction to Élie de Beaumont, that mountains had been elevated

25. C. L., Jr. to his father. 23 May 1840. Kinnordy mss.

gradually throughout long periods of time. In chapter twelve Lyell presented his theory of the origin of plutonic and metamorphic rocks and showed that they had been formed in every geological period. Finally in chapter thirteen he attacked the whole concept that the history of the earth had consisted of periods of relative tranquillity interrupted by episodes of widespread catastrophic upheaval and disorder. Lyell argued that all geological phenomena had been produced by an uninterrupted series of changes which was still going on.

These additional chapters reflected Lyell's deepened knowledge of geology and broadened perspective, acquired during the decade of travel, investigation, and writing since he had published the first edition in 1830. Their total effect was to extend the philosophical argument of the *Principles* to embrace all that had been discovered and written in geology up to the year 1840. In them Lyell presented a powerful, sophisticated, and comprehensive plea for an unbroken series of processes and succession of changes in the history of the earth.

In the sixth edition Lyell established the plan of organization of the *Principles* to which he would adhere, with only minor revisions, through the ninth edition, published in 1853. Thereafter he did not revise the *Principles* again until 1865, when he made a major revision, rearranging the order of chapters and rewriting several, including those on the development of organic life and on climate. Thus in 1840 the *Principles* assumed the form they were to retain for the next twenty-five years.

Shortly after the publication of the new edition of the *Principles* in June 1840, the Lyells went on their geological tour in the Loire valley of France and on their return to London they remained at 16 Hart Street until the annual meeting of the British Association, which opened at Glasgow on 14 September. When the meeting was over they paid a brief visit to Henry Cockburn at Edinburgh and then went to Kinnordy. During their stay at Kinnordy, Lyell, persuaded by Buckland of the reality of glaciation in Scotland, made his study of glacial phenomena in the vale of Strathmore.

After their return to London in November 1840, and during the early months of 1841, Lyell was preparing the second edition of the *Elements* to go through the press. This edition was enlarged from one to two volumes and now included the series of chapters on the Tertiary formations formerly in the *Principles*. Because of the chapters transferred from Book IV of the *Principles* and the subdivision of some of the original chapters of the *Elements* into two, the *Elements* grew from twenty-five to thirty-six chapters, and from 528 pages to a total of 897 pages in two volumes. Yet the book retained the small, attractive, and readable page size and clear, open type of the first edition and Lyell maintained the same style of simple, lucid exposition. Although in the third edition of 1851 Lyell changed the name of the *Elements* to *A Manual of Elementary Geology*, the organization of the book remained unchanged.[26] Through the years successive editions of the *Manual* reflected, to a greater degree than the *Principles*, the steady influx of geological discoveries and increasing knowledge. In 1851 Lyell added chapters on the Permian and Silurian groups of strata, the oolite became the Jurassic and the new red sandstone, the Trias, but the order of topics and many of the chapter headings remained unchanged. Furthermore, despite innumerable minor revisions and interpolations, the book was still recognizably the same work when Lyell restored its original name in the sixth edition of 1865.[27] Thus with the publication of the second edition of the *Elements of Geology* in 1841, Lyell's whole treatment of geology crystallized substantially in the form it would maintain during the next quarter century.

During the spring of 1841 Lyell decided to visit the United States the following summer, and on 14 April he wrote to Professor Silliman of Yale College to tell him of his forthcoming visit and to ask for information to help him in planning his itinerary. Lyell was to go first to Boston, where he would deliver the Lowell lectures, a series of public lectures given under the terms of a bequest by John Lowell (1799–1836).

With these exciting prospects in view, Lyell completed the *Elements* and wrote his paper on the faluns of the Loire, which he read to the Geological Society on 2 June. In June Lyell also made an excursion to Aymestry in Radnorshire, Wales, where he had been invited by the Reverend Thomas Lewis to examine some remarkable corals and encrinites in the Wenlock limestone, a formation of Silurian age. He collected corals, shells, and trilobites from quarries of upper Silurian strata, in part at least so as to be able to take a representative group of Silurian fossils to America. The fossil corals retained the position in which they had grown

26. *A Manual of elementary geology* ... 3rd ed. (1851).
27. *Elements of geology* ... 6th ed. (1865).

originally, "the points of attachment being inclined toward the lower part of each stratum, and the convex surface of the hemispherical masses being upwards."[28] The position of the corals and the thinly bedded calcareous shale surrounding them showed clearly that the materials composing these Silurian strata had been deposited slowly over a long period of time. From the fact, too, demonstrated by Darwin and others, that corals did not grow at depths greater than 120 feet, Lyell concluded that the deposition of these Silurian strata had been accompanied by a slow subsidence. Thus the processes of slow gradual deposition and gradual subsidence which had gone on during the very ancient Silurian epoch had been very similar to those of much more recent periods and to the conditions which Darwin had shown to be existing at present in the Pacific.

By mid-July Lyell had completed the printing of the second volume of the *Elements*. Murray, however, was to withhold its publication until Lyell had a chance to arrange for an edition on the other side of the Atlantic after he arrived there. He was taking the woodcuts with him for this purpose.

In the early nineteenth century a trip to America was still an extraordinary adventure. On the eve of their departure his father wrote a letter of farewell in his graceful eighteenth-century hand:

My dear Charles,

    This is the last post by which I can write to you ere you depart. I will not neglect therefore to bid you farewell, to send you and my dear Mary my love, and to assure you you will seldom be out of my thoughts.—Like old Polonius too I must throw in a little advice.

    Pray have a proper regard to the health of both of ye, and the comfort. Do not fancy you are a man of iron, and never forget that Mary is a wife of gold and that you could not have found another like her. When rough expeditions are to be encountered do not measure her strength by yours. Her spirits, and anxiety never to be a hinderance to the accomplishment of any wish of yours, will always incline her to run risks which you must not suffer. So take especial care of her if you love me.— One word more of addition to this preachment. I have my fears of over-labour of the mind in preparing the Boston lectures, for which "The Elements" has left you so little time. The head

28. "Some remarks on the Silurian strata . . ." (1841) p. 463.

gives friendly notice as soon as it requires rest, attend to it in time, and let nothing induce you to risk the fate of poor Faraday.[29]

Once more Farewell
Your very affectionate father
Cha. Lyell[30]

Kinnordy 14 July 1841

Three days later Lyell received this letter at London and added a postscript to his own parting letter.

This morning brought your very affectionate parting letter & & I assure you I shall not forget your advice

ever yours affectionately
Cha Lyell[31]

Lyell's departure for America was in different respects a turning point in his life. He was to be away a year, and when he returned he would be occupied with new questions evoked by North America, by its vast spaces and the enormous scale of its geology, and by its restlessly active people.

---

29. In 1841 Michael Faraday suffered loss of memory and "giddiness" which had obliged him to give up his research and lectures completely and to go to Switzerland for a complete rest.

30. C. Lyell to C. L., Jr. 14 July 1841. Kinnordy mss.

31. C. L., Jr. to his father. 16–17 July 1841. Kinnordy mss.

Bibliography

Manuscript Sources

Acad. Sci., Paris mss. Miscellaneous Lyell letters in the library of the Académie des Sciences, Institut de France, Paris.

Admiralty records. Public Record Office, London.

APS mss. Manuscripts in the library of the American Philosophical Society, 105 South Fifth Street, Philadelphia, Pennsylvania. These include, among a rich collection of other scientific correspondence, the Darwin-Lyell mss.

Babbage mss. Personal papers and correspondence of Charles Babbage (1792–1877), mathematician and inventor, in the British Museum, Great Russell Street, London.

Darwin mss., Cambridge. These are the personal papers and books of Charles Darwin, including many letters to him, at the Cambridge University Library, Cambridge, England.

Darwin-Lyell mss. These papers in the library of the American Philosophical Society, Philadelphia, include most of the surviving letters written by Charles Darwin to Sir Charles Lyell, plus many letters to Lyell from other scientists, particularly geologists.

De la Beche mss. Some correspondence to Sir Henry de la Beche in the Department of Geology, National Museum of Wales, Cardiff.

Dawson Turner mss. These include correspondence to Dawson Turner (1775–1858), banker of Yarmouth, Norfolk, in the library of Trinity College, Cambridge, England.

Eyles mss. Correspondence to James Sowerby (1757–1822), botanist and conchologist of Lambeth, belonging to Mrs. Joan M. Eyles, The Old Cottage, Great Rissenden, Gloucestershire, England.

Fitzwilliam Museum mss. Manuscripts in the Fitzwilliam Museum, Cambridge, England.

Hawkins mss. Personal papers and correspondence to and from John Hawkins (1761–1841) at the Sussex County Record Office, County Hall, Chichester, Sussex, England.

Hooker mss. The papers of Sir William Jackson Hooker and Sir Joseph Dalton Hooker in the library of the Royal Botanic Garden, Kew, England.

Kinnordy mss. Letters, journals, and notebooks of Sir Charles Lyell and other members of the Lyell family including some letters to Sir Charles Lyell, belonging to the Lord Lyell of Kinnordy, Kinnordy House, Kirriemuir, Angus, Scotland.

Lyell mss., Edinburgh. A large body of correspondence to Sir Charles

Lyell at Edinburgh University Library, Old College, South Bridge, Edinburgh 8, Scotland.

Mantell mss. The papers of Gideon Algernon Mantell (1790–1852), surgeon of Lewes, Sussex, England, including correspondence received by him, at the Alexander Turnbull Library, Wellington, New Zealand.

Murchison mss. Correspondence to Sir Roderick Impey Murchison in the library of the Geological Society of London, Burlington House, Piccadilly, London, W. 1, England.

Murray mss. Lyell's letters to John Murray (1778–1843), property of John Murray (publisher), 50 Albemarle St., London W. 1, England.

Owen mss. Personal papers of Sir Richard Owen (1804–92), anatomist and paleontologist, including correspondence to him, in the library of the British Museum (Natural History), South Kensington, London, England.

Roy. Coll. Surg. mss. Miscellaneous Lyell letters in the library of the Royal College of Surgeons, Lincoln's Inn Fields, London, W.C.1, England.

St. Andrews church, Holborn, London. Baptism register.

Scottish Records Office; Register House. Edinburgh, Scotland.

Somerville mss. Personal papers of Mrs. Mary Somerville, including some correspondence to her in the library of Somerville College, Oxford.

Wedderburn mss. These are the Wedderburn of Pearsie Muniments at Register House, Edinburgh, Scotland, the papers of the Wedderburns of Pearsie, near Kirriemuir in the county of Angus, Scotland. They include a large mass of correspondence to Charles Wedderburn (1748–1829) of Pearsie.

Whewell mss. Personal papers including correspondence to William Whewell (1794–1866) in the library of Trinity College, Cambridge, England.

PUBLISHED SOURCES

Abel-Smith, Brian and Robert Stevens, *Lawyers and the Courts, A Sociological Study of the English Legal System.* Cambridge, Mass.: Harvard Univ. Press, 1967.

Adams, Frank Dawson, *The Birth and Development of the Geological Sciences.* Baltimore, Md.: Williams & Wilkins Co., 1938.

Agassiz, Elizabeth Cary, *Louis Agassiz, his life and correspondence.* 2 vols. Boston: Houghton Mifflin & Co., 1886.

Agassiz, Louis, "Discours prononcé à l'ouverture des séances de la Société Helvétique des Sciences Naturelles à Neuchâtel le 24 Juillet 1837," *Actes Soc. Helv. des Sci. Nat.* 22 (1837): v-xxxii.

"On glaciers and the evidence of their having one existed in Scotland, Ireland and England," [1840] *Proc. Geol. Soc. Lond.* 3 (1838–42): 327–32.

"On glaciers and boulders in Switzerland," *Brit. Assoc. Rept.* 10 (1841): 113–14.

"The Glacial Theory and its recent progress," *Edin. New Phil. J.* 33, ser. 2 (1842): 217–83.

Anon., "On Circuit," *Chambers' Journal* 5 (1856): 97–100.

"Going on Circuit by 'One who goes'," *Chambers' Journal* 7, ser. 5, (1890): 273–75.

Amici, Giovan Battista, "Descrizione di alcune specie nuova di Chara ed osservazioni microscopiche sulla medesime," *Mem. Real. Accad. di Sci., Lett. ed Arti Modena* 1 (1833): 199–221.

Bakewell, Robert, *An Introduction to Geology illustrative of the general structure of the earth; comprising the elements of the science and an outline of the geology and mineral geography of England.* London: J. Harding, 1813.

Second edition, London: J. Harding, 1815.

Travels comprising observations made during a residence in the Tarentaise and various parts of the Grecian and Pennine Alps, and in Switzerland and Auvergne, in the years 1820, 1821 and 1822. 2 vols. London: Longman, et al., 1823.

Ballantine, [William] Mr. Serjeant, *Some experiences of a barrister's life.* 2 vols. London: R. Bentley & Son, 1882.

Basterot, B[arthelemy] de, "Description géologique du bassin tertiaire du sud-ouest de la France," *Mém. Soc. d'Hist. Nat. de Paris* 2 (1825): 1–100.

Beatson, Robert, *Naval and Military Memoirs of Great Britain from 1727 to 1783.* 6 vols. London: Longman, et al., 1804.

Bosc, Louis, "Note sur un fossile remarquable de la montagne de Saint-Gerard-le-Puy entre Moulins et Roanne, departement de l'Allier, appelé l'Indusie tubuleuse," *Journ. Mines* 17 (1804–05): 397–400.

Boué, Aimé, "On the theory of the elevation of mountain chains as advocated by M. Elie de Beaumont," *Edin. New Phil. J.* 17 (1834): 123–50.

Brocchi, Giovanni, *Conchiologia fossile subapennina con osservazioni geologiche sugli Apennini e sul suolo adjacente.* 2 vols. Milan: Royal Printing Office, 1814.

Brongniart, Alexandre, "Sur les terrains qui paroissent avoir été formés sous l'eau douce," *Ann. Mus. Hist. Nat.* (Paris) 15 (1810): 357–405.

"Sur les caractères zoologiques des formations, avec l'application de ces caractères á la détermination de quelques terrains de craie," *Ann. Mines* 6 (1821): 537–72.

"Notes sur les coquilles fossiles qui se trouvent dans les terrains décrits par M. Studer; sur les époques géognostiques qu'elles indiquent, et sur la montagne de Diablerets, au N.-E. de Bex," *Ann. Sci. Nat.* 11 (1827): 266–88.

Tableau des terrains qui composent l'ecorce du globe. Paris: F. G. Levrault, 1829.

Brown, Robert, *Prodromus florae Novae Hollandiae et Insulae Van-Diemen.* 2 vols. London: R. Taylor et socii, 1810.

Buch, Leopold von, *Geognostische beobachtungen auf reisen durch Deutschland und Italien.* 2 vols. Berlin: Haude und Spener, 1802–09.

"Ueber das vorkommen des dolomite in die nahe der vulkanischen gebilde der Eifel," *Taschenb. gesam. mineral.* 18 (1824): 331–34.

Buckland, William, "On the structure of the Alps and adjoining parts of the Continent and their relation to the Secondary and Transition rocks of England," *Ann. Phil.* 1 (1821): 450–68.

Reliquiae Diluvianae; or, observations on the organic remains contained in caves, fissures, and diluvial gravel, and on other geological phenomena, attesting the action of an universal deluge. London: J. Murray, 1823.

"Memoir on the evidences of glaciers in Scotland and North of England," [1840] *Proc. Geol. Soc. Lond.* 3 (1838–42): 332–37.

Burke, Sir Bernard, *A genealogical and heraldic history of the landed gentry of Great Britain and Ireland.* Edited by his sons, 8th ed. 2 vols. London: Harrison and Sons, 1894.

Butler, Joseph, *The analogy of religion, natural and revealed, to the constitution and course of nature.* 3rd ed. London: John and Paul Knapton, 1740.

Candolle, Augustin Pyrâme de, "Géographie botanique" in *Dictionnaire des sciences naturelles.* Strasbourg: F. G. Levrault; Paris: Le Prince le Normant; vol. 18, pp. 359–422.

Chapman, R. W., *Jane Austen's Letters to her sister Cassandra and others.* 2nd ed. Oxford Univ. Press, 1952.

Charlesworth, Edward, "On the Crag of part of Essex and Suffolk," [1835] *Proc. Geol. Soc. Lond.* 2 (1834–37): 195–96.

"Observations on the Crag formation and its organic remains; with a view to establish a division of the Tertiary strata overlying the London Clay in Suffolk," *London. and Edin. Phil. Mag.* 7 (1835): 81–94.

"Reply to Mr. Woodward's remarks on the Coralline Crag; with observations on certain errors which may affect the determination of the age of Tertiary deposits," *Lond. and Edin. Phil. Mag.* 7 (1835): 464–70.

"A notice of the remains of vertebrated animals found in the Tertiary beds of Norfolk and Suffolk," [1836] *Brit. Assoc. Rept., Abstracts* 5 (1837): 84–86.

"Observations on the Crag and on the fallacies involved in the present system of classification of Tertiary deposits," *Lond. and Edin. Phil. Mag.* 10 (1837): 1–9.

"On some fallacies involved in the results relating to the comparative age of Tertiary deposits obtained from the application of the test recently introduced by Mr. Lyell and M. Deshayes," *Edin. New Phil. J.* 22 (1837): 110–16. *Cf. Brit. Assoc. Rept.* 6 (1837): 86.

Charpentier, Jean G. F. de, "Notice sur la cause probable du transport des blocs erratiques de la Suisse," *Ann. Mines* 8 (1835): 219–36.

Clark, John Willis and Thomas McKenny Hughes, *The Life and Letters of the Reverend Adam Sedgwick.* 2 vols. Cambridge Univ. Press, 1890.

Clive, John, *Scotch Reviewers, The Edinburgh Review 1802–1815.* Cambridge, Mass.: Harvard Univ. Press, 1957.

Coleman, William, *Georges Cuvier, zoologist, a study in the history of evolution theory.* Cambridge, Mass.: Harvard Univ. Press, 1964.

Coleridge, Ernest Hartley, *Life and Correspondence of John Duke, Lord Coleridge, Lord Chief Justice of England.* 2 vols. London: W. Heinemann, 1904.

Coleridge, Sir John Taylor, *"My recollections of the Circuit" a lecture delivered at the autumnal session of the Exeter Literary Society.* [28 Sept. 1859] Exeter: C. D. Mayne, 1859.

Conybeare, William D., "Descriptive notes referring to the outline sections presented by a part of the coasts of Antrim and Derry," *Trans. Geol. Soc. Lond.* 3 (1816): 196–216.

"Additional notices on the fossil genera Ichthyosaurus and Plesiosaurus," [1822] *Trans. Geol. Soc. Lond.* 1, ser. 2 (1824): 381–89.

"On the discovery of an almost perfect skeleton of the Plesiosaurus," *Trans. Geol. Soc. Lond.* 1, ser. 2 (1824). 381–89.

"On the hydrographical basin of the Thames, with a view more especially to investigate the causes which have operated in the formation of the valleys of that river, and its tributary streams," [1829] *Proc. Geol. Soc. Lond.* 1 (1826–33): 145–49.

"Answer to Dr. Fleming's view of the evidence from the animal kingdom, as to the former temperature of the Northern Regions," *Edin. New Phil. J.* 7 (1829): 142–52.

Letters and Exercises of the Elizabethan Schoolmaster John Conybeare . . . with Notes and a Fragment of Autobiography. Edited by F. C. Conybeare. London: H. Frowde, 1905.

Conybeare, William D. and William Phillips, *Outlines of the Geology of England and Wales with an introductory compendium of the general principles of that science and comparative views of the structure of foreign countries illustrated by a coloured map and sections.* London: William Phillips, 1822.

Cordier, Louis, "Essai sur la température de l'intérieur de la terre," *Mém. Acad. Roy. Sci. (Paris)* 7 (1827): 473–555.

Crawfurd, John, *Journal of an embassy from the governor general of India to the court of Ava . . . With an appendix containing a description of fossil remains by Professor Buckland and Mr. Clift.* London: H. Colburn, 1829.

Culley, Matthew, "A few facts and observations as to the power which running water exerts in removing heavy bodies," *Proc. Geol. Soc. Lond.* 1 (1826–33): 149.

Curtis, John, *British Entomology; or illustrations and descriptions of the genera of Insects found in Great Britain and Ireland.* 16 (annual) vols. London, 1824–39.

Cuvier, Georges, "Sur les espèces d'animaux dont proviennent les os fossiles répandus dans la pierre à platre des environs de Paris. 1er Mémoire: Restitution de la tête. 2ᵈ Mémoire: Examen des dents, &. c. 3ᵉ & 4ᵉ Mémoire: Restitution des pieds," *Ann. Mus. Hist. Nat. (Paris)* 3 (1804): 275–303, 364–87, 442–72.

Recherches sur les ossemens fossiles de quadrupèdes. 4 vols. Paris: Déterville, 1812.

Cuvier, Georges and Alexandre Brongniart, *Essai sur la géographie minéralogique des environs de Paris, avec une carte géognostique et des coupes de terrain.* Paris: Baudouin, 1811.

Darwin, Charles, *Extracts from Letters addressed to Professor Henslow.* Cambridge: privately printed, 1835.

"Observations of proofs of recent elevation on the coast of Chili, made during the survey of His Majesty's ship *Beagle,* commanded by Capt. Fitzroy R.N.," [1837] *Proc. Geol. Soc. Lond.* 2 (1834–37): 446–49.

"A sketch of the deposits containing extinct Mammalia in the neighbourhood of the Plata," [1837] *Proc. Geol. Soc. Lond.* 2 (1834–37): 542–44.

"On certain areas of elevation and subsidence in the Pacific and Indian oceans as deduced from the study of Coral Formations," [1837] *Proc. Geol. Soc. Lond.* 2 (1834–37): 552–54.

"On the connexion of certain volcanic phenomena in South America; and on the formation of mountain chains and volcanos, as the effect of the same power by which continents are elevated," [1838] *Trans. Geol. Soc. Lond.* 5, ser. 2, pt. 3, (1840): 601–31.

"Darwin's Notebooks on transmutation of species, Part III. Third Notebook July 15th 1838–October 2nd 1838," Sir Gavin de Beer ed. *Bull. Brit. Mus. (Nat. Hist.) Hist.* ser. 2 (1960): 119–50.

Journal of Researches into the Geology and Natural History of the various countries visited by H.M.S. Beagle under the command of Capt. Fitzroy R.N. from 1832–1836. London: H. Colburn, 1839.

"Observations on the Parallel Roads of Glen Roy, and of other parts of Lochaber in Scotland, with an attempt to prove that they are of marine origin," *Phil. Trans. Roy. Soc. Lond.* 129 (1839): 39–81.

More Letters of Charles Darwin. Edited by Francis Darwin and A. C. Seward. 2 vols. London: J. Murray, 1903.

Autobiography. Edited by Nora Barlow. London: Collins, 1858.

"Darwin's Journal," edited by Sir Gavin de Beer, *Bull. Brit. Mus. (Nat. Hist.), Hist. Ser.* 2 (1959): 1–21.

Darwin and Henslow, the growth of an idea. Edited by Nora Barlow. London: J. Murray, 1967.

Darwin, Emma, *Emma Darwin, a century of family letters, 1792–1896.* Edited by Henrietta Litchfield. 2 vols. New York: D. Appleton and Co., 1915.

Darwin, Francis, *The Life and Letters of Charles Darwin.* 3 vols. London: J. Murray, 1887.

Daubeny, Charles, *A description of active and extinct volcanoes with remarks on their origin, their chemical phaenomena and the character of their products, as determined by the condition of the earth during the period of their formation.* London: W. Phillips, 1825.

"Sketch of the geology of Sicily," *Edin. Phil. J.* 13 (1825): 107–18, 254–68.

Davy, Sir Humphry, *Consolations in travel or the last days of a philosopher.* London: J. Murray, 1830.

D'Aubuisson, Jean F., "Extrait d'un mémoire sur les volcans et les basaltes de l'Auvergne," *Journ. de Phys.* 58 (1804): 310–18.

de Beer, Sir Gavin, "The volcanoes of Auvergne," *Ann. Sci.* 18 (1962): 49–61.

Dechen, Heinrich von and Karl von Oeynhausen, "Die insel Arran," (Karsten's) *Arch. Mineral., Geogn., Bergbau and Huttenkunde* 1 (1829): 316–56.

de la Beche, Henry T. and W. D. Conybeare, "Notice of the discovery of a new fossil animal, forming a link between the Ichthyosaurus and Crocodile, together with general remarks on the osteology of the Ichthyosaurus," *Trans. Geol. Soc. Lond.* 5 (1821): 559–94.

Deshayes, Gérard Paul, *Description des coquilles fossiles des environs de Paris.* 2 vols. Paris: the author, 1824–37.

Desmarest, Nicholas, "Mémoire sur l'origine et la nature du basalte," *Mém. Acad. R. Sci. (Paris)* 1771 (publ. 1774): p. 705.

Desnoyers, Jules, "Mémoire sur la craie, et sur les terrains tertiaires de Cotentin," *Mém. Soc. d'Hist. Nat. de Paris* 2 (1825): 176–248.

"Observations sur un ensemble de dépots marins plus récens que les terrains tertiaires du Bassin de la Seine, et constituant une formation géologique distincte; précédées d'un apercu de la non simultanéité des bassins tertiaires," *Ann. Sci. Nat.* 16 (1829): 171–214, 402–91.

Dillenius, John James, *Historia muscorum. . . .* Oxford, at the Sheldonian Theatre, 1741.

Donovan, Edward, *The Natural History of British Insects; explaining them in their several states, with the periods of their transformations, etc.* 16 vols. London: printed for the author and F. & C. Rivington, 1793–1813.

Eaton, Amos, *A Geological and Agricultural Survey of the District adjoining the Erie Canal, in the state of New York.* Albany, N.Y.: Packard and Van Benthuysen, 1824.

Élie de Beaumont, Jean Baptiste Armand Louis Leonce, "Recherches sur quelques-unes des révolutions de la surface du globe, presentant différens exemples de coincidence entre le redressement des couches de certains systèmes de montagnes et les changemens soudains qui ont produit les lignes de démarcation qu'on observe entre certains étages consécutifs des terrains de sédiment," *Ann. Sci. Nat.* 18 (1829): 5–25, 284–416.

"Researches on some of the revolutions which have taken place on the surface of the globe; presenting various examples of the coincidence between the elevation of beds in certain systems of mountains; and the sudden changes which have produced the lines of demarcation observable in certain stages of the sedimentary deposits," *Phil. Mag.* n.s. 10 (1831): 241–64.

Englefield, Sir Henry Charles, Bt., "Observations on some remarkable Strata of flint in a chalk-pit in the Isle of Wight . . .," *Trans. Linn. Soc.* 6 (1802): 103–09.

A Description of the Principal Picturesque Beauties, Antiquities and Geological Phenomena of the Isle of Wight. With additional observations on the Strata of the Island and their continuation in the adjacent parts of Dorsetshire. By Thomas Webster Esq. London: Payne and Foss, 1816.

Eyles, Joan M. "William Smith: the sale of his geological collection to the British Museum," *Ann. Sci.* 23 (1967): 177–212.

Eyles, Victor A., "John Macculloch F.R.S., and his geological map; an account of the first geological survey of Scotland," *Ann. Sci.* 2 (1937): 694–95.

"James Hutton (1726–97) and Sir Charles Lyell (1797–1875)," *Nature* 160 (1947): 694–95.

"A bibliographical note on the earliest printed version of James Hutton's Theory of the Earth, its form and date of publication," [1955] *J. Soc. Bibl. Nat. Hist.* 3 (1953–60): 105–08.

Eyles, Victor A. and Joan M. Eyles, "On the different issues of the first geological map of England and Wales," *Ann. Sci.* 3 (1938): 190–212.

Faujas de Saint-Fond, Barthelemy, *Recherches sur les volcans éteints du Vivarais et du Velay; avec un discours sur les volcans brulans, des mémoires analytiques sur les schols, la zéolite le basalte, la pouzzolane, les laves et les différentes substances qui s'y trouvent engagées etc.* Grenoble: Joseph Cuchet; Paris: Nyon et Née et Masquelier, 1778.

Fitch, Robert, "On the Coralline Crag of Ramsholt and Orford," *Lond. and Edin. Phil. Mag.* 7 (1835): 463–64.

Fitton, William Henry, "Inquiries respecting the geological relations of the beds between the Chalk and the Purbeck Limestone in the Southeast of England," *Ann. Phil.* 8 (1824): 365–83.

"Art. V. *Elements of Geology* by Charles Lyell Esq.," *Edin. Rev.* 69 (1839): 406–66.

Fleming, Rev. John, "On the value of the evidence from the animal kingdom, tending to prove that the arctic regions formerly enjoyed a milder climate than at present," *Edin. New Phil. J.* 6 (1829): 277–86.

Forbes, Edward, *On the Tertiary fluvio-marine formation of the Isle of Wight*. London: *Mem. Geol. Surv. Gt. Brit.*, 1856.

Forchhammer, Georg, "On the chalk formation of Denmark," *Edin. J. Sci.* 9 (1828): 56–68.

Fulton, John F. and Elizabeth H. Thomson, *Benjamin Silliman 1779–1864, Pathfinder in American Science*. New York: Henry Schuman, 1947.

Geikie, Sir Archibald, *Memoir of Sir Andrew Crombie Ramsay*. London: Macmillan & Co., 1895.

The Founders of Geology. 2nd edition. London: Macmillan & Co., 1905.

Gemmellaro, Carlo, "Sopra la fisionomia delle montagne di Sicilia," [1828] *Atti. Acad. Gioen. (Catania)* 5 (1831): 73–94.

Geoffroy St. Hilaire, Étienne, "Memoire où l'on se propose de rechercher dans quels rapports de structure organique et de parenté sont entre eux les animaux des ages historiques et vivant actuellement et les *espèces antédiluviennes et perdues*," *Mem. Mus. Hist. Nat. (Paris)* 17 (1828): 209–29.

Gordon, Mrs. Anna. *The Life and Correspondence of William Buckland, D.D., F.R.S.* New York: Appleton and Co., 1894.

Graham, Henry Grey, *The Social Life of Scotland in the Eighteenth Century*. 4th ed. London: A. C. Black Ltd., 1937.

Great Britain, Government of, *Oxford University Commission Report*. London: H.M. Stationery Office, 1852.

Greenough, George Bellas, "Address delivered at the Anniversary Meeting of the Geological Society on the 21st of February 1834," *Proc. Geol. Soc. Lond.* 2 (1834): 42–70.

"Remarks on the theory of the elevation of mountains," *Edin. New Phil. J.* 17 (1834): 205–27.

Guettard, Jean Étienne, "Mémoire sur quelques montagnes de la France qui ont été des volcans," [1752] *Mem. Acad. R. Sci.* (1756): 27.

Halévy, Élie, *A History of the English People in the Nineteenth Century*. Translated by E. J. Watkin. 6 vols. London: E. Benn, 1927.

Hearnshaw, F. J. C., *The centenary history of King's College London*. London: G. C. Harrap & Co., 1929.

Herschel, John F. W., "Notice of a remarkable occurrence of serpentine at the junction of sienite with the Dolomite of the Tyrol," *Edin. J. Sci.* 3 (1825): 126–29.

A preliminary discourse on the study of natural philosophy. London: Longman et al., 1831.

Hoff, Karl Ernst Adolf von, *Geschichte der durch Ueberlieferung nachgewiesen naturlichen veranderungen der erdoberflache.* 2 vols. Gotha: J. Perthes, 1822–24.

Hogg, Thomas Jefferson, *The Life of Percy Bysshe Shelley.* London: G. Rutledge & Sons, 1906.

Holdsworth, William, *A History of English Law.* 12 vols. London: Methuen, 1938.

Horsfield, Thomas W., *The History and Antiquities of Lewes and its vicinity.* 2 vols. Lewes, 1824–27.

Humboldt, Alexander von, *Essai sur la géographie des plantes; accompagné d'un tableau physique des regions equinoxiales.* . . . Paris: Schoell, 1807.

"*Des lignes isothermes et de la distribution de la chaleur sur la globe,*" *Mem. de Phys. d'Arcueil* 3 (1817): 462–602.

"On isothermal lines, and the distribution of heat over the globe," *Edin. Phil. J.* 3 (1820): 1–20, 256–74; 4 (1821): 23–37, 262–81; 5 (1821): 28–39.

Essai géognostique sur le gisement des roches dans les deux hémitheres. Paris: F. G. Levrault, 1823.

A Geognostical Essay on the Superposition of Rocks in both hemispheres. London: Longman et al., 1823.

Hutton, James, "Theory of the Earth; or an investigation of the laws observable in the composition, dissolution and restoration of land upon the globe," [1785] *Trans. Roy. Soc. Edinb.* 1 (1788): 209–304.

Theory of the Earth with proofs and illustrations. 2 vols. Edinburgh: Cadell and Davies, 1795.

Jameson, Robert, *An outline of the mineralogy of the Shetland Islands, and of the island of Arran.* . . . Edinburgh: W. Creech, 1798.

Johnston, James F. W., "On a gradual elevation of the land in Scandinavia," *Edin. New Phil. J.* 15 (1833): 34–48.

Keilhau, B. M. "Granitens ag de ovrige saakeldte massive Bjergarters samt de Krystalliniske skiferes Theorie," *Nyt. Mag. Naturvid.* 1 (1838): 1–72; *Edin. New Phil. J.* 24 (1838): 387–403; 25 (1838): 80–101, 263–72; 28 (1840): 366–71.

ed., *Gaea Norvegica von mehreren verfassern.* Christiania: J. Dahl, 1838–50.

Kidd, John, *A Geological Essay on the Imperfect Evidence in support of a Theory of the Earth.* Oxford: at the University Press for the author, 1815.

Kiralfy, A. K. R., *Potter's Historical Introduction to English Law and its Institutions.* 4th ed. London: Sweet and Maxwell, 1962.

Kirby, William and William Spence, *An introduction to entomology: or elements of the natural history of insects.* 4th ed. 4 vols. London: Longman et al., 1822–26.

Kirwan, Richard, "On the primitive state of the globe and its subsequent catastrophe," *Trans. Roy. Irish Acad.* 6 (1797): 233–317.

Laizer, Louis (comte de), "Note sur l'existence d'ossemens fossiles dans le tuf volcanique ou peperino d'Auvergne," *Ann. Sci. Nat.* 15 (1828): 415–20.

Lamarck, Jean Baptiste Antoine Pierre de Monnet de, *Philosophie zoologique, ou exposition des considerations relatives à l'histoire naturelle des animaux . . . .* 2 vols. Paris: Dentu, 1809.
Zoological philosophy, an exposition with regard to the natural history of animals. . . . Trans. with an introd. by Hugh Elliott. London: Macmillan & Co., 1914.
Histoire naturelle des animaux sans vertèbres. 7 vols. Paris: Verdière, 1815–22.

Lewis, Michael, *A Social History of the Navy 1793–1815.* London: G. Allen & Unwin, 1960.

Leys, John, "Going on Circuit," *The Month* 55 (1885): 482–88.

Lindsay, Jack, *J. M. W. Turner, his life and work.* London: C. Adams & MacKay, 1966.

Lovejoy, A. O., *The Great Chain of Being.* Cambridge, Mass.: Ha Univ. Press, 1933.

Lurie, Edward, *Louis Agassiz, a life in science.* Chicago: Univ. cago Press, 1960.

Lyell Charles, "On a recent formation of freshwater lim Forfarshire, and on some recent deposits of freshwater m comparison of recent with ancient freshwater formatic appendix on the Gyrogonite or seed-vessel of the C *Trans. Geol. Soc. Lond.* 2, ser. 2 (1829): 73–96.
"On a dike of serpentine, cutting through sandstone, i Forfar," *Edin. J. Sci.* 3 (1825): 112–26.
"Art. X. Letter to Mr. Brougham on the Subject c versity, together with Suggestions respecting the F bell Esq., London, 1825," *Quart. Rev.* 33 (1825–26)
"On the strata of the Plastic Clay Formation e between Christchurch Head, Hampshire, and ' shire," [1826] *Trans. Geol. Soc. Lond.* 2 (1829):
"On the freshwater strata of Hordwell Cliff, ' Cliff, Hampshire," [1826] *Trans. Geol. Soc* 287–92.
"Art. VIII. 1. *Transactions of the Cambr* vol. 1. 2. *Memoirs of the Literary and P' chester.* 2nd Series. vol. iv. London, 1824 *Geological Society of Cornwall, institu*

Penzance. 4. *Report of the Liverpool Royal Institution.* 1822. 5. Bristol Institution. *Proceedings of the Second Annual Meeting held February 10, 1825 etc.* 6. *Annual Report of the Council of the Yorkshire Philosophical Society for 1824," Quart. Rev.* 34 (1826): 153–79.

"Art. IX. *Transactions of the Geological Society of London* vol. i. 2d Series. London 1824," *Quart. Rev.* 34 (1826): 507–40.

"Art. VIII. 'State of the Universities,' " *Quart. Rev.* 36 (1827): 216–68.

"Art. IV. *Memoir on the Geology of Central France; including the Volcanic Formations of Auvergne, the Velay and the Vivarais, with a volume of Maps and Plates.* By G. P. Scrope F.R.S., F.G.S., London 1827." *Quart. Rev.* 36 (1827): 437–83.

Principles of Geology being an attempt to explain the former changes of the earth's surface by reference to causes now in operation. 3 vols. London: J. Murray, 1830–1833.

"Reply to a Note in the Rev. Mr. Conybeare's paper entitled 'An examination of those phaenomena of geology which seem to bear most directly on theoretical speculations.' " *Phil. Mag.* 9 (1831): 1–3.

Principles of Geology. . . . 2nd edition, 3 vols. London: J. Murray, 1832–33.

Principles of Geology. . . . 3d edition, 4 vols. London: J. Murray, 1834.

"Observations on the loamy deposit called 'loess' of the basin of the Rhine," *Edin. New Phil. J.* 17 (1834): 110–22.

"On the change of level of the land and sea in Scandinavia," [1834] *Brit. Assoc. Rept.* 4 (1835): 652–54.

"On the Cretaceous and Tertiary strata of the Danish Islands of Seeland and Moen," [1834] *Proc. Geol. Soc. Lond.* 2 (1834–37): 191–92.

"The Bakerian Lecture. On the proofs of a gradual rising of the land in certain parts of Sweden," *Phil. Trans. Roy. Soc. Lond.* 125 (1835): 1–38.

Principles of Geology. . . . 4th edition, 4 vols. London: J. Murray, 1835.

"Address to the Geological Society, delivered at the Anniversary on the 19th of February 1836," *Proc. Geol. Soc. Lond.* 2 (1834–37): 357–90.

"Address to the Geological Society, delivered at the Anniversary, on the 17th of February, 1837," *Proc. Geol. Soc. Lond.* 2 (1834–37): 479–523.

Principles of Geology. . . . 5th edition, 4 vols. London: J. Murray, 1837.

Elements of Geology. London: J. Murray, 1838.

"On the relative ages of the tertiary deposits commonly called Crag Norfolk and Suffolk," [1838] Proc. Geol. Soc. Lond. 3 (1838–42): –30.

"On certain phaenomena connected with the junction of granitic and transition rocks, near Christiania in Norway," *Brit. Assoc. Rept.* 6 (1838): 67–69.

"Notes on the Silurian strata in the neighbourhood of Christiania in Norway," [1838] *Proc. Geol. Soc. Lond.* 3 (1838–42): 465–67.

"On the relative ages of the Tertiary deposits commonly called 'Crag' in the counties of Norfolk and Suffolk," *Mag. Nat. Hist.* n.s. 3 (1839): 313–30.

"On the origin of the tubular cavities filled with gravel and called 'sandpipes' in the Chalk near Norwich," [1839] *Brit. Assoc. Rept.* 9 (1840): 65–66.

"On remains of Mammalia in the Crag and London Clay of Suffolk," [1839] *Brit. Assoc. Rept.* 9 (1840): 69–70.

"On the Boulder Formation or drift and associated freshwater deposits composing the mud cliffs of eastern Norfolk," *Lond. and Edin. Phil. Mag.* 16 (1840): 345–80.

"On the discovery of fossil teeth of a Leopard, Bear and other animals in a Crag pit at Newbourn in Suffolk," *Ann. Nat. Hist.* 4 (1840): 189–90.

Principles of Geology. . . . 6th edition, 3 vols. London: J. Murray, 1840.

"On the occurrence of two species of shells of the genus *Conus* in the Lias, or inferior Oolite, near Caen in Normandy," [1840] *Brit. Assoc. Rept.* 10 (1841): 110–11.

"On ancient sea-cliffs and needles in the Chalk of the valley of the Seine in Normandy," [1840] *Brit. Assoc. Rept.* 10 (1841): 111–13.

"On the geological evidence of the former existence of glaciers in Forfarshire," [1840] *Proc. Geol. Soc. Lond.* 3 (1838–42): 337–45.

"On the Faluns of the Loire, and a comparison of their fossils with those of the newer Tertiary strata in the Cotentin, and on the relative age of the Faluns and Crag of Suffolk," [1841] *Proc. Geol. Soc. Lond.* 3 (1838–42): 437–44.

"Some remarks on the Silurian strata between Aymestry and Wenlock," [1841] *Proc. Geol. Soc. Lond.* 3 (1838–42): 463–64.

Elements of Geology. 2nd edition, 2 vols. London: J. Murray, 1841.

A Manual of elementary geology: or, the ancient changes of the earth and its inhabitants as illustrated by geological monuments. 3rd edition. London: J. Murray, 1851.

Elements of geology, or the ancient changes of the earth and its inhabitants as illustrated by geological monuments. 6th edition London: J. Murray, 1865.

Lyell, Charles and Roderick Impey Murchison, "On the excavation of valleys, as illustrated by the volcanic rocks of central France," *Edin. New Phil. J.* 7 (1829): 15–48.

"Sur les dépots lacustres tertiaires du Cantal, et leurs rapports avec les roches primordiales et volcaniques," *Ann. Sci. Nat.* 18 (1829): 173–214.

Lyell, Katherine M., *Life, Letters and Journals of Sir Charles Lyell, Bart.* 2 vols. London: J. Murray, 1881.

Memoir of Leonard Horner, F.R.S., F.G.S., consisting of letters to his family and from some of his friends. 2 vols. London: Women's Printing Society, 1890.

Macculloch, John, "On the 'Parallel Roads' of Glen Roy," *Trans. Geol. Soc. Lond.* 4 (1817): 314–92.

A description of the western islands of Scotland, including the Isle of Man: comprising an account of their geological structure. 2 vols. & atlas. London: Hurst, Robinson & Co., 1819.

"Art. III. *Considerations on Volcanoes* . . . by G. Poulett Scrope," *Westminster Rev.* 5 (1826): 356–73.

A system of geology with a theory of the earth and an explanation of its connection with the sacred records. 2 vols. London: Longman et al., 1831.

Maclure, William, "Sur les volcans d'Ollot, en Catalogne," *Journ. de Phys.* 66 (1808): 219–20.

"Observations on the geology of the United States," *Trans. Am. Phil. Soc.* 6 (1809): 411–27.

Mantell, Gideon, *The Fossils of the South Downs; or illustrations of the Geology of Sussex.* London: L. Relfe, 1822.

"On the Iron-Sand formation of Sussex. In a letter to Dr. Fitton, Secretary of the Geological Society" [Read June 14th, 1822], *Trans. Geol. Soc. Lond.* 2, ser. 2 (1829): 131–34.

Outlines of the natural history of the environs of Lewes, Lewes, 1824; being vol. 1 of Thomas W. Horsfield, *The History and Antiquities of Lewes and its vicinity.* 2 vols. Lewes, 1824–27.

"Notice on the Iguanodon, a newly discovered fossil reptile, from the sandstone of Tilgate forest, in Sussex," *Phil. Trans. Roy Soc. Lond.* 115 (1825): 179–86.

Illustrations of the Geology of Sussex. London: L. Relfe, 1827.

"On the ripple marks made by the waves observable in the sandstone strata of Sussex," *Edin. New Phil. J.* 11 (1831): 240–41.

The Journal of Gideon Mantell, surgeon and geologist covering the years 1818–1852. Edited by E. Cecil Curwen. London: Oxford Univ. Press, 1940.

[Marcet, Mrs. Jane (Haldimand)] *Conversations on Chemistry; in which the elements of that science are familiarly explained and illustrated by experiments.* 2 vols. London: Longman et al., 1806.

Martine, F. W., J. H. Chemnitz, G. H. Schubert, and J. A. Wagner, *Neues systematisches Conchylien-Cabinet.* 12 vols. Nurnberg, 1769–

1829. Johann Hieronymus Chemnitz (1730–1800) had prepared volumes 4 to 11, published from 1780 to 1795.

Martineau, Harriet, *Autobiography*. Edited by Maria Weston Chapman, 2 vols. Boston: J. R. Osgood & Co., 1877.

Michell, John, *Conjectures concerning the Cause, and Observations upon the Phaenomena of Earthquakes....* London, 1761.

Montlosier, François Dominique Reynaud de, *Essai sur la théorie des volcans d'Auvergne*. Paris: Landroit et Rousset, 1802.

Montmollin, Auguste de, "Mémoire sur le terrain crétacé de Jura," *Mem. Soc. des Sci. Nat. Neuchatel* 1 (1835): 49–65.

Murchison, Roderick Impey, "Supplementary remarks on the strata of the Oolitic series and the rocks associated with them, in the counties of Sutherland and Ross in the Hebrides," [1827] *Trans. Geol. Soc. Lond.* 2, ser. 2 (1829): 353–68.

Murchison, Roderick Impey and Charles Lyell, Jr. "On the tertiary fresh-water formations of Aix, in Provence, including the coal-field of Fuveau," *Edin. New Phil. J.* 7 (1829): 287–98.

Murchison, Roderick Impey and Adam Sedgwick, "On the structure and relations of the deposits contained between the primary rocks and the oolitic series in the north of Scotland," [1828] *Trans. Geol. Soc. Lond.* 3 (1835): 125–60.

Necker, [de Saussure] Louis Albert, "Sur les filons granitiques et porphyriques de Valorsine et sur le gisement des couches coquillières des montagnes de Sales, des Fizs, et de Platet," *Bibl. univ. sci., belles lettres, arts* 33 (1826): 62–92.

New, Chester W., *The Life of Henry Brougham to 1830*. Oxford: Clarendon Press, 1961.

Newell, Norman D., "Revolutions in the history of life," in Claude C. Albritton, Jr., ed. *Uniformity and Simplicity*, New York: Geological Society of America, 1967, Special Paper 89, pp. 63–91.

Owen, Richard, "A description of the cranium of the *Toxodon Platensis,* a gigantic extinct mammiferous species referrible by its dentition to the *Rodentia,* but with affinities to the *Pachydermata* and the *Herbivorous Cetacea,*" [1837] *Proc. Geol. Soc. Lond.* 2 (1834–37): 541–42.

"Description of the fossil mentioned in the preceding letter," *Mag. Nat. Hist.* n.s. 3 (1839): 446–48.

Parkinson, James, "Observations on some of the strata in the neighbourhood of London, and on the fossil remains contained in them," *Trans. Geol. Soc. Lond.* 1 (1811): 324–54.

Pennant, Thomas, *A Tour in Scotland and Voyage to the Hebrides*. 2nd ed. London: B. White, 1772.

Phillips, William, *Outlines of Mineralogy and Geology. . . .* Second edition. *To which is added an outline of the geology of England and*

Wales, with a map and section of the strata. London: W. Phillips, 1816.

A Selection of Facts from the best authorities arranged so as to form an outline of the Geology of England and Wales. With a map and sections of the Strata. London: W. Phillips, 1818.

Playfair, John, *Illustrations of the Huttonian Theory of the Earth.* Edinburgh: Cadell and Davies, 1802.

"Biographical account of the late Dr. James Hutton, F.R.S. Edin.," *Trans. Roy. Soc. Edin.* 5 (1805): Pt. 3, 39–99. Also in Playfair, *Works.* 4 vols. Edinburgh: A. Constable & Co., 1822; IV, pp. 33–118.

Prevost, Constant, "Sur un nouvel exemple de la réunion de coquilles marines et de coquilles fluviatiles fossiles dans les mêmes couches," *Journ. de Phys.* 92 (1821): 418–28.

"Observations sur les grès coquillers de Beau-Champ et sur les mélanges de coquilles marines et fluviatiles dans les couches inférieures de la formation du gypse des environs de Paris," *Journ. de Phys., de Chim. et d'Hist. Nat.* 94 (1822): 1–18.

"De l'importance de l'étude des corps organisés vivants pour la géologie positive," *Mem. Soc. d'hist. nat. Paris* 1 (1823): 259–68.

"De la formation des terrains des environs de Paris," *Bull. Soc. Philomat. Paris* (1825): 74–77, 88–90.

Prevost, Constant and Anselme Desmarest, "Sur des empreintes de corps marins trouvées à Mont martre, dans plusieùrs couches de la masse inférieure de la formation gypseuse," *Journ. Mines* 25 (1809): 215–26.

Prichard, James Cowles, *Researches into the Physical History of Man.* London: J. and A. Arch, 1813.

Researches into the Physical History of Mankind. 2 vols. London: J. and A. Arch, 1826.

Ramsay, Andrew Crombie, *The geology of the Island of Arran, from original survey.* Glasgow: R. Griffin & Co., 1841.

Rang, Sander, *Manuel de l'histoire naturelle des mollusques et de leurs coquilles ayant pour base de classification celle de M. le baron Cuvier.* Paris: Roret, 1829.

Raspe, Rudolph Erich, *Specimen historiae naturalis globi terraquei praecipue de novis e mari natis insulis et ex his exactius descriptis... confirmanda Hookiana telluris hypothesi de origine montium et corporum petrefactorum.* Amsterdam and Leipzig: J. Schreuder and P. Mortier, 1763.

Reid, Wemyss, *Memoirs and Correspondence of Lyon Playfair.* New York and London: Harper Bros., 1899.

Risso, Giovanni Antonio, *Histoire naturelle des principes productions de l'Europe méridionale et particulièrement de celles des environs de Nice et des Alpes maritimes.* 5 vols. Paris and Strasbourg: F. G. Levrault, 1826.

Robinson, Henry Crabb, *Diary, reminiscences and correspondence.* Edited by Thomas Sadler, 3 vols. London: Macmillan and Co., 1869.

Rossetti, Gabriele, *La Divina Comedia di Dante Alighieri con comento analitico.* 2 vols. London: J. Murray, 1826–27.

Rudwick, Martin J. S. "The foundation of the Geological Society of London: its scheme for co-operative research and its struggle for independence," *Brit. J. Hist. Sci.* 1 (1963): 325–55.

"Lyell on Etna and the antiquity of the Earth," in Cecil J. Schneer ed., *Toward a History of Geology,* Cambridge, Mass.: M.I.T. Press, 1969; pp. 288–304.

Sassi, Agostino, "Essai géologique sur le bassin tertiaire d'Albenga," *Bull. univ. sci. & ind. sect. 2* 18 (1829): 167.

Saussure, Horace-Bénedict de, *Voyages dans les Alpes précédés d'un essai sur l'histoire naturelle des environs de Genève.* 4 vols. Neuchatel: S. Fauche, 1779–96.

Scrope, George Poulett, "Notice on the geology of the Ponza Isles," [1824] *Trans. Geol. Soc. Lond.* 2, ser. 2 (1826): 195–236.

Considerations on Volcanoes, the probable causes of their phenomena, the laws which determine their march, the disposition of their products, and their connexion with the present state and past history of the globe; leading to the establishment of a new theory of the earth. London: W. Phillips, 1825.

Memoir on the Geology of Central France; including the Volcanic Formations of Auvergne, the Velay and the Vivarais, with a volume of Maps and Plates. London: Longman et al., 1827.

"On the volcanic district of Naples," [1827] *Trans. Geol. Soc. Lond.* 2, ser. 2 (1829): 337–52.

[review of] "Principles of Geology . . . by Charles Lyell," *Quart. Rev.* 43 (1830): 411–69.

"On the rippled markings of many of the Forest Marble strata north of Bath and the foot-tracks of certain animals occurring in great abundance on their surfaces," [1831] *Proc. Geol. Soc. Lond.* 1 (1826–33): 317–18.

Sedgwick, Adam, "Address to the Geological Society, delivered on the evening of the 18th of February, 1831," *Proc. Geol. Soc. Lond.* 1 (1826–33): 281–316.

"Remarks on the structure of large mineral masses, and especially on the chemical changes produced in the aggregation of stratified rocks during different periods after their deposition," *Trans. Geol. Soc. Lond.* 3, ser. 2 (1835): 461–86.

Sedgwick, Adam and Roderick Impey Murchison, "On the geological relations of the Secondary strata in the isle of Arran," [1828] *Trans. Geol. Soc. Lond.* 3, ser. 2 (1835): 21–36.

Serres, Marcel de, "Observations sur des terrains d'eau douce récemment découverts dans les environs de Sète, à très peu de distance de la Mediterranée, et inférieurs au niveau de cette mer," *Mem. Mus. Hist. Nat. Paris* 11 (1824): 372–419.

"Notes sur les Arachnides et les insectes fossiles et spécialement sur ceux des terrains d'eau douce," *Ann. Sci. Nat.* 15 (1828): 98–108.

Sinclair, Sir John, *The Statistical Account of Scotland drawn up from the communications of the Ministers of the Different Parishes.* 21 vols. Edinburgh: W. Creech, 1791–99.

Smiles, Samuel, *A publisher and his friends, memoir and correspondence of the late John Murray with an account of the origin and progress of the house. 1768–1843.* 2 vols. London: J. Murray, 1891.

Smith, William, *A delineation of the strata of England and Wales, with part of Scotland; exhibiting the collieries and mines, the marshes and fen lands originally overflowed by the sea and the varieties of soil according to the variations in the substrata, illustrated by the most descriptive names.* London: J. Cary, 1815.

A memoir to the map and delineation of the strata of England and Wales with part of Scotland. London: J. Cary, 1815.

Strata identified by organized fossils, containing prints on colored paper of the most characteristic specimens in each stratum. London: J. Cary, 1816.

Stratigraphical system of organized fossils with reference to the specimens of the original geological collection in the British Museum explaining their state of preservation and their use in identifying the British strata. London :E. Williams, 1817.

Somerville, Mary, *Personal Recollections from early life to old age. With selections from her correspondence* [edited] by her daughter Martha Somerville. London: J. Murray, 1873.

Sowerby, James, *English Botany.* 36 vols. London: printed for the author by J. Davis, 1790–1814.

The Mineral Conchology of Great Britain; or coloured figures . . . of . . . Shells which have been preserved . . . in the Earth. (continued by J. de C. Sowerby) 7 vols. London: J. Sowerby, 1812–46.

Spokes, Sidney, *Gideon Algernon Mantell L.L.D., F.R.C.S., surgeon and geologist.* London: J. Bale, Sons & Daniellson Ltd., 1927.

Studer, Bernhard, *Beytrage zu einer Monographie der Molasse. . . .* Berne, 1825.

"Remarques géognostiques sur quelques parties de la chaine septentrionale des Alpes," *Ann. Sci. Nat.* 11 (1827): 5–47.

"Notices géognostiques sur quelques parties de la chaîne de Stockhorn, et sur la Houille du Simmenthal, canton de Berne," *Ann. Sci. Nat.* 11 (1827): 249–65.

Stukeley, William, *Itinerarium curiosum: or An account of the antiquities, and remarkable curiosities in nature or art, observed in travels through Great Britain* . . . 2d ed., with large additions. 2 vols. London: Baker and Leigh, 1776. [1st ed. 1724]

Taylor, R[ichard] C., *On the Geology of East Norfolk; with remarks on the hypothesis of J. W. Robberds respecting the former level of the German Ocean.* London, 1827.

Thurmann, Jules, *Essai sur les soulèvements jurassiques.* 2 vols., vol. I, Strasbourg, 1832; vol. II, Porrentrui, 1836.

Townsend, Joseph, *The character of Moses established for veracity as an historian, recording events from the Creation to the Deluge.* 2nd ed. 2 vols. in one. Bath, 1815.

Tuckwell, Rev. W., *Reminiscences of Oxford.* London: Cassell and Co., 1901.

Ure, Andrew, *A new system of geology, in which the great revolutions of the earth and animated nature are reconciled at once to modern science and sacred history.* London: Longman et al., 1829.

Venn, J. A., *Alumni Cantabrigiensis. A biographical list.* Cambridge Univ. Press, 1922.

Vincent, E. R., *Gabriele Rossetti in England.* Oxford: Clarendon Press, 1936.

Ward, Humphrey, *History of the Athenaeum 1824–1925.* London: printed for the Club, 1926.

Warden, Alex J., *Angus or Forfarshire, the Land and People, Descriptive and Historical.* 5 vols. Dundee: Alexander and Co., 1880–85.

Webster, Thomas, "On the freshwater formations in the Isle of Wight, with some observations on the strata over the Chalk in the South-east part of England," *Trans. Geol. Soc. Lond.* 2 (1814): 161–254.

——— "On the geognostical situation of the Reigate Stone and of the Fuller's Earth at Nutfield," [1819] *Trans. Geol. Soc. Lond.* 5 (1821): 353–57.

——— "On a fresh-water formation in Hordwell Cliff, Hampshire; and on the subjacent beds from Hordwell to Muddiford," [1821] *Trans. Geol. Soc. Lond.* 1, ser. 2 (1824): 90–94.

——— "Reply to Dr. Fitton's paper in the 'Annals of Philosophy' for November, entitled 'Inquiries respecting the geological relations of the beds between the Chalk and the Purbeck Limestone in the South-east of England,' " *Ann. Phil.* 9 (1825): 33–51.

[Whewell, William] [review of] "Principles of Geology . . . by Charles Lyell," *Brit. Critic, Quart. Theol. Rev. and Ecclesiastical Record,* 9 (1831): 180–206.

Wilson, Leonard G., "The emergence of geology as a science in the United States," *J. World Hist.* 10 (1967): 416–37.

Withering, William, *A Botanical Arrangement of all the Vegetables Naturally growing in Great Britain.* . . . 2 vols. Birmingham: M. Swinney for T. Cadell, P. Emsley, and G. Robinson, London, 1776.

Wood, S. W., "The discovery of fossil quadrumanous remains near Woodbridge, Suffolk," *Mag. Nat. Hist.* n.w. 3 (1839): 444–45.

Woodward, Horace B., *The History of the Geological Society of London*. London: Geological Society, 1907.

Woodward, Samuel, *An outline of the geology of Norfolk*. Norwich, Eng., 1833.

"Some remarks upon the Crag formation of Norfolk and Suffolk," *Lond. and Edin. Phil. Mag.* 7 (1835): 353–55.

Index

The entry under the name of Charles Lyell (1797–1875) has been limited to those references which cannot be readily located under other entries. The abbreviation C. L. has been used throughout for Charles Lyell (1797–1875) and M. E. L. for his wife, Mary Elizabeth Lyell. Charles Lyell's father, also Charles Lyell, is referred to as C. Lyell, Esq.

Acephala, 484

Aconcagua, Chile, 454

Addington, Henry, Viscount Sidmouth (*1757–1844*), 15

Agassiz, Louis (*1807–73*), 371–72, 409, 421, 422, 469, 501; theory of glacial movement, 496–500

Agricultural laborers' revolt, 320

Agrigento. *See* Girgenti, Sicily

l'Aiguille de Brevent (mountain), 62

Aix-en-Provence, France: insect bed, 208–10

Albion, H.M.S., 3

Alcyonium, 97

Aldborough, Suffolk, 481, 486

Alexander, Capt., 481–82

Allier River, 178, 191

Alps: C. L. visits (*1818*), 60–63

Altoona, Germany, 392

Alum Bay, Isle of Wight, 19–20

Amici, Giovan Battista (*1786–1868*), 171–72

Ammonites Bucklandi, 45

Anapa River valley, 242, 244

Ancylus, 201

Andes, 452

Andrews, Sophy, 409, 423

Angers, France, 493

Anning, Mary, 128

Anoplotherium, 82

Appleton, D. and Co., 426

Arago, Dominique-François (*1786–1853*), 414

Ardèche (district), France: C. L. and R. Murchison tour (*1828*), 206–08

Ardèche River valley, 262

Arduino, Giovanni (*1713–95*), 66–67

Armadillo, 437

Arnold, Joseph (*1782–1818*), 46, 47–48, 49

Arno valley, Italy, 224

Arran, Isle of, 71, 429–31

Arve valley, Switzerland, 60

Athenaeum, 135

Athol, Duke of. *See* Murray, John, 4th Duke of Athol

D'Aubuisson de Voisins, Jean François (*1769–1819*), 74, 174, 296

Auchenia, 437

Audebard de Férussac, Baron André Étienne Justin Pascal Joseph François d'. *See* Férussac, André

Augustus Frederick, Duke of Sussex (*1773–1843*), 304

Aurillac, France, 201, 203–04

Austen, Jane (*1775–1817*), 21

Auvergne (district), France, 74, 80, 81, 173–74, 176–79; C. L. and R. Murchison tour (*1828*), 191–200, 207–08

Ava, Burma, 185

Avallon, France, 60

Ax-les-Thermes, France, 296

Aymestry, Radnorshire, 515–16

Babbage, Charles (*1792–1871*), 354, 386, 411; Ninth Bridgewater Treatise, 435, 461–62

Bagnères de Luchon, France, 299

Bahia Blanca, Argentina, 442, 445

Bakewell, Robert (*1768–1843*), 77, 176, 276, 409; *Introduction to Geology*, 41–42

Bakie Loch, Angus, 131–33

Ballentine, William, 138

Baltic Sea: small size of shells of, 396–97, 400

Banks, Sir Joseph (*1743–1820*), 53, 332

Barcelona, Spain, 297

Bardi, Baron, 224

Bar in England, 136–37; circuit system, 138–40; western circuit, 138–39; C. L. travels with western circuit, (*1825*), 138, (*1826*), 153, 159, (*1827*), 172

Baring, Alexander (*1774–1848*), 345

Barrat, France, 204

Barrow, John (*1764–1848*), 159

Basalt, question of origin, 73–74, 174–75; British view (*1813*), 74

Basterot, Barthelemy de (d. *1887*), 220, 221

Battle beds, 105, 107

Bayreuth, Germany, 384

Beagle, H. M. S., 424, 425, 433, 450, 451

Beale, Mary. *See* Lyell, Mary Beale

Beauchamp, Sandstone of, 120

Beaufort, Sir Francis (*1774–1857*), 272

Beauley, Bay of, Inverness, 499

Beaumont, Jean Baptiste Armand Louis Leonce Élie de. *See* Élie de Beaumont, Jean

Beche, Sir Henry Thomas de la (*1796–1855*), 125, 343–44, 424, 456

Beck, Heinrich (*1796–1863*), 422, 423, 443–44, 470, 472, 475

Belgium: C. L.'s observations, 89

Bertrand (of Puy-en-Velay, France), 206

Berzelius, Jöns Jakob (*1779–1848*), 399–400, 402, 405, 415

Bex, Switzerland, 369

Biddulph, Constance, 20

Birmingham, Warwickshire, 126–28

Bischof, Karl Gustav Christoph (*1792–1870*), 347

Black, Joseph (*1728–99*), 69

Blackadder (of Glamis), 87

Black Hambleton Hills, Yorkshire, 49

Blue lias formation, 83, 103, 125

Bologna, Italy, 224

Bonelli, Franco Andrea (*1784–1830*), 221, 224, 257

Bonn, Germany, 362–63, 384, 420–21

Bonpland, Aimé Jacques Alexandre (*1773–1858*), 332

Bordeaux, France, 220, 221, 296

Borrer, William (*1781–1862*), 20, 25

Bosc, D'Antic Louis-Augustin-Guillaume (*1759–1828*), 81

Bosson (glacier), Switzerland, 60–62

Bourg Madame, France, 296

Bray, Valley of, France, 382

Bright, Richard (*1781–1858*), 261

Brighton, Sussex, 409

British Association, 420, 468, 475; Agassiz paper on movement of glaciers (Sept. *1840*), 496

—meetings attended by C. L.: gives report on Sweden (Sept. *1834*), 409; Aug. *1838;* papers on tubular cavities in

chalk and Suffolk fossils (Aug.–Sept. *1839*), 489, 512

British Critic, 292, 305, 308

Brocchi, Giovanni Battista (*1772–1826*), 218–19

Broderip, William John (*1789–1859*), 181, 273, 277, 299, 304, 313, 317, 328

Brongniart, Adolphe T. (*1801–76*), 146–47

Brongniart, Alexandre (*1770–1847*), 93, 101, 118, 218, 279–80, 367, 413–15; concept of a Cretaceous formation, 202–03

—work on Paris Basin, 76, 78–83, 133; discovery of freshwater formation, 80–81

Bronn, Heinrich Georg (*1800–62*), 366

Brougham, Henry Peter, first Baron Brougham (*1779–1868*), 58

Brown, Robert (*1773–1858*), 25, 304, 325, 332, 452, 459

Bruncrona, Colonel, 402

Buccinum undatum, 444

Buch, Christian Leopold von (*1774–1853*), 53–54, 74, 174–75, 414–15, 417, 420, 473; theory of origin of dolomites, 317

Buckland, William (*1784–1856*), 34, 42–45, 48, 53–54, 59, 74, 84, 85, 95, 113, 114, 143, 147, 157, 159, 164, 168, 173, 176, 186, 196, 231, 264, 266, 273, 278, 314, 358, 409, 420, 501; and Agassiz study glaciation, 498–501; and C. L. tour in Scotland (*1824*), 129; Bridgewater Treatise, 461; C. L. gathers information for (*1817*), 46, 48, 54

Buffon, Georges Louis Leclerc, Comte de (*1707–88*), 334

Bulimus, 81, 201

Bullock's museum, 46, 56

Burnet, Thomas (*1635?–1715*), 278

Butler, Joseph (*1692–1752*), 158, 277, 281–82

Butte de Montpensier, France, 193

Byrne, Frances, 476–77

Byron, John (*1723–86*), 3, 10

Caddis fly. *See Phryganea*

Cadibona coal basin, Italy, 221

Caen, France, 492

Caillaud, Frédéric (*1787–1869*), 493

Calcair grossier. *See* Paris limestone

Caltagirone, Sicily, 249, 250, 251

Caltanissetta, Sicily, 249–50

Cambridge University, 165–69, 173, 314;

Cambridge University (*cont.*)
C. L. receives honorary M.A. degree (*1831*), 314

Campbell, Thomas (*1777–1844*): *Letter to Mr. Brougham on the Subject of a London University* reviewed by C. L., 144–45

Candolle, Augustin Pyrâme de, 257, 258–59, 331, 333

Candolle family, 7, 91

Cantal (district), France: freshwater formations, 80, 178, 200–01; C. L. and R. Murchison tour (*1828*), 200–06

Cape Passaro, Sicily, 245

Capybara, 438

Carcary, Farnell, Angus, 1

Cardium edule, 394, 396–97, 400

Cardwell, Edward (*1787–1861*), 167–68

Caroline of Brunswick, Queen (*1768–1821*), 88, 91

Castrogiovanni, Sicily, 249, 251–52

Catania, Sicily, 237–38, 240

Celsius, Anders (*1701–44*), 385, 406

Chain of being: C. L.'s concept of, 158

Chambezon, France, 201

Chamonix, Switzerland, 60, 62

Champeix, France, 200

Les Chapelles, France, 201

Chara, 81, 119, 140, 149, 151, 172, 178, 201, 204; *C. ulvoides*, 172

Charlesworth, Edward (*1813–93*), 480, 481; fossil shell collection from the Crag, 415, 422, 464
—publishes papers on the Crag: *1835*, 465–67; *1836*, 468–69; *1837*, 469

Charpentier, Jean G. F. de (*1786–1855*), 369, 496–97, 498

Charters, William, 171

Chemnitz, Johann Hieronymus (*1730–1800*), 470

Chilean earthquakes: *1822*, 157, 425, 435; *1835*, 451

Cholera epidemic, London, 340

Christian, Prince, of Denmark (*1818–1906*), 395–96, 470, 471–72

Christiania, Norway, 472–74

Clam-shell cave, Staffa, 54

Clermont-Ferrand, France, 193, 196, 197; *puys* near, 179

Clift, William (*1775–1849*), 142, 434

Climate: C. L.'s theory of, 285–87

Cockburn, Henry (*1779–1854*), 319, 345, 391, 514

Colchester, William, 478, 480, 488

Coleridge, Sir John Taylor (*1790–1876*), 38, 137, 139, 143–44

Coleridge, Samuel Taylor (*1772–1834*); *Christabel*, 38

Combe Wood, Surrey, 352

Côme, Cheire of, France, 196

Compton Bay, Isle of Wight, 114

Concepción, Chile, 451, 453, 454

Conus, 492

Conybeare, John Josias (*1779–1824*), 43–44

Conybeare, William Daniel (*1787–1857*), 74, 83–84, 102–103, 108, 128, 142, 267, 273, 278, 314; challenges Webster's view on firestone, 102; volcanic theory, 109–10; influence on C. L., 110–11; work on fossil reptiles, 124–25; "On the hydrographical basin of the Thames . . . ," 262–65; review of C. L.'s *Principles*, vol. 1, 305; honorary M.A. degree, Cambridge University (*1831*), 314

Conybeare, William Daniel, and William Phillips: *Outlines of the Geology of England*, 102, 107–08, 114, 170, 219

Cooke, S. E., and C. L. tour Pyrenees (*1830*), 273, 294–97, 299–301

Copenhagen, Denmark, 394, 396, 443, 470–72

Copleston, Edward (*1776–1849*), Bishop of Llandaff, 274, 308–13
—letters re C. L.'s orthodoxy of views: from C. L. (28 Mar. *1831*), 310; to C. L. (30 Mar. *1831*), 311–12

Coquebert de Montret, Baron, 118

Corbett, Thomas George (*1796–1889*), 52

Cordier, Pierre L. A. (*1777–1862*), 386–88

Corsica: flora of, 258

Cortachy, Bridge of, Angus, 56

Coseguina (volcano), 454

Costa (former professor, University of Otranto), 228–29, 252, 257

Coulon, Louis, 417

Cousdes, France, 201

Cowes, Isle of Wight, 19

Crag: recent formation, 219–20, 266

Crag controversy, 463–69; fossil shells examined by G. Deshayes, 415, 468; C. L.'s opinion on dating, 415, 463, 464, 466–67; fossil shells examined by H. Beck, 422, 468; C. L.'s letter to Darwin, 475–76; C. L. affirms Charlesworth's conclusions, 480, 482, 483–84,

Crag controversy (*cont.*)
486; C. L. publishes paper confirming Charlesworth's conclusions, 485
—E. Charlesworth papers on: *1835*, 465–67; *1836*, 468–69; *1837*, 469
—C. L. examines Crag: April *1838*, 478–80; July *1838*, 481–82; June *1839*, 486–89
Crawfurd, John (*1783–1868*), 185
Cretaceous formations, 202–03
Croft, Sir John (*1778–1862*), 117, 118
Croker, John Wilson (*1780–1857*), 135
Cromer, Norfolk, 484, 486, 487
Cruachan, Ben, Argyll, 52
Culley, Matthew, 265
Culver Cliff, Isle of Wight, 97
Cuming, Hugh (*1791–1865*), 425
Curtin, John (*1791–1862*), 147, 210
Cuvier, Georges Léopold Chrétien Frédéric Dagobert, Baron, (*1769–1832*), 44, 59, 93, 101, 116–17, 218, 261, 329, 358, 371; work on Paris basin, 76, 78–84, 133; catastrophic theory, 81, 83; *Discours sur les Revolutions de la Globe*, 155–56
Cyclops, Island of, 237
Cyclostoma, 81
Cypris, 149, 151, 191–93, 201
Cypris faba, 132
Cypris ornata, 132

Danemora, Sweden, 404
Daniell, John Frederic (*1790–1845*), 386, 388
Darwin, Charles Robert (*1809–82*), 314, 339, 424–25, 458, 462, 505, 509, 516; student life at Cambridge, 5; return from voyage, 433–35; friendship with C. L., 434, 441, 457, 460; studies South American fossils, 436–38, 440–42; work on transmutation of species, 441, 443, 444–47; natural selection, 446–47; origin of coral reefs and atolls, 447–50; theory of origin of elevated plains in South America, 450–52; Glen Roy paper (*1839*), 456–57; engagement and marriage, 458–59
—Geological Society: drafts of papers read by C. L., 435; addresses on elevation of Chile coast (Jan. *1837*), 435; addresses on South American fossils (May *1837*), 441–42; addresses on theory of coral reefs (May *1837*), 450;

addresses on earthquakes and volcanoes (March *1838*), 453–56
—*Journal of Researches*, 452, 507; work on, 434, 442, 444; proofs read by C. L., 452–53
Darwin, Emma Wedgwood (*1808–96*), 458, 459
Daubeny, Charles Giles Bridle (*1795–1867*), 175–77, 231, 314; *A Description of Active and Extinct Volcanoes . . .*, 294; *Sketch of the Geology of Sicily*, 243–44, 247–49
Davy, Sir Humphry (*1778–1829*), 49, 135, 388; *Consolations in Travel*, 284–85, 289–90
Dechen, Ernest Heinrich Carl von (*1810–69*), 431
Deluc, Jean André (*1727–1817*), 72
Denmark: C. L. tours (*1834*), 394–96
Deshayes, Gérard Paul (*1797–1875*), 259–60, 301–03, 371, 382, 413, 422, 443, 444
Deslongchamps, Jacques Amand Eudes. *See* Eudes-Deslongchamps, Jacques Amand
Desmarest, Anselme-Gaetan (*1784–1838*), 119
Desmarest, Nicholas (*1725–1815*), 174, 176
Desnoyers, Jules Pierre François Stanislas (*1800–87*), 219–20, 259, 486
Dogger Bank, North Sea, 279
Dôle, France, 60
Donovan, Edward, *The Natural History of British Insects*, 22
Doué, France, 493, 494
Dourtol, France, 197
Drammen, Norway, 474
Dufrénoy, Ours Pierre Armand Petit (*1792–1857*), 295
Dujardin, Felix (*1801–62*), 477, 486
Duncombe Park, Yorkshire, 49
Durdle Cove, Isle of Wight, 99
Durdlestone Point, Dorsetshire, 172–73

Eaton, Amos (*1776–1842*), 77
Edinburgh, 49–50, 87; Carlton Hill, 50; School of Arts, 163
Edinburgh Academy, 163
Edinburgh Review, 509
Egerton, Francis Henry, 8th Earl of Bridgewater (*1756–1829*), 461
Egerton, Sir Philip de Malpas Grey (*1806–81*), 272
Eiffel (district), Germany, 317

Elbe River, 392

Élie de Beaumont, Jean Baptiste Armand Louis Leonce (1798–1874), 382, 391, 414, 420, 497; theory of elevation of mountain chains, 259, 293, 294–96, 347–50, 378–79, 383, 455

Elsa River valley: lacustrine formation, 225

Englefield, Sir Henry Charles (1752–1822), 96–101

Eocene: coining of term, 307

Epernay, France, 383

Epine, Edward 1', 3

Erycina, 451

Esjko Klubb, Island of, 403–04

d'Espagne, Count, 297

Estaing, Charles Hector Théodat, Comte d' (1729–94), 3

Etna, 233–37, 279; Valley of St. Giacomo, 233–35; Rocca di Calanna, 235; Val di Calanna, 235, 236; C. L.'s ascent of, 238–39; mass indicative of its age, 253–54; C. L. demonstrates age, King's College lecture, 359

—Val del Bove, 233, 235–37; C. L.'s sketch of, 239

Eucalypta streptocarpa, 31

Eudes-Deslongschamps, Jacques Amand (1794–1867), 492

Euganean Hills, Italy, 223

Exeter College, Oxford, 35

Eyles, Victor A., and Joan M. Eyles, 76

Fahlun, Sweden, 404

Fairfax, Mary. See Somerville, Mary

Fairfax, Sir William George (1739–1813), 10

Faraday, Michael (1791–1867), 135, 388, 396, 409

Faujas de Saint-Fond, Barthelemy (1741–1819), 174

Ferguson, James, 2

Férussac, André Étienne Justin Pascal Joseph François d'Audebard de, Baron (1786–1836), 122–23, 275

Fingal's cave, Staffa, 53–54

Finhaven, Angus, 52

Firebrand, H. M. sloop, 1–2

First Cause, 310–11

Fitch, Robert, 466, 482, 484

Fitton, William Henry (1780–1861), 151, 304, 326, 353, 360–61, 456, 459; review of C. L.'s Elements, 1st ed., 509–12

Fitzroy, Robert (1805–65), 425, 452

Flanders, 89

Fleming, John (1785–1857), 269, 283, 323, 469

Florence, Italy, 224–25

Flumen, Olof, 402–03

Fluvialist-diluvialist dispute, 263; A. Sedgwick converted, 269

Fontainebleau, forest of, France, 60, 79, 119, 122

Forbes, Edward (1815–54), 126, 494

Forchhammer, Johann Georg (1794–1865), 394–96, 470

Forfar, Angus: popular feeling re Reform Bill, 324

Forfar Loch, Angus, 133

Forfarshire [Angus]: paper on deposits by C. L., Geological Society (Dec. 1824 and Jan. 1825), 131, 135; geological map made by C. L. for Macculloch, 129, 131

Fox, Henry Richard Vassall, 3rd Baron Holland (1773–1840), 461

France, visits of C. Lyell, Esq.: 1788, 6; 1792, 7

Frankfurt, Germany, 364

French Revolution: effects of (1820), 89

Fuveau, France, coal mines of, 209–10

Galapagos Islands, 445

Gardner (American consul, Sicily), 252

Gault beds, Cambridgeshire, 113–14

Gefle, Sweden, 402–03

Gelk-Ay, Argyll, 52

Gemmellaro, Giuseppe, 238, 239

Genesis, 59

Geneva, Switzerland, 257–59, 369, 371

Genoa, Italy, 220–21, 257

Geoffroy Saint-Hilaire, Étienne (1772–1884), 329

Geognosy, 66

Geological Society of London, 43, 74–75, 105–08, 125–26, 146–47, 163, 185, 256, 262, 264–65, 293, 325–26, 343, 349–50, 353–54, 412, 464; C. L. elected fellow (1819), 64; formation and purpose, 65, 74; addressed by Agassiz on glaciers (1840), 499–500

—Transactions, 65, C. L. on editorial staff, 112, 126; reviewed by C. L. in Quarterly Review (1826), 154–59, 281–82

—anniversary meetings: attended by

544

Geological Society of London (cont.)
C. L., 1822, 95, 1828, 186, 1833, 389–90; C. L. president, 1835, 411, 1836, 424, 468, 497, 1837, 435–36
—papers read by Darwin (see Darwin, Charles Robert)
—papers read by C. L.: Forfarshire deposits (Dec. 1824), 131; Forfarshire deposits (Jan. 1825), 135; plastic clay formations (March 1826), 148; Hordwell Cliff (June 1826), 149, 201; Cretaceous and Tertiary strata of Seeland and Moen (May 1835), 394–96; Silurian strata near Christiania (June 1841), 475; Crag (May 1839), 480, 485, 509; glaciation in Forfarshire (Nov., Dec. 1840), 501; boulder formation, Norfolk (Jan. 1840), 512; faluns of the Loire (June 1841), 515; Silurian strata, Aymestry and Wenlock (June 1841), 515–16
—C. L. secretary, 125–26; resigns (1825), 147
—Wollaston Medal: to G. Mantell (1834), 411; to L. Agassiz (1835), 422
George IV (1762–1830), 88
German Association for the Advancement of Science, 420
Giant's Causeway, Ireland, 8–9, 74
Gifford, William (1756–1826), 143
Gilbert (formerly Giddy), Davies (1767–1839), 304
Gioenian Society of Catania, 239–40
Girgenti, Sicily, 247–48
Glaux maritima, 402
Glen Carity, Angus, 501
Glen Prosen, Angus, 501
Glen Roy, Argyll, 130, 456–57, 500
Glen Tilt, Perthshire, 70, 130
Godesberg, Germany, 315–16, 363, 421
Gorleston, Norfolk, 47
Gozzo degli Martiri, Sicily, 242
Grammichele, Sicily, 250
Granite, theory of, in mountain building: P. Pallas, 67; J. Hutton, 70
Graves, Louis (1791–1857), 382
Gray, Thomas (1716–71), 27
Grays, Essex, 484
Greenough, George Bellas (1778–1855), 43, 75, 76, 104, 108, 112–13, 264, 326, 389–90, 501
Green sand: A. Werner, 56; T. Webster, 97, 101–02, 107; W. Smith, 102; Isle of Wight, correlated to Sussex, 111, 113–14
Grey, Charles, 2nd Earl (1764–1845), 320, 321, 356–57
Grindelwald (glacier), 419, 499
Guettard, Jean Étienne (1715–86), 174
Guidotti, Professor, of Parma, 223–24
Gulf of Bothnia, 402–04
Gullholmen, Island of, 406–07
Gurnigel, Switzerland, 368
Gypsum: Montmartre, 44, 79, 119–20; Paris basin, 79–82
Gyrogonites. See Chara

Hahl (geologist at Stuttgart), 384
Hall, Basil (1788–1844), 303, 326
Hall, George (clerk to C. L.), 190, 193, 194, 261, 304, 319, 325, 326, 352, 354, 372, 373, 374, 375, 423
Hall, Sir James, of Dunglass (1761–1832), 71, 130, 502
Hallstrom, Colonel, 404
Handfast, Point, Dorsetshire, 99
Happisburgh, Norfolk, 487, 489
Hartmann, J. D. Wilhelm (1793–1862), 384
Hastings, Sussex, 410–11
Hawkins, John Sidney (1758–1842), 266
Head, Sir Edmund Walker (1805–68), 370–71
Headlam, Dr., 49
Heathcote, Ann Lyell (d. 1854), 340; engagement, 21; marriage, 23
Heathcote, Gilbert (1779–1831), 21, 185; marriage, 23
Heathcote, William (1746–1819), 23
Heathcote family: at Isle of Wight with C. Lyell family (1806), 19
Heidelberg, Germany, 364, 384
Helix, 81, 201
Helmesley, Yorkshire, 49
Helvellyn, Cumberland, 86
Henslow, John Stevens (1796–1861), 160, 173, 314, 459
Herculaneum, Italy, 229
Herschel, John F. W. (1792–1871), 141, 196, 223, 238, 286, 304, 426, 438
Heyland (friend of C. Lyell, Esq.), 63, 124
Hoff, Karl Ernst Adolf von (1771–1837), 170, 267, 276
Hogg, Thomas Jefferson (1792–1862), Life of Shelley, 33

Holland, Lord. *See* Fox, Henry Richard Vassall, 3rd Baron Holland

Holmstrand, Norway, 474

Hooker, William Jackson (*1785–1865*), 24, 31, 32, 111

Hopkins, William (*1793–1866*), 455

Hordwell Cliff, Hampshire, 149, 201, 208

Horner, Frances, 412, 422

Horner, Leonard (*1785–1864*), 162–63, 315–16, 317, 345, 408, 420, 505

Horner, Leonora, 459

Horner, Mary Elizabeth: engagement to C. L. (12 July *1831*), 315–17, 323; marriage to C. L. (12 July *1832*), 362–64, 374

Horsham sandstone: C. L. studies ripple marks (*1822*), 105–07

Humboldt, Freiherr Heinrich Alexander von (*1769–1859*), 48, 117, 124, 170, 285–86, 332; tables of earthquakes and volcanic activity, 453

Hutton, James (*1726–97*), 42, 430, 510

—theory of the earth, 69–73, 156, 157; cyclical process of rock formation, 69–70, 72; on uplift of mountains, 70–71; paper to Royal Society of Edinburgh on (*1785*), 70

Huttonian-Wernerian controversy, 49–50, 73, 74

Hydrochaerus capybara, 441

Hypnum molluscum, 19

Iceland: plan for trip abandoned by C. L., 270

Ichthyosaurus, 44, 83–84, 125, 128

Iguanodon, 142

Ilford, Essex, 484

Indusia tubulata, 81, 193

Inns of Court, 137–38

Inocerami, 114

Inula helenium, 19

Inverary, Argyll, 499

Invercarity, Angus, purchase of (*1782*), 3–4

Iona, Island of, 55

Irawaddi River, 185

Ireland: visited by C. Lyell, Esq. (*1795*), 8–9

Iron sand, Isle of Wight, 102, 103, 105, 111

Ischia, Isle of: C. L. collects shells from Mt. Epomeo, 226–28

Isle of Wight, 95, 149; visited by C. Lyell and family (*1806*), 19–20; history of geological exploration, *1799–1822*, 96–102; explored by T. Webster, *1811*, 97–99, *1812*, 99; strata below chalk described by T. Webster, 101; visited by C. L. to correlate strata with Sussex (*1822*), 111, 113–14; visited by C. L. and W. Buckland (*1823*), 113–15; Auvergne freshwater formations compared, 201

Isle of Wight basin, 101

Issoire, France, 201

Italy: visited by C. Lyell, Esq. and C. L. (*1820*), 88–91

Jaeger, Georg Friedrich von (*1785–1866*), 384

Jameson, Robert (*1774–1854*), 49–50, 73, 87, 430, 431; *Mineralogy of the Scottish Isles*, 73

Jardin des Plantes, 59

Jardin du Roi, 117, 477

Jarlsberg, Count Wedel, 473, 474

Jedburgh, Berwickshire, 71, 156

Jed River, 71

Jeffrey, Francis (*1773–1850*), 131

Johnson, John Robert (interpreter for C. L. in Sweden), 397–405

Johnston, James Finlay Weir (*1796–1855*), 400

Juan Fernandez, Island of, 453

Jungermannia ciliaris, 18

Jungfrau (Switzerland), 418

Jura Mountains, 60

Kander River, 417–18

Keilhau, Baltazar Mathias (*1797–1858*), 473–74

Kerrera, Argyll, 52

Keyser, Jens Jacob (*1780–1847*), 473

Kidd, John (*1775–1851*), 34, 84, 93

King's College. *See* Lyell, Charles (*1797–1875*)

Kingston Hill, Surrey: Zoological Society farm, 352

Kinnordy: purchased by C. Lyell (*1734–96*) (*1782*), 3–4; agricultural changes by C. Lyell (*1734–96*), 4–5; visited by C. Lyell, Esq., *1804*, 15–16, *1815*, 31, *1816*, 38–39, *1817*, 44, 55, *1819*, 85, 87; C. L. visits, *1817*, 44, 52, 55, *1819*, 85, 87, *1829*, 267, *1830–31*, 304–05, 307, *1831*, 319–25, *1838*, 507–08; C. Lyell,

Kinnordy (cont.)
Esq. moves household to (1826), 154; situated in a glacial landscape, 501
Kinnordy, Loch of, Angus, 131
Kirriemuir, Angus, 3–4; heritor, 10; industries, 11; economic depression (1816), 39
Kirwan, Richard (1733–1812), 72
König, Charles Dietrich Eberhard (1774–1851), 83

Lake Albano, Italy, 225–26
Lake District: explored by C. L., (1819), 86–87
Lamarck, Jean Baptiste Antoine Pierre de Monnet, Chevalier de (1744–1829), 78, 116, 440, 444; Philosophie zoologique, 161, 180, 181, 329, 332
Latreille, Pierre André (1762–1833), 116
Lauterbrunner, Switzerland, 418
Le Havre, France, 490
Lehman, Johann Gottlob (d. 1767), 67
Leibniz, Gottfried Wilhelm, Baron von (1646–1716), 386–87
Lempdes, France, 201
Lentini, Sicily, 240–41
Leonhard, Carl Cäsar von (1779–1862), 366, 384
Lewes, Sussex: C. L. meets G. Mantell (1822), 92
Lewis, Ben, Argyll, 52
Lewis, Thomas, 515
Lhuyd, Edward (1660–1709), 94
Licata, Sicily, 246–47, 248
Lichen pollinarius, 20
Liège, Belgium, 385
Limagne, France: freshwater formations, 176, 178, 191–93, 197
Limnea, 201
Lincoln's Inn. See Lyell, Charles, Esq.; and Lyell, Charles (1797–1875)
Linnaeus, Carolus (1707–78), 331, 470
Linnaeus's garden, 402
Linnean Society: elects as fellow C. Lyell, Esq. (1813), 25; elects as fellow C. L., (1819), 64; collection of moths and butterflies exhibited by C. L. (1825), 147
Lismore, Island of, 52–53
Lithodomus, 230
Llandaff, Bishop of. See Copleston, Edward
Loch Awe, Argyll, 52

Loch Treig, Argyll, 499
Lockhart, John Gibson (1794–1854), 144, 148, 152, 159, 179, 188, 189, 273–74, 309, 327
Löfgrund, Island of, 403
Loire River, 178
Loire valley, excavation of, 206
London basin, 101
Lonsdale, William (1794–1871), 433, 494
Louans, France, 494
Lowell, John (1799–1836), 515
Lucina divaricata, 422, 444
Lund, Sweden, 397
Lundstedt, Lt. Col., 400
Lunel, France, 208
Lyell, Ann. See Heathcote, Ann Lyell
Lyell, Caroline (1802–86), 14, 56, 85, 87, 185, 322, 340, 345, 358, 410
Lyell, Charles (1734–96): years at sea, 1–3; marriage to Mary Beale, 2; birth of son Charles, 2; death, 9
Lyell, Charles, Esq. of Kinnordy (1769–1849), 361, 421; parents, 2; education to 1796, 2, 5–10, portrait by Miss Singleton (1794), 8; Lincoln's Inn (1788–95), 6–9; marriage to Frances Smith (1796), 10; births of children, 10–31 passim; Bartley Lodge at Lyndhurst, 14, 24, 146; commands company of volunteers (1803–05), 15, 16–17; botanical interest, 18–19; lichen named for him (1806), 19; need to borrow money (1813–14), 25; education of C. L., 35; letter to C. L. on departure for America (1841), 516–17
—travel: Continent (1788, 1792), 6–7; Ireland (1795), 8–9; Isle of Wight (1806), 19–20; Continent (1818), 58–63; Italy (1820), 88–91
Lyell, Charles (1797–1875)
—early years: birth, 10; inoculated for smallpox (1798), 12; fifth birthday, 14; first letter to parents (12 March 1805), 16; illness (1808), 21–22; interest in aquatic insects, 22–23; botanical expedition with W. Hooker (1815), 31; interest in geology, 41–56; letters (excerpts) to C. Lyell, Esq., on geological observations (1817), 47–48; trouble with eyes (1819–), 64, 85, 88, 89, 92, 98, 112, 118, 124; publishes first geological paper (1826), 131; insect collection, 147, 151–52, 160–61

Lyell, Charles (*cont.*)

—education: Ringwood (*1805*), 16; Mr. Radcliffe's School, Salisbury (*1808*), 21; Mr. Bayley's School, Midhurst (*1810–15*), 24–31; Oxford (*1816–21*), 33, 35–43, 58, 94; Lincoln's Inn (*1819–25*), 63, 88, 91, 94–95, 112, 136

—Mary Elizabeth Horner: first meeting, 315; engagement, 315–17, 323; marriage, 361–64, 374

—King's College: seeks professorship of geology at (*1831*), 308–13, 323; lectures at (*1832*), 318, 353–60, (*1833*), 376; resigns from (*1832*), 340, 360, (*1833*), 376

—travel on Continent: with C. Lyell, Esq. (*1818*), 58–63; Italy with C. Lyell, Esq. (*1820*), 88–91; Paris (*1823*), 116–24; France with R. Murchison (*1828*), 187, 190–217; Italy (*1828*), 220–32; Sicily (*1828*), 232–56; Paris (*1829*), 259–61; Pyrenees (*1830*), 273, 294–301; Paris (*1830*), 301–03; Eiffel district (*1831*), 315–17; Rhine valley with M. E. L. (*1832*), 364–67; Switzerland with M. E. L. (*1832*), 367–71; Paris with M. E. L. (*1832*), 371–72; Rhine valley with M. E. L. (*1833*), 384–85; Denmark (*1834*), 394–96; Sweden (*1834*), 391, 396–407; Paris with M. E. L. (*1835*), 413–15; Switzerland with M. E. L. (*1835*), 415–20; Paris with M. E. L. (*1837*), 477; Copenhagen with M. E. L. (*1837*), 470–72, 475–76; Norway with M. E. L. (*1837*), 472–75; France with M. E. L. (*1840*), 490–94. *See also place names.*

—*Principles of Geology*, 1st ed.: *Vol. 1*, 278–91, 318; thoughts leading up to, 164, 169–71, 172, 184, 186, 256; writing of, 265–73; comments other than reviews, 299, 303, 325–26; reviews, 273–77, 291–92, 293, 305; *Vol. 2*, 328–39; work on, 303, 313, 317, 318, 320, 322, 326–27; review by W. Whewell for *Quarterly Review*, 327, 350–51; *Vol. 3*, 346–47, 351–52, 359, 377–81; work on, 345–46, 350–53, 366, 371–72, 375–76

—*Principles of Geology*, 2nd ed.: *Vol. 1*, 360, 373; *Vol. 2*, 360, 374

—*Principles of Geology*, 3rd ed., 385, 387, 389, 390–91

—*Principles of Geology*, 4th ed., 411, 413

—*Principles of Geology*, 5th ed., 428, 461

—*Principles of Geology*, 6th ed., 513–14; work on, 483, 490, 508

—*Elements of Geology*, 1st ed., 506–07; work on, 409, 457, 461, 478, 480, 481, 503–05; C. Darwin comments on, 505–06; reviewed by W. Fitton, 509–12

—*Elements of Geology*, 2nd ed., 514–15, 516

—*Manual of Elementary Geology*, 515

Lyell, Charles, and R. Murchison, "On the excavation of valleys . . . ," 211, 223, 256, 262–63

Lyell, Eleanor (*1805–66*), 17, 111

Lyell, Elizabeth (*1814–35*), 31, 410, 412, 421

Lyell, Frances (Fanny) (*1800–73*), 14, 111

Lyell, Frances Smith (d. *1850*), 8, 410; marriage to C. Lyell, Esq., 10. *See also* Lyell, Charles, Esq. of Kinnordy.

Lyell, Henry (*1804–75*), 17, 88, 410–11, 428

Lyell, James of Carcary, 1

Lyell, John of Carcary, 1

Lyell, Katherine M. Horner, 136

Lyell, Margaret Mudie, 1

Lyell, Maria (*1808–43*), 22

Lyell, Marianne (*1801–81*), 14, 85, 87, 112, 185, 319, 322, 340, 345, 358

Lyell, Mary (d. *1843*), 340

Lyell, Mary Beale (d. *1813*): marriage to C. Lyell (*1734–96*), 2; birth of son Charles, 2; death, 30

Lyell, Sophia Georgina (*1812–97*), 30

Lyell, Thomas (*1798–1871*), 12, 323–24, 340; Ringwood School (*1805*), 16; Mr. Radcliffe's School, Salisbury (*1808*), 21; Mr. Bayley's School, Midhurst (*1810–13*), 24; joins the British Navy (*1813*), 30; made Lieutenant (*1820*), 88

Lyellia, 25

Lyme Regis, Somerset, 83, 124–25, 128

Lymnea, 81, 405

Lyndhurst, Hampshire, 14

Macbean (solicitor), 319, 325

Macculloch, John (*1773–1835*), 126, 128, 129, 164, 175, 424, 430, 431, 457; *System of Geology*, 316

MacLure, William (*1763–1840*), 77, 294, 297

Macrauchenia, 442

Mactra, 394

Maestricht beds, 83, 394–95

Magazine of Natural History, 485, 509

Magnan River, 214

Mallet, John Lewis, 358, 375, 423

Malmö, Sweden, 396–97

Malthus, Thomas Robert *(1766–1834)*, *Essay on the Principle of Population*, 446–47

Mantell, Gideon Algernon *(1790–1852)*, 92–95, 103–07, 112–13, 124, 147, 153, 184, 271, 313, 409, 410, 462; *Fossils of the South Downs*, 103–04; discovers Iguanodon, 141–142; *Illustrations of the Geology of Sussex (1827)*, 151; C. L. buys fossils from Deshayes for *(1829)*, 260; receives specimens from C. L. *(1821)*, 94, *(1827)*, 183–84; receives Wollaston medal from G. S. 411

Marcet, Jane Haldimand *(1769–1858)*, *Conversations on Chemistry*, 164, 169, 409

Marginella muscaria Lam., 229

Marl deposits, 87, 140; Paris basin, 78–80

Marstand, Island of, 407

Mason, Laing, 50

Massanite, Spain, 294

Mayence basin, Germany, 394

Megatherium, 437, 443

Melilli, Sicily, 241–42

Mendoza, Argentina, 452

Mer de Glace, 62

Merivale, Herman *(1806–74)*, 375

Mermaid, H. M. S., 2

Merstham, firestone of, 102, 104

Messina, Sicily, 232

Meyer, Christian Friedrich Herrmann von *(1801–69)*, 364, 371

Meyringen, Switzerland, 419–20

Michell, John *(1724–93)*, 389

Midhurst, Sussex, 24, 25–31, 92

Millar, David, 87

Millet (naturalist), 493

Mill-stone grit, 77

Milne-Edwards, Henri *(1800–85)*, 414, 469

Milton, John *(1608–74)*, 48; quoted by C. L., 27

Miocene: coining of term, 307

Moën, Island of, 394–95

Mont Blanc, 62

Mont Dore, 198–99

Monte Nuovo, 231

Montmartre gypsum quarries. *See* Gypsum, Montmartre

Montmollin, Auguste de *(1808–98)*, 417

Montpellier, France, 208

Mont Perdu, 299, 303

Montrose, Angus, 1

Moore, Sir Graham *(1764–1843)*, 188

Muc Airn, Argyll, 499

Mudie, Margaret. *See* Lyell, Margaret Mudie.

Muddiford, Hampshire, 56

Muirhouses, purchase of *(1784)*, 5

Mull, Island of, 53, 55; McLeod's bay, 55

Mundesley, Norfolk, 484, 486, 487

Munster, Count, 384–85

Murchison, Charlotte Hugonin (d. *1869*), 271, 354; tours France *(1828)*, 190–91, 194, 207

Murchison, Roderick Impey *(1792–1871)*, 135–36, 147, 328, 354, 411, 501; tours France with C. L. *(1828)*, 187, 190–217; urges C. L. to go to Sicily *(1828)*, 215; tours Italy with C. L. *(1828)*, 220–23; "On the excavation of valleys . . . ," 211, 223, 256, 262–63; *Silurian System*, 507

Murray, John, 4th Duke of Athol *(1755–1830)*, 70

Murray, John *(1778–1843)*, 135, 143–44, 154, 159, 160, 173, 189, 302, 303, 340, 343–44

—publication of C. L.'s works: *Principles*, 1st ed., *vol. 1*, 170, 268–72, *vol. 2*, 341–43, *vol. 3*, 376; *Principles*, 2nd ed., 374–75; *Principles*, 3rd ed., 385, 407–09, 411; *Principles*, 4th ed., 411, 413, 426; *Principles*, 5th ed., 504; *Principles*, 6th ed., 508, 512; *Elements*, 1st ed., 503, 505; *Elements*, 2nd ed., 516

Mytilus, 149, 394; *M. edulis*, 396–97, 400, 406

Nantes, France, 493

Naples, Italy, 225–32

Necker de Saussure, Louis Albert *(1786–1861)*, 369–70

Neckers, France, 200

Needles, Isle of Wight, 19

Nelson, Horatio, Viscount Nelson, Duke of Bronte *(1758–1805)*: C. L. hears of his death, 17

Neptune, H. M. S., 3

Nerita helicina, 229

Neritina, 405

Nesti (professor at Florence), 224

Neuchâtel, Switzerland, 417, 498–99
New Forest, Hampshire, 14; botanical interest for C. Lyell, Esq., 18–19, 25; Ravens Nest Inclosure, 19
Nice, France, 211, 213, 220
Nicolosi, Sicily, 238, 239
Nilsson, Sven (1787–1883), 397
Nismes, France, 208
Northampton, Lord, 252
North Sea, 406
Norwich, Norfolk, 47, 481–82
Noto, Sicily, 245

Oban, Argyll, 52–53, 55
Oersted, Hans Christian (1777–1851), 396, 470
Oeynhausen, Karl von (1795–1865), 431
Ogilvy, Donald, 321–22, 323
Ogilvy, Sir John, 3
Ogilvy, Thomas: describes parish of Kirriemuir (1792), 4
Olot, Spain, 294, 297, 318
Orbigny, Alcide d' (1802–57), 477
Oregrund, Sweden, 402–03
Orthotrichum lyelli, 25
Orust, Island of, 406–07
Osorno, Chile, 454
Owen, Richard (1804–92), 482, 488; examines fossil bones brought by Darwin, 434, 436–38, 442, 445; reads to G. S. description of Toxodon, 440–41
Oxford University, 33–35. See also Lyell, Charles (1797–1875)

Pachydermata, 82
Padua, Italy, 223
Paestum, Italy, 229
Palaeotherium, 82
Palermo, Sicily, 252
Pallas, Peter Simon (1741–1811): formation of mountains, 67
Paludina, 394
Pariou, France: lava currents, 193
Paris basin, 76, 78, 80, 83, 93, 120–21, 124, 179; Auvergne freshwater formation compared, 201
Paris limestone, 78–79, 80, 120
Parkinson, James (1755–1824), 92, 219, 464
Parma, Italy, 224
Patagonia, 450
Patteson, John (1790–1861), 88, 138
Peel, Sir Robert (1788–1850), 490

Pennant, Thomas (1726–98), A Tour in Scotland and Voyage to the Hebrides, 53
Penny, Taylor, 1–2
Pentalica caves, Sicily, 242
Peterhead, Aberdeenshire, 203
Peterhouse College, Cambridge, 5
Petit Puy, France, 193
Petworth marble, 114
Pewsey, Vale of, 101–02
Phillips, John (1800–74), 266, 456, 469, 501
Phillips, Thomas (1770–1845): portrait of three Lyell sons (1819), 63
Phillips, William (1775–1828), 170; Outlines of Mineralogy and Geology, 46. See also Conybeare, William Daniel, and William Phillips
Philosophical Magazine, 304–05, 465, 466
Phryganea, 81, 193
Planorbis, 81, 201, 204
Plastic clay, Paris basin, 78, 80
Playfair, John (1748–1819), 49, 71, 156, 171; Illustrations of the Huttonian Theory, 72
Playfair, Lyon, 1st Baron Playfair of St. Andrews (1818–98), 429
Pleistocene: coining of term, 485
Plesiosaurus, 84, 124–25
Pliocene: coining of term, 307
Pompeii, Italy, 229
Pont Gibaud, France, 194, 262
Porrentrui, Switzerland, 417
Potamides, 81, 201
Prandi, Fortunato, 318
Prevost, Louis Constant (1787–1856), 118–24, 190, 259, 275–76, 301, 382, 420; tours S. W. England with C. L. (1824), 126–29
Prevost, Pierre (1751–1839), 370
Prichard, James Cowles (1786–1848), Researches into the Physical History of Man, 331, 333–34
Primosole, Sicily, 240–41
Princess Royal, H. M. S., 3
Puycerda, Valley of, Spain, 297
Puy-de-Dôme, France, 193
Puy de Sancy, France, 198
Puy-en-Velay, France, 205–06
Puzzuoli, Italy, 230–31
Pyrenees: C. L. tours (1830), 273, 294–301

Quarterly Review, 143–44

Quarterly Review (cont.)
—articles by C. L.: review of Campbell, *Letter . . . London University (1825)*, 144–45; "On Scientific Institutions" *(1826)*, 152–53; *Transactions of the G. S. of London (1826)*, 154–59; "State of the Universities" *(1827)*, 164–69; review of Scrope's *Memoir on the Geology of Central France (1827)*, 177–79

Raddusa, Sicily, 251
Ramsay, Andrew Crombie *(1814–91)*, 429
Ramsay, George, 29
Ramsay, Sir James, 8th Bt. of Banff *(1797–1859)*, 29, 52, 55
Ramsay, Lady, of Banff, 29
Rang, Paul Karel Sander Leonard *(1784–1859)*, 477
Ranville La Place, France, 492
Raspe, Rudolph Erich *(1737–94)*, *Specimen historiae naturalis globi terraquei*, 266
Ravenna, Italy, 90
Reform Bill, 340; debate *(1831)*, 321; defeat in House of Lords *(1831)*, 326
Reigate, firestone of, 102, 104, 107, 111
Reynaud de Montlosier, Comte François Dominique *(1755–1838)*, 175, 197
Rhine River, 316, 364, 384, 390, 420
Rhone delta, 208
Richardson, Benjamin, 43
Richardson, William *(1740–1820)*, 8–9
Rigi, Switzerland, 62
Rio Colorado, 450
Rio de la Plata, 450
Rio Negro, 450
Ripple marks, C. L.'s first theory of, 300–01
Risso, Giovanni Antonio *(1777–1845)*, 213–14
Ritchie, John, 1
Rivaulx Abbey, Yorkshire, 49
Robinson, Henry Crabb, 355
Rogers, Henry Darwin *(1808–66)*, 100
Rogers, William Barton *(1804–82)*, 100
Rome, 90, 225, 256
Romney, H. M. S., 2
Rose, William Stewart *(1775–1843)*, 149
Rosen, Geheimrath von, 392
Rosenlaui (glacier), 499
Rossetti, Gabriele: friendship with C. Lyell, Esq., 188–90; edition of Dante's *Divine Comedy*, C. L.'s review not published, 187–90
Royal College of Surgeons, 434
Royal Institution: lecture series by C. L. *(1833)*, 376
Royal Society of Edinburgh, 69
Royal Society of London, 183, 304, 396; elects G. Mantell FRS *(1825)*, 147; elects C. L. FRS *(1826)*, 148; Bakerian lecture on Sweden by C. L. *(1834)*, 410; royal medal awarded to C. L., 410
Rudolphi, Karl Asmund *(1771–1832)*, 331
Rudwick, Martin J. S., 75, 238–39
Rumford, Count. *See* Thompson, Benjamin
Russell, Lord John *(1792–1878)*, 320

St. Abb's Head, Berwickshire, 71, 156
Saint Andrews University, 5
St. Helena, 335
Sainte-Claire Deville, Charles Joseph *(1814–76)*, 347
Sala, Sweden, 404
Salisbury, H. M. S., 3
Sandown Bay, Isle of Wight, 97, 113–14
Santa Maria, Island of (Chile), 451
Santiago, Chili, 451
Sassi, Agostino, 221, 257
Saussure, Horace-Bénédict de *(1740–99)*, 67; *Voyages dans les Alpes*, 7, 347, 498
Savigné, France, 493
Savona, Italy, 221
Saxony, 74
Schaffhausen, falls of, 62, 367
Scheibenberg, Germany, 74
Scheuchzer, Johann Jacob *(1672–1733)*, 498
Schmerling, Philippe Charles *(1791–1836)*, 385
Schumacher, Heinrich Christian Friedrich *(1757–1830)*, 392
Scogletti, Sicily, 246
Scotland, agricultural revolution in (ca. *1750*), 4–5
Scott, Sir Walter *(1771–1832)*, 27, 144, 159
Scrope, George Julius Poulett *(1797–1876)*, 164, 175, 187, 225, 256, 271, 294, 350; review by C. L. of *Geology of Central France (1827)*, 164, 177–79; reviews C. L.'s *Principles*, vol. 1, 273–77, 291–92, 303
Sedberg, Westmorland, 6–7
Sedgwick, Adam *(1785–1873)*, 168, 201, 264–65, 268–69, 273, 276–77, 314, 357,

Sedgwick, Adam (*cont.*)
  412–13, 440, 461–62, 501; comments on C. L.'s *Principles,* vol. 1, 293; praises Beaumont's new theory, 293, 349–50
Seeland, Island of, 394–95
Segeberg, Germany, 392
Seine valley, 44, 83
Serapis, Temple of, 230–31
Serpula, 149
Serres, Pierre Marcel Toussaint de (*1780–1862*), 208, 209, 210
Sèvres, France, 415
Sèvres porcelain: use of plastic clay, 78
Shelley, Percy Bysshe (*1792–1822*), 33, 34
Shells: C. L. finds identity of species inconsistent, 462–63, 469, 475
Sheppard, Samuel Philip (*1766–1832*), 8
Shielhill, purchase of (*1783*), 5
Siccar point (St. Abb's Head), 71
Sicily: C. L. visits (*1828*), 215, 232–56; fossil shells of living species, 252; flora and fauna older than land, 255. *See also place names.*
Sidlaw Hills, Angus, 129
Siena, Italy, 225, 256
Silliman, Benjamin (*1779–1864*), 426–28, 515
Sioule River, 194, 196, 262–63
Skaptár Jokul, 280
Smith, Sir Andrew (*1797–1872*), 445
Smith, Frances. *See* Lyell, Frances Smith (d. *1850*)
Smith, James, of Jordanhill (*1782–1867*), 456–57
Smith, Sir James Edward (*1759–1828*), 20, 25, 46
Smith, Thomas, 8
Smith, William (*1769–1839*), 42–43, 75, 102, 103; *A delineation of the strata of England and Wales . . . ,* 75–76; fossils used to identify strata, 75–76, 77–78, 218; *A memoir to the map . . . ,* 75–76; influence on geology, 76; fossil collection exhibited at B. M., 76; *Stratigraphical system of organized fossils,* 76, 77–78, 84
Smyth, William (*1765–1849*), 167, 226
Sodertelje, Sweden, 401–02
Solander, Daniel (*1736–82*), 332
Solen callosum, 229
Solna, Sweden, 400, 401
Somersetshire, W. Smith's survey of, 75

Somerville, Mary (*1780–1872*), 171, 314–15, 383
Somerville, William (*1771–1860*), 171
Sorgenfrei, 472
South American fauna, 436, 438, 440–42
Southampton, 12
Southwold, Suffolk, 481, 482
Sowerby, George Brettingham (*1788–1854*), 443, 469, 483, 484, 486, 494, 509
Sowerby, James (*1757–1822*), 24–25, 151; letters from C. Lyell, Esq. (*1806*), 18–20; C. L. visits (*1817*), 45
Sowerby, James de Carle (*1787–1871*), 45, 141
Species: adapt to environment, C. L. observes, 255; origin of, C. L.'s treatment of (*Principles,* vol. 1), 289; dynamic interaction among, 336; consequences of spread, 337; change of climate, 338; how new arise, C. L.'s theory, 339, 439–40; transmutation of, Darwin's theory, 446
Spedding, Thomas Story (*1800–70*), 115, 160
Staffa, Island of: C. L. visits (*1817*), 52–55; Fingal's cave, 53–54; Clam-shell cave, 54
Starch Factory Creek (New York), 77
Steno, Nicolaus (*1638–86*), 69
Stephenson, George (*1781–1848*), 49
Stevenson, Robert (*1772–1850*), 276
Stockholm, Sweden, 399, 402, 404, 405
Stokes, Charles (*1783–1853*), 147, 273, 277, 359–60, 501
Stonesfield, Oxfordshire, 84, 93; resemblance of fossils to those of Tilgate Forest, 94
Strankaer, Inverness, 499
Stratford-on-Avon, Warwickshire, 85
Strathmore, Angus, 4
Strathmore, Vale of, 129, 131, 500–01
Studer, Bernhard (*1794–1887*), 367–68, 417
Stukeley, William (*1687–1765*), *Itinerary Curiosities,* 103
Stutchbury, Samuel, 142
Stutton, Essex, 484
Sumatra, 157, 450
Superga, Hill of, Italy, 221, 253, 255
Sussex, Duke of. *See* Augustus Frederick, Duke of Sussex.
Sutton, Suffolk, 480
Swanage, Dorsetshire, 172
Sweden: question of land elevation, 385,

Sweden (cont.)
400–01; C. L.'s tour (1834), 391, 396–407

Switzerland: visit of C. Lyell, Esq. (1792), 7

Syracuse, Sicily, 242, 244–45, 250, 251; fossil clay bed discovered by C. L. on south side of harbor, 244

Targioni-Tozzetti, Antonio (1785–1856), 224

Taylor, Richard C. (1789–1851), 463, 464

Tellina, 394

Tellina baltica, 400

Temperature of earth's interior, 386–88

Terebratula, 466, 484

Terranuova, Sicily, 246

Thames valley, Conybeare's theory of formation, 262–65

Thompson, Sir Benjamin Count von Rumford (1753–1814), 97

Thomson, James (1700–48): writing influences C. L., 27–28, 48

Thorpe, Suffolk, 481

Thueyts, France, 206–07, 262

Thun, Lake of, 417–18

Thurmann, Jules (1804–55), 417

Tilgate Forest Beds, Sussex, 93, 94, 103, 105–07, 116, 141, 142, 151

Time: effect on interpretation of geological evidence, 282

Titus Hiero, 57

Tortworth Rectory, Gloucestershire, 128

Townsend, Joseph (1739–1816), 101–02

Toxodon, 440, 443

Travemunde, Germany: shells collected by C. L., 392–94

Triglochina maritimus, 402

Turbo littoreus, 394

Turin, Italy, 221, 257

Turner, Dawson (1775–1858), 20, 24, 32, 35, 38–39, 41, 46, 47–48, 53, 57

Turner, Elizabeth (1799–1852), 48

Turner, Harriet (1806–69), 46

Uddevalla, Sweden, 406

Unterseen, Switzerland, 418

Upsala, Sweden, 402

Urbach Thal, Switzerland, 419

Ure, Andrew (1778–1857), A New System of Geology, 265

Uspallata Mountains, petrified forest of, 452

Val di Noto limestone (Sicily), 242–54

Valdivia, Chile, 451

Valognes, France, 492

Valorsine, Switzerland, 370–71

Valparaiso, Chile, 451

Vanikoro, Island of, 448

Veaurs, France, 201

Venetz, Ignace (1788–1859), 497

Verrus rugosa, 228

Vesuvius, 74, 229, 279

Vévayre River, 368

Vicenza, Italy, 223

Vichy, France, 196–97

Victoria, Queen (1819–1901), 471, 505

Visconti, Ferdinand, 226

Viviani, Domenico (1772–1840), 221

Vizzini, Sicily, 249; C. L. finds fossil oyster bed between lava layers, 251

Volvic, France, 196

Wahlenberg, Goran (1780–1851), 402

Warrington, Daniel Richard, 8

Warspight, H.M.S., 3

Watson, Joshua (1771–1855), 268, 308

Waulkmiln, purchase of (1784), 5

Weald strata, 93, 102, 113–14, 391

Weaver, Thomas (1773–1885), 128

Webster, Thomas (1773–1844), 105, 149, 218; geological exploration of Isle of Wight, 96–102; discovery of the anticline, 99–100; theory of chalk strata (1814), 100–01

Wedderburn, Charles (1748–1829): at Isle of Wight with C. Lyell family (1806), 19; consulted regarding C. L.'s illness (1808), 22

Wedgwood, Emma. See Darwin, Emma Wedgwood

Wellesley, Arthur, 1st Duke of Wellington (1769–1852), 59, 320, 356

Werner, Abraham Gottlob (1749–1817), 48, 65; geognosy, 66; studies basalt, 74; mineralogical classification found invalid, 202–03

—theories: origin of earth, 65–68; classification of strata, 66; identification of strata, 76–77, 80, 109

Wernerian Natural History Society, 50

Western Circuit. See Bar in England.

Weybourne, Norfolk, 487, 489

Whewell, William (1794–1866), 301, 314, 326, 449, 456; reviews C. L.'s Principles, vol. 1, 292–93, 301, 305; reviews C. L.'s

Whewell, William (*cont.*)
Principles, vol. 2, 327, 350–51
—letters on naming of Tertiary formations: from C. L., (21 Jan. *1831*), 305–06, (17 Feb. *1831*), 307; to C. L. (31 Jan. *1831*), 306–07
Wigham, J. B. (collector of Crag shells), 482
Wilberforce, Samuel (*1805–73*), 86
Willdenow, Karl Ludwig (*1765–1812*), 332
William IV (*1765–1837*), 471
Winch, Nathaniel John (*1769?–1838*), 49
Winchelsea, Sussex, 105, 106, 115
Winchester, Hampshire, 24, 25

Wood, Searles (*1798–1880*), 464, 465, 483, 484, 486, 509
Woodbridge, Suffolk, 478, 480
Woodstock, Oxfordshire, 85
Woodward, Samuel Peckworth (*1821–65*), 464, 465–66
Wordsworth's garden, 86
Wrottesley, Sir John, 1st Baron Wrottesley (*1771–1841*), 62

Yare River, 47
Yarmouth, Isle of Wight, 19
Yarmouth, Norfolk, 47

Zoological Society of London, 421, 352